British Catalogue of Music

1976

A record of music and books about music recently published in Great Britain, based upon the material deposited at the Copyright Receipt Office of the British Library, arranged according to a system of classification with a Composer and Title Index, a Subject Index, and a List of Music Publishers.

The British Library BIBLIOGRAPHIC SERVICES DIVISION

CITY OF BIRMINGHAM LIBRARY POLYTECHNIC

The British Catalogue of Music is compiled within

The British Library

BIBLIOGRAPHIC SERVICES DIVISION

Store Street London WC1E 7DG

Telephone : 01-636 0755

Telex : 22787

ISBN 0–900220–60–0

ISSN 0068–1407

© The British Library Board 1977

CITY OF BIRMINGHAM
POLYTECHNIC LIBRARY

BOOK
No. 649068

SUBJECT
No. R 016.78. Bir

British Library Cataloguing in Publication data

British Catalogue of Music
1976

1. Music—Bibliography
I British Library. Bibliographic Services Division
016.78   ML118

ISBN 0–900220–60–0
ISSN 0068–1407

Produced by computer-controlled phototypesetting by Computaprint Ltd London
Printed by William Clowes & Sons, Limited, London, Beccles and Colchester

BI 0649068 9

BIRMINGHAM CITY
UNIVERSITY
DISCARDED

 **CITY OF BIRMINGHAM
POLYTECHNIC LIBRARY** M

FOR REFERENCE ONLY

NOT TO BE TAKEN AWAY

P43036 B1(C)

Preface

The British Catalogue of Music is a record of new music—with the exception of certain types of popular music—published in Great Britain. In addition, it records foreign music available in this country through a sole agent and books about music. It is based on the works deposited at the Copyright Receipt Office of the British Library where copies of all new publications must be sent by law and is the most complete list of current British music available. The Catalogue is presented in three sections:

Classified Section
Composer and Title Index
Subject Index

Instruments, musical forms

While the Classified Section displays the works systematically according to the instrument or combination for which a work is written, the Subject Index lists the principle musical forms and musical character and it shows by means of the class symbol where works having such forms or musical character are to be found in the Classified Section. For example, in the Subject Index under the word Sonatas the following entries may be found:

Sonatas : Arrangements for 2 pianos	QNUK/AE
Sonatas : Organ	RE
Sonatas : Piano duets, 4 hands	QNVE
Sonatas : Violin solos, Unaccompanied	SPME

It will be seen that this group of entries enables you to assemble all the works in sonata form no matter for what instrument the music is, or was originally, written. Under the word Violin the following may be found:

Violin	S
Violin : Accompanying female voices : Choral works	FE/S
Violin : Books	AS
Violin & orchestra	MPS
Violin & string orchestra	RXMPS

This group directs you first to the place S in the Classified Section, where music for the violin is found, including works composed originally for other instruments and arranged for violin. It also directs you to works in which the violin figures in combination with other instruments. It thus provides at one and the same time the link between an instrument and its place in the Classified Section and an exhaustive guide to all the works in which that particular instrument figures. It should be borne in mind that class symbols which include () "brackets" or / "stroke" precede letters in the arrangement.
Thus:

	A
is followed by	A(....)
which is followed by	A/....
which is followed by	AA
which is followed by	AB
which is followed by	B. etc.

Music literature

Books about music which normally appear in the *British National Bibliography* are also included in this catalogue. They occur in the sequences lettered A and B of the Classified Section. They are indexed in exactly the same way as musical works in the Composer and Title Index and are designated by the qualification "Books" in the Subject Index. Thus, in the second group above, the entry Violin: Books, directing you to AS, indicates that books about the violin will be found at that place.

Composers

When the composer or author of a work is known, look under his name in the Composer and Title Index. The information given here, including the publisher and price, will be adequate for most purposes. If, on the other hand, the fullest information about a work is required, turn to the entry in the Classified Section. This may be found by means of the class symbol (group of letters) at the end of the entry in the Composer and Title Index.

Titles, series, editors and arrangers

Entries are made in the Composer and Title Index under the titles of all works, so that, if you do not know the composer or author, a work can be found by looking up its title in the Composer and Title Index.
If you do not know either the composer or the title, it may still be possible to trace the work if the name of the editor or arranger is known and, in the case of vocal works, the author of the words.

Prices

Prices given are those current at the time of the first recording of an entry in this catalogue. In a few cases prices of parts are not given but can be obtained on application to the publishers.

Abbreviations

Most of the abbreviations used in describing musical works are self-explanatory. The size of a musical work is indicated by one of the following conventional symbols: *8vo* for works up to $10\frac{1}{2}$ and 12 in. in height, and *fol.* for works over 12 in. in height. The abbreviation *obl.* (oblong) is added to show when a work is of unusual proportions, and a single sheet is designated by the abbreviations *s.sh.* The abbreviations used for the description of books in the sections A and B are those in use in the *British National Bibliography*.

Patrick Mills
Editor
British Catalogue of Music

Outline of the Classification

The following outline is given for general information only. Users are advised to consult the Subject Index to discover the exact location of required material in the Classified Section.

MUSICAL LITERATURE

A	General Works
	Common sub-divisions
A(B)	Periodical
A(C)	Encyclopaedias
A(D)	Composite works, symposia, essays by several writers
A(E)	Anecdotes, personal reminiscences
A(K)	Economics
A(M)	Persons in music
A(MM)	Musical profession
A(MN)	Music as a career
A(P)	Individuals
A(Q)	Organisations
A(QT)	Terminology
A(QU)	Notation
A(R)	Printing
A(S)	Publishing
A(T)	Bibliographies
A(U)	Libraries
A(V)	Musical education
A(X)	History of music
A(Y)	Music of particular localities
A/AM	Theory of music
A/CC	Aesthetics
A/CY	Technique of music
A/D	Composition
A/E	Performance
A/F	Recording
A/FY	Musical character
A/G	Folk music
A/GM	Music associated with particular occupations
A/H	Dance music
A/HM	Ballet music
A/J	Music accompanying drama
A/JR	Film music
A/KD	Music to accompany social customs
A/L	Religious music
A/LZ	Elements of music
A/R	Harmony
A/S	Forms of music
A/Y	Fugue
AB	Works on vocal music
AC	Works on opera
ACM	Works on musical plays
AD-AX	Works on music for particular vocal or instrumental performers, enumerated like D-X below
B	Works on individual composers (including libretti and other verbal texts of particular musical works)
BZ	Works on non-European music

MUSIC: SCORES AND PARTS

C/AY	Collections not limited to work of particular composer, executant, form or character
C/AZ	Collections of a particular composer not otherwise limited
C/G-C/Y	Collections illustrating music of particular form, character, etc., enumerated like A/G-A/Y above
CB	Vocal music
CC	Opera. Vocal scores
CM	Musical plays. Vocal scores
D	Choral music
DC	Oratorios, Cantatas, Masses
DF	Liturgical, Service music
DH	Motets, Anthems, Hymns
DW	Songs, etc.
E	Choral music with instruments other than keyboard
EZ	Choral music unaccompanied
F	Choral music. Female voices
G	Choral music. Male voices
J	Unison vocal works
K	Vocal solos
L	Instrumental music
M	Orchestral music
N	Chamber music
PVV	Music for individual instruments and instrumental groups
PW	Keyboard instruments
Q	Piano
R	Organ
RW	String instruments
S	Violin
SQ	Viola
SR	Cello
SS	Double bass
TQ	Harp
TS	Guitar
U	Wind instruments
V	Woodwind
VR	Flute
VS	Recorder
VT	Oboe
VU	Saxophone
VV	Clarinet
VW	Bassoon
W	Brass
WS	Trumpet
WT	Horn
WU	Trombone
WX	Bass tuba
X	Percussion instruments
Z	Non-European music

CORRIGENDA

The entries given below do not appear in their appropriate places in the Classified Section, and to ensure that they are not overlooked their correct places have been marked with a†.

A/FD/GB/YT(XPK11) — United States. Popular music, 1950–1960
Propes, Steve
  Those oldies but goodies : a guide to 50's record collecting / [by] Steve Propes. — New York : Collier Books ; London : Collier Macmillan, 1973. — xi,192p ; 21cm.
  Originally published: New York : Macmillan, 1973. — Lists of gramophone records.
  ISBN 0-02-061430-6 Pbk : £0.95

(B76-12802)

BVE(N/XHK19) — Verdi, Giuseppe. Biographies, 1830–1848
Burrows, Donald
  Music and revolution, Verdi / prepared for the Course Team by Donald Burrows. — Milton Keynes : Open University Press, 1976. — 47p : ill, port ; 30cm. — (Arts, a third level course : the revolutions of 1848 ; unit 12) (A321 ; 12)
  ISBN 0-335-05059-x Pbk : Unpriced

(B76-23700)

BWCAC — Wagner, Richard. Ring des Nibelungen. Librettos
Wagner, Richard
  [Der Ring des Nibelungen. English & German]. The ring / [by] Richard Wagner ; English translation by Andrew Porter ; illustrations by Eric Fraser. — Folkestone : Dawson, 1976. — xli, 362p ; 25cm.
  Parallel German and English texts, English preliminaries. — Bibl.: p.xli.
  ISBN 0-7129-0698-3 : £15.00

(B76-31122)

Classified section

This section contains entries under Subjects, Executants and Instruments according to a system of classification, a synopsis of which appears in the preliminary pages. The Composer and Title Index and the Subject Index which follow this section are the key to both the classification and to this section.

The following are used for sizes of musical works:

8vo. for works up to 10½ in. in height.
4vo. for works between 10½ in. and 12 in. in height.
fol. for works over 12 in. in height.
obl. indicates a work of unusual proportions.
s.sh. means a single sheet.

A — MUSICAL LITERATURE
Bernstein, Leonard
The unanswered question : six talks at Harvard / [by] Leonard Bernstein. — Cambridge, Mass. ; London : Harvard University Press, 1976. — [9],428p : ill, music, ports ; 21x24cm & 3 sound discs(6s. ; 7in. 33 1/3 rpm.). — (Charles Eliot Norton lectures ; 1973)
In slipcase.
ISBN 0-674-92000-7 : £12.75

(B76-22851)

Corbett, Jane
Music for GCE 'O' Level / [by] Jane Corbett, Vera Yelverton. — 2nd ed., revised. — [London] : Barrie and Jenkins, 1975. — 176p : ill, music ; 19cm.
Previous ed.: i.e. Revised ed., London : Barrie and Rockliff, 1967. — Bibl.: p.173. — Index.
ISBN 0-214-15676-1 Pbk : £1.95

(B76-05035)

Willson, Robina Beckles
The voice of music / [by] Robina Beckles Willson ; foreword by Yehudi Menuhin ; designed and illustrated by Jeroo Roy. — London : Heinemann, 1976. — 223p : ill, music ; 24cm.
Bibl.: p 214. — List of records: p.212-213. — Index.
ISBN 0-434-97258-4 : £4.50

(B76-22073)

A(C) — Encyclopaedias
Blom, Eric
Everyman's dictionary of music / compiled by Eric Blom. — 5th ed. / revised by Sir Jack Westrup ; with the collaboration of ... [others]. — London : Dent, 1974. — xiii,793p : music ; 19cm. — (Aldine paperbacks) (Everyman's reference library)
Previous ed.: i.e. 5th ed., 1971.
ISBN 0-460-02151-6 Pbk : £1.95

(B76-31911)

Grove, *Sir* George
Grove's dictionary of music and musicians. — 5th ed. / edited by Eric Blom. — London [etc.] : Macmillan, 1975. — 9v. : ill, facsims, music, ports ; 24cm.
In 10 vols. — Fifth ed. originally published: 1954. — Bibl.
ISBN 0-333-00949-5 : £75.00(for vols 1-9 and supplementary vol. 10)
ISBN 0-333-19262-1 Set of 10 vols. Pbk : £35.00

(B76-19247)

A(D) — Essays
Newman, Ernest
Essays from the world of music : essays from 'The Sunday Times' / [by] Ernest Newman ; selected by Felix Aprahamian. — London : J. Calder, 1976. — 190p : music, port ; 23cm.
'Volume One'. — This collection originally published: as 'From the world of music', 1956.
ISBN 0-7145-3548-6 : £6.50
ISBN 0-7145-3587-7 Pbk : Unpriced

(B76-34776)

Newman, Ernest
More essays from the world of music : essays from the 'Sunday Times' / [by] Ernest Newman ; selected by Felix Aprahamian. — London : J. Calder, 1976. — ix,260p : music, ports ; 23cm.
'Volume two'. — This collection originally published: 1958.
ISBN 0-7145-3549-4 : £7.50
ISBN 0-7145-3598-2 Pbk : Unpriced

(B76-34777)

A(M/YC) — Musicians. Great Britain
British Association of Concert Agents
Composite list of artists showing sole representation, by members of the British Association of Concert Agents, as at January 1, 1976 / compiled for members of the British Association of Concert Agents. — London (c/o The Secretary, 44 Castelnau Gardens, Arundel Terrace, SW13 9DU) : [The Association], [1976]. — [1],75p ; 30cm.
Index.
ISBN 0-904892-01-8 Ls : Unpriced

(B76-15528)

A(QM/XD101) — Ornaments, 1500-1600
Brown, Howard Mayer
Embellishing sixteenth-century music / [by] Howard Mayer Brown. — London : Oxford University Press, 1976. — xiv,79p : ill, music ; 21cm. — (Early music series ; 1)
Index.
ISBN 0-19-323175-1 Pbk : £2.95

(B76-14364)

A(QU) — Notation
Boustead, Alan
Writing down music / [by] Alan Boustead. — London [etc.] : Oxford University Press, 1975. — xiii,137p : music ; 21cm.
Bibl.: p.137.
ISBN 0-19-317104-x Pbk : £3.75

(B76-14363)

A(S/YEF/XWK91) — Publishing. Frankfurt, 1620-1730
Schaefer, Hartmut
Die Notendrucker und Musik verleger in Frankfurt am Main von 1630 bis um 1720 : eine bibliographisch-drucktechnische Untersuchung / [von] Hartmut Schaefer. — Kassel [etc.] ; London ([32 Great Titchfield St., W.1]) : Bärenreiter, 1975. — 2v.(711p) : ill, facsims ; 23cm. — (Catalogus musicus ; 7)
Pbk : £28.13
ISBN 3-7618-0531-4

A(T) — Bibliographies
Library Association. *Public Libraries Group*
Introduction to music / Library Association, Public Libraries Group ; [compiled by L.W. Duck]. — [Chippenham] ([c/o A.L. Bamber, Divisional Library, Timber St., Chippenham, Wilts.]) : [The Group], 1975. — 69p ; 19cm. — (Readers' guide ; no.3)
ISBN 0-85365-168-x Sd : £0.40

(B76-19568)

University of Lancaster. *Library*
Catalogue of the Hans Ferdinand Redlich Collection of musical books and scores : (including material on the Second Viennese School) / [University of Lancaster Library] ; [cataloguing by Graham Royds]. — Lancaster (University Library, Bailrigg, Lancaster LA1 4YH) : The University, 1976. — xi,117p : port ; 30cm. — (Miscellaneous publications series)
Limited ed. of 100 copies. — Index.
ISBN 0-901699-35-7 Pbk : £3.00

(B76-31432)

A(TC) — Bibliographies of scores
Whistling, Carl Friedrich
Handbuch der musikalischen Litteratur / by Carl Friedrich
Whistling and Friedrich Hofmeister. — 1817 ed. [reprinted with]
the ten supplements, 1818-1827 ; with a new introduction by Neil
Ratliff. — New York ; London : Garland ; [London] ([2 Rugby
St., WC1N 3QU]) : [Distributed by George Prior Associated
Publishers Ltd], 1975. — 134p in various pagings ; 23cm. —
(Garland reference library of the humanities ; vol.21)
Facsimile reprints. — English introduction. — Bibl.: p.xvi-xviii.
ISBN 0-8240-1064-7 : £33.35

(B76-04592)

A(VC/M/BC) — Teachers. Directories
Professional register of private teachers of music / the Incorporated
Society of Musicians. — London (48 Gloucester Place, W1H
3HJ) : The Society.
1975-76. — [1976]. — [4],48p : map ; 21cm.
ISBN 0-902900-08-0 Sd : £1.00

(B76-14360)

A(VC/P) — Boulanger, Nadia. Biographies
Kendall, Alan, b.1939
The tender tyrant, Nadia Boulanger : a life devoted to music : a
biography / by Alan Kendall ; introduction by Yehudi Menuhin.
— London : Macdonald and Jane's, 1976. — xvi,144p,[8]p of
plates : ill, ports ; 23cm.
Index.
ISBN 0-356-08403-5 : £5.95

(B76-29098)

A(VCC) — Teaching methods. Pre-school children
Moog, Helmut
The musical experience of the pre-school child / [by] Helmut
Moog ; translated [from the German] by Claudia Clarke. —
London (48 Great Marlborough St., W1V 2BN) : Schott Music,
1976. — ix,140p : music ; 21cm.
Translation of: 'Das Musikerleben des vorschulpflichtigen Kindes'. Mainz :
Schott, 1968. — Bibl.: p.137-140.
ISBN 0-901938-06-8 Pbk : £2.00

(B76-35594)

A(VF) — Teaching
Todd, Dennis
Teaching music-reading in class / [by] Dennis Todd. — London :
Evans Bros, 1976. — 64p : ill, music ; 21cm. — (Education in
action)
Bibl.: p.62-64.
ISBN 0-237-29164-9 Pbk : £0.95

(B76-06886)

A(VG) — Primary schools
Walker, Robert, b.1936
Sound projects / [by] Robert Walker. — London : Oxford
University Press, Music Department, 1976. — v,33p : ill, music ;
24cm.
ISBN 0-19-321804-6 Sd : £1.25

(B76-21743)

A(VK/AL) — Secondary schools. Examinations
**Associated Examining Board for the General Certificate of
Education**
Report on the music examination in 1974 relating to the proposed
single system of examining at 16+ / Associated Examining Board
for the General Certificate of Education [and] the West Yorkshire
and Lindsey Regional Examining Board for the Certificate of
Secondary Education. — [Aldershot] ([Wellington House,
Aldershot, Hants. GU11 1BQ]) : [The Board], [1976]. — 157p in
various pagings : ill, forms, music ; 30cm.
ISBN 0-901893-07-2 Sd : £0.50

(B76-15048)

A(VMMX/YDL) — Gifted children. Scotland
**Working Group on Provision for Children of Exceptional Gifts in
Music and Dance**
Gifted young musicians and dancers : report of a Working Group
[i.e. Working Group on Provision for Children of Exceptional
Gifts in Music and Dance] set up to consider their general and
specialised education / [for the] Scottish Education Department.
— Edinburgh : H.M.S.O., 1976. — 28p ; 25cm.
'Working Group on Provision for Children of Exceptional Gifts in Music
and Dance'- p.25.
ISBN 0-11-491405-2 Sd : £0.80

(B76-24278)

A(VMWM) — Maladjusted children
Music in developmental therapy : a curriculum guide / edited by
Jennie Purvis and Shelley Samet ; with contributions by
Clementine Gigliotti, Beleta Griffith, Sarah McGinley. —
Baltimore ; London [etc.] : University Park Press, 1976. — x,
254p : ill, music ; 22x30cm.
Bibl.: p.237-238. — Index.
ISBN 0-8391-0895-8 Sp : £6.25

(B76-30972)

A(VMWR) — Backward children
Dickinson, Pamela Ingeborg
Music with ESN children : a guide for the classroom teacher /
[by] Pamela I. Dickinson. — Windsor : NFER, 1976. — 174p :
ill, form, music ; 22cm.
Bibl.: p.169-174. — List of books and music: p.153.
ISBN 0-85633-085-x Pbk : £3.65

(B76-14728)

A(VMX) — Handicapped children
Alvin, Juliette
Music for the handicapped child / [by] Juliette Alvin. — 2nd ed.
— London : Oxford University Press, 1976. — viii,150p ; 19cm.
Previous ed : 1965. — Bibl.: p.149-150.
ISBN 0-19-314920-6 Pbk : £2.75

(B76-25691)

A(VQ) — Professional education
Careers Research and Advisory Centre
Music and drama / Careers Research and Advisory Centre. —
Cambridge (Bateman St., Cambridge CB2 1LZ) : Hobsons Press
(Cambridge) Ltd for CRAC.
1975-76 / [by] B.W. Blackwood. — 1975. — [2],35p ; 21cm. — (Degree
course guide)
Bibl.
ISBN 0-86021-038-3 Sd : £0.85

(B76-04296)

A(VS/YDFKC/X) — Canford Summer School of Music. History
Hale, Noel
Point and counterpoint : an account of the founding and first
twenty-five years of the Canford Summer School of Music / [by]
Noel Hale. — Croydon (250 Purley Way, Croydon CR9 4QD) :
Belwin Mills Music Limited, 1976. — [5],43p ; 22cm.
ISBN 0-9503671-3-3 Sd : £0.80

(B76-35347)

A(VX/P) — Dent, Edward Biographies
Radcliffe, Philip
E.J. Dent : a centenary memoir / [by] Philip Radcliffe. —
Rickmansworth (22 Pheasants Way, Rickmansworth, Herts.) :
Triad Press [for] the E.J. Dent Centenary Committee, [1976]. —
3-32p,plate : port ; 23cm.
Limited ed. of 400 numbered copies.
ISBN 0-902070-18-5 Sd : £1.50

(B76-20005)

**A(W/YB/XHK19/Z) — Concerts. Europe, 1830-1848 - related to
social class**
Weber, William
Music and the middle class : the social structure of concert life in
London, Paris and Vienna / [by] William Weber. — London :
Croom Helm, 1975. — [9],172p ; 23cm. — ([Comparative studies
in European social history])
Bibl.: p.129-137. — Index.
ISBN 0-85664-215-0 : £5.95

(B76-32961)

A(X) — History
Baker, Richard, b.1925
The magic of music / [by] Richard Baker. — London : Sphere,
1976. — 128p,[16]p of plates : ill, music, ports ; 20cm.
Originally published: London : Hamilton, 1975. — Bibl.: p.118. — Index.
ISBN 0-7221-1421-4 Pbk : £0.95

(B76-29099)

Rosen, Charles
The classical style : Haydn, Mozart, Beethoven / [by] Charles
Rosen. — Revised ed. — London : Faber, 1976. — 467p : music ;
23cm.
Previous ed.: 1971. — Index.
ISBN 0-571-04916-8 : £9.00
ISBN 0-571-04905-2 Pbk : £4.25

(B76-35348)

A(XCR181) — History, 1420-1600
Brown, Howard Mayer
Music in the Renaissance / [by] Howard Mayer Brown. —
Englewood Cliffs ; London : Prentice-Hall, 1976. — xv,384p :
music ; 24cm. — (Prentice-Hall history of music series)
Index.
ISBN 0-13-508505-9 : £8.00
ISBN 0-13-508497-4 Pbk : £5.30

(B76-26567)

A(XGQ160) — History, 1815-1975
Raynor, Henry
Music and society since 1815 / [by] Henry Raynor. — London :
Barrie and Jenkins, 1976. — viii,213p ; 24cm.
Bibl.: p.203-206. — Index.
ISBN 0-214-20220-8 : £6.00

(B76-20705)

A(XMA77/C) — History, 1901-76. Encyclopaedias
Fink, Robert
The language of twentieth century music : a dictionary of terms / [compiled] by Robert Fink and Robert Ricci. — New York : Schirmer Books ; London : Collier Macmillan, 1975. — viii,125p : ill, music ; 25cm.
Bibl.: p.117-125.
ISBN 0-02-870600-5 : £5.50

(B76-05036)

A(XM76) — History, 1900-1975
Bray, Trevor
Contemporary music, case stuwies II / prepared by Trevor Bray ; for the [Open University] Course Team. — Milton Keynes : Open University Press, 1974. — 71p : ill, music, ports ; 30cm. — (Arts, a third level course : the development of instruments and their music ; units 31-32) (A304 ; 31-32)
Bibl.: p.68. — List of gramophone records: p.68-70.
ISBN 0-335-00870-4 Pbk : £1.60

(B76-50756)

A(XN9) — History, 1920-1930
Shead, Richard
Music in the 1920s / [by] Richard Shead. — London : Duckworth, 1976. — [7],148p,plate : port ; 23cm.
List of sound discs: p.136-144. — Index.
ISBN 0-7156-0972-6 : £5.95

(B76-35349)

A(Y) — MUSIC OF PARTICULAR LOCALITIES
A(YC/BC) — Great Britain. Directories
British music yearbook : a survey and directory with statistics and reference articles. — London [etc.] : Bowker.
1976 / edited by Arthur Jacobs. — 1976. — xvi,751p : ill, 2 ports ; 21cm.
List of gramophone records: p.15-30. — Bibl. — Index.
ISBN 0-85935-035-5 : £10.50
ISSN 0306-5928

(B76-20706)

Brody, Elaine
The music guide to Great Britain : England, Scotland, Wales, Ireland / [by] Elaine Brody, Claire Brook. — London : Hale, 1976. — xv,240p : maps ; 22cm.
Originally published: New York : Dodd, Mead, 1975. — Index.
ISBN 0-7091-5662-6 : £5.50

(B76-24539)

A(YC/WE/Q) — Great Britain. Festivals. Organisations
British Federation of Music Festivals
Year book / the British Federation of Music Festivals incorporating the Music Teacher's Association. — London (106 Gloucester Place, W1H 3DB) : The Federation.
1976. — [1976]. — [4],107p ; 21cm.
Index.
ISBN 0-901532-06-1 Sd : £1.00

(B76-13568)

A(YD/XCE841/D) — England, 900-1740. Essays
Essays on opera and English music : in honour of Sir Jack Westrup / edited by F.W. Sternfeld, Nigel Fortune, Edward Olleson. — Oxford : Blackwell, 1975. — x,189p,[3] leaves of plates,[4]p of plates : ill, music, port ; 24cm.
Bibl.: p.177-189.
ISBN 0-631-15890-1 : £7.00
Also classified at 782.1

(B76-15050)

A(YDHW/XHD152) — Belper, 1824-1975
Makin, Denis
Music in Belper (1824-1975) / compiled by Denis Makin. — [Milford] ([1 Derwent Ave., Milford, Derby DE5 1RB]) : [The author], [1976]. — [1],24p : facsims, geneal table, ports ; 26cm.
ISBN 0-9504990-0-5 Sd : £0.60

(B76-50350)

A(YDJF/XYN201) — Liverpool, 1773-1973
Taylor, Stainton de Boufflers
Two centuries of music in Liverpool : a scrap-book of information concerning musical activities both professional and amateur / compiled and written by Stainton de B. Taylor ; with a foreword by Sir Charles Groves. — Liverpool (Long Lane, Aintree, Liverpool) : Rockliff Brothers Limited, [1976]. — x,126p : ill, facsims, ports ; 30cm.
Bibl.: p.viii.
ISBN 0-9505143-0-6 Pbk : £4.50

(B76-25957)

A(YE/X) — Germany. History
Of German music : a symposium / edited and introduced by Hans-Hubert Schönzeler. — London : Wolff [etc.], 1976. — 328p : ill, facsim, geneal table on lining paper, ports ; 24cm.
Bibl.: p.323-324. — Index.
ISBN 0-85496-401-0 : £6.50
Also classified at 781.7'436

(B76-14365)

A(YH/X) — France. History
Blunt, Sir Anthony
French art and music since 1500 / [by] Anthony Blunt and Edward Lockspeiser. — London : Methuen, 1974. — x,101p,[30]p of plates, leaf of plate : ill ; 22cm. — (University paperbacks ; 548)
Index.
ISBN 0-416-81650-9 Pbk : £1.35

(B76-50351)

A(YJ/WJ) — Italy. Fitzwilliam Museum. Exhibitions
Italian music and the Fitzwilliam : a collection of essays and a catalogue of an exhibition of Italian in the Fitzwilliam Museum in May 1976 on the occasion of four concerts of Italian music. — Cambridge : Fitzwilliam Museum, 1976. — 48p,[4]p of plates : ill, ports ; 25cm.
ISBN 0-904454-02-9 Pbk : £1.00

(B76-26569)

A(YVD) — Israel
Brod, Max
Die Musik Israels / [von] Max Brod. — Revidierte Ausg., mit einen zweiten Teil 'Werden und Entwicklung der Musik in Israel' ; von Yehuda Walter Cohen. — Basel [etc.] ; London ([32 Great Titchfield St., W.1]) : Bärenreiter Kassel, 1976. — 164p,24p of plates : music, ports ; 23cm.
Previous ed.: s.l. : s.n., 1951. — Index.
Pbk : £10.50
ISBN 3-7618-0513-6

A(Z) — MUSIC IN RELATION TO OTHER SUBJECTS
A(ZC) — Music - expounding symbolism
De ratione in musica : Festschrift Erich Schenk, zu 5.Mai 1972 / herausgegeben von Theophil Antonicek, Rudolf Flotzinger und Othman Wessely. — Basel [etc.] ; London ([32 Great Titchfield St., W.1]) : Bärenreiter Kassel, 1975. — xiii,300p,plate : 2 ill, music, port ; 24cm.
Bibl.: p.286-300.
Pbk : £18.00
ISBN 3-7618-0420-2

A(ZF) — Music - influenced by ethnic factors
Blacking, John
How musical is man? / [by] John Blacking. — London : Faber, 1976. — viii,120p,[12]p of plates : ill, music ; 23cm.
Sound tape of Venda music to accompany this book available from the University of Washington Press, Seattle. — Originally published: Seattle ; London : University of Washington Press, 1973. — Bibl.: p.117-118. — Index.
ISBN 0-571-10790-7 : £4.95
ISBN 0-571-10803-2 Pbk : £2.20
Also classified at BZNR

(B76-22078)

A/B — PHYSICS OF MUSIC
Benade, Arthur Henry
Fundamentals of musical acoustics / [by] Arthur H. Benade. — New York ; London [etc.] : Oxford University Press, 1975. — xii, 596p ; 24cm.
Index.
ISBN 0-19-502030-8 : £11.50

(B76-25959)

Taylor, Charles Alfred
Sounds of music / [by] Charles Taylor. — London : British Broadcasting Corporation, 1976. — [6],183p : ill, facsims, music, ports ; 26cm.
' ... a fuller version of Professor Taylor's Royal Institution Christmas lectures' - book jacket. — Bibl.: p.177. — Index.
ISBN 0-563-12228-5 : £6.50

(B76-10250)

Wood, Alexander
Alexander Wood's the physics of music. — 7th ed. / revised by J.M. Bowsher. — London : Chapman and Hall [etc.], 1975. — xiv,258p,xvi p of plates : ill, music, plans ; 23cm.
Previous ed.: published as 'The physics of music'. London : Methuen, 1962. — Bibl.: p.252. — Index.
ISBN 0-412-13250-8 : £5.50
ISBN 0-412-21140-8 Pbk : £2.95

(B76-23699)

A/D — COMPOSITION
A/D(VJ) — Composition. Junior schools
Tillman, June
Exploring sound : creative musical projects for teachers / [by] June Tillman. — London : Galliard [etc.], 1976. — 102p : ill, music ; 25cm.
Bibl.: p.98. — Index.
ISBN 0-85249-310-x Pbk : £2.50

(B76-22855)

A/D(YB/M) — Europe. Composers
Borge, Victor
My favourite intervals / [by] Victor Borge and Robert Sherman ;
drawings by Thomas Winding. — London : Sphere, 1976. —
189p : ill ; 18cm.
Originally published as: 'My favorite intermissions', Garden City, N.Y. :
Doubleday, 1971 ; and as 'My favourite intervals', London : Woburn Press,
1974.
ISBN 0-7221-1779-5 Pbk : £0.60

(B76-28392)

A/D(YC/M) — Composers. Great Britain
British music now : a guide to the work of younger composers /
edited by Lewis Foreman. — London : Elek, 1975. — 246p :
music ; 23cm.
Bibl.: p.199-212. — List of records: p.216-237. — Index.
ISBN 0-236-30933-1 : £6.50

(B76-08493)

A/D(YM/M/T) — Composers. Russia. Bibliographies
Moldon, David
A bibliography of Russian composers / [by] David Moldon. —
London [etc.] : White Lion Publishers, 1976. — xviii,364p ; 26cm.
Index.
ISBN 0-7284-0101-0 : £15.00

(B76-28683)

A/D(YSX/XN55/M) — Composers. Canada, 1920-1974
Contemporary Canadian composers / edited by Keith Macmillan
and John Beckwith. — Toronto ; London [etc.] : Oxford
University Press, 1975 [i.e. 1976]. — xxiv,248p,[8]p of plates : ill,
music, ports ; 25cm.
Published in Canada: 1975. — Bibl.
ISBN 0-19-540244-8 : £11.75

(B76-25955)

A/E — PERFORMANCE
A/EC(M) — Conductors
Conversations with conductors : Bruno Walter, Sir Adrian Boult,
Leonard Bernstein, Ernest Ansermet, Otto Klemperer, Leopold
Stokowski / edited by Robert Chesterman ; photographs by
Godfrey MacDomnic ; photograph of Bruno Walter by Fred
Plant. — London : Robson Books, 1976. — 128p : ports ; 24cm.
'The principal conversations in this book are taken from recordings, made
between the years 1966 and 1969 ... ' - p.11.
ISBN 0-903895-44-7 : £4.50

(B76-33375)

A/EC(P) — Karajan, Herbert von. Biographies
Robinson, Paul
Karajan / [by] Paul Robinson ; discography by Bruce Surtees. —
London : Macdonald and Jane's, 1976. — [3],158p,[8]p of plates :
ill, ports ; 23cm. — (The art of the conductor)
Originally published: Toronto : Lester and Orpen, 1975. — List of sound
discs: p.125-156. — Index.
ISBN 0-354-04031-6 : £3.95

(B76-35356)

A/EC(P) — Toscanini, Arturo. Biographies
Marek, George Richard
Toscanini / [by] George R. Marek. — London : Vision Press,
1976. — xiv,322p,[20]p of plates : ill, facsim, ports ; 24cm.
Originally published: New York : Atheneum, 1975. — Bibl.: p.302-304. —
Index.
ISBN 0-85478-463-2 : £7.80

(B76-21367)

A/EC(P) — Weingartner, Felix. Biographies
Felix Weingartner : recollections & recordings / [edited by]
Christopher Dyment. — Rickmansworth (22 Pheasants Way,
Rickmansworth, Herts.) : Triad Press, 1976. — 5-116p : ill,
facsims, music, ports ; 30cm. — (Triad Press bibliographical
series ; no.5)
List of gramophone records: p.72-92. — Index.
ISBN 0-902070-17-7 Pbk : £5.95

(B76-17083)

**A/EC(P/ZD) — Smart, Sir George - influencing the attitudes of
Great Britain towards Beethoven**
Young, Percy Marshall
Beethoven : a Victorian tribute based on the papers of Sir George
Smart / by Percy M. Young. — London : Dobson, 1976. — xiii,
125p,[16]p of plates : ill, facsims, music, ports ; 24cm.
Bibl.: p.119-120. — Index.
ISBN 0-234-77672-2 : £5.00

(B76-33367)

A/FD — RECORDED MUSIC
A/FD(K) — Recorded music. Economic aspects
Electric and Musical Industries
World record markets / Electric and Musical Industries. — 3rd
ed. — London (23 Ridgmount St., WC1E 7AH) : Henry Melland
for EMI, 1976. — 110p : ill(chiefly col), col facsims ; 22cm.
Previous ed.: 1971.
ISBN 0-9500730-1-6 Pbk : £2.50

(B76-28828)

A/FD(P) — Gaisberg, Fred. Biographies
Moore, Jerrold Northrop
A voice in time : the gramophone of Fred Gaisberg, 1873-1951 /
[by] Jerrold Northrop Moore. — London : Hamilton, 1976. —
viii,248p,xvi p of plates : ill, facsims, ports ; 23cm.
Index.
ISBN 0-241-89374-7 : £5.50

(B76-13200)

A/FD(WT) — Lists
Music master / [designed and compiled by John Humphries]. —
London (48 Shacklewell La., E8 2EY) : John Humphries.
1976. — 1976. — 472p ; 31cm.
English text, preliminaries in English, French and German.
ISBN 0-904520-01-3 : £15.00(£22.50 including monthly supplements)
ISSN 0308-9347

(B76-29926)

Music master. — London (10 Kingsland High St., E8 2JP) : R.P.C.
1974 / [compiled by John Humphries]. — 1975. — 5-1006p ; 30cm.
Versos of most leaves blank. — Originally published: 1974.
ISBN 0-904520-00-5 Pbk : Unpriced
ISSN 0308-9347

(B76-35030)

The art of record buying : a list of recommended microgroove
recordings. — London : E.M.G
1976. — [1976]. — [2],285p : map ; 23cm.
£5.00

A/FD(WT) — Phrynis records. Lists
Première liste générale des disques à saphir Phrynis de 30
centimètres de diamètre. — Bournemouth (19 Glendale Rd,
Bournemouth BH6 4JA) : Talking Machine Review, 1975. —
48p ; 21cm.
French text, English introduction. — Facsimile reprint of first catalogue of
'Phrynis' records.
ISBN 0-902338-23-4 Sd : £0.60

(B76-50352)

A/FE(P/X) — Sterling Cylinder Records. History
Carter, Sydney Horace
'Sterling' / ... compiled by Sydney H. Carter, Frank Andrews
[and] Leonard L. Watts. — Bournemouth (19 Glendale Rd,
Bournemouth BH6 4JA) : 'Talking Machine Review', 1975. —
[108]p : facsims, ports ; 21cm.
Contents: A catalogue of 'Sterling' cylinder records / compiled by Sydney
H. Carter - A history of their manufacture / by Frank Andrews - 'Sterling'
records on 'Pathé' discs / compiled by Leonard L. Watts and F. Andrews.
ISBN 0-902338-22-6 Sd : £1.60

(B76-09865)

A/FE(WT) — Cylinder records. Lists
Annand, Herbert Harry
The catalogue of the United States Everlasting Indestructible
cylinders, 1908-1913 / by H.H. Annand. — 2nd ed. —
Bournemouth (19 Glendale Rd, Bournemouth BH6 4JA) : The
Talking Machine Review International, 1973. — [36]p ; 21cm.
Previous ed.: 1966.
ISBN 0-902338-21-8 Sd : £0.45

(B76-27984)

A/FF(WT) — Stereophonic records. Lists
Greenfield, Edward
The Penguin stereo record guide / [by] Edward Greenfield,
Robert Layton, Ivan March ; edited by Ivan March. —
Harmondsworth [etc.] : Penguin, 1975. — xix,1114p ; 20cm. —
(A Penguin handbook)
ISBN 0-14-046223-6 Pbk : £3.50

(B76-03703)

A/FY — MUSICAL CHARACTER
A/G(BC) — Directories
The folk directory / [English Folk Dance and Song Society]. —
London : The Society.
1976 / edited by Mira S. Curtis. — 1976. — 177p : ill, map ; 22cm.
Index.
ISBN 0-85418-111-3 : £2.00(£1.00 to members)
ISBN 0-85418-110-5 Pbk : £1.00 (£0.50 to members)

(B76-25961)

A/G(D) — Folk music. Essays
Bartók, Béla
Béla Bartók essays / selected and edited by Benjamin Suchoff. —
London : Faber, 1976. — xvi,567p,[2]leaves of plates,[8]p of
plates : ill, facsims, music, port ; 26cm. — (New York Bartók
Archive. Studies in musicology ; no.8)
'Translation of Hungarian and other foreign language essays was made for
the most part by Richard Tószeghy and by ... the late Elma Laurvik,
Marianne Kethly, and Ida Kohler. The pieces on Liszt were translated by
the late Colin Mason ...' - Editors preface. — Bibl.: p.527-555. — Index.
ISBN 0-571-10120-8 : £38.50

(B76-36283)

A/G(YDM) — Folk music. Ireland
Eigse cheol tíre = Irish folk music studies. — Dublin (3 Sydenham Rd, Dundrum, Dublin 14) : Folk Music Society of Ireland.
Includes Irish text. — Bibl.
Vol.2 : 1974-1975 / edited by Hugh Shields, Seóirse Bodley & Breandán Breathnach. — 1976. — 87p : facsim, music ; 21cm.
ISBN 0-905733-00-2 Pbk : £1.00

(B76-35799)

Léachtaí Cholm Cille VII : an ceol i litríocht la Gaeilge / in eagar ag Pádraig O Fiannachta. — Má Nuad [i.e. Maynooth] ([Maynooth, Co. Kildare]) : [St Patrick's College], 1976. — 166p ; 21cm.
ISBN 0-901519-17-0 Pbk : £0.50

(B76-34780)

A/GB(VK) — Popular music. Secondary schools
Pop music in school / edited by Graham Vulliamy and Ed Lee. — Cambridge [etc.] : Cambridge University Press, 1976. — viii,207p : ill, music ; 24cm. — (The resources of music series ; 13)
Bibl.: p.181-194. — List of sound discs: p.195-204. — Index.
ISBN 0-521-20836-x : £4.75
ISBN 0-521-09968-4 Pbk : £2.25

(B76-25953)

A/GB(W/Z) — Popular music. Concerts - related to safety
Greater London Council
Code of practice for pop concerts : a guide to safety, health and welfare at one day events / Greater London Council. — [London] : G.L.C., [1976]. — [34]p : 1 ill ; 30cm.
ISBN 0-7168-0732-7 : £1.50

(B76-32962)

A/GB(XN10) — Popular music, 1920-1929
Pearsall, Ronald
Popular music of the twenties / [by] Ronald Pearsall. — Newton Abbot [etc.] : David and Charles [etc.], 1976. — 176p : ill, facsims, ports ; 22cm.
Bibl.: p.172-173. — Index.
ISBN 0-7153-7036-7 : £4.95

(B76-32590)

A/GCW(C) — Country 'n' western music. Encyclopaedias
Stambler, Irwin
Encyclopedia of folk country and Western music / by Irwin Stambler and Grelun Landon ; illustrated with photographs. — New York : St Martin's Press ; London : St James Press, 1969. — ix,396p : ill, music, ports ; 24cm.
Bibl.: p.393-396. — List of gramophone records: p.377-390.
ISBN 0-900997-24-9 : £5.00

(B76-00666)

A/GR(VH) — Activities. Infants schools
Hope-Brown, Margaret
Activities in music with children under six / [by] Margaret Hope-Brown. — London : Evans Bros, 1976. — 46p : ill, music ; 21cm. — (Education in action)
ISBN 0-237-29165-7 Sd : £0.80

(B76-04797)

A/HK(C) — Rock 'n' roll. Encyclopaedias
The *encyclopedia* of rock / edited by Phil Hardy and Dave Laing. — St Albans : Panther.
In 3 vols.
Vol.1 : The age of rock'n'roll. — 1976. — 352p ; 18cm.
Index.
ISBN 0-586-04267-9 Pbk : £0.95

(B76-14358)

Vol.2 : From Liverpool to San Francisco. — 1976. — 398p ; 18cm.
Index.
ISBN 0-586-04268-7 Pbk : £0.95

(B76-16549)

Vol.3 : The sounds of the seventies. — 1976. — 320p ; 18cm.
Index.
ISBN 0-586-04269-5 Pbk : £0.95

(B76-31912)

A/HK(XQK11) — Rock 'n' roll, 1965-1975
Downing, David
Future rock / [by] David Downing. — St Albans : Panther, 1976. — 172p ; 18cm.
List of sound discs: p.170-172.
ISBN 0-586-04308-x Pbk : £0.60

(B76-30334)

A/JR — Films
Bazelon, Irwin
Knowing the score : notes on film music / [by] Irwin Bazelon. — New York ; London [etc.] : Van Nostrand Reinhold, 1975. — 352p : ill, music, ports ; 24cm.
Index.
ISBN 0-442-20594-5 : £6.25

(B76-05914)

Manvell, Roger
The technique of film music / written and compiled by Roger Manvell and John Huntley ... — Revised and enlarged ed. / by Richard Arnell and Peter Day. — London [etc.] : Focal Press, 1975. — 310p : ill, facsims, music ; 23cm. — (The library of communication techniques)
Previous ed.: 1957. — Bibl.: p.291-302. — Index.
ISBN 0-240-50848-3 : £5.00

(B76-12128)

A/JV/E(P) — Powell, Sandy. Biographies
Powell, Sandy
'Can you hear me, mother?' : Sandy Powell's lifetime of music-hall / Sandy Powell's story told to Harry Stanley. — London : Jupiter Books, 1976. — 3-192p : ill, facsims, ports ; 24cm.
ISBN 0-904041-38-7 : £3.50

(B76-13584)

A/KB — Programme music
Brace, Geoffrey
Listen! music and nature / [by] Geoffrey Brace and Ian Burton. — Cambridge [etc.] : Cambridge University Press, 1976. — v, 66p : ill, music, port ; 21cm.
ISBN 0-521-20706-1 Pbk : £1.60

(B76-13569)

A/KB(X) — Programme music. History
Orrey, Leslie
Programme music : a brief survey from the sixteenth century to the present day / [by] Leslie Orrey. — London : Davis-Poynter, 1975. — 223p : music ; 23cm.
Bibl.: p.211-215. — List of programme music: p.193-210. — Index.
ISBN 0-7067-0171-2 : £6.00

(B76-01879)

A/LD(T) — Church music. Bibliographies
Yeats-Edwards, Paul
English church music : a bibliography / [by] Paul Yeats-Edwards. — London [etc.] : White Lion Publishers, 1975. — [6],xviii,217p : ill, facsims ; 26cm.
Index.
ISBN 0-7285-0020-5 : £15.00

(B76-50000)

A/LD(YD/D) — Church music. England. Essays
English church music : essays, reports and reviews. — Croydon (Addington Place, Croydon CR9 5AD) : Royal School of Church Music.
1976. — [1976]. — 62p : music ; 22cm.
ISBN 0-85402-062-4 Pbk : £1.50

(B76-50353)

A/LD/E — Church music. Performance
Dakers, Lionel
A handbook of parish music : a working guide for clergy and organists / by Lionel Dakers. — London [etc.] : Mowbrays, 1976. — xv,133p : music ; 19cm.
Bibl.: p.122-127. — Index.
ISBN 0-264-66261-x Pbk : £1.95

(B77-00345)

A/LZ — ELEMENTS OF MUSIC
Berry, Wallace
Structural functions in music / [by] Wallace Berry. — Englewood Cliffs ; London [etc.] : Prentice-Hall, 1976. — xiii,447p : ill, music ; 24cm.
Index.
ISBN 0-13-853903-0 : £8.40

(B76-11503)

A/M — Rudiments
Joseph, Jack
Notes on music / compiled by Jack Joseph. — Gillingham, Kent (38 Ferndale Rd, Gillingham, Kent) : Lindley Press, 1975. — [1], 24p : ill ; 13cm.
ISBN 0-9504506-0-x Sd : £0.40

(B76-24540)

Puopolo, Vito
Music fundamentals / [by] Vito Puopolo. — New York : Schirmer ; London : Collier Macmillan, 1976. — xiii,219p : ill, music ; 26cm.
Index.
ISBN 0-02-871890-9 Pbk : £5.25

(B76-25958)

Roe, Betty
An ABC of music for actors / [compiled by B. Roe]. — London (14 Barlby Rd, W10 6AR) : Thomas Publishing, 1975. — 11p : music ; 25cm.
ISBN 0-905210-00-x Sd : £0.30
Also classified at 781'.24

(B76-05037)

A/NM — Rhythm
Yeston, Maury
    The stratification of musical rhythm / [by] Maury Yeston. —
    New Haven [Conn.] ; London : Yale University Press, 1976. — ix,
    155p : ill, music ; 24cm.
    Bibl.: p.154-155.
    ISBN 0-300-01884-3 : £6.00

(B76-18372)

A/R — Harmony
Benjamin, Thomas
    Techniques and materials of tonal music : with an introduction to
    twentieth-century techniques / [by] Thomas Benjamin, Michael
    Horvit, Robert Nelson. — Boston [Mass.] [etc.] ; London :
    Houghton Mifflin, 1975. — xiii,236p : ill, music ; 26cm.
    Bibl.: p.231. — Index.
    ISBN 0-395-19095-9 : £7.95

(B76-22853)

A/R(XE331) — Harmony, 1600-1930
La Motte, Diether de
    Harmonielehre : 1600-1730-1790-1810-1840-1860-1880-1910-1930 /
    [von] Diether de la Motte. — Kassel [etc.] ; London : Bärenreiter
    [etc.], 1976. — 281p : ill, music ; 18cm.
    Pbk : £12.00
    ISBN 3-7618-0540-3

A/RM — Counterpoint
Ziehn, Bernhard
    Canonic studies / [by] Bernhard Ziehn. — [1st ed. reprinted] /
    edited and introduced by Ronald Stevenson. — London : Kahn
    and Averill, 1976. — 216p : chiefly music, port ; 23cm.
    Originally published: as 'Canonical studies'. Milwaukee : Kaun Music Co.,
    1912. — Bibl.: p.20-21.
    ISBN 0-900707-38-0 : £4.50

(B76-35798)

AB — MUSICAL LITERATURE. VOCAL MUSIC
AB(TCT/WT) — Titles. Lists
Hodgson, Julian
    Music titles in translation : a checklist of musical compositions /
    compiled by Julian Hodgson. — London : Bingley [etc.], 1976. —
    viii,370p ; 23cm.
    ISBN 0-85157-198-0 : £7.50

(B76-14368)

AB/E — Singing
Husler, Frederick
    Singing : the physical nature of the vocal organ : a guide to the
    unlocking of the singing voice / by Frederick Husler and Yvonne
    Rodd-Marling ; illustrated by Frederick Husler. — London :
    Hutchinson, 1976. — xviii,148p,[7]leaves of plates,[10]p of plates :
    ill(some col), port ; 25cm.
    Previous ed.: London : Faber, 1965. — Bibl.: p.133-134. — Index.
    ISBN 0-09-126860-5 : £6.50

(B76-26571)

AB/ED — Diction
Marshall, Madeleine
    The singer's manual of English diction / [by] Madeleine Marshall.
    — New York : Shirmer Books ; London : Collier Macmillan,
    [1975]. — [4],198p ; 24cm.
    Originally published: New York : Schirmer, 1953.
    ISBN 0-02-871100-9 Pbk : £3.50

(B76-23702)

AC — MUSICAL LITERATURE. OPERA
Knapp, John Merrill
    The magic of opera / [by] J. Merrill Knapp. — London : Hale,
    1975. — x,371p : ill, facsim, music, ports ; 24cm.
    Originally published: New York : Harper and Row, 1972. — Bibl. — Index.
    ISBN 0-7091-5254-x : £6.50

(B76-00668)

Kobbé, Gustave
    Kobbé's complete opera book. — 9th ed. / edited and revised by
    the Earl of Harewood. — London : Putnam, 1976. — xvii,1694p,
    40p of plates : ill, music ; 22cm.
    Previous ed.: 1969. — Index.
    ISBN 0-370-10020-4 : £15.00

(B76-31916)

AC(C) — Encyclopaedias
The encyclopedia of opera / edited by Leslie Orrey ; advisory editor
    Gilbert Chase. — London : Pitman, 1976. — 376p : ill(some col) ;
    26cm.
    Ill. on lining papers.
    ISBN 0-273-00237-6 : £13.50(£10.50 until January 1 1977)

(B76-31915)

AC(DE) — Questions and answers
Taylor, Ian, *b.1932*
    The opera lover's quiz book / compiled by Ian Taylor ; illustrated
    with drawings by Enrico Caruso. — London : Luscombe, 1975. —
    95p : ill ; 20cm.
    With answers. — Index.
    ISBN 0-86002-084-3 Pbk : £0.95

(B76-15052)

AC(WB/XPD28/P) — Webster, Sir David. Biographies, 1944-1971
Haltrecht, Montague
    The quiet showman : Sir David Webster and the Royal Opera
    House / [by] Montague Haltrecht. — London : Collins, 1975. —
    319p, leaf of plate,[16]p of plates : ill, ports ; 24cm.
    Bibl.: p.308. — Index.
    ISBN 0-00-211163-2 : £6.00

(B76-03866)

AC(XG41) — Opera, 1800-1840
Dent, Edward Joseph
    The rise of romantic opera / [by] Edward J. Dent ; edited by
    Winton Dean. — Cambridge [etc.] : Cambridge University Press,
    1976. — x,198p ; 23cm.
    'Lectures originally delivered at Cornell University, 1937-8' - Library of
    Congress Cataloging in Publication data. — Index.
    ISBN 0-521-21337-1 : £6.50

(B77-00341)

AC(XM75/WT) — Opera, 1900-1974. Lists
Northouse, Cameron
    Twentieth century opera in England and the United States / [by]
    Cameron Northouse. — Boston, Mass. : G.K. Hall ; London :
    Prior, 1976. — viii,400p ; 22cm.
    Index.
    ISBN 0-86043-002-2 : £14.95

(B76-35928)

AC/E(YHXM/QB/XKU31) — Monte Carlo Opera, 1879-1909
Walsh, T J
    Monte Carlo opera, 1879-1909 / [by] T.J. Walsh. — Dublin : Gill
    and Macmillan ; [London] : Macmillan, 1975. — xix,321p,[16]p of
    plates : ill, facsim, ports ; 24cm.
    Facsims on lining papers. — Bibl.: p.305-306. — Index.
    ISBN 0-7171-0725-6 : £9.75

(B76-05913)

**AC/E/K/QB(YTXHS) — Seattle Opera Association. Economic
        aspects**
Salem, Mahmoud
    Organizational survival in the performing arts : the making of the
    Seattle Opera / [by] Mahmoud Salem. — New York [etc.] ;
    London : Praeger ; [London] : [Distributed by Martin Robertson],
    1976. — xiii,211p : ill ; 25cm. — (Praeger special studies in US
    economic, social and political issues)
    Bibl.: p.188-201. — Index.
    ISBN 0-275-05670-8 : £10.25

(B76-22516)

ACH — MUSICAL LITERATURE. OPERA-BALLET
**ACLM(XFWK61/ZC) — Ballad operas, 1730-1790. Expounding
        seafaring**
Topical and nautical operas / selected and arranged by Walter H.
    Rubsamen. — New York ; London : Garland, 1974 [i.e. 1976]. —
    366p in various pagings : ill, music ; 23cm. — (The ballad opera ;
    vol.14)
    Facsimile reprints. — Published in the United States: 1974.
    ISBN 0-8240-0913-4 £400.00 the 28 volume series
    Primary classification ACLM(XFWK61/ZC)

(B76-20707)

**ACLM(XFWK61/ZC) — Ballad operas, 1730-1790. Expounding social
        life**
Topical and nautical operas / selected and arranged by Walter H.
    Rubsamen. — New York ; London : Garland, 1974 [i.e. 1976]. —
    366p in various pagings : ill, music ; 23cm. — (The ballad opera ;
    vol.14)
    Facsimile reprints. — Published in the United States: 1974.
    ISBN 0-8240-0913-4 : £400.00 the 28 volume series
    Also classified at ACLM(XFWK61/ZC)

(B76-20707)

**ACLM(XFWK61/ZC) — Ballad operas, 1730-1790. Expounding the
        legal profession**
The **medical** and legal professions / selected and arranged by Walter
    M. Rubsamen. — New York ; London : Garland, 1974 [i.e. 1976].
    — 360p in various pagings : music ; 23cm. — (The ballad opera ;
    vol.4)
    Facsimile reprints. — Published in the United States: 1974.
    ISBN 0-8240-0903-7 : £400.00 the 28 vol. series
    Primary classification ACLM(XFWK61/ZC)

(B76-19251)

**ACLM(XFWK61/ZC) — Ballad operas, 1730-1790. Expounding the
        medical profession**
The **medical** and legal professions / selected and arranged by Walter
    M. Rubsamen. — New York ; London : Garland, 1974 [i.e. 1976].
    — 360p in various pagings : music ; 23cm. — (The ballad opera ;
    vol.4)
    Facsimile reprints. — Published in the United States: 1974.
    ISBN 0-8240-0903-7 : £400.00 the 28 vol. series
    Also classified at ACLM(XFWK61/ZC)

(B76-19251)

ACM — MUSICAL LITERATURE. MUSICAL PLAYS
ACM/JR(YT/XNF8) — Musical plays. Films. United States, 1926-1933
The movie musical from Vitaphone to 42nd Street : as reported in a great fan magazine / edited by Miles Kreuger. — New York : Dover Publications [etc.] ; London : Constable, 1975. — xi,367p : ill, ports ; 29cm.
' ... an anthology of selected articles and illustrations from "Photoplay" magazine which appeared between 1926 and 1933 ... ' - title page verso. — Index.
ISBN 0-486-23154-2 Pbk : £4.55

(B76-12805)

ACPF — Masques
The maske of flowers / [by I.G., W.D., T.B.]. — Leeds ([5 Albert Grove, Leeds LS6 4DA]) : Boethius Press, [1975]. — [37]p : music ; 21cm. — (Early music reprinted ; 2)
Facsimile reprint of: 1st ed., London : Printed by N.O. for Robert Wilson, 1614.
ISBN 0-904263-02-9 : £3.20

(B76-10977)

AD — MUSICAL LITERATURE. CHORAL MUSIC
AD/LE(YDKPB/X) — Cathedral music. Bangor Cathedral. History
Paul, Leslie Douglas
Music at Bangor Cathedral Church : some historical notes / by Leslie D. Paul. — [Bangor] ([The Cathedral Chaplain's House, Glanrafon, Bangor, Caernarvonshire LL57 1LH]) : [Bangor Cathedral], 1975. — 24p ; 21cm. — (Bangor Cathedral. Monographs ; no.1)
' ... first published in the issue of "Welsh Music" for Spring, 1971 ... ' - cover.
ISBN 0-905229-00-2 Sd : £0.25

(B76-24542)

ADD/LH(YG/XD301) — Passions. Hungary, 1500-1800
Bárdos, Kornél
Volksmusikartige Variierungstechnik in den ungarischen Passionen, 15. bis 18. Jahrhundert / von Kornél Bárdos ; [aus dem ungarischen übertragen von Tilda und Paul Alpári]. — Kassel [etc.] ; London ([32 Great Titchfield St., W.1]) : Bärenreiter, 1975. — 240p,6p of plates : facsims, music ; 25cm. — (Musicologica Hungarica : neue Folge ; 5)
Originally published: in Hungarian. Budapest : Akadémiai Kiadó, 1975. — Bibl.: p.229-240.
£16.25
ISBN 3-7618-0504-7

ADGTCW(X) — Protestant church music. History
Blume, Friedrich
Protestant church music : a history / by Friedrich Blume in collaboration with Ludwig Finscher ... [et al.] ; [translated from the German] ; foreword by Paul Henry Lang. — London : Gollancz, 1975. — xv,831p : ill, facsims, music, ports ; 24cm.
This translation originally published: New York : Norton, 1974. — Translation of: 'Geschichte der Evangelischen Kirchenmusik', 2 Aufl. Kassel : Bärenreiter-Verlag, 1965. — Bibl.: p.733-800. — Index.
ISBN 0-575-01996-4 : £15.00

(B76-01876)

ADP(YD) — Carols. England
Iles, Norman
The pagan carols restored / by Norman Iles. — Morecambe (381 Marine Rd, Morecambe, Lancs.) : The author.
Vol.1. — 1971. — [4],30p ; 21cm.
The author attempts to reconstruct the pagan originals of 18 Christian carols.
ISBN 0-9500776-4-x Sd : £0.50

(B76-15054)

ADW/G(YD/XG61) — Folk songs. England, 1800-1860
The rigs of the fair : popular sports and pastimes in the nineteenth century through songs, ballads and contemporary accounts / selected and edited by Roy Palmer and Jon Raven. — Cambridge [etc.] : Cambridge University Press, 1976. — 64p : ill, facsims, music ; 28cm. — (The resources of music series ; 12)
Bibl.: p.62-64. — Index.
ISBN 0-521-20908-0 : £1.25(non-net)
Also classified at 784.6'8'301570941

(B76-12389)

ADW/G(YDCR) — Folk songs. Sussex
Copper, Bob
A song for every season / [by] Bob Copper. — St Albans : Paladin, 1975. — xiii,288p,[8]p of plates : ill, music, ports ; 20cm.
Originally published: London : Heinemann, 1971.
ISBN 0-586-08229-8 Pbk : £1.25
Also classified at 784.4'9422'5

(B76-02079)

We wunt be druv : songs and stories from Sussex / [compiled] by Tony Wales. — London : Galliard : English Folk Dance and Song Society, 1976. — 60p : ill, music ; 21x25cm.
Bibl.: p 60.
ISBN 0-85249-307-x Pbk : £2.80

(B76-17456)

ADW/G(YDMG/T) — Folk songs. Ireland. Galway. Bibliographies
Ní Fhlathartaigh, Ríonach
Clár amhrán Bhaile na hInse : clár na n-amhrán i mbarúntacht Bhaile na hInse / [le] Ríonach Ní Fhlathartaigh. — Baile Atha Cliath [Dublin] ([15 Bóthar Ghráinseach an Déin, An Charraig Dhubh, Co. Atha Cliath]) : An Clóchomhar Tta, 1976. — xv, 480p,plate : map ; 23cm. — (Leabhair thaighde ; 25)
Index.
ISBN 0-903758-06-7 : £3.50

(B76-17862)

ADW/G(YMUL) — Folk songs. Lvov
Lwowskie piosenki / Stefan Uhma ; w opracowaniu i z uzupelnieniami Mariana Wagnera. — Londyn [London] : Kolo Lwowian.
Część 5 : Zbrodnia i Kara ; oraz uzupelnienia poprzednio wydanych cześci / [ilustracje Marek Gramski]. — 1975. — [2],92p : ill, music, port ; 23cm.
ISBN 0-9503005-3-5 Sd : £0.75

(B76-05915)

ADW/G(YUBR) — Folk songs. Mexico. Rio Grande
A Texas-Mexican cancionero : folksongs of the Lower Border / [compiled by] Américo Paredes. — Urbana [etc.] ; London : University of Illinois Press, 1976. — xxiv,194p,[10]p of plates : ill, map, music, ports ; 26cm. — (Music in American life)
English text, Spanish and English lyrics. — Bibl.: p.187-189. — Index.
ISBN 0-252-00522-8 : £6.50

(B76-22856)

ADW/GB — Popular songs
Rock file. — St Albans : Panther.
4 / edited by Charlie Gillett and Simon Frith. — 1976. — 400p ; 18cm.
'... incorporating some of the material originally published in "Rock file 1"' - note.
ISBN 0-586-04370-5 Pbk : £1.25

(B76-25952)

ADW/GB(XL95/WT) — Songs, 1884-1974. Lists
Blacklock, Robert Shedden
Which song and when : a handbook of selected song titles from 1880 to 1974 / compiled by R.S. Blacklock. — Edinburgh (10 Antigua St., Edinburgh EH1 3NH) : Bandparts Music Stores Ltd, 1975. — 84p ; 21cm.
Index.
ISBN 0-9504826-0-9 Sd : £0.40

(B76-06890)

ADW/GB(YTLD/X) — Afro-American popular songs. History
Cummings, Tony
The sound of Philadelphia / [by] Tony Cummings. — London : Eyre Methuen, 1975. — 157p : ill, facsims, ports ; 27cm.
Index.
ISBN 0-413-34080-5 Pbk : £2.75

(B76-04295)

ADW/GB/FD(XPQ21/WT) — Popular songs. Recorded music. Lists, 1955-1975
20 years of British record charts, 1955-1975 / with commentary by Peter Jones & Tony Jasper ; edited by Tony Jasper. — London : Queen Anne Press, 1975. — 208p ; 18cm.
'... Top Twenty singles charts as listed weekly in "Record Mirror" from early January 1955 to the end of September 1975' - Foreword and acknowledgements.
ISBN 0-362-00263-0 Pbk : £0.75

(B76-08789)

ADW/GJ — Children's songs
Ten green bottles / illustrated by Susanna Gretz. — Harmondsworth [etc.] : Puffin Books, 1976. — 32p : chiefly col ill, music ; 20cm. — (A puffin easy reader)
Also published: Harmondsworth : Kestrel Books, 1976.
ISBN 0-14-050144-4 Sd : £0.50

(B76-14369)

ADW/GR — Songs. Activities
Action rhymes / [compiled] by Dorothy Taylor ; with illustrations by Kathy Layfield & Brian Price Thomas and photographs by John Moyes. — Loughborough : Ladybird Books, 1976. — 52p : col ill, music ; 18cm. — (Learning with traditional rhymes ; book 5)
Text on lining papers.
ISBN 0-7214-0439-1 : £0.24

(B76-30340)

ADW/H — Dance songs
Dancing rhymes / [compiled] by Dorothy Taylor ; with illustrations by Martin Aitchison, Frank Humphris and Brian Price Thomas and photographs by John Moyes. — Loughborough : Ladybird Books, 1976. — 52p : col ill, music ; 18cm. — (Learning with traditional rhymes ; book 6)
Text on lining papers.
ISBN 0-7214-0440-5 : £0.24

(B76-30341)

AK — MUSICAL LITERATURE. VOCAL SOLOS
AKDW(YE) — Songs. Germany
The **Fischer-Dieskau** book of Lieder : the texts of over 750 songs in
German / chosen and introduced by Dietrich Fischer-Dieskau ;
with English translations by George Bird and Richard Stokes. —
London : Gollancz : Pan Books, 1976. — 3-433p ; 24cm.
Parallel German text and English translation, with English introduction. —
German text with German introduction originally published: as 'Texte
deutscher Lieder'. München : Deutscher Taschenbuch, 1968. — Index.
ISBN 0-575-01852-6 : £7.50

(B76-33373)

AKDW/E(P) — Menzies, Ivan. Biographies
Magor, Cliff
The song of a merryman : Ivan Menzies of the D'Oyly Carte
Gilbert & Sullivan operas / by Cliff & Edna Magor. — London :
Grosvenor Books, 1976. — 108p,[8]p of plates : ill, ports ; 19cm.
— (A Grosvenor biography)
ISBN 0-901269-18-2 Pbk : £1.00

(B76-19249)

AKDW/E(YH) — Songs. Performance. France
Bernac, Pierre
The interpretation of French song / by Pierre Bernac ;
translations of song texts by Winifred Radford. — London :
Gollancz, 1976. — xvi,327p : music ; 21cm.
Originally published: London : Cassell, 1970. — Index.
ISBN 0-575-02207-8 : £7.50

(B77-00346)

AKDW/G/E(YDTF/P) — Folk songs. Singers. Co. Fermanagh.
Maguire, John. Biographies
Maguire, John, *b.1902*
Come day, go day, God send Sunday : the songs and life story
told in his own words, of John Maguire, traditional singer and
farmer from Co. Fermanagh / collated by Robin Morton. —
London : Routledge and Kegan Paul, 1973 [i.e. 1976]. — xiv,
188p,leaf of plate,[2]p of plates : ill, music, ports ; 22cm.
Originally published: 1973. — Index.
ISBN 0-7100-8388-2 Pbk : £1.50
Also classified at 784.4'9416

(B76-21366)

AKDW/GB/E(M) — Popular songs. Singers
Top pop scene. — Maidenhead : Purnell.
[1976]. — 1976. — 3-63p : chiefly ill(some col), ports(some col) ; 27cm.
Ports. on lining papers.
ISBN 0-361-03505-5 : £0.85

(B76-31913)

AKDW/GB/E(M/XQK7) — Popular songs. Singers, 1970-1976
Superstars of the 70's. — London : Octopus Books, 1976. —
5-92p : ill(chiefly col), col facsim, ports(chiefly col) ; 31cm.
Col. ill. on lining papers. — ' ... adapted from "The story of pop"' - title
page verso.
ISBN 0-7064-0447-5 : £1.99

(B76-34774)

AKDW/GB/E(P) — Beatles, The
Mellers, Wilfrid
Twilight of the gods : the Beatles in retrospect / [by] Wilfrid
Mellers. — London : Faber, 1976. — 3-215p : music ; 20cm.
Originally published: 1973. — List of sound discs: p.208-209. — Index.
ISBN 0-571-10998-5 Pbk : £1.50

(B76-33370)

AKDW/GB/E(P) — Crosby, Bing. Biographies
Thompson, Charles
Bing : the authorised biography / [by] Charles Thompson. —
London : Star Books, 1976. — 223p,[8]p of plates : ports ; 18cm.
Originally published: London : W.H. Allen, 1975.
ISBN 0-352-39887-6 Pbk : £0.70

(B76-25963)

AKDW/GB/E(P) — Essex, David. Biographies
Tremlett, George
The David Essex story / by George Tremlett. — London [etc.] :
White Lion Publishers, 1976. — 140p,[16]p of plates : ill, ports ;
21cm.
Originally published: London : Futura Publications, 1974.
ISBN 0-7274-0113-0 : £3.25

(B76-16550)

AKDW/GB/E(P) — Formby, George. Biographies
Fisher, John, *b.1945*
George Formby / [by] John Fisher. — London : Woburn Press,
1975. — 96p : ill, facsims, ports ; 21cm. — (The entertainers)
ISBN 0-7130-0144-5 : £2.95

(B76-17647)

AKDW/GB/E(P) — John, Elton
Gambaccini, Paul
Paul McCartney in his own words / written and edited by Paul
Gambaccini ... — London [etc.] ([78 Newman St., W1P 3LA]) :
Omnibus Press, 1976. — 112p : chiefly ill, facsim, chiefly ports ;
26cm.
ISBN 0-8256-3063-0 Pbk : £1.95

(B76-25962)

Tatham, Dick
Elton John / [by] Dick Tatham & Tony Jasper. — London :
Octopus Books : Phoebus, 1976. — 5-92p : chiefly ill(chiefly col),
ports(chiefly col) ; 31cm.
Col. ill. on lining papers. — List of gramophone records.
ISBN 0-7064-0548-x : £1.99

(B76-28395)

AKDW/GB/E(P) — Jolson, Al. Biographies
Anderton, Barrie
Sonny boy! : the world of Al Jolson / [by] Barrie Anderton. —
London : Jupiter Books, 1975. — 3-160p : ill, facsims, ports ;
26cm.
List of gramophone records: p.121-133. — List of films: p.135-160.
ISBN 0-904041-35-2 : £3.95

(B76-12797)

AKDW/GB/E(P) — Joplin, Janis. Biographies
Caserta, Peggy
Going down with Janis / [by] Peggy Caserta ; as told to Dan
Knapp. — London : Futura Publications, 1975. — 267p ; 18cm.
Originally published: Secausus, N.J. : Lyle Stuart ; London : Talmy
Franklin, 1975.
ISBN 0-86007-231-2 Pbk : £0.65

(B76-01877)

AKDW/GB/E(P) — Lynn, Vera. Biographies
Lynn, *Dame* Vera
Vocal refrain : an autobiography / by Vera Lynn. — London :
W.H. Allen, 1975. — 192p,leaf of plate,[40]p of plates : ill, ports ;
23cm.
Facsim. on lining papers. — Index.
ISBN 0-491-01795-2 : £3.00

(B76-00673)

AKDW/GB/E(P) — McCartney, Paul. Biographies
Tremlett, George
The Paul McCartney story / [by] George Tremlett. — London
[etc.] : White Lion Publishers, 1976. — 192p,16p of plates : ill,
ports ; 21cm.
Originally published: London : Futura Publications, 1975.
ISBN 0-7274-0118-1 : £3.25

(B76-34782)

AKDW/GB/E(P) — Mitchell, Joni. Biographies
Fleischer, Leonore
Joni Mitchell / by Leonore Fleischer. — New York : Flash
Books ; London (78 Newman St., W1P 3LA) : Book Sales Ltd,
1976. — 79p : ill, ports ; 26cm.
ISBN 0-8256-3907-7 Pbk : £1.95

(B76-35355)

AKDW/GB/E(P) — Osmonds, The. Biographies
Dunn, Paul H
The Osmonds : the official story of the Osmond family / by Paul
H. Dunn. — London : W.H. Allen, 1975. — ix,246p : ill, ports ;
24cm.
Also published: Salt Lake City : Bookcraft, 1975.
ISBN 0-491-01835-5 : £2.95

(B76-00672)

AKDW/GB/E(P) — Rolling Stones. Biographies
Jagger, Mick
The Rolling Stones file / [words and music by Mick Jagger and
Keith Richard ; biographical details written and research by
'Miles']. — London (78 Newman St., WIP 3LA) : Music Sales
Ltd, [1976]. — 82p : ill, music, ports ; 31cm.
ISBN 0-86001-245-x Pbk : £2.95

(B76-26570)

Jasper, Tony
The Rolling Stones / [by] Tony Jasper. — London : Octopus
Books, 1976. — 5-92p : ill(some col), ports(some col) ; 30cm.
Col. ports on lining papers. — List of sound discs: p.84-89.
ISBN 0-7064-0549-8 : £1.99

(B76-31917)

Tremlett, George
The Rolling Stones story / [by] George Tremlett. — London
[etc.] : White Lion Publishers, 1976. — 190p,[16]p of plates :
ports ; 21cm.
Originally published: London : Futura Publications, 1974.
ISBN 0-7274-0123-8 : £3.25

(B76-28394)

AKDW/GB/E(P) — Sinatra, Frank. Biographies
Wilson, Earl
Sinatra / by Earl Wilson. — London : W.H. Allen, 1976. — xv,
380p,[16]p of plates : ill, ports ; 24cm.
Also published: New York : Macmillan, 1976. — List of sound discs:
p.378-380.
ISBN 0-491-01967-x : £5.00

(B76-35802)

AKDW/GB/E(P) — Streisand, Barbra. Biographies
Jordan, René
 Streisand : an unauthorised biography / [by] René Jordan. — 1st
 British ed. — London : W.H. Allen, 1976. — 253p ; 23cm.
 Originally published: as 'The greatest star'. New York : Putnam, 1975.
 ISBN 0-491-01775-8 : £3.95

(B76-11504)

AKDW/GC(M) — Country music. Singers
Davis, Paul
 New life in country music / by Paul Davis ; with foreword by
 Cliff Richard and introduction by George Hamilton IV ;
 illustrations by Richard Deverell. — Worthing : Walker, 1976. —
 111p : ports ; 18cm.
 ISBN 0-85479-591-x Pbk : £1.00

(B76-35353)

AKDW/GCW/E(M) — Country 'n' western songs. Singers
Chalker, Bryan
 Country music / [written by Bryan Chalker ; with additional
 material by others]. — London : Phoebus, 1976. — 95p : ill(some
 col), ports(some col) ; 31cm.
 Ill. on lining papers.
 ISBN 0-7026-0015-6 : £2.50

(B76-34775)

AKDW/GCW/E(P) — Cash, Johnny. Biographies
Cash, Johnny
 Man in black / [by] Johnny Cash. — London [etc.] : Hodder and
 Stoughton, 1976. — 5-244p,[24]p of plates : ill, ports ; 23cm.
 Originally published: Grand Rapids : Zondervan, 1975.
 ISBN 0-340-20627-6 : £3.75

(B76-22082)

AKDW/GCW/E(P) — Wills, Bob. Biographies
Townsend, Charles R
 'San Antonio Rose' : the life and music of Bob Wills / [by]
 Charles R. Townsend ; with a discography and filmusicography by
 Bob Pinson. — Urbana [etc.] ; London : University of Illinois
 Press, 1976. — xvii,395p,[90]p of plates : ill, facsims, maps, ports ;
 26cm. — (Music in American life)
 Bibl.: p.334-335. — List of gramophone records : p.337-372. — List of
 films : p.373-376. — Index.
 ISBN 0-252-00470-1 : £8.75

(B76-31914)

AKDW/GNF/E(M) — Cowboy songs. Singers
White, John Irwin
 Git along, little dogies : songs and songmakers of the American
 West / [by] John I. White ; with a foreword by Austin E. Fife. —
 Urbana [etc.] ; London : University of Illinois Press, 1975. — xiii,
 221p : ill, facsims, music, ports ; 26cm & sound disc(2s. ; 171/2in.
 331/3 rpm.). — (Music in American life)
 Bibl.: p.203-206. — List of gramophone records.: p.206-214. — Index.
 ISBN 0-252-00327-6 : £7.00

(B76-33374)

AKDW/HHW — Blues
Blues / [compiled by] Robert Neff & Anthony Connor. —
 London : Latimer New Dimensions, 1976. — [9],141p : ill, ports ;
 26cm.
 Index.
 ISBN 0-901539-49-x : £5.00
 ISBN 0-901539-50-3 Pbk : £2.95

(B76-29101)

AKDW/HHW/E(M) — Blues. Singers
Haralambos, Michael
 Right on : from blues to soul in Black America / [by] Michael
 Haralambos. — London (2 Greycoat Place, [SW1P 1SB]) :
 Eddison Press Ltd, 1974. — 187p : ill, facsims, map, ports ; 23cm.
 — (Eddison blues books)
 Bibl.: p.175-178. — List of gramophone records: p.179-181. — Index.
 ISBN 0-85649-016-4 : £2.50

(B76-20008)

AKDW/HHW/E(P) — Smith, Bessie. Biographies
Albertson, Chris
 Bessie / [by] Chris Albertson. — London : Abacus, 1975. —
 224p,[16]p of plates : ill, facsims, ports ; 20cm.
 Originally published: New York : Stein and Day ; London : Barrie and
 Jenkins, 1972. — Bibl.: p.214-215. — List of gramophone records :
 p.209-213. — Index.
 ISBN 0-349-10054-3 Pbk : £1.00

(B76-31123)

AKDW/HJ/E(P) — Lane, Cleo. Biographies
Cleo and John : a biography of the Dankworths / [compiled and
 edited] by Graham Collier. — London : Quartet Books, 1976. —
 [9],187p,[34]p of plates : ports ; 23cm.
 Index.
 ISBN 0-7043-2113-0 : £4.95
 Also classified at AMT(P)

(B76-33371)

AKDW/HJ/L/E(P) — Jackson, Mahalia. Biographies
Goreau, Laurraine
 Mahalia / [by] Laurraine Goreau. — Berkhamsted : Lion
 Publishing : Aslan, 1976. — 592p,[16]p of plates : ill, ports ;
 20cm.
 Originally published: as 'Just Mahalia, baby'. Waco : Word Books, 1975.
 ISBN 0-85648-061-4 Pbk : £1.95

(B76-36285)

AKDW/HK/E(P) — Led Zeppelin
Mylett, Howard
 Led Zeppelin / [by] Howard Mylett. — St Albans : Panther,
 1976. — 156p,[8]p of plates : ports ; 18cm.
 ISBN 0-586-04390-x Pbk : £0.60

(B76-34781)

AKDW/HK/E(P) — Presley, Elvis. Biographies
Harbinson, William Allen
 Elvis Presley : an illustrated biography / by W.A. Harbinson ;
 designed by Stephen Ridgeway. — London : Joseph, 1975. —
 160p : chiefly ill, ports ; 28cm.
 ISBN 0-7181-1469-8 : £5.50
 ISBN 0-7181-1431-0 Pbk : £3.75

(B76-03356)

Jones, Peter, b.1930
 Elvis / [by] Peter Jones. — London : Octopus Books, 1976. —
 88p : ill(some col), ports(some col) ; 31cm.
 Col. ill. on lining papers.
 ISBN 0-7064-0550-1 : £1.99

(B76-34783)

AKDW/K/G(YDM) — Ballads. Ireland
Soodlum's selection of Irish ballads with guitar chords / [chord
 arrangements Pat Conway]. — [Dublin] ([153 Downpatrick Rd,
 Dublin 12]) : [International Music Publications].
 Vol.1. — [1976]. — [1],16p ; 23cm.
 ISBN 0-905326-00-8 Sd : Unpriced

(B76-07531)

 Vol.2. — [1976]. — [1],[20]p : ill ; 22cm.
 Cover titles: Pat Conway presents Soodlum's selection of Irish ballads with
 guitar chords.
 ISBN 0-905326-01-6 Sd : Unpriced

(B76-07532)

AKDW/KG(YC/XNU25) — Military songs. Great Britain, 1939-1963
For gawdsake don't take me! : the songs, ballads, verses,
 monologues, etc. of the call-up years, 1939-1963 / edited by
 Martin Page ; illustrated by Bill Tidy. — London : Hart-Davis,
 MacGibbon, 1976. — 3-190p : ill ; 26cm.
 Ill. on lining paper. — Index.
 ISBN 0-246-10859-2 : £2.95

(B76-50757)

AKDW/L/HJ/E(P) — Gordon, Taylor. Biographies
Gordon, Taylor
 Born to be / by Taylor Gordon ; with an introduction by Muriel
 Draper, a foreword by Carl Van Vechten and illustrations by
 Covarrubias. — [1st ed. reprinted] ; new introduction by Robert
 Hemenway. — Seattle ; London : University of Washington Press,
 1975. — liv,236p,[9]leaves of plates,[8]p of plates : ill, ports ;
 21cm.
 Originally published: New York : Covici-Friede, 1929.
 ISBN 0-295-95428-0 Pbk : £3.50

(B76-33369)

AKFL/E(P) — Callas, Maria. Biographies
Galatopoulos, Stelios
 Callas : prima donna assoluta / [by] Stelios Galatopoulos. —
 London : W.H. Allen, 1976. — xviii,353p,leaf of plate,[40]p of
 plates : ill, ports ; 24cm.
 Index.
 ISBN 0-491-01518-6 : £7.50

(B76-35800)

AKGX/E(P) — Shaliapin, Fedor Ivanovich. Biographies
Shaliapin, Fedor Ivanovich
 Chaliapin : an autobiography / as told to Maxim Gorky ; with
 supplementary correspondence and notes, translated from the
 Russian ; compiled and edited by Nina Froud and James Hanley.
 — London [etc.] : White Lion Publishers, 1976. — 320p,[1]
 leaf,[62]p of plates : ill, facsims, ports ; 23cm.
 This translation originally published: London : Macdonald, 1968 [i.e. Dec.
 1967]. — Translation of: 'Fedor Ivanovich Shaliapin' published in 2 vols.
 Moscow : Iskusstvo, 1957-8. — Bibl.: p.307-308. — Index.
 ISBN 0-7274-0191-2 : £6.50

(B76-07530)

AKGX/E(P) — Wallace, Ian. Biographies
Wallace, Ian, b.1919
 Promise me you'll sing 'Mud'! : the autobiography of Ian Wallace.
 — London (18 Brewer St., W1R 4AS) : John Calder, 1975. —
 240p,[12]p of plates : ill, ports ; 23cm.
 Index.
 ISBN 0-7145-3500-1 : £5.75

(B76-00669)

AL — MUSICAL LITERATURE. INSTRUMENTAL MUSIC
AL/B — Instruments
Gammond, Peter
   Musical instruments in colour / [by] Peter Gammond ;
   photography Richard Bird. — Poole : Blandford Press, 1975. —
   173p : ill(chiefly col) ; 20cm.
   Bibl.: p.166-168.
   ISBN 0-7137-0628-7 : £2.60

(B76-00667)

AL/B(XCD801) — Instruments, 800-1600
Munrow, David
   Instruments of the Middle Ages and Renaissance / [by] David
   Munrow ; foreword by André Previn. — London : Oxford
   University Press, Music Department, 1976. — 97p : ill, music,
   ports ; 29cm.
   Index.
   ISBN 0-19-321321-4 Pbk : £3.50

(B76-18373)

AL/BC — Instruments. Manufacture
Roberts, Ronald
   Musical instruments, made to be played / [by] Ronald Roberts. —
   6th ed. — Leicester : Dryad Press, 1976. — [2],84p,plate : ill,
   music ; 25cm.
   Ill. on fold sheet ([2]p.) in pocket. — Bibl.: p.83. — Index.
   ISBN 0-85219-095-6 Pbk : £1.95

(B76-15863)

AL/E(M) — Musicians
Jacobson, Robert
   Reverberations : interviews with the world's leading musicians /
   by Robert Jacobson. — London : Vision Press, 1976. — [7],308p ;
   22cm.
   Originally published: New York : Morrow, 1974.
   ISBN 0-85478-453-5 : £5.95

(B76-15049)

AL/E(VF) — Instrumental music. Schools. Books
Self, George
   Make a new sound / [by] George Self. — London : Universal
   Edition, 1976. — x,135p : ill, music ; 24cm.
   ISBN 0-900938-46-3 Pbk : £3.90

(B76-13570)

AL/E(VG) — Instrumental music. Performance. Primary schools
Diamond, Dorothy Mary
   Musical instruments / [by] Dorothy Diamond and Robert Tiffin.
   — London [etc.] : Macdonald Educational for Chelsea College,
   University of London, 1976. — [4],44p : ill(some col) ; 22cm. —
   (Teaching primary science)
   Bibl.: p.41-42. — Index.
   ISBN 0-356-05077-7 Pbk : £1.50

(B76-30110)

AL/E(VG) — Performance. Primary schools
Dennis, Brian
   Projects in sound / [by] Brian Dennis. — London : Universal
   Edition, 1975. — x,49p : ill, music ; 21x26cm.
   ISBN 0-900938-45-5 Sd : £2.00

(B76-22854)

AM — MUSICAL LITERATURE. ORCHESTRAL MUSIC
AM/B — Orchestra. Instruments
Harding, David
   The orchestra / by David Harding ; ... illustrated by Virginia
   Smith. — London : F. Watts, 1976. — 48p : ill(some col), music,
   port ; 18x22cm.
   Index.
   ISBN 0-85166-558-6 : £1.45

(B76-05039)

AMT — MUSICAL LITERATURE. JAZZ
Berendt, Joachim
   The jazz book / [by] Joachim Berendt ; [translated from German
   and edited by Dag Morgenstern]. — St Albans : Paladin, 1976. —
   xvii,459p : 1 ill, music ; 20cm.
   This translation also published: St Albans : Hart-Davis, MacGibbon, 1976.
   — Originally published: New York : Hill, 1973. — Translation of : 'Das
   Jazzbuch'. — List of records: p.413-442. — Index.
   ISBN 0-586-08260-3 Pbk : £1.50

(B76-33376)

Freeman, Bud
   If you know of a better life please tell me / [by] Bud Freeman. —
   Dublin (65 Dublin Industrial Estate, Glasnevin, Dublin 11) :
   Bashall Eaves, [1976]. — [3],62p ; 18cm.
   ISBN 0-902638-02-5 Pbk : £0.80

(B76-31126)

AMT(M/XN10) — Musicians, 1920-1929
Hadlock, Richard
   Jazz masters of the Twenties / by Richard Hadlock. — New
   York : Collier Books ; London : Collier Macmillan, 1974. —
   255p,[12]p of plates : ports ; 21cm. — (The Macmillan jazz
   masters series)
   Originally published: 1966. — Bibl. — List of gramophone records.
   ISBN 0-02-060770-9 Pbk : £1.80

(B76-12130)

AMT(M/XP10) — Musicians, 1940-1949
Gitler, Ira
   Jazz masters of the Forties / by Ira Gitler. — New York : Collier
   Books ; London : Collier Macmillan, 1974. — 290p,[10]p of
   plates : ill, ports ; 21cm. — (The Macmillan jazz masters series)
   Originally published: New York : Macmillan, 1966 ; London : Collier
   Macmillan, 1967. — Bibl.: p.283-285. — List of gramophone records. —
   Index.
   ISBN 0-02-060610-9 Pbk : £1.80

(B76-12131)

AMT(P) — Armstrong, Louis. Biographies
Jones, Max
   Louis : the Louis Armstrong story, 1900-1971 / [by] Max Jones &
   John Chilton. — St Albans : Mayflower, 1975. — 302p,[32]p of
   plates : ill, facsims, ports ; 18cm.
   Originally published: London : Studio Vista, 1971. — List of films:
   p.294-295. — Index.
   ISBN 0-583-12710-x Pbk : £0.95

(B76-01204)

AMT(P) — Coltrane, John. Biographies
Thomas, J C
   Chasin' the Trane : the music and mystique of John Coltrane /
   [by] J.C. Thomas. — London : Elm Tree Books, 1976. — [4],
   188p,[8]p of plates : ill, facsim(on lining papers), ports ; 22cm.
   Originally published: Garden City, N.Y. : Doubleday, 1975. — List of
   gramophone records: p.161-179. — Index.
   ISBN 0-241-89340-2 : £4.50

(B76-10255)

AMT(P) — Dankworth, John. Biographies
Cleo and John : a biography of the Dankworths / [compiled and
   edited] by Graham Collier. — London : Quartet Books, 1976. —
   [9],187p,[34]p of plates : ports ; 23cm.
   Index.
   ISBN 0-7043-2113-0 : £4.95
   Primary classification AKDW/HJ/E(P)

(B76-33371)

AMT(P) — Fox, Roy. Biographies
Fox, Roy
   Hollywood, Mayfair, and all that jazz : the Roy Fox story. —
   London : Frewin, 1975. — 248p,plate : ill, music, ports ; 23cm.
   ISBN 0-85632-171-0 : £4.25

(B76-17648)

AMT(P) — Parker, Charlie. Biographies
Russell, Ross
   Bird lives! / [by] Ross Russell. — London : Quartet Books, 1976.
   — [9],405p,[16]p of plates : ill, facsims, music, ports ; 22cm.
   Originally published: 1972. — Bibl.: p.381-383. — List of gramophone
   records : p.384-388. — Index.
   ISBN 0-7043-3094-6 Pbk : £2.25

(B76-31128)

AMT(P/XP11) — Green, Benny. Biographies, 1940-1950
Green, Benny
   Swingtime in Tottenham / [by] Benny Green ; illustrations by
   Ross. — London (Basset Chambers, 27 Bedfordbury, W.C.2) :
   Lemon Tree Press Ltd, 1976. — 107p : ill ; 20cm.
   ISBN 0-904291-11-1 Pbk : £1.25

(B76-35803)

AMT(YC) — Great Britain
Jazz now : the Jazz Centre Society guide / edited by Roger
   Cotterrell ; preface by Spike Milligan. — London : Quartet Books,
   1976. — [8],216p : ports ; 20cm.
   Bibl.: p.200-203. — List of films: p.204-210. — Index.
   ISBN 0-7043-3097-0 : £1.75

(B76-27767)

AMT(YC/XTA15) — Great Britain, 1941-1975
Godbolt, Jim
   All this and 10% / [by] Jim Godbolt. — London : Hale, 1976. —
   208p,[12]p of plates : ports ; 23cm.
   Index.
   ISBN 0-7091-5841-6 : £4.95

(B77-00347)

AP — MUSICAL LITERATURE. INDIVIDUAL INSTRUMENTS & INSTRUMENTAL GROUPS
APV — Electronic music
Jenkins, John, *b.1936*
Electric music : a practical manual for musicians / [by] John
Jenkins and Jon Smith. — Newton Abbot [etc.] : David and
Charles, 1975. — 168p : ill ; 23cm.
Index.
ISBN 0-7153-6815-x : £4.95

(B76-33378)

APW — MUSICAL LITERATURE. KEYBOARD INSTRUMENTS
APW/B(YDBCF/WJ) — Keyboard instruments. Fenton House.Benton Fletcher Collection. Exhibitions
National Trust
A catalogue of early keyboard instruments : the Benton Fletcher
collection / [National Trust] ; [compiled by Raymond Russell ;
photographs by John Bethell]. — [London] : The Trust, 1976. —
21p,[4]p of plates : ill ; 22cm.
ISBN 0-7078-0061-7 Sd : £0.12

(B76-22083)

APW/E — Keyboard instruments. Performance
Bach, Carl Philipp Emanuel
[Versuch über die wahre Art das Clavier zu spielen. English].
Essay on the true art of playing keyboard instruments / by Carl
Philipp Emanuel Bach ; translated [from the German] and edited
by William J. Mitchell. — London (48 Great Marlborough St.,
W1V 2BN) : Eulenburg Books, 1974. — xiii,449p : ill, facsims,
music, ports ; 22cm.
This translation originally published: London : Cassell, 1949. — Translation
of: 'Versuch über die wahre Art das Clavier zu spielen'. Berlin, 1753. —
Bibl.: p.446-449.
ISBN 0-903873-14-1 : £3.00
ISBN 0-903873-01-x Pbk : £1.50

(B76-15055)

AQ — Piano music
Brendel, Alfred
Musical thoughts & afterthoughts / [by] Alfred Brendel. —
London : Robson Books, 1976. — 168p,[4]p of plates : facsims,
music, ports ; 24cm.
Bibl.: p.162-165. — Index.
ISBN 0-903895-43-9 : £5.25

(B76-33377)

Kentner, Louis
Piano / [by] Louis Kentner. — London : Macdonald and Jane's,
1976. — xi,204p,[4]p of plates : ill, music ; 23cm. — (Yehudi
Menuhin music guides)
Bibl.: p.190. — List of gramophone records: p.191-198. — Index.
ISBN 0-356-04713-x : £3.95
ISBN 0-356-04714-8 Pbk : £2.25
Primary classification AQ/B

(B76-10253)

AQ/B — Pianos. Instruments
Kentner, Louis
Piano / [by] Louis Kentner. — London : Macdonald and Jane's,
1976. — xi,204p,[4]p of plates : ill, music ; 23cm. — (Yehudi
Menuhin music guides)
Bibl.: p.190. — List of gramophone records: p.191-198. — Index.
ISBN 0-356-04713-x : £3.95
ISBN 0-356-04714-8 Pbk : £2.25
Also classified at AQ; 786.2'1

(B76-10253)

AQ/B(X) — Piano. Instruments. History
Ehrlich, Cyril
The piano : a history / [by] Cyril Ehrlich. — London : Dent,
1976. — 254p,[8]p of plates : ill, facsims ; 26cm.
Bibl.: p.225-232. — Index.
ISBN 0-460-04246-7 : £6.95

(B76-20709)

Van Barthold, Kenneth
The story of the piano / [by] Kenneth van Barthold and David
Buckton. — London : British Broadcasting Corporation, 1975. —
109p,[16]p of plates : ill, music, ports ; 23cm.
ISBN 0-563-12580-2 : £3.50

(B76-05040)

AQ/CY(M) — Pianists. Technique
Gerig, Reginald R
Famous pianists & their technique / [by] Reginald R. Gerig. —
Newton Abbot [etc.] : David and Charles, 1976. — xvi,560p : ill,
music ; 24cm.
Originally published: Washington, D.C. : Luce, 1974. — Bibl.: p.519-542. —
Index.
ISBN 0-7153-7220-3 : £8.50

(B76-32593)

AQ/E — Piano music. Performance
Cooper, Peter, *b.1918*
Style in piano playing / [by] Peter Cooper. — London : John
Calder : [Distributed by Calder and Boyars], 1975. — 181p,[10]p
of plates : ill, music, ports ; 23cm.
ISBN 0-7145-3512-5 : £6.50

(B76-15056)

AQ/E(P) — Ashburnham, George. Biographies
Ashburnham, George
The story of unique piano tuition / [by George Ashburnham]. —
[3rd ed.]. — [Sutton] ([22 Effingham Close, Sutton, Surrey SM2
6AG]) : Ashburnham School of Music, [1976]. — [3],55p : music,
port ; 26cm.
ISBN 0-905329-00-7 Pbk : £1.15

(B76-05916)

AQ/P — Piano. Tuning
Fischer, Jerry Cree
Piano tuning : a simple and accurate method for amateurs / [by]
J. Cree Fischer. — [Abridged ed.]. — New York : Dover
Publications [etc.] ; London : Constable, 1975 [i.e. 1976]. — [2],
201p,[2]leaves of plates : ill ; 21cm.
Abridged ed. published in the United States: 1975. — Full ed. originally
published: as 'Piano tuning, regulating and repairing'. Philadelphia : Presser,
1907. — Index.
ISBN 0-486-23267-0 Pbk : £2.10

(B76-31127)

AR(Q) — Organ Club
Organ Club
The Organ Club golden jubilee, 1976. — Hornchurch (c/o Jubilee
Treasurer, 84 Haynes Rd, Hornchurch, Essex RM11 2HU) :
[Organ Club], [1976]. — [1],117p : ill, ports(1 col) ; 21cm.
Cover title.
ISBN 0-9505260-0-2 Pbk : £1.80
Primary classification AR/B(XNF51)

(B76-31918)

AR(YH/PU/XE201) — Organ music. France. Registration, 1600-1800
Diederich, Susanne
Originale Registrieranweisungen in der französischen Orgelmusik
des 17. und 18. Jahrhunderts : Beziehungen zwischen Orgelbau
und Orgelkomposition im Zeitalter Ludwigs XIV / [von] Susanne
Diederich. — Kassel [etc.] ; London ([32 Great Titchfield St.,
W.1]) : Bärenreiter, 1975 [i.e. 1976]. — xv,427p : ill, facsims,
music ; 26cm. — (Orgelwissenschaftliche Forschungsstelle,
Westfälische Wilhelmsuniversität. Veröffentlichungen ; no.9)
Published in Germany: 1975. — Includes transcripts of French texts.
Pbk : £11.00
ISBN 3-7618-0527-6

AR/B — Organ. Instruments. Forster and Andrewes
Elvin, Laurence
Forster and Andrews : their barrel, chamber and small church
organs / by Laurence Elvin ; foreword by Philip Marshall. —
Lincoln (10 Almond Ave., Swanpool, Lincoln) : The author, 1976.
— [4],140p : ill, facsims ; 25cm.
Limited ed. of 1000 copies. — A companion volume to 'Forster and
Andrews organ builders, 1843-1956'. — Bibl.: p.131-132. — Index.
ISBN 0-9500049-3-6 Pbk : £4.75

(B76-20009)

AR/B(XNF51) — Organs, 1926-1976
Organ Club
The Organ Club golden jubilee, 1976. — Hornchurch (c/o Jubilee
Treasurer, 84 Haynes Rd, Hornchurch, Essex RM11 2HU) :
[Organ Club], [1976]. — [1],117p : ill, ports(1 col) ; 21cm.
Cover title.
ISBN 0-9505260-0-2 Pbk : £1.80
Also classified at AR(Q)

(B76-31918)

AR/B(YDDLI) — Organs. Ipswich
Woodward, Michael, *b.1928*
A trinity of organs : notes on the history of the organs in three
Ipswich public buildings / by Michael Woodward. — [Ipswich]
([c/o The Chief Executive, Civic Centre, Civic Drive, Ipswich IP1
2EE]) : Borough of Ipswich, 1975. — 36p : ill, ports ; 25cm. —
(An Ipswich book)
ISBN 0-904023-08-7 Sd : £0.50

(B76-09328)

AR/B(YDHRHB/X) — Organs. Hereford Cathedral. History
Shaw, Watkins
The organists and organs of Hereford Cathedral / by Watkins
Shaw ; with a note by Roy Massey. — Hereford : Friends of
Hereford Cathedral Publications Committee, 1976. — 47p,leaf of
plate,iv p of plates : ill, facsim, ports ; 22cm.
Bibl.: p.46-47.
ISBN 0-904642-01-1 Sd : £0.50
Also classified at 786.6'2424'46

(B76-35357)

AR/B(YDHWD) — Organs. Derby. St John the Evangelists' Church
Johnson, David Sturgess
The organs of the Church of St John : a history / by David S.
Johnson. — [Derby] ([Mill St., Derby]) : [Church of St John the
Evangelist], [1976]. — [1],9p ; 21cm.
ISBN 0-9505280-0-5 Sd : £0.10

(B76-31919)

AR/B(YDJHH/X) — Organ. Instruments. St. Michael and All
Angels, Houghton-le-Spring. Durham County
Gelston, Anne
The history of the organ in the parish church of St Michael and
All Angels, Houghton-le-Spring / by Anne Gelston. —
[Houghton-le-Spring] (['Lesbury', Hetton Road,
Houghton-le-Spring, Co. Durham DH5 8JW]) : [The author],
1975. — [15]p : ill, port ; 22cm.
ISBN 0-9504842-0-2 Sd : £0.25

(B76-06891)

AR/BC(YEH/P) — Organ builders. Hanover. Christian Vater
Der **hannoversche** Orgel Christian Vater, 1679-1756 /
[zusammengestellt von] Reinhard Skupnik. — Kassel [etc.] ;
London ([32 Great Titchfield St., W.1]) : Bärenreiter, 1976. — xi,
447p ; 26cm. — (Orgelwissenschaftliche Forschungsstelle,
Westfälische Wilhelmsuniversität. Veröffentlichungen ; nr.8)
Bibl.: p.439-447.
Pbk : £13.00
ISBN 3-7618-0543-8

ARPV/BC — Electronic organs. Instrument building
Douglas, Alan
The electronic musical instrument manual : a guide to theory and
design / [by] Alan Douglas. — 6th ed. — London [etc.] : Pitman,
1976. — vii,205p : ill ; 26cm.
Previous ed.: 1968. — Bibl.: p.200. — Index.
ISBN 0-273-36193-7 : £7.50

(B76-12801)

ARW — MUSICAL LITERATURE. STRING INSTRUMENTS
AS/B — Violin. Instruments
Robinson, Marjorie
The violin and viola / by Marjorie Robinson ; illustrated by
Virginia Smith ; general editor J.P. Rutland. — London [etc.] : F.
Watts, 1976. — 48p : ill(some col), col map, music, ports ;
18x22cm.
Bibl.: p.46. — Index.
ISBN 0-85166-595-0 : £1.75
Also classified at 787'.2

(B77-00349)

AS/BC — Violin. Instrument making
Roberts, Ronald
Making a simple violin and viola / [by] Ronald Roberts ; with 27
photographs, 17 line drawings and 5 scale diagrams. — Newton
Abbot [etc.] : David and Charles, 1975. — 112p : ill ; 18x22cm.
Bibl.: p.110. — Index.
ISBN 0-7153-6964-4 : £4.50
Also classified at ASQ/BC

(B76-09330)

AS/CY — Violin. Technique
Whone, Herbert
The integrated violinist / by Herbert Whone ; with illustrations by
the author. — London : Gollancz, 1976. — 128p : ill, music ;
24cm.
Index.
ISBN 0-575-02148-9 : £4.75

(B76-27768)

AS/E — Violin. Performance
Menuhin, Yehudi
Violin and viola / [by] Yehudi Menuhin and William Primrose ;
with a section on the history of the instrument by Denis Stevens.
— London : Macdonald and Jane's, 1976. — xiii,250p,leaf of
plate,[12]p of plates : ill, facsim, music, ports ; 23cm. — (Yehudi
Menuhin music guides)
Bibl.: p.233. — List of gramophone records: p.235-243. — Index.
ISBN 0-356-04715-6 : £4.50
ISBN 0-356-04716-4 Pbk : £2.25
Also classified at ASQ/E

(B76-06892)

AS/EV — Violin. Vibrato
Hauck, Werner
Vibrato on the violin / [by] Werner Hauck ; translated [from the
German] by Kitty Rokos. — London : Bosworth, 1975. — [4],
95p : ill, music ; 21cm.
Translation of: 'Das Vibrato auf der Violine'. Cologne : Bosworth Edition,
1971. — Bibl.: p.90-92. — Index.
ISBN 0-900180-71-4 Sd : £3.00

(B76-09329)

ASQ/BC — Viola. Instrument making
Roberts, Ronald
Making a simple violin and viola / [by] Ronald Roberts ; with 27
photographs, 17 line drawings and 5 scale diagrams. — Newton
Abbot [etc.] : David and Charles, 1975. — 112p : ill ; 18x22cm.
Bibl.: p.110. — Index.
ISBN 0-7153-6964-4 : £4.50
Primary classification AS/BC

(B76-09330)

ASQ/E — Viola. Performance
Menuhin, Yehudi
Violin and viola / [by] Yehudi Menuhin and William Primrose ;
with a section on the history of the instrument by Denis Stevens.
— London : Macdonald and Jane's, 1976. — xiii,250p,leaf of
plate,[12]p of plates : ill, facsim, music, ports ; 23cm. — (Yehudi
Menuhin music guides)
Bibl.: p.233. — List of gramophone records: p.235-243. — Index.
ISBN 0-356-04715-6 : £4.50
ISBN 0-356-04716-4 Pbk : £2.25
Primary classification AS/E

(B76-06892)

ASQQ/B — Viola d'amore
Danks, Harry
The viola d'amore / by Harry Danks. — Halesowen (7 Summit
Gardens, Halesowen, West Midlands B63 4SP) : Bois de
Boulogne, 1976. — 104p,[24]p of plates : ill, music, col port ;
31cm.
Limited ed. of 500 numbered copies. — Bibl.: p.7.
ISBN 0-900998-15-6 : £15.40

(B76-17084)

AT — MUSICAL LITERATURE. PLUCKED STRING
INSTRUMENTS
ATS/HK/E(P) — Clapton, Eric. Biographies
Pidgeon, John
Eric Clapton : a biography / [by] John Pidgeon. — St Albans :
Panther, 1976. — 144p,[8]p of plates : ports ; 18cm.
List of sound discs: p.139-144.
ISBN 0-586-04292-x Pbk : £0.60

(B76-27135)

ATW(YD) — Lute music. England
The **Mynshall** lute book / [compiled by] Richard Mynshall ; with
an introductory study by Robert Spencer. — Leeds (5 Albert
Grove, Leeds 6) : Boethius Press, 1975. — [65]p : ill, facsims,
music, port ; 32cm. — (Reproductions of early music ; 3)
Facsimile of the lute book of Richard Mynshall (c.1597-99). — Bibl.:
p.[63-65].
ISBN 0-904263-03-7 : £6.25

(B76-11505)

ATWT/B(X) — Psaltery. History
Kettlewell, David
All the tunes that ever there were : an introduction to the
dulcimer in the British Isles / [by] David Kettlewell. — Tisbury
(Tisbury, Wilts.) : Spoot Books, 1975. — ix,65p : ill, music, ports ;
30cm.
Versos of some leaves blank. — Bibl.: p.53. — List of sound discs: p.53.
ISBN 0-9505111-0-2 Sp : £3.25
Also classified at AXTQ/B(X)

(B76-50758)

AU — MUSICAL LITERATURE. WIND INSTRUMENTS
AU/B(YDBL) — Wind instruments. Horniman Museum
Horniman Museum
Wind instruments of European art music / Horniman Museum,
London ; [prepared by E.A.K. Ridley]. — London : Inner London
Education Authority, 1974. — 107p,20p of plates : ill ; 20cm.
Bibl.: p.102-104. — Index.
ISBN 0-7168-0545-6 : £0.45

(B76-21368)

AU/E — Wind instruments. Performance
Weisberg, Arthur
The art of wind playing / by Arthur Weisberg. — New York :
Schirmer Books ; London : Collier Macmillan, 1975. — xi,145p :
ill, music ; 24cm.
Index.
ISBN 0-02-872800-9 : £5.00

(B76-05041)

AVV/E — Clarinet. Performance
Brymer, Jack
Clarinet / [by] Jack Brymer. — London : Macdonald and Jane's,
1976. — xii,259p,[12]leaves of plates : ill, music ; 22cm. —
(Yehudi Menuhin music guides)
Bibl.: p.246-247. — List of music : 211-245. — Index.
ISBN 0-356-08414-0 : £4.50
ISBN 0-356-08415-9 Pbk : £2.95
Also classified at 788'.62'0712

(B76-36286)

AVV/E(VC) — Clarinet. Teaching
Weston, Pamela
    The clarinet teacher's companion / [by] Pamela Weston. —
    London : Hale ; London : Distributed to the music trade by
    Breitkopf and Härtel, 1976. — 117p : ill, music ; 21cm.
    ISBN 0-7091-5482-8 : £2.00

(B76-14370)

AVW/E(MN) — Bassoon playing. Careers
Burness, John
    Bars rest / by John Burness. — London (38 Wigmore St., W1H
    0EX) : Paterson's Publications, 1975. — 32p : music ; 19cm.
    ISBN 0-9503608-1-3 Sd : £0.50

(B76-09331)

AW/B(X) — Brass instruments. History
Baines, Anthony
    Brass instruments : their history and development / [by] Anthony
    Baines. — London : Faber, 1976. — 3-298p,xvi p of plates : ill,
    music, ports ; 23cm.
    Bibl.: p.267-278. — Index.
    ISBN 0-571-10600-5 : £12.50

(B77-00350)

AWM(VF/VC) — Brass band music. Schools. Teaching
Lawrence, Ian
    Brass in your school / [by] Ian Lawrence. — London [etc.] :
    Oxford University Press, 1975. — [6],140p,[4]p of plates : ill,
    music ; 19cm.
    Bibl.: p.139-140.
    ISBN 0-19-318705-1 Pbk : £3.15

(B76-50355)

AWM/E(YC/BC) — Brass bands. Great Britain. Directories
Directory of British brass bands : associations, societies, contests. —
    York (c/o F.H. Bradbury, 47 Hull Rd, York YO1 3JP) : British
    Federation of Brass Bands.
    Vol.1 : 1975-76. — 1975. — 76p : ill, ports ; 21cm.
    ISBN 0-905170-00-8 Sd : £0.50
    ISSN 0307-6261

(B76-01203)

AWM/E(YDJED/X) — Dobcross Band. History
Livings, Henry
    That the medals and the baton be put on view : the story of a
    village band, 1875-1975 / [by] Henry Livings. — Newton Abbot
    [etc.] : David and Charles, 1975. — 96p : ill, facsims, map, ports ;
    23cm.
    ISBN 0-7153-7071-5 : £3.95

(B76-00675)

**AX — MUSICAL LITERATURE. PERCUSSION
    INSTRUMENTS**
AX/B(XCG551) — Percussion instruments, 1100-1650
Blades, James
    Early percussion instruments : from the Middle Ages to the
    Baroque / [by] James Blades and Jeremy Montagu. — London :
    Oxford University Press, 1976. — x,77p : ill, music ; 21cm. —
    (Early music series ; 2)
    Bibl.: p.77.
    ISBN 0-19-323176-x Pbk : £2.95
    Also classified at 789'.01'0714

(B76-14371)

AX/BC — Percussion instruments. Instrument making
Montagu, Jeremy
    Making early percussion instruments / [by] Jeremy Montagu. —
    London : Oxford University Press, 1976. — xiii,49p : ill ; 21cm.
    — (Early music series ; 3)
    Bibl.: p.49.
    ISBN 0-19-323177-8 Pbk : £2.95

(B76-14372)

Southworth, Mary
    Making musical sounds / [by] Mary Southworth. — London :
    Studio Vista [etc.], 1976. — 28p : col ill ; 22cm.
    Adaptation of: 'How to make musical sounds' / by Mary Southworth.
    London : Studio Vista, 1973. — Index.
    ISBN 0-289-70711-0 : £0.45

(B76-50356)

AXS/BC(YDDLI/XEXK300) — Bell founding. Ipswich, 1650-1951
Bevis, Trevor Allen
    The Ipswich bellfounders / by Trevor A. Bevis. — Hadlow ;
    [Oxford] ([36 Great Clarendon St., Oxford]) : J. Hannon and Co.,
    [1976]. — [10]p ; 23cm.
    Originally published: Hadlow : Press of John Hilton, 1966.
    £2.00

AXSR/B(YDHR) — Church bells. Herefordshire
Sharpe, Frederick
    The church bells of Herefordshire : their inscriptions and
    founders / by Frederick Sharpe. — [Launton] (['Derwen',
    Launton, Oxon.]) : The author.
    In 5 vols.
    Vol.5 : Summarised accounts of the bells at the Reformation and the present
    day and details of bellfounders. — 1975. — [7]p,p600-836 : ill, facsims ;
    21cm.
    Bibl.: p.817-820. — Index.
    ISBN 0-9500835-9-3 Pbk : £3.20

(B76-09332)

AXSR/E — Change ringing
Chant, H
    Method splicing / by H. Chant. — Tonbridge (19 Lonewood
    Way, Hadlow, Tonbridge, Kent) : Press of John Hilton.
    Part 1 : Minor methods. — [1976]. — [1],88p ; 22cm.
    ISBN 0-900465-06-9 : £2.00

(B76-35807)

Cleaver, A W T
    The theory of change ringing : an introduction / [by] A.W.T.
    Cleaver. — [Oxford] ([36 Great Clarendon St., Oxford]) : J.
    Hannon and Co. (Publishers) Oxford, [1976]. — [1],32p ; 21cm.
    Originally published: Hadlow, Kent : Press of John Hilton, 1965.
    ISBN 0-904233-10-3 : £0.60

(B76-35358)

Crabtree, Anthony John
    Touches in popular doubles methods / [compiled by A.J.
    Crabtree]. — [Beeston] ([202 Attenborough La., Beeston,
    Nottingham NG9 6AL]) : The author, [1975]. — [1],16p ; 16cm.
    ISBN 0-904233-11-1 : £1.75

(B76-35805)

Trollope, J Armiger
    Grandsire / by J. Armiger Trollope. — 3rd ed. — Kettering ([22
    Duke St.], Burton Latimer, Kettering, Northants.) : Christopher
    Groome, 1973. — 128p ; 19cm. — (Jasper Snowdon change
    ringing series)
    Third ed. originally published: Leeds : Whitehead and Miller, 1948.
    ISBN 0-904233-09-x : £2.50

(B76-35806)

AXSR/E(XA1935) — Change ringing. History, to 1935
Snowdon, Jasper Whitfield
    Ropesight : Jasper Whitfield Snowdon's introduction to the art of
    change ringing, as revised by William Snowdon. — Burton
    Latimer ([22 Duke St., Burton Latimer, Northants.]) : C. Groome,
    1975. — [5],144p : ill ; 19cm. — (Jasper Snowdon change ringing
    series)
    Facsimile reprint of: ?9th ed. Cartmel : M.E. Snowdon, 1936. — This
    reprint originally published: 1970. •
    ISBN 0-905334-00-0 : £2.50

(B76-35804)

AXTQ/B(X) — Dulcimer. History
Kettlewell, David
    All the tunes that ever there were : an introduction to the
    dulcimer in the British Isles / [by] David Kettlewell. — Tisbury
    (Tisbury, Wilts.) : Spoot Books, 1975. — ix,65p : ill, music, ports ;
    30cm.
    Versos of some leaves blank. — Bibl.: p.53. — List of sound discs: p.53.
    ISBN 0-9505111-0-2 Sp : £3.25
    Primary classification ATWT/B(X)

AY/BC — Other instruments. Manufacture
Burton, John Andrew
    Musical instruments from odds and ends / [by] John Burton ;
    illustrated by Andrew Burton. — London : Carousel, 1976. —
    80p : ill ; 20cm. — (Carousel books)
    ISBN 0-552-54096-x Pbk : £0.45

(B76-14366)

B — INDIVIDUAL COMPOSERS
BAO — Alkan, Charles Valentin
Smith, Ronald
    Alkan / [by] Ronald Smith. — London : Kahn and Averill.
    In 2 vols.
    Vol.1 : The enigma. — 1976. — 120p : ill, facsims, geneal table, music,
    ports ; 23cm.
    Bibl.: p.113-114. — Index.
    ISBN 0-900707-39-9 : £3.00

(B76-07533)

BBJARXNS — Beethoven, Ludwig van. String quartets
Kerman, Joseph
    The Beethoven quartets / [by] Joseph Kerman. — London [etc.] :
    Oxford University Press, 1975. — [11],386,viii,[3]p : music ; 25cm.
    Originally published: New York : Knopf ; London : Oxford University
    Press, 1967. — Bibl.: p.383-386. List of works: p.i-iv. — Index.
    ISBN 0-19-315135-9 : £6.00

(B77-00348)

BBP — Bizet, Georges
Dean, Winton
  Bizet / by Winton Dean. — [3rd ed.]. — London : Dent, 1975. — x,306p,[8]p of plates : ill, facsims, music, ports ; 20cm. — (The master musicians series)
  Previous ed.: published as 'Georges Bizet'. 1965. — Bibl.: p.280-282. — List of works: p.260-273. — Index.
  ISBN 0-460-03163-5 : £3.95

(B76-12126)

BBQ(N) — Bliss, Sir Arthur. Biographies
Palmer, Christopher
  Bliss / [by] Christopher Palmer. — Sevenoaks : Novello, 1976. — 24p ; 19cm. — (Novello short biographies)
  List of works: p.23-24.
  ISBN 0-85360-064-3 Sd : £0.42

(B76-30335)

BBTN(N) — Brian, Havergal. Biographies
Eastaugh, Kenneth
  Havergal Brian : the making of a composer / [by] Kenneth Eastaugh. — London : Harrap, 1976. — xi,337p,[16]p of plates : ill, facsims, music, ports ; 23cm.
  List of sound discs: p.324. — Index.
  ISBN 0-245-52748-6 : £10.00

(B76-33366)

Foreman, Lewis
  Havergal Brian and the performance of his orchestral music : a history and source book / [by] Lewis Foreman. — London (14 Barlby Rd, W10 6AR) : Thames Publishing, 1976. — 112p : ill, facsims, music, ports ; 27cm.
  Facsims., ports., on lining papers. — List of music: p.105-106. — Index.
  ISBN 0-905210-01-8 : £6.95

(B76-23704)

Nettel, Reginald
  Havergal Brian and his music / by Reginald Nettel ; with a catalogue of his music by Lewis Foreman. — London : Dobson, 1976. — xiii,223p,[8]p of plates : ill, facsims, music, ports ; 23cm. — (The student's music library, historical and critical studies)
  Bibl.: p.205-214. — Index.
  ISBN 0-234-77861-x : £7.50

(B76-25956)

BBTNAC — Brian, Havergal. The tigers. Librettos
Brian, Havergal
  The tigers : satirical anti-war opera in a prologue and three acts / by Havergal Brian ; editor James Reid Baxter. — Centennial ed. — Aberdeen ([7 Gaitside Drive, Aberdeen]) : Aberdeen Branch of the Havergal Brian Society, 1976. — [3],vi,26p : ill, facsims, port ; 31cm.
  Text only. — 'The text ... is reproduced from the published Vocal Score [London : Cranz and Co., 1932] ...'. — Bibl. and list of records: p.[3].
  ISBN 0-9505185-0-6 Sd : £0.40

(B76-30338)

BBTP — Bridge, Frank
Payne, Anthony, *b.1936*
  The music of Frank Bridge / [by] Anthony Payne, Lewis Foreman, John Bishop. — London (14 Barlby Rd, W10 6AR) : Thames Publishing, 1976. — 88p : ill, music, ports ; 21cm.
  Bibl.: p.81-83. — List of works: p.58-80. — List of records: p.84-86. — Index.
  ISBN 0-905210-02-6 Sd : £3.20

(B76-29100)

BBUACF — Britten, Benjamin. Paul Bunyan. Librettos
Auden, Wystan Hugh
  Paul Bunyan : an operetta in two acts and a prologue / libretto by W.H. Auden ; set to music by Benjamin Britten. — London (38 Russell Sq., WC1B 5DA) : Faber Music Limited [for] Faber, 1976. — [4],39p ; 20cm.
  ISBN 0-571-10015-5 Sd : £0.80

(B76-10251)

BCE(N) — Chopin, Frédéric. Biographies
Orga, Ateş
  Chopin : his life and times / [by] Ateş Orga. — Tunbridge Wells : Midas Books, 1976. — 144p : ill, facsims, ports ; 26cm.
  Bibl.: p.7. — Index.
  ISBN 0-85936-057-1 : £5.95

(B76-29713)

BCMEACM — Coleman, Cy. See-saw. Librettos
Fields, Dorothy
  Seesaw : a musical / music by Cy Coleman; lyrics by Dorothy Fields ; based on the play 'Two for the Seesaw' by William Gibson ; written, directed and choreographed by Michael Bennett. — New York ; London [etc.] : French, 1975. — 70p ; 21cm. — (French's musical library)
  Four men, 4 women.
  ISBN 0-573-68069-8 Sd : £1.25

(B76-06887)

BDL — Delius, Frederick
  A Delius companion / edited with a preface by Christopher Redwood. — London : John Calder : [Distributed by Calder and Boyars], 1976. — 270p,[18]p of plates : ill, facsims, music, ports ; 23cm.
  '... tribute to Eric Fenby' - Introduction. — Index.
  ISBN 0-7145-3526-5 : £7.50

(B76-17646)

Palmer, Christopher
  Delius : portrait of a cosmopolitan / [by] Christopher Palmer ; with a foreword by Eric Fenby. — London : Duckworth, 1976. — xi,199p,leaf of plate,[18]p of plates : ill, facsim music, ports ; 24cm.
  Bibl.: p.195-196. — Index.
  ISBN 0-7156-0773-1 : £9.80

(B76-22079)

BDL(Z) — Delius, Frederick - relations with Warlock
Tomlinson, Fred
  Warlock and Delius / [by] Fred Tomlinson. — London (14 Barlby Rd, W10 6AR) : Thames Publishing [for the Peter Warlock Society], 1976. — 31p : facsims, music, ports ; 24cm.
  '... basically the script of a talk given to the Delius Society in London on 29th January 1976' - Preface.
  ISBN 0-905210-05-0 Sd : £1.50

(B76-27764)

BDTARWNR — Dowland, John. Lachrimae
Dowland, John
  Lachrimae / [by] John Dowland. — [1st ed.], reprinted / under the direction of Leslie Hewitt ; with a commentary by Warwick Edwards ; general editor Richard Rastall. — Leeds (5 Albert Grove, Leeds 6) : Boethius Press, 1974. — [61]p : facsims, chiefly music ; 36cm. — (Early music reprinted ; 1)
  Facsimile reprint of: 1st ed., London : Printed by John Windet, 1605.
  ISBN 0-904263-04-5 : £6.60

(B76-10254)

BDUACM — Dubey, Matt. Smith. Librettos
Dubey, Matt
  Smith : a musical / music and lyrics by Matt Dubey and Dean Fuller ; book by Dean Fuller, Tony Hendra and Matt Dubey. — New York ; London [etc.] : French, 1975. — 67p ; 19cm. — (French's musical library)
  Seven men, 1 woman.
  ISBN 0-573-68066-3 Sd : £1.25

(B76-00671)

BDVAMBN — Dukas, Paul. L'Apprenti sorcier. Stories
Yanagihara, Ryohei
  P. Dukas' 'The sorcerer's apprentice' / illustrated by Ryohei Yanagihara ; adapted by Makoto Oishi ; translated by Ann Brannen. — London : F. Warne, 1976. — [30]p : chiefly col ill ; 25x27cm. — (Fantasia pictorial, stories from famous music)
  Sheet of music ([2]p.) as insert. — These illustrations originally published: with Japanese text. Tokyo : Gakken, 1971.
  ISBN 0-7232-1834-x : £2.25

(B76-18582)

BFNRACP — Forster, John. Pretzels. Librettos
Forster, John
  Pretzels : a musical revue / music and lyrics by John Forster ; written by Jane Curtin, Fred Grandy, and Judy Kahan. — New York ; London [etc.] : French, 1975. — 73p ; 21cm. — (French's musical library)
  ISBN 0-573-68071-x Sd : £1.25

(B76-06889)

BG — Gabrieli, Giovanni
Müller-Blattau, Wendelin
  Tonsatz und Klanggestaltung bei Giovanni Gabrieli / [von] Wendelin Müller-Blattau. — Kassel [etc.] ; London ([32 Great Titchfield St., W.1]) : Bärenreiter, 1975. — 246p : music ; 24cm. — (Saarbrücker Studien zur Musikwissen-schaft ; Band 4)
  Bibl.: p.142-146.
  Pbk : £24.00
  ISBN 3-7618-0502-0

(B76-06888)

BGGTACM — Geld, Gary. Shenandoah. Librettos
Udell, Peter
  Shenandoah : a musical / based on an original screenplay by James Lee Barrett, lyrics by Peter Udell, music by Gary Geld ; book by James Lee Barrett, Peter Udell and Philip Rose. — New York ; London [etc.] : French, 1975. — 78p : plans ; 21cm. — (French's musical library)
  Eighteen men, 2 women.
  ISBN 0-573-68073-6 Sd : £1.25

(B76-06888)

BGRT(N) — Grainger, Percy Aldridge. Biographies
Bird, John, *b.1941*
  Percy Grainger / [by] John Bird. — London : Elek, 1976. — xvi, 317p,[16]p of plates : ill, facsim, ports ; 25cm.
  Facsims. on lining papers. — Bibl : p.258-260. — List of music: p.262-282. — List of sound discs and piano rolls: p.292-308. — Index.
  ISBN 0-236-40004-5 : £10.00

(B76-35350)

BGSEACM — Grant, Micki. The prodigal sister. Librettos
Franklin, J E
The prodigal sister : a new black musical / book and lyrics by
J.E. Franklin ; music and lyrics by Micki Grant. — New York ;
London [etc.] : French, [1976]. — 60p : plan ; 21cm. — (Frengh's
musical library)
Thirteen men, 12 women. — Published in the United States: 1975.
ISBN 0-573-68075-2 Sd : £1.35

(B76-50357)

BGYU(N) — Gurney, Ivor. Biographies
Moore, Charles Willard
Maker and lover of beauty : Ivor Gurney, poet and songwriter /
[by] Charles W. Moore ; with decorations by Richard Walker and
an introduction by Herbert Howells. — Rickmansworth (22
Pheasants Way, Rickmansworth, Herts.) : Triad Press, 1976. —
28p : ill, music, port ; 28cm.
Limited ed. of 200 numbered copies.
ISBN 0-902070-16-9 Sd : £2.65

(B76-50358)

BHKMACM — Herman, Jerry. Mack and Mabel. Librettos
Stewart, Michael
Mack & Mabel : a musical love story / book by Michael Stewart ;
music and lyrics by Jerry Herman. — New York [etc.] ; London :
French, 1976. — 63p ; 21cm. — (French's musical library)
Ten men, 5 women.
ISBN 0-573-68074-4 Sd : £1.35

(B76-19250)

BHUAC — Humperdinck, Engelbert. Hänsel und Gretel. Librettos
Hammond, Tom
Hansel and Gretel : a fairy opera in three acts / by Adelheid
Wette ; translated and adapted into English by Tom Hammond ;
the music composed by E. Humperdinck. — London (48 Great
Marlborough St., W1V 2BN) : Schott and Co. Ltd, [1976]. —
42p ; 20cm.
Vocal score of this adaptation published: 1972. — Adaptation of : 'Hänsel
und Gretel'.
ISBN 0-901938-14-9 Sd : £0.50

(B76-18375)

BHUACBN — Humperdinck, Engelbert. Hänsel und Gretel
Isaka, Yoshitaro
E. Humperdinck's 'Hansel and Gretel' : based on E.
Humperdinck's opera after the story by the Brothers Grimm /
illustrated by Yoshitaro Isaka ; adapted by Eriko Kishida ;
translated by Ann Brannen. — London : F. Warne, 1976. — [30]
p : chiefly col ill ; 25x27cm. — (Fantasia pictorial, stories from
famous music)
Sheet of music ([2]p.) as insert. — These illustrations originally published:
with Japanese text, Tokyo : Gakken, 1971.
ISBN 0-7232-1835-8 : £2.25

(B76-19463)

BIV(N) — Ives, Charles. Biographies
Rossiter, Frank Raymond
Charles Ives and his America / [by] Frank R. Rossiter. —
London : Gollancz, 1976. — v-xv,420p,[8]p of plates,[2]leaves of
plates : ill, facsim, music, ports ; 23cm.
Originally published: New York : Liveright, 1975. — Bibl.: p.385-395. —
Index.
ISBN 0-575-02103-9 : £8.50

(B76-20007)

BJRP(N) — Joplin, Scott. Biographies
Gammond, Peter
Scott Joplin and the ragtime era / [by] Peter Gammond. —
London : Abacus, 1975. — 223p,[32]p of plates : ill, facsims,
ports ; 20cm.
Bibl.: p.189-192. — List of music : p.195-198. — List of records : p.201-218.
— List of works : p.221-223.
ISBN 0-349-11412-9 Pbk : £1.25

(B76-29712)

BLDACF — Lehár, Franz. Friederike, Librettos
Dunn, Bernard
Frederica : operetta in three acts / new book by Bernard Dunn,
lyrics by Harry S. Pepper, additional lyrics by Bernard Dunn ;
original book and lyrics by L. Herzer and F. Löhner ; music by
Franz Lehar ; adapted & arranged by Ronald Hanmer. — London
(10 Rathbone St., W1P 2BJ) : Glocken Verlag Ltd, 1976. — [2],
iii,117p : 2 plans ; 20cm.
Pbk : £1.00

BMKS — Messiaen, Oliver
Samuel, Claude
Conversations with Olivier Messiaen / [by] Claude Samuel ;
translated [from the French] by Felix Aprahamian. — London :
Stainer and Bell, 1976. — [2],140p,plate : port ; 23cm.
Translation of: 'Entretiens avec Olivier Messiaen'. Paris : Belfond, 1967. —
Index.
ISBN 0-85249-308-8 : Unpriced

(B76-18371)

BMS(N) — Mozart, Wolfgang Amadeus. Biographies
Hutchings, Arthur
Mozart : the man, the musician / [by] Arthur Hutchings. —
London : Thames and Hudson, 1976. — viii,113,131p,48p of
plates : ill(some col), facsims, map, music, ports(some col) ; 31cm.
Index.
ISBN 0-500-01161-3 : £16.00

(B76-34778)

Mozart, Wolfgang Amadeus
Briefe und Afzeichnungen / [von] Mozart ; herausgegeben von der
Internationalen Stiftung Mozarteum Salzburg ; gesammelt von
Wilhelm A. Bauer und Otto Erich Deutsch ; auf Grund deren
Vorarbeiten erläutert von Joseph Heinz Eibl. — Gesamtuasg. —
Kassel [etc.] ; London ([32 Great Titchfield St., W1P 7AD]) :
Bärenreiter.
Band 7 : Register / zusammengestellt von Joseph Heinz Eibl. — 1975. —
xxiv,645p ; 24cm.
£37.50

BMSAC — Mozart, Wolfgang Amadeus. La Clemenza di Tito.
Librettos
Metastasio, Pietro
La Clemenza di Tito : Opera seria in zwei Akten : Textbuch
italiebisch-deutsch / Text nach Pietro Metastasio ; von Caterino
Mazzolà ; wortgetreue deustche Ubersetzung von Erna Neunteufel.
— Kassel [etc.] ; London ([32 Great Titchfield St., W1P 7AD]) :
Bärenreiter, 1976. — 119p ; 19cm. — (Internationale Stiftung
Mozarteum Salzburg. Mozarts italienische Texte mit deutscher
Übersetzung ; Band 2)
Parallel Italian and German text.
Pbk : £1.13
ISBN 3-7618-0548-9

BMUAMBN — Mussorgsky, Modest. A night on the bare mountain.
Stories
Semba, Taro
M.P. Mussorgsky's 'A night on bare mountain' / illustrated by
Taro Semba ; adapted by Satoru Sato ; translated by Ann King
Herring. — London : F. Warne, 1976. — [30]p : chiefly col ill ;
25x27cm. — (Fantasia pictorial, stories from famous music)
Sheet of music ([2]p.) as insert. — These illustrations originally published:
with Japanese text. Tokyo : Gakken, 1971.
ISBN 0-7232-1836-6 : £2.25

(B76-18581)

BOLAC — Oliver, Stephen. Tom Jones. Librettos
Oliver, Stephen
Tom Jones : a comedy for music, based on the novel by Henry
Fielding / [libretto and music] by Stephen Oliver. — Sevenoaks :
Novello, [1976]. — [3],viii,56p ; 20cm.
ISBN 0-85360-063-5 Sd : £0.85

(B76-21365)

BPEMACM — Pember, Ron. Jack the Ripper. Librettos
Pember, Ron
Jack the Ripper : a musical play / book and lyrics by Ron
Pember and Denis de Marne ; music by Ron Pember. — London
[etc.] : French, 1976. — [7],53p : plan ; 22cm.
Eight men, 8 women, supers.
ISBN 0-573-08042-9 Pbk : £0.90

(B76-10909)

BPU — Puccini, Giacomo
Carner, Mosco
Puccini : a critical biography / by Mosco Carner. — 2nd ed. —
London : Duckworth, 1974. — xvi,520p,leaf of plate,[22]p of
plates : ill, facsims, geneal table, music, ports ; 26cm.
Previous ed.: 1958. — Bibl.: p.507-508. — Index.
ISBN 0-7156-0795-2 : £14.00

(B76-22081)

BRC — Rachmaninoff, Sergei
Norris, Geoffrey, b.1947
Rachmaninov / by Geoffrey Norris. — London : Dent, 1976. —
xi,211p,[8]p of plates : ill, music, ports ; 20cm. — (Master
musicians series)
Bibl.: p.200-203. — List of works: p.179-194. — Index.
ISBN 0-460-03145-7 : £3.50

(B76-04297)

BRHEACM — Reiser, Dave. What a spot! Librettos
Sharkey, Jack
What a spot! : a musical farce in three acts / by Jack Sharkey &
Dave Reiser. — New York ; London [etc.] : French, [1976]. —
76p : plan ; 19cm.
Three men, 2 women. — Published in the United States: 1975.
ISBN 0-573-61814-3 Sd : £1.45
Primary classification BSGNHACM

(B76-30339)

BRK(N) — Rodgers, Richard. Biographies
Rodgers, Richard
Musical stages : an autobiography / [by] Richard Rodgers. —
London : W.H. Allen, 1976. — ix,341p,[24]p of plates : ill,
facsims, music, ports ; 25cm.
Originally published: New York : Random House, 1975. — Index.
ISBN 0-491-01777-4 : £5.95
(B76-32591)

BRRACBN — Rossini, Giacchino Antonio. Guillaume Tell. Stories
Mizusawa, Hiroshi
G.A. Rossini's 'William Tell' / illustrated by Hiroshi Mizusawa ;
adapted by Tamao Fujita ; translated by Ann Brannen. —
London : F. Warne, 1976. — [26]p : chiefly col ill ; 25x27cm. —
(Fantasia pictorial, stories from famous music)
Sheet of music ([2]p.) as insert. — These illustrations originally published:
with Japanese text. Tokyo : Gakken, 1971.
ISBN 0-7232-1833-1 : £2.25
(B76-18578)

BSET — Schoenberg, Arnold
MacDonald, Malcolm, b.1948
Schoenberg / [by] Malcolm MacDonald. — London : Dent, 1976.
— xiv,289p,[8]p of plates : ill, facsim, music, ports ; 20cm. —
(The master musicians series)
Bibl.: p.276-281. — List of works : p.258-266. — Index.
ISBN 0-460-03143-0 : £4.25
ISBN 0-460-02183-4 Pbk : Unpriced
(B76-31120)

Rosen, Charles
Schoenberg / [by] Charles Rosen. — [London] : Fontana, 1976.
— 124p : music ; 18cm. — (Fontana modern masters)
Originally published: as 'Arnold Schoenberg.' New York : Viking, 1975. —
'Schoenberg' also published: London : Marion Boyars, 1976. — Bibl.:
p.123-124.
ISBN 0-00-633558-6 Pbk : £0.75
(B76-34779)

Rosen, Charles
Schoenberg / [by] Charles Rosen. — London : Marion Boyars :
Distributed by Calder and Boyars, 1976. — [1],124p : music ;
23cm.
Originally published: as 'Arnold Schoenberg'. New York : Viking, 1975. —
'Schoenberg' also published: London : Fontana, 1976. — Bibl.: p.123-124.
ISBN 0-7145-2566-9 : £4.25
(B76-14361)

BSFAKDW — Schubert, Franz. Songs, etc
Fischer-Dieskau, Dietrich
Schubert : a biographical study of his songs / [by] Dietrich
Fischer-Dieskau ; translated [from the German] and edited by
Kenneth S. Whitton. — London : Cassell, 1976. — [9],331p ;
23cm.
Translation of: 'Auf den Spuren der Schubert-Lieder'. Wiesbaden :
Brockhaus, 1971. — Bibl.: p.319-320. — Index.
ISBN 0-304-29002-5 : £5.95
(B76-33372)

BSG(N) — Schumann, Robert. Biographies
Walker, Alan, b.1930
Schumann / [by] Alan Walker. — London : Faber, 1976. —
3-128p : ill, facsims, geneal table, music, ports ; 22cm. — (The
great composers)
List of music: p.123-124. — Index.
ISBN 0-571-10269-7 : £3.25
(B76-21364)

BSGADW — Schumann, Robert. Songs, etc
Sams, Eric
The songs of Robert Schumann / [by] Eric Sams ; foreword by
Gerald Moore. — 2nd ed. — London (48 Great Marlborough St.,
W1V 2BN) : Eulenburg Books, 1975. — xii,292p : music ; 23cm.
Previous ed.: London : Methuen, 1969. — Index.
ISBN 0-903873-17-6 : £4.50
ISBN 0-903873-18-4 Pbk : £3.00
(B76-10252)

BSGNHACM — Sharkey, Jack. What a spot! Librettos
Sharkey, Jack
What a spot! : a musical farce in three acts / by Jack Sharkey &
Dave Reiser. — New York ; London [etc.] : French, [1976]. —
76p : plan ; 19cm.
Three men, 2 women. — Published in the United States: 1975.
ISBN 0-573-61814-3 Sd : £1.45
Also classified at BRHEACM
(B76-30339)

BSH(N) — Sibelius, Jean. Biographies
Tawaststjerna, Erik
Sibelius / by Erik Tawaststjerna ; translated [from the Swedish] by
Robert Layton. — London : Faber.
Vol.1 : 1865-1905. — 1976. — xv,316p,[12]p of plates : ill, music, ports ;
25cm.
Translation of: 'Sibelius'. Stockholm : Bonnier, 1968. — Bibl.: p.295. —
Index.
ISBN 0-571-08832-5 : £12.50
(B76-30336)

BSHLACM — Simpson, Bland. Diamond studs. Librettos
Wann, Jim
Diamond studs : the life of Jesse James / book by Jim Wann ;
music and lyrics by Bland Simpson and Jim Wann. — New York
[etc.] ; London : French, 1976. — 59p : plan ; 21cm. — (French's
musical library)
Twelve men, 8 women.
ISBN 0-573-68076-0 Sd : £1.60
Also classified at BWKBACM
(B77-00344)

BSNK — Stockhausen, Karlheinz
Maconie, Robin
The works of Karlheinz Stockhausen / [by] Robin Maconie ; with
a foreword by Karlheinz Stockhausen. — London [etc.] : Oxford
University Press, 1976. — x,341p : ill, facsims, music ; 26cm.
Jacket title: Stockhausen. — Bibl.: p.330-333. — Index.
ISBN 0-19-315429-3 : £17.50
(B76-20708)

BSU — Strauss, Richard
Kennedy, Michael, b.1926
Richard Strauss / by Michael Kennedy. — London : Dent, 1976.
— xii,274p,[8]p of plates : ill, music, ports ; 20cm. — (The master
musicians series)
List of works: p.241-253. — Bibl.: p.259-260. — Index.
ISBN 0-460-03148-1 : £3.95
ISBN 0-460-02176-1 Pbk : £1.95
(B76-14362)

BTB — Tallis, Thomas
Doe, Paul
Tallis / [by] Paul Doe. — 2nd ed. — London [etc.] : Oxford
University Press, 1976. — 71p : music ; 22cm. — (Oxford studies
of composers ; 4)
Previous ed.: 1968. — List of works: p.66-71.
ISBN 0-19-314122-1 Pbk : £2.20
(B76-15053)

BVB(N) — Varèse, Edgard. Biographies
Varèse, Louise
Varèse : a looking-glass diary / [by] Louise Varèse. — London (48
Great Marlborough St., W1V 2BN) : Eulenburg Books.
In 2 vols.
Vol.1 : 1883-1928. — 1975. — 3-290p,[16]p of plates : ill, facsims, ports ;
23cm.
Originally published: New York : Norton, 1972 ; London : Davis-Poynter,
1973. — Index.
ISBN 0-903873-04-4 Pbk : £3.00
(B76-12127)

BVD — Vaughan Williams, Ralph
Day, James
Vaughan Williams / by James Day. — Revised ed. — London :
Dent, 1975. — x,228p,[8]p of plates : ill, facsim, music, ports ;
20cm. — (The master musicians series)
Previous ed.: 1961. — Bibl.: p.214-215. — Catalogue of works: p.194-205. —
Index.
ISBN 0-460-03162-7 : £3.75
(B76-01202)

BWC — Wagner, Richard
Gàl, Hans
Richard Wagner / [by] Hans Gàl ; translated [from the German]
by Hans-Hubert Schönzeler. — London : Gollancz, 1976. —
224p : music ; 23cm.
Translation of: 'Richard Wagner'. Frankfurt am Main : Fischer Bücherei,
1963. — Bibl.: p.211-212. — List of works: p.213-215. — Index.
ISBN 0-575-01847-x : £5.50
(B76-05038)

BWC(D) — Wagner, Richard. Essays
Wagner 1976 : a celebration of the Bayreuth festival / [edited by
Stewart Spencer]. — London ([c/o 25 Balcombe St., NW1 6HE]) :
The Wagner Society, 1976. — 287p,leaf of plate,[24]p of plates :
ill, facsims, music, ports ; 22cm.
English text, parallel German text and English translation. — Index.
ISBN 0-905800-00-1 Pbk : £3.75
(B77-00342)

BWC(N) — Wagner, Richard. Biographies
Newman, Ernest
The life of Richard Wagner / [by] Ernest Newman. — Cambridge
[etc.] : Cambridge University Press, 1976. — 4v. : music ; 23cm.
Originally published: New York : Knopf, 1933. — Indexes.
ISBN 0-521-29149-6 Pbk : £17.50
(B76-33368)

BWCAC — Wagner, Richard. Der Ring des Nibelungen
Culshaw, John
Reflections on Wagner's 'Ring' / [by] John Culshaw ;
[photographs by Frank Dunand]. — London : Secker and
Warburg, 1976. — xvi,107p : ill ; 23cm.
The first four chapters are based on a series of intermission features on the
Texaco Metropolitan Opera radio network broadcasts of the "Ring" cycle
during the 1974-75 season. The last chapter is expanded from an article
which appeared in "Opera News"' - title page verso. — Also published: New
York : Viking Press, 1976. — Bibl.: p.103-105.
ISBN 0-436-11801-7 : £3.50
(B76-13571)

Westernhagen, Curt von
The forging of the 'Ring' : Richard Wagner's composition sketches
for 'Der Ring des Nibelungen' / [by] Curt von Westernhagen ;
translated [from the German] by Arnold and Mary Whittall. —
Cambridge [etc.] : Cambridge University Press, 1976. — ix,248p :
facsims, music ; 24cm.
Translation of: 'Die Entstehung des "Ring"'. Zürich : Atlantis, 1973. —
Bibl.: p.244-246. — Index.
ISBN 0-521-21293-6 : £7.50

(B77-00343)

BWCAC/E(YEB) — Wagner, Richard. Opera. Bayreuth
Skelton, Geoffrey
Wagner at Bayreuth : experiment and tradition / [by] Geoffrey
Skelton ; foreword by the late Wieland Wagner. — New and
revised ed. — London [etc.] : White Lion Publishers, 1976. —
251p,[16]p of plates : ill, ports ; 22cm.
Previous ed.: London : Barrie and Rockliff, 1965. — Bibl.: p.241-242. —
Index.
ISBN 0-85617-068-2 : £5.75

(B76-14367)

BWCAC/E(YEB) — Wagner, Richard. Performance. Bayreuth
Shaw, Bernard
Wagner in Bayreuth / by Bernard Shaw. — London (15 Mortimer
Terrace, N.W.5) : Broadsheet King, 1976. — 12p : ill, facsims,
plan, ports ; 22x23cm.
'... originally appeared in the "English Illustrated Magazine" of 1889'.
ISBN 0-902617-17-6 Sd : Unpriced

(B76-35352)

BWCB(XKR101/EM) — Wagner family, 1876-1976. Illustrations
The **Wagner** family albums, Bayreuth 1876-1976 / [compiled by]
Wolf Siegfried Wagner; translated from the German by Susanne
Flatauer. — London : Thames and Hudson, 1976. — 160p :
chiefly ill, geneal table, ports ; 28cm.
Translation of: 'Die Geschichte unserer Familie in Bildern, Bayreuth
1876-1976'. Munich : Rogner und Bernhard, 1976. — Bibl.: p.160.
ISBN 0-500-01158-3 : £5.95

(B76-19493)

BWKBACM — Wann, Jim. Diamond studs. Librettos
Wann, Jim
Diamond studs : the life of Jesse James / book by Jim Wann ;
music and lyrics by Bland Simpson and Jim Wann. — New York
[etc.] ; London : French, 1976. — 59p : plan ; 21cm. — (French's
musical library)
Twelve men, 8 women.
ISBN 0-573-68076-0 Sd : £1.60
Primary classification BSHLACM

(B77-00344)

BWL(YDB/XHF) — Weber, Carl Maria von, Freiherr. London, 1826
Weber in London, 1826 / edited by David Reynolds ... — London :
Wolff, 1976. — 51p : ill, facsims, maps, music, ports ; 21x27cm.
Bibl.: p.5. — Includes: Selections from Weber's letters to his wife /
translated by Noel Currer-Briggs - London in 1826 / by Hermione
Hobhouse - Weber's legacy / by John Warrack.
ISBN 0-85496-403-7 Pbk : £1.95

(B76-22852)

BWPAC — Wolf, Hugo. Der Corregidor
Cook, Peter, *b.1924*
Hugo Wolf's 'Corregidor' : a study of the opera and its origins /
[by] Peter Cook. — [London] ([8 Upper Wimpole St., W.1.]) :
The author, 1976. — 171p,plate : 1 ill, music ; 21cm.
Bibl.: p.171.
ISBN 0-9504360-0-3 Pbk : £3.90

(B76-05912)

BZ — LITERATURE ON NON-EUROPEAN MUSIC
BZC — Turkey
Bartók, Béla
Turkish folk music from Asia Minor / by Béla Bartók ; edited by
Benjamin Suchoff ; with an afterword by Kurt Reinhard. —
Princeton ; London : Princeton University Press, 1976. — [7],
288p : ill, facsims, music, ports ; 23cm. — (New York Bartók
Archive. Studies in musicology ; no.7)
Index.
ISBN 0-691-09120-x : £12.20

(B76-36284)

BZCWIAL/B(YDB/WJ) — Islam. Instruments. Horniman Museum.
Exhibitions
Jenkins, Jean
Music and musical instruments in the world of Islam / [by] Jean
Jenkins and Poul Rovsing Olsen ; line drawings by John Pringle.
— London ([85 Cromwell Rd, SW7 5BW]) : World of Islam
Festival Publishing Co. Ltd, 1976. — iv,100p,[8]p of plates :
ill(some col), music ; 25cm.
Catalogue of an exhibition held 6th April-6th October at the Horniman
Museum. — Bibl.: p.90-100.
ISBN 0-905035-12-7 Pbk : £1.50

(B76-22080)

BZGH — Thailand
Morton, David
The traditional music of Thailand / [by] David Morton. —
Berkeley [etc.] ; London : University of California Press, 1976. —
xv,258p : ill, music, ports ; 29cm.
Bibl.: p.244-251. — List of records : p.252. — Index.
ISBN 0-520-01876-1 : £11.55

(B76-31121)

BZHPAL — Japan. Court music
Garfias, Robert
Music of a thousand autumns : the Tōgaku style of Japanese court
music / by Robert Garfias. — Berkeley [etc.] ; London :
University of California Press, 1976. — x,361p : ill, music, ports ;
29cm.
Published in the United States: 1975. — Bibl.: p.285-294. — List of
recordings: p.297-301. — List of works: p.305-314. — Index.
ISBN 0-520-01977-6 : £17.45

(B76-19253)

BZK/FD(WT) — Africa. Recorded music. Lists
Stone, Ruth M
African music oral data : a catalog of field recordings,
1902-1975 / [by] Ruth M. Stone, Frank J. Gillis. —
Bloomington ; London : Indiana University Press ; [London] :
[Distributed by Bell], 1976. — xix,412p : forms ; 25cm.
The African Field Recording Survey project has produced a new and
detailed source of information about African music. — Index.
ISBN 0-253-30262-5 : £12.00

(B76-50759)

BZNDAT — Sudan. Plucked string instruments
Plumley, Gwendolen Alice
El tanbur : the Sudanese lyre or the Nubian kissar / [by]
Gwendolen A. Plumley. — Cambridge (c/o Book Production
Consultants, 12 Hills Rd, Cambridge [CB2 1PG]) : Town and
Gown Press, [1976]. — 70p : ill, maps, music ; 21cm.
ISBN 0-905107-02-0 Pbk : £1.25

(B76-13572)

BZNR — South Africa. Venda tribe
Blacking, John
How musical is man? / [by] John Blacking. — London : Faber,
1976. — viii,120p,[12]p of plates : ill, music ; 23cm.
Sound tape of Venda music to accompany this book available from the
University of Washington Press, Seattle. — Originally published: Seattle ;
London : University of Washington Press, 1973. — Bibl.: p.117-118. —
Index.
ISBN 0-571-10790-7 : £4.95
ISBN 0-571-10803-2 Pbk : £2.20
Primary classification A(ZF)

(B76-22078)

C/AY — GENERAL COLLECTIONS
C/AY(XCSK76) — 1450-1525
An **anthology** of early renaissance music / edited by Noah
Greenberg and Paul Maynard. — London : Dent, 1975. — xiv,
318p ; 4to.
ISBN 0-460-04300-5 : £9.95

(B76-50001)

C/AYD — England
Musica Britannica : a national collection of music. — 2nd, revised
ed. — London : Stainer and Bell.
Vol.28 : William Byrd : Keyboard music 2 / transcribed and edited by Alan
Brown. — 1976. — xxii,211p ; fol.
ISBN 0-85249-426-2 : Unpriced
Also classified at PWP/AZ

(B76-50359)

Musica Britannica : a national collection of music. — London :
Stainer and Bell.
This volume brings together all Locke's settings of Latin and English sacred
texts that are scored for four or more voices - Editor's note.
Vol.38 : Matthew Locke : anthems and motets / transcribed and edited by
Peter le Huray. — 1976. — xx,158p ; fol.
ISBN 0-85249-397-5 : Unpriced
Also classified at ERXMDH

(B76-50360)

C/CY — COLLECTIONS, EXERCISES, ETC. , ILLUSTRATING
TECHNIQUES OF PERFORMANCE
C/JR — Theatre music
Goehr, Alexander
[Triptych, no.2. Op.30]. Shadowplay, Op.30 : music theatre from
book 7 of the Republic of Plato / [by] Alexander Goehr ; utilizing
a translation and original material by Kenneth Cavander ; deutsch
von Frederik Prausnitz. — London : Schott, 1976. — 39p ; 4to.
The work performed by an actor playing the role of the prisoner, tenor
(narrator), alto flute in G, alto saxophone in E flat, horn in F, cello and
piano.
Unpriced

(B76-50002)

Goehr, Alexander
[Triptych, no.3. Op.31]. Sonata about Jerusalem. Op.31 : cantata / [by] Alexander Goehr ; texts from the Jewish, Christian and Arab history of the city of Jerusalem, English version by the composer ; German version by Frederick Prausnitz. — London : Schott, 1976. — 78p ; 4to.
The work performed by bass solo (narrator), soprano solo (mad boy), female chorus, boy's voice (speaking role), flute (doubling piccolo), clarinet in B flat, horn in F, trumpet in B flat, piano, violin, cello, double bass. — Text in English and German.
Unpriced

(B76-50003)

CB — VOCAL MUSIC
CB/AY — Collections
Gweithdy cerddorol y plant. — Llandybie [Swansea] : C. Davies.
Staff & tonic sol-fa notation. — Book 1 was classified in CB/NM.
Llyfr 2 : Carolau / wedi eu trefnu gan E. Olwen Jones. — 1974. — 28p : music ; obl. 4to.
ISBN 0-7154-0188-2 : Unpriced
Also classified at CB/LF/AY

(B76-50361)

CB/AY(XCH301) — 1200-1500
Invitation to medieval music / newly transcribed and edited by Thurston Dart and Brian Trowell. — London : Stainer and Bell.
3 : Music of the mid-fifteenth century (1). — 1976. — viii,48p ; 8vo.
ISBN 0-85249-316-9 : Unpriced

(B76-50362)

CB/AYT — United States
America's bicentennial songs from the great sentimental age, 1850-1900, Stephen C. Foster to Charles E. Ives : for unison, two- and four-part vocal ensembles with piano accompaniment / compiled and edited by Gregg Smith. — New York ; London : Schirmer, 1975. — vi,140p ; 4to.
Unpriced

(B76-50004)

CB/LF/AY — Christmas. Collections
Gweithdy cerddorol y plant. — Llandybie [Swansea] : C. Davies.
Staff & tonic sol-fa notation. — Book 1 was classified at CB/NM.
Llyfr 2 : Carolau / wedi eu trefnu gan E. Olwen Jones. — 1974. — 28p : music ; obl. 4to.
ISBN 0-7154-0188-2 : Unpriced
Primary classification CB/AY

(B76-50361)

CC — OPERA. VOCAL SCORES
Dan, Ikuma
[Yuzuru. *Vocal score*]. Yuzuru = The twilight heron : opera in one act / [by] Ikuma Dan ; libretto by Junji Kinoshita ; English translation [from the Japanese] by Dorothy G. Britton ; German translation by E. Hartogs. — London : Boosey and Hawkes, 1976. — 194p ; 4to.
Text in Japanese, English & German.
Unpriced

(B76-50363)

Humperdinck, Engelbert
[Hänsel und Gretel. *Vocal score*]. Hansel and Gretel : opera in two acts / [by] Engelbert Humperdinck ; text by Adelheid Wette ; translated and adapted by Norman Kelley. — New York ; [London] : Boosey and Hawkes, 1976. — 179p ; 8vo.
Vocal score by R. Kleinmichel.
£9.00

(B76-50005)

Luening, Otto
[Evangeline. *Vocal score*]. Evangeline : opera in 3 acts / libretto and music by Otto Luening. — New York ; London : Peters, 1974. — [8],141p ; 4to.
Duration 180 min.
Unpriced

(B76-50760)

CF — OPERETTAS. VOCAL SCORES
Korngold, Erich
[Eine Nacht in Venedig. *Vocal score*]. A night in Venice / adapted from the music of Johann Strauss by Erich Korngold ; original book and lyrics by Zell and Genes ; additional German lyrics by E. Marischka and A. Jergen ; English translation and book adaptation by Murray Dickie ; additional musical adaptation and orchestrations by Anton Paulik and Laszlo Imre. — London : Weinberger, 1976. — 199p ; 8vo.
Unpriced

(B76-50364)

Lehár, Franz
[Friederike. *Vocal score*]. Frederica : operetta in three acts / [by] Franz Lehar ; adapted and arranged by Ronald Hanmer, original book by Ludwig Herzer and Fritz Löhner, new book by Bernard Dunn, original English lyrics by Harry S. Pepper, additional lyrics by Bernard Dunn. — London : Glocken, 1976. — 196p ; 4to.
Unpriced

(B76-50761)

Offenbach, Jacques
[La Fille du tambour major. *Vocal score*]. The drum-major's daughter : comic opera in three acts / by Jacques Offenbach ; music adapted and arranged by Max Morris, original libretto by Alfred Duru and Henri Chivot in a new English translation by Geoffrey Wilson. — Paris : Choudens ; London : United Music, 1976. — 192p ; 4to.
Unpriced

(B76-50762)

CM — MUSICAL PLAYS. VOCAL SCORES
Previn, André
[The good companions. *Vocal score*]. The good companions : the musical of the novel by J.B. Priestley / [by] André Previn ; lyrics by Johnny Mercer. — London : Chappell, 1976. — iv,185p ; 4to.
Unpriced

(B76-50763)

CM/L — Religious musical plays. Vocal scores
Fargo, Milford
[Away he run. *Vocal score*]. Away he run : a musical based on the story of the prodigal son / music by Milford Fargo ; words by Dane Gordon. — London : Stainer and Bell, 1976. — 63p ; 4to.
ISBN 0-85249-315-0 : Unpriced

(B76-50764)

CN — Children's musical plays with keyboard accompaniment
Parry, William Howard
The beast of Bettesthorne / music written and arranged for voices, piano and optional instruments by W.H. Parry ; words by S. Jackson-Smith. — London : Chester, 1976. — 39p ; obl.4to. — (Musicplay series ; no.2)
Children's musical play.
Unpriced

(B76-50765)

Tobias, Henry
Twelve musical plays for children (based on famous fairy tales) / by Henry Tobias and David Ormont ; edited by Lee Snider ; illustrations by Judi Weiser. — New York : Henry Tobias : Chappell ; [London] : [Chappell], 1976. — 293p ; 4to.
Unpriced

(B76-50006)

Walker, Raymond
[Cinderella in Salerno. *Vocal score*]. Cinderella in Salerno : an opera for schools in three acts based on Rossini's 'La Cenerentola' / by Raymond Walker and William Beaumont. — Sevenoaks : Novello, 1976. — 108p ; 8vo.
£1.70

(B76-50766)

CQC — OPERA. FULL SCORES
Delius, Frederick
Fennimore und Gerda = Fennimore and Gerda / [von] Frederick Delius ; zwei Episoden aus dem Leben Niels Lyhnes in elf Bildern nach dem Roman von J.P. Jacobsen ; English version by Philip Heseltine. — London : Boosey and Hawkes, 1976. — 140p ; 8vo. — (Hawkes Pocket Score ; no.896)
Miniature score. — Text in German and English.
£6.50

(B76-50007)

Henze, Hans Werner
We come to the river = Wir erreichen den Fluss : Handlungen für Musik / von Edward Bond ; [von] Hans Werner Henze ; deutsche Fassung vom Komponisten. — Mainz ; London : Schott, 1976. — xix,555p ; fol.
£39.20

(B76-50767)

Holst, Gustav
Savitri, Op 25 : an episode from the Mahābhārata / [by] Gustav Holst ; foreword by Imogen Holst. — Revised ed. / edited by Imogen Holst. — London : Eulenburg, 1976. — ix,43p ; 8vo. — (Edition Eulenburg ; no.1097)
Miniature score.
Unpriced

(B76-50768)

CQM — MUSICAL PLAYS. FULL SCORES
CQN — Children's musical plays. Full scores
Burnett, Michael
The poltergoose : for recorder, percussion, voices and piano / by Michael Burnett ; words, R.C. Scriven. — London : Chester, 1976. — 51p ; obl.4to. — (Musicplay series ; no.1)
Children's musical play.
Unpriced

(B76-50769)

Odam, George
Inca : a project in sound for young performers / [by] George Odam ; words by Ruth Phelps. — London : Chester, 1976. — 87p ; 4to. — (Musicplay series ; no.4)
Children's musical play.
Unpriced

(B76-50770)

Odam, George
The legend of Robin Hood : for descant recorders, pitched percussion, voices and piano / words and music by George Odam. — London : Chester, 1976. — 28p ; obl.4to. — (Musicplay series ; no.3)
Children's musical play.
Unpriced
(B76-50771)

Oliver, Stephen
Three instant operas for children / [by] Stephen Oliver. — Sevenoaks : Novello, 1976. — 43p ; 4to.
Contents: Old Haunts - Paid off - Time flies.
£1.35
(B76-50772)

Thackray, Roy
The heavenly archer / words and music by Roy Thackray. — London : Chester, 1976. — 51p ; 4to.
Unpriced
(B76-50365)

DACM — MUSICAL PLAYS. CHORAL WORKS. CHORAL SCORES
Rutter, John
[Bang. *Choral Score*]. Bang! / music, John Rutter ; words, David Grant. — London : Oxford University Press, 1976. — 27p ; 8vo.
ISBN 0-19-338051-x : Unpriced
(B76-50773)

DADK — ANTHEMS. CHORAL SCORES.
DADM — Hymns. Choral scores
[The **Cambridge** hymnal. *Choral score*]. The Cambridge hymnal : vocal edition / edited by Elizabeth Poston, music, and David Holbrook, words. — Cambridge : Cambridge University Press, 1976. — xv,192p ; 8vo.
ISBN 0-521-20398-8 : £1.50
(B76-50008)

DE — RELIGIOUS CANTATAS WITH KEYBOARD ACCOMPANIMENT
Argento, Dominick
[Jonah and the whale. *Vocal score*]. Jonah and the whale : tenor and bass soli, mixed chorus, narrator and instrumental ensemble / [by] Dominick Argento. — New York ; [London] : Boosey and Hawkes, 1976. — 148p ; 8vo.
Duration 60 min.
£10.00
(B76-50774)

Bennett, Robert Russell
[The fun and faith of William Billings, American. *Vocal score*]. The fun and faith of William Billings, American / composed by Robert Russell Bennett, on songs by William Billings. — New York ; [London] : Chappell, 1976. — 80p ; 4to.
Unpriced
(B76-50366)

Buxtehude, Dietrich
[Cantate Domino. *arr*]. Cantate Domino, canticum novum / [by] Dietrich Buxtehude ; arranged for four-part chorus of mixed voices, SATB, with soprano, tenor and bass soli and piano accompaniment by Walter Ehret. — New York ; London : Schirmer, 1975. — 29p ; 8vo.
English and Latin text.
Unpriced
(B76-50009)

Buxtehude, Dietrich
In te Domine speravi : Kantate für Sopran, Alt, Bass und Basso continuo / [von] Dietrich Buxtehude ; zum ersten Mal herausgegeben von Traugott Fedtke, Generalbassaussetzung vom Herausgeber. — Frankfurt : Litolff ; London : Peters, 1975. — 7p ; 8vo.
Unpriced
(B76-50010)

Einem, Gottfried von
[An die Nachgeborenen. Op.42. *Vocal score*]. An die Nachgeborenen, Op.42 : Kantate für Mezzosopran, Bariton, gemischte Chor und Orchester / [von] Gottfried von Einem. — London : Boosey and Hawkes, 1976. — 143p ; 4to.
£12.50
(B76-50777)

Grünberger, Theodor
[German mass, no.2, G. major. *Vocal score*]. Zweite deutsche Messe, 'Hier liegt vor deiner Majestät', für Sopran, Alt, Bass ad libitum (solistisch oder chorisch) und Orgel / [von] Theodor Grünberger ; herausgegeben von Eberhard Kraus. — Regensburg : Bosse ; [London] : [Bärenreiter], 1975. — 31p ; 4to. — (Musik der Oberpfalz)
The text is largely a metrical version of the Mass text in German.
£8.75
(B76-50367)

Mendelssohn, Felix
[O Haupt voll Blut und Wunden. *Vocal score*]. O Haupt voll Blut und Wunden : für Bass, gemischten Chor und Orchester / [von] Felix Mendelssohn-Bartholdy ; Klavierauszug vom Herausgeber. — Zum ersten Mal / herausgegeben von Theo Molich. — Frankfurt : Litolff ; London : Peters, 1976. — 28p ; 8vo.
Cantata.
Unpriced
(B76-50775)

Rooper, Jasper
[Cantata for all seasons. *Vocal score*]. Cantata for all seasons : for solos and mixed voices with orchestra or organ / by Jasper Rooper. — London : Thames, 1976. — 16p ; 8vo.
Unpriced
(B76-50368)

Rorem, Ned
[Little prayers. *Vocal score*]. Little prayers : for soprano and baritone solos, mixed chorus, and orchestra / [by] Ned Rorem ; texts by Paul Goodman. — New York ; [London] : Boosey and Hawkes, 1976. — 59p ; 4to.
£6.00
(B76-50776)

DFF — ROMAN LITURGY
DGB — Ordinary of the Mass. Kyrie
Rossini, Gioacchino Antonio
[Messe solennelle. Kyrie. *Vocal score*]. Kyrie / [by] Gioacchino Rossini ; edited for four-part chorus of mixed voices with piano by Edwin Earle Ferguson. — Wendover : Roberton, 1976. — 19p ; 8vo. — (Lawson-Gould sacred choral series)
£0.28
(B76-50778)

DGC — Ordinary of the Mass. Gloria
Freed, Arnold
[Gloria. *Vocal score*]. Gloria : mixed chorus, brass ensemble, timpani with piano (alternate accompaniment) / [by] Arnold Freed. — Revised ed. — New York ; [London] : Boosey and Hawkes, 1976. — 16p ; 8vo.
£0.50
(B76-50779)

Rutter, John
[Gloria. *Vocal score*]. Gloria for mixed voices with brass, percussion and organ / [by] John Rutter. — London : Oxford University Press, 1976. — 44p ; 8vo.
Duration 17 min.
ISBN 0-19-338062-5 : Unpriced
(B76-50369)

DGE — Ordinary of the Mass. Sanctus
Schubert, Franz
[Gesänge zur Feier des heiligen Opfers der Messe. D.872. Zum Sanctus. *arr*]. Zum Sanctus : for 4-part chorus of mixed voices with organ or piano / [by] Franz Schubert ; edited by Abraham Kaplan ; English text by A.K. — Wendover : Roberton, 1975. — 7p ; 8vo. — (Kaplan, Abraham. Choral series)
£0.14
Primary classification DH
(B76-50019)

DGKAV — Requiems
Ligeti, György
[Requiem. *Vocal score*]. Requiem für Sopran, Mezzosopran, zwei gemischte Chöre und Orchester / [von] György Ligeti ; Klavierauszug von Zsigmond Szathmáry. — Frankfurt : Litolff ; London : Peters, 1975. — 84p ; fol.
Unpriced
(B76-50011)

DGM — ANGLICAN LITURGY
Festival service book. — Addington : Royal College of Church Music.
8 : The city : a meditation with words and music. — 1976. — 72p ; 8vo. — ISBN 0-85402-064-0 : Unpriced
(B76-50780)

Hanson, Geoffrey
Brecon service : for mixed voice chorus and organ / by Geoffrey Hanson. — Wendover : Roberton.
No.1 : Venite, exultemus Domino. — 1976. — 8p ; 8vo. — £0.14
(B76-50370)
No.2 : Benedictus. — 1976. — 15p ; 8vo. — £0.22
(B76-50371)
No.3 : Te Deum laudamus. — 1976. — 11p ; 8vo. — £0.18
(B76-50372)

Hanson, Geoffrey
Brecon service : for mixed voice chorus and organ / by Geoffrey Hanson. — Wendover : Robertson.
No.4 : Magnificat and Nunc dimittis. — 1976. — 16p ; 8vo. — £0.22
(B76-50373)

No.5 : Preces and responses. — 1976. — 4p ; 16mo. —
£0.10

(B76-50374)

DGPP — Evening prayer. Canticles
Walton, *Sir* **William**
Magnificat and Nunc dimittis : S.A.T.B. and organ / by William
Walton. — London : Oxford University Press, 1976. — 15p ; 8vo.
— (Oxford church services ; S.609)
ISBN 0-19-351650-0 : Unpriced

(B76-50012)

Wesley, Samuel Sebastian
Magnificat and Nunc dimittis in E / [by] Samuel Sebastian
Wesley ; Garrett's edition edited with introduction and notes by
Watkins Shaw. — London : Oxford University Press, 1976. — iv,
28p ; 8vo. — (Church Music Society. Reprints ; no.53)
ISBN 0-19-395317-x : Unpriced

(B76-50375)

DGS — Communion
Appleford, Patrick
Music for series 3 : new Communion hymns, Morning and
Evening Prayer / [by] Patrick Appleford. — London :
Weinberger, 1976. — 18p ; 8vo.
Unpriced
Primary classification DM

(B76-50390)

Ellis, Martin
Communion service, series 3 (including two Communion hymns) :
SATB (or unison) / by Martin Ellis. — York : Banks, 1976. —
12p ; 8vo. — (Eboracum choral series ; 19)
Unpriced
Also classified at JDGS

(B76-50376)

Hancock, Gerre
Communion service 'Missa resurrectionis' : based upon the hymn
tune 'St Magnus', for mixed choir and organ / [by] Gerre
Hancock. — New York ; [London] : Oxford University Press,
1976. — 16p ; 8vo.
Unpriced

(B76-50781)

DGSKAD/LL — Communion. Sentences. Easter
Middleton, James Roland
The Easter anthems : SATB and organ / [by] J. Roland
Middleton ; words from Book of Common Prayer. — York :
Banks, 1976. — 4p ; 8vo. — (Eboracum choral series ; no.46)
Unpriced

(B76-50013)

DH — MOTETS, ANTHEMS, HYMNS, ETC.
Antes, John
[Die mit Thränen saën. *Vocal score].* Who with weeping soweth
= Die mit Thränen saën / [by] John Antes ; ed. and arr.
S.A.T.B. and organ by Karl Kroeger ; German text from Psalm
126 ; English version by K.K. — New York ; London : Boosey
and Hawkes, 1976. — 13p ; 8vo. — (Moramus edition)
£0.30

(B76-50377)

Antes, John
[Gelobet sey der Herr. *Vocal score].* All praises be to the Lord =
Gelobet sey der Herr / by John Antes ; ed. and arr. S.A.T.B. and
organ by Karl Kroeger ; German text from 1 Chronicles 17 ;
English version by K.K. — New York ; [London] : Boosey and
Hawkes, 1976. — 12p ; 8vo. — (Moramus edition)
£0.30

(B76-50378)

Antes, John
[Gott hat uns angenehm gemacht. *Vocal score].* The Lord has
been gracious unto us = Gott hat uns angenehm gemacht / [by]
John Antes ; ed. and arr. S.A.T.B. and organ by Karl Kroeger ;
German text from Ephesians 1 ; English versions by K.K. — New
York ; [London] : Boosey and Hawkes, 1976. — 15p ; 8vo. —
(Moramus edition)
£0.40

(B76-50379)

Antes, John
[My heart shall rejoice in His salvation. *Vocal score].* My heart
shall rejoice in His salvation / [by] John Antes ; ed. and arr.
S.A.T.B. and organ by Karl Kroeger, text from Psalm 13. — New
York ; London : Boosey and Hawkes, 1976. — 19p ; 8vo. —
(Moramus edition)
£0.40

(B76-50380)

Antes, John
[Sing and rejoice, O daughter of Zion. *Vocal score].* Sing and
rejoice, O daughter of Zion / by John Antes ; ed. and arr.
S.A.T.B. and organ by Karl Kroeger ; text from Zechariah 2. —
New York ; [London] Boosey and Hawkes, 1976. — 14p ; 8vo.
— (Moramus edition)
£0.40

(B76-50381)

Antes, John
[Unser Seele wartet auf den Herrn. *Vocal score].* Our soul doth
wait upon the Lord = Unser Seele wartet auf den Herrn / [by]
John Antes ; ed. and arr. S.A.T.B. and organ by Karl Kroeger,
German text fron Psalm 130, English version by K.K. — New
York ; London : Boosey and Hawkes, 1976. — 12p ; 8vo. —
(Moramus edition)
£0.30

(B76-50382)

Artman, Ruth
Today is the first day … (of the rest of my life) : SATB chorus
and piano, (optional flute, recorder or harmonica) / words and
music by Ruth Artman. — New York : Warner ; [London] :
[Blossom], 1976. — 8p ; 8vo.
The part for optional flute, recorder or harmonica is printed on page 8.
Unpriced

(B76-50014)

Aston, Peter
The true glory / [by] Peter Aston ; words by Francis Drake and
Richard Hakluyt. — Croydon : Royal School of Church Music,
1976. — 8p ; 8vo.
For S.A.T.B. and organ.
Unpriced

(B76-50782)

Atkinson, Condit
I yield thee praise : for mixed chorus and piano / [by] Condit
Atkinson ; words by Philip Jerome Cleveland. — New York :
Galaxy ; [London] : [Galliard], 1976. — 8p ; 8vo.
Unpriced

(B76-50383)

Frith, Michael
The river flows, the seasons turn : anthem for S.A.T.B., soprano
solo and organ / [by] Michael Frith ; words by T.S. Eliot. —
London : Oxford University Press, 1976. — 6p ; 8vo. — (Oxford
anthems ; no.A.318)
Unpriced

(B76-50015)

Gardner, John
A song for St Cecilia's Day. Op.119 : SATB / [by] John
Gardner ; words from John Dryden. — London : Oxford
University Press, 1976. — 6p ; 8vo. — (Oxford anthems ; A 315)
ISBN 0-19-350355-7 : Unpriced

(B76-50384)

Hanson, Geoffrey
Let the whole Creation cry : for soprano solo and four-part chorus
of mixed voices with organ / [by] Geoffrey Hanson ; words by
Stopford A. Brooke. — Wendover : Roberton, 1976. — 12p ; 8vo.
£0.18

(B76-50016)

Jackson, Francis
Lift up your heads, Opus 44, no.2 : SATB / [by] Francis
Jackson ; words by Joseph Beaumont. — London : Oxford
University Press, 1976. — 10p ; 8vo. — (Oxford anthems ; A320)
With organ.
ISBN 0-19-350360-3 : Unpriced

(B76-50385)

Jackson, Francis
People of Sion : introit for Advent II (Populus Sion), A.T.B. /
[by] Francis Jackson. — York : Banks, 1976. — 6p ; 8vo. —
(Eboracum choral series ; no.61)
With organ.
Unpriced

(B76-50783)

Joubert, John
Lord make me an instrument of thy peace. Op.84 : S. solo,
S.S.A.A.T.T.B.B. / [by] John Joubert ; words by St Francis of
Assisi. — London : Oxford University Press, 1976. — 15p ; 8vo.
— (Oxford anthems ; A 319)
Duration 5 mins.
ISBN 0-19-350359-x : Unpriced

(B76-50386)

King, Jeffrey
I thank you God : SATB and piano accompaniment / [by] Jeffrey
King ; poem by E.E. Cummings. — New York ; [London] :
Boosey and Hawker, 1976. — 20p ; 8vo.
£0.50

(B76-50017)

Rossini, Gioacchino Antonio
Ave Maria : for four-part chorus of mixed voices with piano / by
Gioacchino Rossini ; edited by Abraham Kaplan ; English text by
A.K. — Wendover : Roberton, 1976. — 8p ; 8vo. — (Kaplan,
Abraham. Choral series)
£0.14

(B76-50018)

Schubert, Franz
[Gesänge zur Feier des heiligen Opfers der Messe. D.872. Zum
Sanctus. *arr*]. Zum Sanctus : for 4-part chorus of mixed voices
with organ or piano / [by] Franz Schubert ; edited by Abraham
Kaplan ; English text by A.K. — Wendover : Roberton, 1975. —
7p ; 8vo. — (Kaplan, Abraham. Choral series)
£0.14
Also classified at DGE

(B76-50019)

Wills, Arthur
The light invisible / [by] Arthur Wills ; words by T.S. Eliot. —
London : Weinberger, 1976. — 12p ; 8vo.
For S.A.T.B. semichorus, S.A.T.B. chorus and organ.
Unpriced

(B76-50784)

DH/AY — Collections
King of glory : a collection of anthems. — Sevenoaks : Novello,
1975. — 76p ; 8vo.
£1.00

(B76-50020)

Sing to the Lord : a collection of twelve anthems. — Sevenoaks :
Novello, 1975. — 51p ; 8vo.
£0.75

(B76-50021)

DJ — MOTETS
Donizetti, Gaetano
[Ave Maria. *Vocal score*]. Ave Maria : für Sopran, gemischten
Chor und Streicher / [von] Gaetano Donizetti ; herausgegeben
von Oliver Nagy ; Klavierauszug von Herausgeber. — Budapest :
Editio musica ; Frankfurt ; London : Litolff, 1975. — 8p ; 8vo.
Unpriced

(B76-50387)

Milani, Francesco
[Litanie et motetti. Ave verum corpus]. Ave verum corpus :
S.A.T.T.B. [and organ] / [by] Francesco Milani ; edited by Jerome
Roche. — London : Oxford University Press, 1975. — 8p ; 8vo.
— (Oxford anthems ; A 317)
ISBN 0-19-350357-3 : Unpriced

(B76-50022)

DK — ANTHEMS
Boyce, William
Blessing and glory : for full chorus of mixed voices with organ /
[by] William Boyce ; edited by John R. Van Nice, realization by
Louis F. Chenette, [text from Revelation 7]. — Wendover :
Roberton, 1976. — 7p ; 8vo.
£0.14

(B76-50388)

Boyce, William
Save me, O God : for 4-part chorus of mixed voices with piano or
organ / [by] William Boyce ; edited by John R. Van Nice,
realization by Louis F. Chenette, [text from] Psalm 54. —
Wendover : Roberton, 1976. — 11p ; 8vo.
£0.18

(B76-50389)

Phillips, John Charles
The lot is fallen unto me : anthem for SATB with divisions and
organ / [by] John C. Phillips ; text from Psalms 16, 81, 21, 122,
and 125. — Sevenoaks : Novello, 1975. — 12p ; 8vo. — (Novello
church music ; no.43)
£0.20

(B76-50023)

Weelkes, Thomas
Alleluia! I heard a voice : anthem for SATBB or SSATB / [by]
Thomas Weelkes ; edited by S. Townsend Warner, text from Rev.
5. — Revised edition / by Roger Bray. — London : Oxford
University Press, 1976. — 12p ; 8vo.
ISBN 0-19-352090-7 : Unpriced

(B76-50024)

DK/AY — Collections
Anthems for choirs. — London : Oxford University Press.
Vol.4 : Twenty-six anthems for mixed voices by twentieth-century
composers / compiled by Christopher Morris. — 1976. — 207p ; 8vo.
ISBN 0-19-353016-3 : Unpriced

(B76-50025)

DM — HYMNS
Appleford, Patrick
Music for series 3 : new Communion hymns, Morning and
Evening Prayer / [by] Patrick Appleford. — London :
Weinberger, 1976. — 18p ; 8vo.
Unpriced
Also classified at DGS

(B76-50390)

Edwards, D W
The Lord's Prayer plus two hymn tunes for choir or organ solo /
music by D.W. Edwards. — West Kirby (67 Lang Lane, West
Kirby, Wirral, Merseyside) : D.W. Edwards, 1976. — 4p ; 8vo.
Contents: 1: Nearer my God to thee - 2: The Lord's Prayer - 3: Break thou
the bread of life.
Unpriced
Also classified at DTF

(B76-50391)

Edwards, William Llewelyn
Clychau'r maes : detholiad o donau / [gan] W. Llewelyn Edwards.
— Bow Street (Ruel Uchaf, Bow Street, Dyfed) : The composer,
1976. — 8vo.
Staff notation ed. (48p.) - Tonic sol-fa ed. (50p.).
Unpriced

(B76-50785)

Nelson, Havelock
My God and King! : S.A.T.B. organ or piano / [by] Havelock
Nelson ; [words by] Henry Vaughan. — York : Banks, 1976. —
6p ; 8vo. — (Eboracum choral series ; 52)
Unpriced

(B76-50392)

DM/AY — Collections
Hymns for choirs / arranged for mixed voices and organ by David
Willcocks. — London : Oxford University Press, 1976. — 64p ;
8vo.
ISBN 0-19-353556-4 : Unpriced

(B76-50026)

The **Stanbrook** Abbey hymnal / [text and music by the Benedictines
of Stanbrook]. — Revised ed. — Worcester ([Stanbrook Abbey,
Callow End, Worcester WR2 4TD]) : Stanbrook Abbey Music,
1974. — 32p ; 8vo.
Cover title. — Previous ed.: 1971.
Unpriced

(B76-50786)

DM/AYND — Collections. Sweden
Songs and hymns from Sweden / edited by Anders Frostenson and
translated by Fred Kaan. — London : Stainer and Bell, 1976. —
24p ; 8vo.
ISBN 0-85249-440-8 : Unpriced

(B76-50787)

DP — CAROLS
Davies, Laurence Hector
Gather gladness from the skies : spring carol, unison or SATB /
music by Laurence H. Davies ; words by Gerard Manley Hopkins.
— London : Ashdown, 1975. — 3p ; 8vo. — (Unison songs ;
no.101)
£0.08
Primary classification JDP

(B76-50103)

DP/LF — Christmas
Cattouse, Nadia
[Red and green Christmas. *arr*]. Red and green Christmas : for
SATB chorus and keyboard / words and music by Nadia
Cattouse ; based on an arrangement by Donald Swann. — New
York : Galaxy ; [London] : [Galliard], 1976. — 7p ; 8vo.
Unpriced

(B76-50393)

Davis, William Robert
[The builders. *Vocal score*]. The builders : Angevin carol, in a
festival setting : for combined mixed and unison choirs, soprano
solo and optional instruments / [by] William R. Davis ; words
paraphrased by Geoffrey Dearmer. — New York ; London :
Oxford University Press, 1976. — 11p ; 8vo.
Unpriced

(B76-50788)

Flanders, Michael
[The wassail of Figgy Duff. *arr*]. The wassail of Figgy Duff : for
mixed chorus and keyboard / traditional words and music
invented by Michael Flanders ; choral arrangement by Donald
Waxman. — New York : Galaxy ; [London] : [Galliard], 1976. —
6p ; 8vo.
Unpriced

(B76-50394)

Garden, Edward
Angel voices singing : Christmas carol for four-part chorus of mixed, female or boys' voices with organ or unison voices with piano / by Edward Garden ; words by Nicola Garden. — Wendover : Roberton, 1976. — 8p ; 8vo.
£0.15
Also classified at FDP/LF

(B76-50789)

Jackson, Francis
Two carols arrangements / arranged S.A.T.B. by Francis Jackson. — York : Banks, 1976. — 8p ; 8vo. — (Eboracum choral series ; 36)
Contents: 1: Ding dong! merrily on high: 16th cent French tune, words by G.R. Woodward - 2: I saw three ships: (traditional).
Unpriced

(B76-50395)

Klusmeier, R T
Gift of new sight : Christmas anthem, S.A.T.B. / music by R.T. Klusmeier ; text by W.H. Farquharson. — Oakville : Harmuse ; [South Croydon] : [Lengnick], 1974. — 11p ; 8vo.
£0.21

(B76-50790)

Madden, John
The babe of Bethlehem : SATB / [by] John Madden ; traditional Kentish words. — London : Oxford University Press, 1976. — 11p ; 8vo. — (Oxford choral songs ; X259)
With organ.
ISBN 0-19-343060-6 : Unpriced

(B76-50396)

Ropartz, Joseph Guy
[Berceuse. *arr*]. You will see an angel tonight / [by] J. Guy Ropartz ; choral version for mixed chorus and keyboard with mezzo-soprano solo by Katherine K. Davis ; text based on a poem by Hippolyte Lucas ; translated and adapted by K.K.D. — New York : Galaxy ; [London] : [Galliard], 1976. — 8p ; 8vo.
Unpriced

(B76-50397)

Rutter, John
[Donkey carol. *Vocal score*]. Donkey carol : S.A.T.B. accompanied / words and music by John Rutter. — London : Oxford University Press, 1976. — 15p ; 8vo. — (Oxford choral songs ; X254)
ISBN 0-19-343055-x : Unpriced

(B76-50398)

Tate, Phyllis
Peace on earth to men : SATB / [by] Phyllis Tate ; words by St. Germanus, translated by J.M. Neale. — London : Oxford University Press, 1976. — 7p ; 8vo. — (Oxford choral songs ; X256)
Carol.
ISBN 0-19-343057-6 : Unpriced

(B76-50399)

DP/LF/AY — Christmas. Collections
The **apple** tree : Christmas music from 'The Cambridge hymnal' / edited by David Holbrook and Elizabeth Poston. — London : Cambridge University Press, 1976. — xiii,115p ; 8vo.
ISBN 0-521-21479-3 : £4.00

(B76-50791)

A **carol** for to sing : 6 new carols for SATB. — Eastwood : Basil Ramsey ; Wendover : Roberton, 1976. — 24p ; 8vo.
Composed by Ian Kellam, John Joubert, David Sanger, Christopher Bowers-Broadbent, Peter Hurford and Barry Ferguson.
Unpriced
Also classified at EZDP/LF/AY

(B76-50400)

DP/LL — Easter
Walmsley, Henry
God is gone up on high : melody from Corner, 1625 / arr. S.A.T.B. by Henry Walmsley, 15th century text. — York : Banks, 1976. — 4p ; 8vo. — (Eboracum choral series ; no.34)
Unpriced

(B76-50027)

DPDE — CAROL CANTATAS
DPDE/LF — Carol cantatas. Christmas
Wills, Arthur
The child for today : a carol sequence for SATB and organ / [by] Arthur Wills. — Sevenoaks : Novello, 1976. — 34p ; 8vo.
Duration 15 min.
£0.90

(B76-50792)

DR — PSALMS
Agay, Denes
The first psalm : for SATB chorus and piano with optional guitar and bass / music by Denes Agay. — New York : Warner ; [London] : [Blossom], 1976. — 12p ; 8vo.
Duration 5 min.
Unpriced

(B76-50793)

Berkeley, Sir Lennox
The Lord in my shepherd, Op.91, no.1 / [by] Lennox Berkeley. — London : Chester, 1976. — 7p ; 8vo.
For treble solo, SATB chorus and organ.
Unpriced

(B76-50401)

Liszt, Franz
[Psalm 13. *Vocal score*]. Der 13. Psalm : für Tenor, gemischten Chor und Orchester / [von] Franz Liszt ; herausgegeben von Marta Papp, Klavierauszug von Oliver Nagy. — Frankfurt : Litolff ; New York ; London : Peters, 1975. — 52p ; 8vo.
Unpriced

(B76-50794)

Rutter, John
[I will lift up mine eyes. *Vocal score*]. I will lift up mine eyes : SATB / [by] John Rutter ; text, Psalm 121. — London : Oxford University Press, 1976. — 16p ; 8vo. — (Oxford anthems ; A 313)
ISBN 0-19-350353-0 : Unpriced

(B76-50402)

DTF — LORD'S PRAYER
Edwards, D W
The Lord's Prayer plus two hymn tunes for choir or organ solo / music by D.W. Edwards. — West Kirby (67 Lang Lane, West Kirby, Wirral, Merseyside) : D.W. Edwards, 1976. — 4p ; 8vo.
Contents: 1: Nearer my God to thee - 2: The Lord's Prayer - 3: Break thou the bread of life.
Unpriced
Primary classification DM

(B76-50391)

DW — SONGS, ETC.
Harbison, John
Music when soft voices die : SATB (divisi), with keyboard accompaniment / [by] John Harbison ; words by Percy Bysshe Shelley. — New York ; London : Associated Music, 1975. — 7p ; 8vo.
Unpriced

(B76-50028)

Hoddinott, Alun
Two Welsh songs / arranged for mixed voices and piano, S.A.T.B. by Alun Hoddinott. — London : Oxford University Press, 1976. — 10p ; 8vo. — (Oxford choral songs ; X260)
Contents: 1: Lisa Lan = Fair Lisa - 2: Dadl dan = The lazy wife.
ISBN 0-19-343061-4 : Unpriced

(B76-50403)

Keats, Donald
The hollow men : mixed chorus and piano / [by] Donald Keats ; text by T.S. Eliot. — New York ; [London] : Boosey and Hawkes, 1976. — 28p ; 8vo.
£0.75

(B76-50029)

Kleyn, Howard
A sheaf of sonnets, Op 36 / by Howard Kleyn. — Kowloon : Sonia Archer ; [South Croydon] : [Lengnick], 1975. — 15p ; 8vo.
Contents: 1: Hers will I be (Francesco Petrarca, translated by Henry Howard) - 2: Time is flying (Pierre de Ronsard, translated by Andrew Lang - 3: Remember me (Christina Rossetti).
Unpriced

(B76-50795)

Lombardo, Maria
[Hungry for hope. *arr*]. Hungry for hope / music by Mario Lombardo ; arranged by Maria Lombardo for SATB chorus, lyrics by Bill Margaretten. — New York ; [London] : Chappell, 1976. — 8p ; 8vo.
Unpriced

(B76-50030)

Sumerlin, Macon
Jalapeño : SATB chorus and piano / words and music by Macon Sumerlin. — New York : Warner ; [London] : [Blossom], 1976. — 5p ; 8vo.
Unpriced

(B76-50031)

Thomson, Virgil
[Cantata on poems of Edward Lear. The Akond of Swat]. The Akond of Swat : for four-part chorus of mixed voices with baritone solo and piano accompaniment / [by] Virgil Thomson. — New York ; London : Schirmer, 1975. — 17p ; 8vo.
Unpriced

(B76-50032)

Thomson, Virgil
[Cantata on poems of Edward Lear. The Jumblies]. The Jumblies : for four-part chorus of mixed voices with soprano solo and piano accompaniment / [by] Virgil Thomson. — New York ; London : Schirmer, 1975. — 20p ; 8vo.
Unpriced
(B76-50033)

DW/LC — Spirituals
Hudson, Hazel
The gospel train. (This train is bound for glory) : a quodlibet, for two mezzo-sopranos and baritone or two baritones / arranged with optional parts for rhythm instruments by Hazel Hudson. — London : Ashdown, 1976. — 8p ; 8vo. — (Ashdown vocal duets ; no.387)
£0.15
Primary classification FNDW/LC
(B76-50449)

DW/X — Canons
Thomson, Virgil
[Cantata on poems of Edward Lear. Half an alphabet]. Half an alphabet : canons for chorus, for four-part chorus of mixed voices with piano accompaniment / [by] Virgil Thomson. — New York ; London : Schirmer, 1975. — 17p ; 8vo.
Unpriced
(B76-50034)

DW/XC/LF — Rounds. Christmas
Crawley, Cliff
Aroundabout Christmas : 16 rounds for voices and/or instruments / set to music by Cliff Crawley. — Oakville : Frederick Harris Music ; [South Croydon] : [Lengnick], 1974. — 8p ; obl. 8vo.
£0.25
Primary classification EZDW/XC/LF

DX — SECULAR CANTATAS
Dvořák, Antonín
[The American flag. Op.102. *Vocal score*]. The American flag. Op.102 : cantata for four-part chorus of mixed voices and alto, tenor and bass soli / [by] Antonín Dvořák ; arranged with piano or organ accompaniment, words by Joseph Rodman Drake ; preface by Mario di Bonaventura. — New York ; London : Schirmer, 1975. — 46p ; 8vo.
Unpriced
(B76-50035)

Rorem, Ned
[The poets' requiem. *Vocal score*]. The poets' requiem : mixed chorus, soprano solo and orchestra / by Ned Rorem ; texts compiled by Paul Goodman. — New York ; London : Boosey and Hawkes, 1976. — 80p ; 8vo.
£5.00
(B76-50404)

E — CHORAL WORKS WITH ACCOMPANIMENT OTHER THAN KEYBOARD
ELDW — With instruments. Songs, etc
Sansom, Clive A
Happiness blues : for S.A.T.B. (or S.S.A., S.A.B., T.T.B.) with instrumental accompaniment / words and music by Clive A. Sansom. — London : Paterson, 1975. — 15p ; 8vo.
Duration 3 min.
Unpriced
Also classified at FE/LDW; GE/LDW
(B76-50036)

EMDD — With orchestra. Oratorios
Bach, Carl Philipp Emanuel
Die Israeliten in der Wuste = The Israelites in the wilderness : oratorio for soli, chorus and orchestra / [by] Carl Philipp Emanuel Bach ; edited by Gábor Darvas ; English text by Hans Hubert Schönzeler. — London : Eulenburg, 1976. — 180p ; 8vo. — (Edition Eulenburg ; no.1359)
Miniature score.
Unpriced
(B76-50037)

Liszt, Franz
Christus : oratorio for soli, chorus, organ and orchestra / [by] Franz Liszt ; edited by Gábor Darvas ; foreword by Klara Hamburger. — London : Eulenburg, 1976. — [12],412p ; 8vo. — (Edition Eulenburg ; no.948)
Miniature score.
Unpriced
(B76-50038)

EMDD/LK — With orchestra. Oratorios. Good Friday
Bach, Johann Sebastian
[St John passion. S.245]. Johannes-Passion, BWV 245 / [von] Johann Sebastian Bach ; herausgegeben von Arthur Mendel. — Cassel ; London : Bärenreiter, 1975. — x,265p ; 8vo. — (Taschenpartituren ; 197)
Miniature score.
£6.50
(B76-50405)

EMDE — With orchestra. Religious cantatas
Bach, Johann Sebastian
[Cantatas. *Selections*]. Eleven great cantatas : in full vocal and instrumental score / by Johann Sebastian Bach ; literal translation of texts by Stanley Applebaum. — New York : Dover Publications ; London : Constable, 1976. — [2],350p ; 4to.
Bach-Gesellschaft editions.
ISBN 0-486-23268-9 : £5.25
(B76-50797)

Einem, Gottfried von
An die Nachgeborenen, Op.42 : Kantate für Mezzosopran, Bariton, gemischten Chor und Orchester / [von] Gottfried von Einem. — London : Boosey and Hawkes, 1976. — 187p ; 8vo. — (Hawkes pocket scores ; no.900)
£8.50
(B76-50796)

EMDG — With orchestra. Roman liturgy. Ordinary of the Mass
Haydn, Joseph
[Mass, no.7, G major, 'Sancti Nicolai']. Missa Sancti Nicolai / [by] Joseph Haydn ; edited by H.C. Robbins Landon. — London : Eulenburg, 1976. — xix,48p ; 8vo. — (Edition Eulenburg ; no.1099)
Scored for SATB soloists, choir and orchestra. — Miniature score.
Unpriced
(B76-50039)

EMDGKHB — With orchestra. Roman liturgy. Divine Office. Matins. Te Deum
Berlioz, Hector
Te Deum / by Hector Berlioz ; edited with a foreword by Denis McCaldin. — London : Eulenburg, 1976. — xix,160p ; 8vo. — (Edition Eulenburg ; no.1095)
Miniature score.
Unpriced
(B76-50798)

EMDGKK — With orchestra. Roman liturgy. Divine Office. Magnificat
Bach, Carl Philipp Emanuel
Magnificat for soli, chorus and orchestra / [by] Carl Philipp Emanuel Bach ; edited by Gábor Darvas. — London : Eulenburg, 1976. — 188p ; 8vo.
Miniature score.
Unpriced
(B76-50040)

Penderecki, Krzysztof
Magnificat : für Bass solo, 7 Männerstimmen, 2 gemischte Chore (je 24 stimmig), Knabenstimmen und Orchester / [von] Kryzsztof Penderecki. — Mainz ; London : Schott, 1976. — 118p ; fol.
Study score. — Duration 40 min.
£10.00
(B76-50041)

EMDR — With orchestra. Psalms
Liszt, Franz
[Psalm 13]. Der 13 Psalm : für Tenor, gemischten Chor und Orchester / [von] Franz Liszt ; herausgegeben von Marta Papp. — Frankfurt : Litolff ; London : Peters, 1975. — 96p ; 4to.
Unpriced
(B76-50406)

ENWSDE — With recorders & keyboard. Religious cantatas
Hand, Colin
[In the beginning. *Vocal score*]. In the beginning : a dramatic cantata, for speaker, baritone solo, chancel choir, nave choir and orchestra / [by] Colin Hand. — London : Schott, 1975. — 4to & 8vo.
Vocal score (63p.) chancel choral score (8p.) nave choral score (10p.) & 2 recorder parts. — Duration 70 min.
Unpriced
(B76-50042)

ENWXUNPDX — With trombones & keyboard septet. Secular cantatas
Kagel, Mauricio
Abend : für Doppelvokalquartett, Posaunenquintett, elektrische Orgel und Klavier / von Mauricio Kagel. — London : Universal, 1975. — v,18p ; 4to.
Duration 6 min.
Unpriced
(B76-50043)

ENYFPNSDP/LF — With woodwind, keyboard & percussion quartets. Carols. Christmas
Younger, John B
Twas in the moon of wintertime. The Huron carol : old French folk melody / arranged S.A.T.B. by John B. Younger, words, Huron Indian, 1642, English text by J.E. Middleton. — Oakville : Frederick Harris Music ; [South Croydon] : [Lengnick], 1974. — 12p ; 8vo. — (Harris sacred choral series)
With flute, recorder, hand drum and organ or piano; the parts for flute, recorder and hand drum are in score on page 12.
£0.21
(B76-50799)

ENYHDW — With wind & percussion. Songs, etc
Feldman, Morton
Voices and instruments / [by Morton Feldman. — Toronto ;
London : Universal, 1975. — 36p ; 4to.
Wordless. — Dureation 11 min. — For SATB choir and instrumental
ensemble.
Unpriced

(B76-50044)

ENYLDW — With percussion & keyboard. Songs, etc
Sculthorpe, Peter
Sun music : for voices and percussion / [by] Peter Sculthorpe. —
London : Faber Music, 1976. — 15p ; 4to.
Duration 9 min.
Unpriced

(B76-50045)

**ENYLNSDE — With percussion & keyboard quartet. Religious
cantatas**
Poos, Heinrich
Ein jegliches hat seine Zeit : Suite für Männerchor, Sopransolo,
Sprecher, in der Fassung für zwei Klaviere, Pauken und
Schlagzeug (1 Spieler) / [von] Heinrich Poos. — Mainz ;
London : Schott, 1976. — 103p ; 4to.
£19.20

(B76-50800)

EPV — With electronic instruments
Ferneyhough, Brian
Time and motion study III : 16 solo voices with percussion and
electronic amplification / [by] Brian Ferneyhough. — London :
Peters, 1974. — 44p ; fol.
Unpriced

(B76-50801)

**ERXMDGKJ — With string orchestra. Roman liturgy. Divine Office.
Vespers**
Scarlatti, Alessandro
Dixit Dominus : for SATB soli and chorus, string orchestra and
organ continuo / [by] Alessandro Scarlatti ; edited from Milan
Biblioteca del Conservatorio 'G Verdi' Musica sacra manuscritta
710 by John Steele. — Sevenoaks : Novello, 1975. — 70p ; 8vo.
Duration 30 min.
£1.20
Also classified at ERXMDR

(B76-50046)

ERXMDH — With string orchestra. Motets, Anthems, Hymns, etc
Musica Britannica : a national collection of music. — London :
Stainer and Bell.
This volume brings together all Locke's settings of Latin and English sacred
texts that are scored for four or more voices - Editor's note.
Vol.38 : Matthew Locke : anthems and motets / transcribed and edited by
Peter le Huray. — 1976. — xx,158p ; fol.
ISBN 0-85249-397-5 : Unpriced
Primary classification C/AYD

(B76-50360)

ERXMDJ — With string orchestra. Motets
Donizetti, Gaetano
Ave Maria : für Sopran, gemischten Chor und Streicher / [von]
Gaetano Donizetti ; herausgegeben von Oliver Nagy. —
Budapest : Editio musica ; Frankfurt ; London : Litolff, 1975. —
10p ; 4to.
Unpriced

(B76-50407)

ERXMDR — With string orchestra. Psalms
Scarlatti, Alessandro
Dixit Dominus : for SATB soli and chorus, string orchestra and
organ continuo / [by] Alessandro Scarlatti ; edited from Milan
Biblioteca del Conservatorio 'G Verdi' Musica sacra manuscritta
710 by John Steele. — Sevenoaks : Novello, 1975. — 70p ; 8vo.
Duration 30 min.
£1.20
Primary classification ERXMDGKJ

(B76-50046)

EUMMDE — With military band. Religious cantatas
Berlioz, Hector
[Symphonie funébre et triomphale. Op.15]. Grande symphonie
funébre et triomphale. Op.15 / [by] Hector Berlioz ; edited with a
foreword by Hugh MacDonald. — London : Eulenburg, 1975. —
xvi,90p ; 8vo. — (Edition Eulenburg ; no.599)
Miniature score. — From 'Hector Berlion : new edition of the Complete
Works issued by the Berlioz Centenary Committee', vol.19.
Unpriced

(B76-50047)

EWSNUDH — With trumpets (2). Motets, Anthems, Hymns, etc
Tull, Fisher
The seasons of man : mixed chorus and two trumpets / [by]
Fisher Tull ; [text] Ecclesiastes 3. — New York ; [London] :
Boosey and Hawkes, 1976. — 8p ; 8vo.
£0.20

(B76-50408)

EZ — UNACCOMPANIED CHORAL WORKS
EZDE — Religious cantatas
Rose, Gregory
Vespers for Mary Magdalen : for 21 solo voices, (5 sopranos, 5
altos, 5 tenors, 6 basses) / [by] Gregory Rose ; words and
plainchant from the Liber usualis for St Mary Magdalen's day,
additional words by Gregory Rose. — Sevenoaks : Novello, 1976.
— 22p : obl. 8vo.
£0.42
Also classified at EZDGKJ

(B76-50048)

EZDG — Roman liturgy. Ordinary of the Mass
Kubelík, Rafael
[Mass]. Messe für Sopran und Männerchor / [von] Rafael
Kubelík. — Frankfurt : Litolff ; London : Peters, 1976. — 45p ;
8vo.
Unpriced

(B76-50409)

Sheppard. John
Masses / [by] John Sheppard ; translated and edited by Nicholas
Sandon. — London : Stainer and Bell, 1976. — xiii,169p ; 8vo. —
(Early English church music ; no.18)
ISBN 0-85249-392-4 : Unpriced

(B76-50410)

Victoria, Tomás Luis de
[Missae totius anni, 1592. Mass 'O magnum mysterium']. Missa O
magnum mysterium : for four voices / [by] Tomás Luis de
Victoria ; edited and arranged for modern use by Henry
Washington. — London : Chester, 1976. — 33p ; 8vo.
'If Dona nobis pucem is required in the Agnus Dei, this invocation may
easily replace the given Miserere nobis, as the syllables and accents exactly
correspond' - Editor's note.
Unpriced

(B76-50411)

**EZDG/AYD(XCUE6S) — Roman liturgy. Ordinary of the Mass.
Collections. England, 1485-1545**
Early Tudor masses / transcribed and edited by John D. Bergsagel.
— London : Stainer and Bell. — (Early English church music ;
no.16)
Volume 2. — 1976. — xv,211p ; 8vo.
ISBN 0-85249-385-1 : Unpriced

(B76-50049)

**EZDGKH/LHM — Roman liturgy. Divine Office. Matins. Maundy
Thursday**
Lasso, Orlando di
[Selectissimae cantiones. In monte Oliveti]. In monte Oliveti :
responsory, S.A.A.T.B.B. / music, Roland de Lassus, edited by
Bill Tamblyn. — London : Chiswick Music, 1975. — 4p ; 4to.
Unpriced

(B76-50050)

EZDGKH/LN — Roman liturgy. Divine Office. Matins. Whitsun
Gabrieli, Giovanni
[Sacrae symphoniae, bk.2. Hodie completi sunt]. Hodie completi
sunt, Magnificat antiphon for Whit Sunday : double chorus
SATB-SATB / music, Giovanni Gabrieli ; edited by Bill Tamblyn.
— London (83 Stilehall Gdns, W4 3BT) : Chiswick Music, 1975.
— 8p ; 4to.
Unpriced

(B76-50051)

EZDGKJ — Roman liturgy. Divine Office. Vespers
Rose, Gregory
Vespers for Mary Magdalen for 21 solo voices, (5 sopranos, 5
altos, 5 tenors, 6 basses) / [by] Gregory Rose ; words and
plainchant from the Liber usualis for St Mary Magdalen's day,
additional words by Gregory Rose. — Sevenoaks : Novello, 1976.
— 22p ; obl. 8vo.
£0.42
Primary classification EZDE

(B76-50048)

EZDGKRM — Roman liturgy. Divine Office. Complin. Hymns
Tallis, Thomas
[Cantiones sacrae. Te lucis ante terminum]. Te lucis ante
terminum : festal and ferial tones, S.A.A.T.B. (unacc.) / [by]
Thomas Tallis ; transcribed and edited by Simon R. Hill. —
London : Oxford University Press, 1976. — 6p ; 8vo. — (Oxford
anthems ; A 316)
ISBN 0-19-350356-5 : Unpriced

(B76-50052)

EZDGMM — Anglican liturgy. Preces and responses
Holmes, John
The preces and responses ('for trebles') : S.S.A.T.B. unacc. / [by]
John Holmes ; edited by John Whitworth. — London : Oxford
University Press, 1976. — 8p ; 8vo. — (Oxford church services ;
S610)
ISBN 0-19-351651-9 : Unpriced

(B76-50412)

Tunnard, Thomas
Versicles and responses : SATB / [by] Thomas Tunnard. —
York : Banks, 1976. — 4p ; 8vo. — (Eboracum choral series ;
no.20)
Unpriced

(B76-50053)

EZDGTC — Eastern Orthodox liturgy
Tchaikovsky, Peter
[Liturgical music. *Selections*]. Four anthems : for mixed chorus /
[by] Tchaikovsky ; edited by Jennifer Baker. — Eastwood :
Ramsey ; Wendover : Roberton, 1976. — 33p ; 8vo.
Unpriced
Also classified at EZDH

(B76-50413)

EZDH — Motets, Anthems, Hymns, etc
Baker, Richard Charles
Three short introits : S.A.T.B. / by Richard C. Baker. —
Oakville : Frederick Harris Music ; [South Croydon] : [Lengnick],
1974. — 15p ; 8vo. — (Harris sacred choral series)
£0.27

(B76-50802)

Beaumont, Adrian
The spacious firmament on high : anthem for SSATTB
unaccompanied / music by Adrian Beaumont ; words by Joseph
Addison. — Wendover : Roberton, 1976. — 11p ; 8vo.
£0.18

(B76-50414)

Colville, Thomas
God's world : for unaccompanied mixed chorus, S.S.A.T.B. / [by]
Thomas Colville ; words by Edna St Vincent Millay. — New
York : Galaxy ; [London] : Stainer and Bell, 1976. — 11p ; 8vo.
Unpriced

(B76-50803)

Curtis, James Gilbert
Jesus by thy wounded feet : for unaccompanied four-part choir /
[by] J. Gilbert Curtis ; words by Richard Crashaw. — London :
Cramer, 1976. — 7p ; 8vo. — (Cramer's library of anthems and
church music ; no.24)
£0.12

(B76-50415)

Liszt, Franz
Salve regina : for 4-part chorus of mixed voices unaccompanied /
[by] Franz Liszt ; edited by Robert S. Hines ; English text by
R.S.H. — Wendover : Roberton, 1976. — 7p ; 8vo.
English and Latin text.
£0.14

(B76-50416)

Reutter, Hermann
Trost der Nacht : Chorvariationen für vierstimmigen gemischten
Chor a cappella oder mit Flöte und Klavier ad lib. / [von]
Hermann Reutter ; text von Jakob Christophel von
Grimmelshausen. — Mainz ; London : Schott, 1976. — 4to.
Score & flute part.
£5.20

(B76-50804)

Tchaikovsky, Peter
[Liturgical music. *Selections*]. Four anthems : for mixed chorus /
[by] Tchaikovsky ; edited by Jennifer Baker. — Eastwood :
Ramsey ; Wendover : Roberton, 1976. — 33p ; 8vo.
Unpriced
Primary classification EZDGTC

(B76-50413)

Wilbye, John
Homo natus de maliere : S.S.A.T.B. / [by] John Wilbye ;
transcribed and edited by David Brown ; text from Job 14. —
London : Oxford University Press, 1976. — 8p ; 8vo. — (Oxford
anthems ; no.A312)
ISBN 0-19-350352-2 : Unpriced

(B76-50054)

EZDJ — Motets
Byrd, William
[Liber primus sacrarum cantionum. O quam gloriosum]. O quam
gloriosum : S.S.A.T.B. / [by] William Byrd ; edited by A.
Ramsbotham. — Revised ed. / by Roger Bray. — London :
Oxford University Press, 1976. — 14p ; 8vo. — (Tudor church
music ; T.C.M.30 (revised))
ISBN 0-19-352060-5 : Unpriced

(B76-50417)

Harness, Marjorie
Bone pastor, panis vere : SATB unacc / [by] Marjorie Harness ;
[words by] St Thomas Aquinas. — York : Banks, 1976. — 4p ;
8vo. — (Eboracum choral series ; no.37)
Unpriced

(B76-50055)

EZDK — Anthems
Gibbons, Orlando
Hosanna to the Son of David : S.S.A.A.T.T.B. / [by] Orlando
Gibbons ; edited by Edmund H. Fellowes, revised ed., by Anthony
Greening. — London : Oxford University Press, 1976. — 11p ;
8vo. — (Tudor church music ; no.39)
ISBN 0-19-352078-8 : Unpriced

(B76-50418)

Roe, Betty
Like as the hart : soprano solo and mixed chorus / [by] Betty
Roe. — London : Thames, 1975. — 15p ; 8vo.
Unpriced

(B76-50419)

Rose, Bernard
Behold, I make all things new : anthem for four-part mixed choir
with organ / by Bernard Rose ; [text from] Revelation 21. —
Wendover : Roberton, 1976. — 7p ; 8vo.
Duration 3 1/4 min.
£0.15

(B76-50805)

Tomblings, Philip
Behold, I show you a mystery : anthem for SATB and optional
organ / by Philip Tomblings ; text from 1 Corinthians. —
Hoddesdon : St Gregory Publications, 1974. — 4p ; 8vo.
Unpriced

(B76-50056)

EZDM — Hymns
Appleyard, Patrick
[Golden cross]. The Hereford Festival hymn : written for the
Hereford Diocesan 13th Centenary Festival, 1976 / words and
music by Patrick Appleford. — London : Weinberger, 1976. — s.
sh ; 8vo.
£0.05

(B76-50057)

Bach, Johann Sebastian
[Geistliche Lieder aus Schmelli's Gesangbuch und dem Notenbuch
der Anna Magdelena Buch. Jesus ist das schönste Licht. S.474.
arr]. Jesus is the loveliest light / by J.S. Bach ; arranged for
four-part male voice choir with optional accompaniment by F.
Wüllner ; edited [with] English words [translated from the
German] by Laurence H. Davies. — Wendover : Roberton, 1976.
— 4p ; 8vo.
£0.10

(B76-50420)

EZDP/LEZ — Carols. Advent
Hanson, Geoffrey
Down in yon forest : Advent or Christmas carol for 6-part chorus
of mixed voices unaccompanied / [by] Geoffrey Hanson ; words,
traditional. — Wendover : Roberton, 1976. — 4p ; 8vo.
Duration 4 1/2 min.
£0.10

(B76-50421)

Hanson, Geoffrey
People look east : Advent carol, for four-part chorus of mixed
voices unaccompanied / music by Geoffrey Hanson ; words by
Eleanor Farjeon. — Wendover : Roberton, 1976. — 4p ; 8vo.
Duration 2 1/4 min.
£0.10

(B76-50806)

EZDP/LF — Carols. Christmas
Aston, Peter
Make we joye : four carols set to anonymous 15th century texts,
for S.A.T.B. / by Peter Aston. — Ilford : Chappell, 1976. —
19p ; 4to.
Unpriced

(B76-50807)

Byrd, William
[Pavane & galliard, 'The Earl of Salisbury'. Pavane. *arr*]. The 'Earl
of Salisbury' carol / adapted and arranged, S.A.T.B. unacc. from
[Byrd's] 'The Earl of Salisbury's pavane', by Richard Graves ;
[words by] W. Ballet. — York : Banks, 1976. — 7p ; 8vo. —
(Eboracum choral series ; 56)
Unpriced

(B76-50422)

Carter, Andrew
Sans day carol : Cornish, S.A.T.B. unacc. / arr. Andrew Carter.
— York : Banks, 1976. — 3p ; 8vo. — (Eboracum choral series ;
63)
Unpriced

(B76-50423)

Davis, William Robert
Gloria tibi Domine. A little child there is yborn : Christmas carol, for unaccompanied mixed choir with soprano solo / [by] William R. Davis ; words from a 15th century MS. in the Bodleian Library, Oxford. — New York ; [London] : Oxford University Press, 1976. — 10p ; 8vo.
Unpriced

(B76-50808)

Gibbs, Douglas
In a stable bare : two Christmas carols for unaccompanied mixed voice choir / words and music by Douglas Gibbs. — Wendover : Roberton, 1976. — 8p ; 8vo.
Duration 3 min. — Staff and tonic sol-fa notation. — Contents: 1 : I heard a maiden softly sing - 2 : Carol gently carol.
£0.15

(B76-50809)

Hanson, Geoffrey
Lute book lullaby : for soprano solo and four-part chorus of mixed voices unaccompanied / [by] Geoffrey Hanson ; words from W. Ballett's 17th century lute book. — Wendover : Roberton, 1976. — 4p ; 8vo.
Duration 2 1/4 min.
£0.10

(B76-50058)

James, Donald
Three carols of the nativity : for S.A.T.B. / by Donald James. — London : Chappell, 1976. — 20p ; 4to.
Contents: There is no rose - Lullaby - Alleluia.
Unpriced

(B76-50810)

Lees, Heath
Two mediaeval carols : for 4-part chorus of mixed voices unaccompanied / by Heath Lees. — Wendover : Roberton, 1975. — 8p ; 8vo.
Contents: 1: Nowell, nowell - 2: Jesu, fili Dei.
Unpriced

(B76-50059)

Parfrey, Raymond
Mary's dream / [by] Raymond Parfrey ; words by Mary Dawson. — London : Thames, 1976. — [4]p ; 8vo.
Carol.
Unpriced

(B76-50424)

EZDP/LF/AY — Carols. Christmas. Collections
A carol for to sing : 6 new carols for SATB. — Eastwood : Basil Ramsey ; Wendover : Roberton, 1976. — 24p ; 8vo.
Composed by Ian Kellam, John Joubert, David Sanger, Christopher Bowers-Broadbent, Peter Hurford and Barry Ferguson.
Unpriced
Primary classification DP/LF/AY

(B76-50400)

Three carols for Christmas / arranged for mixed voices by Philip Ledger. — London : Oxford University Press, 1976. — 12p ; 8vo.
Contents: 1: I saw three ships : English traditional carol. unaccompanied - 2: Away in a manger / tune by W.J. Kirkpatrick, unaccompanied - 3: Come leave your sheep : French traditional carol, accompanied.
ISBN 0-19-353246-8 : Unpriced

(B76-50425)

EZDP/LP — Carols. Harvest
Hanson, Geoffrey
Two harvest carols : for four-part chorus of mixed voices unaccompanied / music by Geoffrey Hanson. — Wendover : Roberton, 1976. — 4p ; 8vo.
Contents: 1: Sing to the Lord of harvest (Monsell) - 2: I praised the earth in beauty seen (Heber).
£0.10

(B76-50060)

EZDR — Psalms
Schütz, Heinrich
[Psalmen Davids. De profundis]. Psalm 130 : for double choir, S.A.T.B.-S.A.T.B. / [by] Heinrich Schütz ; text adapted by Bill Tamblyn. — London : Chiswick Music, 1975. — 7p ; 4to.
Text in English.
Unpriced

(B76-50061)

EZDU — Madrigals
Bartolino da Padova
[Madrigals. *Selections*]. Three madrigals for voices and/or instruments / [by] Bartolino da Padova ; edited by Nigel Wilkins. — Newton Abbott : Antico, 1976. — 4to.
Score (12p.) & 3 parts. — Contents: 1: Qual lege move - 2: Imperial sedendo - 3: La dolce sere.
Unpriced
Also classified at LNT

(B76-50426)

EZDU/AY — Madrigals. Collections
Invitation to madrigals. — London : Stainer and Bell.
9 : for S.S.A.T.B. / by Thomas Weelkes ; selected from volumes 10 and 11 of 'The English Madrigalists' ; edited by E.H. Fellowes, revised by Thurston Dart. — 1976. — 48p ; 8vo.
ISBN 0-85249-346-0 : Unpriced

(B76-50811)

Invitation to madrigals. — London : Staines and Bell.
9 : for S.S.A.T.B. / by Thomas Weelkes ; selected from volumes 10 and 11 of 'The English Madrigalists' ; edited by E.H. Fellowes, revised by Thurston Dart. — 1976. — 48p ; 8vo.
ISBN 0-85249-345-2 : Unpriced

(B76-50812)

Twelve madrigals : for SSA(A). — Sevenoaks : Novello, 1975. — 66p ; 8vo.
£1.00

(B76-50062)

EZDU/AYJ — Madrigals. Collections. Italy
Popular Italian madrigals of the sixteenth century : for mixed voices / edited by Alec Harman. — London : Oxford University Press, 1976. — 81p ; 8vo.
ISBN 0-19-343646-9 : Unpriced

(B76-50063)

EZDU/AYK — Madrigals. Collections. Spain
Linoi : clarinet in A and piano / [by] Harrison Birtwistle. — Lustleigh : Antico, 1976. — 12p ; 4to.
Unpriced
Also classified at LNS/AYK

(B76-50813)

EZDU/AZ — Madrigals. Collected works of individual composers
Nicolson, Richard
[Madrigals. *Collections*]. Collected madrigals / [by] Richard Nicolson ; transcribed and edited by John Morehen. — London : Stainer and Bell, 1976. — xi,106p ; 8vo. — (English madrigalists ; no.37)
ISBN 0-85249-382-7 : Unpriced

(B76-50064)

EZDW — Songs, etc
Bach, Jan
Dirge for a minstrel : SATB, soprano and tenor soli a cappella / [by] Jan Bach ; words by Thomas Chatterton. — New York ; London : Associated Music, 1974. — 16p ; 8vo.
Unpriced

(B76-50065)

Balada, Leonardo
Voices no.1 : for four-part chorus of mixed voices a cappella / [by] Leonardo Balada. — New York ; London : Schirmer, 1975. — 19p ; 8vo.
Wordless. — Duration 7 min.
Unpriced

(B76-50066)

Bedford, David
The golden wine is drunk : for 16 solo voices divided into 2 eight-part choirs of SSAATTBB / [by] David Bedford ; words by Ernest Dowson. — London : Universal, 1976. — 31p ; fol.
Duration 12 min.
Unpriced

(B76-50427)

Binkerd, Gordon
For the infant Michael : SATB / [by] Gordon Binkerd ; poem by Babette Deutsch. — New York ; [London] : Boosey and Hawkes, 1976. — 8p ; 8vo.
£0.20

(B76-50067)

Burtch, Mervyn
Three sonnets of John Donne : for four-part choir of mixed voices unaccompanied / by Mervyn Burtch. — Wendover : Roberton, 1976. — 19p ; 8vo. — (Roberton mixed voice series)
Duration 8 min. — Contents: 1: Oh! my black soule - 2: Batter my heart - 3: Death be not proud.
£0.28

(B76-50814)

Clark, Keith
[Metaphysical fragments. Our murmers have their musick too]. Our murmers have their musick too : for 4-part chorus of mixed voices unaccompanied / [by] Keith Clark ; words by Richard Crashaw. — Wendover : Roberton, 1974. — 4p ; 8vo. — (Lawson-Gould choral series)
£0.10

(B76-50428)

Druckman, Jacob
Antiphonies : for mixed chorus unaccompanied / [by] Jacob
Druckman ; poems by Gerard Manley Hopkins. — New York ;
[London] : Boosey and Hawkes.
[No.] 1. — 1975. — 19p ; 8vo.
£0.55
(B76-50429)

[No.] 2. — 1976. — 23p ; 8vo.
£0.70
(B76-50430)

[No.] 3. — 1976. — 36p ; 8vo.
£1.00
(B76-50431)

Gardner, John
[Five philanders. Contentment. Op.125, no.4]. Contentment :
S.A.T. unacc. / [by] John Gardner ; words from a Nottingham
broadside. — London : Oxford University Press, 1976. — 4p ;
8vo. — (Oxford choral songs ; X258)
ISBN 0-19-343059-2 : Unpriced
(B76-50432)

Gardner, John
[Five philanders. Rejection. Op.125, no.1]. Rejection : S.A.T.B.
unacc. / words and music by John Gardner. — London : Oxford
University Press, 1976. — 4p ; 8vo. — (Oxford choral songs ;
X257)
ISBN 0-19-343058-4 : Unpriced
(B76-50433)

Goldsmith, Owen
Benediction : for unaccompanied mixed chorus / [by] Owen
Goldsmith ; words, traditional. — New York : Galaxy ;
[London] : [Galliard], 1976. — 4p ; 8vo.
Unpriced
(B76-50434)

Holloway, Robin
Five madrigals : for unaccompanied mixed voices / [by] Robin
Holloway ; poems by James Joyce and T.S. Eliot. — London :
Oxford University Press, 1976. — 22p ; 8vo.
Contents: 1: Ecce puer - 2: Children's voices - 3: Eyes that last I saw in
tears - 4: Voices of birds - 5: Red river.
Unpriced
(B76-50435)

Joplin, Scott
[The entertainer. arr]. The entertainer / [by] Scott Joplin ; vocal
arrangement S.S.A.A. by Herbert Chappell. — London : Chappell,
1975. — 16p ; 8vo.
Unpriced
(B76-50068)

Kreutz, Robert
Spring grass : part song, SATB / [by] Robert Kreutz ; poem by
Carl Sandberg. — New York ; [London] : Boosey and Hawkes,
1976. — 20p ; 8vo.
Unpriced
(B76-50069)

Liddell, Claire
Fine flowers in the valley : Scottish folk ballad / arranged for
unaccompanied mixed voice choir with female solo by Claire
Liddell, words, anon. — Wendover : Roberton, 1976. — 8p ; 8vo.
Duration 4 min.
£0.14
(B76-50071)

Liddell, Claire
Ae fond kiss : old Highland melody / arranged for
unaccompanied mixed voice choir with soprano and tenor soli by
Claire Liddell ; words by Robert Burns. — Wendover : Roberton,
1976. — 8p ; 8vo.
Staff & tonic sol-fa notation.
£0.14
(B76-50070)

Liddell, Claire
Where are the joys? : traditional Scottish air / arranged for
unaccompanied mixed voice choir with tenor solo by Claire
Liddell, words by Robert Burns. — Wendover : Roberton, 1976.
— 7p ; 8vo.
Duration 3 1/2 min.
£0.14
(B76-50072)

Liddell, Claire
Ye banks and braes / arranged for unaccompanied mixed voice
chorus by Claire Liddell ; words by Robert Burns. — Wendover :
Roberton, 1976. — 4p ; 8vo.
Duration 2 1/2 min. — Staff & tonic sol-fa notation.
£0.10
(B76-50073)

Liszt, Franz
[Vier kleine Klavierstücke, nos. 3, 4. arr]. Two Browning
choruses : S.A.T.B. [unaccompanied] / adapted from [the music
of] Liszt by Gordon Binkerd ; poems by Elizabeth Barrett
Browning. — New York ; [London] : Boosey and Hawkes, 1976.
— 10p ; 8vo.
Contents: 1: The lost bower - 2: The little friend.
Unpriced
(B76-50436)

Rossini, Gioacchino Antonio
Il pianto delle Muse, in morte di Lord Byron = The weeping of
the Muse on the death of Lord Byron : canzone for soloists,
chorus and piano / music by Gioacchino Rossini ; words
ananymous. — Sevenoaks : Novello, 1976. — 12p ; 8vo.
Editorial notes on page 12.
£0.75
(B76-50815)

Rutter, John
It was a lover and his lass : S.A.T. Bar.B. unacc / [by] John
Rutter ; words by Shakespeare. — London : Oxford University
Press, 1976. — 8p ; 8vo. — (Oxford choral songs ; X255)
ISBN 0-19-343056-8 : Unpriced
(B76-50074)

Rutter, John
Two American folk songs : SATB unacc. / arranged by John
Rutter. — London : Oxford University Press, 1976. — 12p ; 8vo.
— (Oxford choral songs ; X247)
These two songs may be performed as part of a set of three American
folk-songs arranged by John Rutter with Down by the riverside (piano or
orchestral accompaniment) as the final song in the group. — Contents: 1:
Sourwood mountain - 2: Black sheep.
ISBN 0-19-343048-7 : Unpriced
(B76-50437)

Terri, Salli
A child of God : American folk song for four-part chorus of
mixed voices and solo (or soli) unaccompanied / arranged by Salli
Terri. — Wendover : Roberton, 1974. — 12p ; 8vo. — (Terri,
Salli. Choral series)
£0.20
(B76-50816)

Thomas, Elizabeth
Frog went a-courtin' : traditional American song, SATBB
unaccompanied / arranged by Elizabeth Thomas. — Wendover :
Roberton, 1976. — 8p ; 8vo.
Duration 1 3/4 min.
£0.14
(B76-50075)

Wilkinson, Stephen
The nightingale : English North Countrie song / arranged for
unaccompanied mixed choir by Stephen Wilkinson. — Wendover :
Roberton, 1976. — 12p ; 8vo.
Staff & tonic sol-fa notation.
£0.18
(B76-50076)

EZDW/AY — Songs, etc. Collections
Gaudeamus : a Leicestershire garland for Europa Cantat 6 for
mixed voices a cappella / with an introduction by Sir Michael
Tippett. — London : Oxford University Press for the British
National Committee for Europa Cantat 6, 1976. — 60p ; 8vo.
This collection was commissioned by the British Committee for Europa
Cantat 6 with funds provided by the East Midlands Arts Association. —
Works by John Joubert, Robin Holloway, John Gardner, Nicholas Maw,
Phyllis Tate, Alan Ridout, Alun Hoddinott, Gordon Crosse, William
Mathias.
Unpriced
(B76-50438)

EZDW/LC/AY — Spirituals. Collections
Spirituals reborn / compiled, edited and arranged by Michael Paget.
— Cambridge : Cambridge University Press.
For unaccompanied voices.
Choral edition. — 1976. — 112p ; 8vo.
Bibl.: p.110-111. — List of sound discs: p.112.
ISBN 0-521-08713-9 : £3.75
(B76-50439)

EZDW/XC/LF — Rounds. Christmas
Crawley, Cliff
Aroundabout Christmas : 16 rounds for voices and/or
instruments / set to music by Cliff Crawley. — Oakville :
Frederick Harris Music ; [South Croydon] : [Lengnick], 1974. —
8p ; obl. 8vo.
£0.25
Also classified at LN/XC; DW/XC/LF
(B76-50817)

EZDX — Secular cantatas
Bauld, Alison
Van Diemen's land : a choral fantasy for mezzo soprano, bass, 2
tenors, baritones, male speaker and a capella / music and text by
Alison Bauld. — Sevenoaks : Novello, 1976. — v,26p ; 4to.
A facsimile of the composer's autograph.
£1.30

(B76-50818)

Fleischmann, Aloys
Poet in the suburbs : for unaccompanied mixed voices / [by]
Aloys Fleischmann ; words by Thomas Kinsella. — London :
Oxford University Press, 1976. — 25p ; 8vo.
Duration 5 3/4 min.
ISBN 0-19-336108-6 : Unpriced

(B76-50077)

F — FEMALE VOICES, CHILDREN'S VOICES
FDK — Anthems
Hemingway, Roger
Consider and hear me, O Lord my God / music by Roger
Hemingway ; text from Psalm 13. — Sevenoaks : Novello, 1976.
— 4p ; 8vo.
£0.12

(B76-50078)

FDP/LF — Carols. Christmas
Balent, Andrew
What Child is this? : Old English melody / arranged for unison or
two-part chorus and piano with optional flute by Andrew Balent,
words by William Chatterton Dix. — New York : Warner ;
[London] : [Blossom], 1976. — 7p ; 8vo.
Carol.
Unpriced
Primary classification JDP/LF

Garden, Edward
Angel voices singing : Christmas carol for four-part chorus of
mixed, female or boys' voices with organ or unison voices with
piano / by Edward Garden ; words by Nicola Garden. —
Wendover : Roberton, 1976. — 8p ; 8vo.
£0.15
Primary classification DP/LF

Rocherolle, Eugénie R
Christmas lullaby : unison, two part or SSA chorus and piano /
[by] Eugénie R. Rocherolle. — New York : Warner ; [London] :
[Blossom], 1976. — 7p ; 8vo.
Unpriced
Primary classification JDP/LF

(B76-50455)

FDW — Songs, etc
Bacon, Ernst
Bennington riflemen : realized for SA, TB, or two soloists [and
piano] / by Ernst Bacon. — New York ; London : Boosey and
Hawkes, 1976. — 7p ; 8vo.
£0.20
Also classified at GDW

(B76-50079)

Hurd, Michael
[Flower songs. *Vocal score*]. Flower songs : for S(S)A and string
orchestra (or piano) / [by] Michael Hurd ; words by Robert
Herrick. — Sevenoaks : Novello, 1974. — 22p ; 8vo.
Duration 14 min.
£0.50

(B76-50080)

Rocherolle, Eugénie R
Along the sand : SSAA chorus and piano with optional alto /
words and music by Eugenie R. Rocherolle. — New York :
Warner ; [London] : [Blossom], 1976. — 10p ; 8vo.
Unpriced

(B76-50081)

FDW/LC — Spirituals
Hudson, Hazel
Roll the old chariot along (with other things) : a quodlibet /
arranged from three negro spitituals [sic] by Hazel Hudson. —
London : Ashdown, 1976. — 7p ; 8vo. — (Ashdown vocal duets ;
no.385)
£0.15

(B76-50440)

Johnson, Stuart
The gospel train : negro spiritual, two-part (with optional
recorders) / arranged by Stuart Johnson. — London : Oxford
University Press, 1975. — 8p ; 8vo. — (Oxford choral songs ; T
108)
ISBN 0-19-341508-9 : Unpriced

(B76-50082)

FDX — Secular cantatas
Hurd, Michael
Rooster rag : a cantata in popular style for unison voices (with
divisions) and piano, with guitar chord symbols / words and
music by Michael Hurd. — Sevenoaks : Novello, 1976. — 26p ;
8vo.
Duration 13 min.
£0.50

(B76-50441)

FE/LDW — With instruments. Songs, etc
Sansom, Clive A
Happiness blues : for S.A.T.B. (or S.S.A., S.A.B., T.T.B.) with
instrumental accompaniment / words and music by Clive A.
Sansom. — London : Paterson, 1975. — 15p ; 8vo.
Duration 3 min.
Unpriced
Primary classification ELDW

(B76-50036)

FE/NWSDW/LC — With recorders & keyboard. Spirituals
Wastall, Peter
Babylon's falling : a jazz spiritual, for voices, recorders, guitars
(optional) and piano / arranged by Peter Wastall and Derek
Hyde, traditional words adapted by Peter Wastall. — London :
Boosey and Hawkes, 1975. — 4to.
Score (8p.) & 9 parts. — With several copies of various parts.
£1.75

(B76-50083)

Wastall, Peter
Did't my Lord deliver Daniel : a jazz spiritual for voices,
recorders, guitars (optional) and piano / arranged by Peter
Wastall and Derek Hyde, traditional words adapted by Peter
Wastall. — London : Boosey and Hawkes, 1975. — 4to.
Score (7p.) & 9 parts. — With several copies of various parts.
£1.75

(B76-50084)

Wastall, Peter
Joshua fought the battle of Jericho : a jazz spiritual, for voices,
recorders, guitars (optional) and piano / arranged by Peter
Wastall and Derek Hyde, traditional words adapted by Peter
Wastall. — London : Boosey and Hawkes, 1975. — 4to.
Score (7p.) & 9 parts. — With several copies of various parts.
£1.75

(B76-50086)

FE/NYFPNTDP/LF — With woodwind, keyboard & percussion
          trios. Carols. Christmas
Roe, Betty
Rocking / music by Betty Roe. — London : Thames, 1975. — [4]
p ; 8vo.
Carol. — For two voices, woodwind, keyboard & percussion.
Unpriced

(B76-50442)

FE/NYGNSDW — With strings, keyboard & percussion quartet.
          Songs, etc
Bacon, Ernst
Buttermilk hill : song of 1776. SA, TB or soloist, with instruments
and percussion / realized by Ernst Bacon. — New York ;
[London] : Boosey and Hawkes, 1976. — 6p ; 8vo.
£0.20
Also classified at GE/NYGNSDW; KE/NYGNSDW

(B76-50087)

FE/TSDW/LC/AY — With guitar. Spirituals. Collections
Spirituals reborn / compiled, edited and arranged by Michael Paget.
— Cambridge : Cambridge University Press.
Melody and guitar edition. Part 1 : for male and female voices, with chords
for piano and guitar and additional parts for voices. — 1976. — 56p ; 8vo.
List of sound discs: p.55.
ISBN 0-521-08714-7 : £1.00
Also classified at GE/TSDW/LC/AY

(B76-50443)

Melody and guitar edition. Part 2 : for male and female voices, with chords
for piano and guitar and additional parts for voices. — 1976. — 64p ; 8vo.
List of sound discs: p.63.
ISBN 0-521-21332-0 : £1.00
Also classified at GE/TSDW/LC/AY

(B76-50444)

FE/XPQDW — With melodic percussion. Songs, etc
Withams, Eric L
Three epitaphs : for voices and percussion / [by] Eric L.
Withams ; words by Brian Adams. — London : Boosey and
Hawkes, 1975. — 8p ; 8vo. — (Tonal perspective series for tuned
percussion ; no.13)
£0.35

(B76-50088)

FEZDH — Unaccompanied voices. Motets, Anthems, Hymns, etc
Lees, Heath
Breathe on me, breath of God : anthem for 3-part female voice
choir unaccompanied / by Heath Lees ; words by Edwin Hatch.
— Wendover : Roberton, 1976. — 4p ; 8vo.
Duration 4 min.
£0.10

(B76-50089)

FEZDJ/LF — Unaccompanied voices. Motets. Christmas
Sweelinck, Jan Pieterzoon
[Cantiones sacrae. Hodie Christus natus est. *arr*]. Hodie Christus
natus est / music by J.P. Sweelinck ; arr. for 4-part female
choir unaccompanied by Hilda Morgan. — Wendover : Roberton,
1976. — 8p ; 8vo.
Staff & tonic sol-fa notation.
£0.15

(B76-50819)

FEZDP/LF — Unaccompanied voices. Carols. Christmas
Carter, Andrew
Adam lay y-bounden : S.A. unacc. / [by] Andrew Carter ; [words]
15th century. — York : Banks, 1976. — 2p ; 8vo. — (Eboracum
choral series ; 59)
Unpriced

(B76-50445)

Carter, Andrew
Ding dong! merrily on high : 16th cent. French tune / arr. S.S.A.
unacc. [by] Andrew Carter ; [words by] G.R. Woodward. —
York : Banks, 1976. — 4p ; 8vo. — (Eboracum choral series ; 64)
Unpriced

(B76-50446)

**FEZDP/LF/AYH — Unaccompanied voices. Carols. Christmas.
Collections. France**
Six French carols / arranged S.S.A. unacc. by Lionel Lethbridge ;
texts paraphrased from the French by Lionel Lethbridge. —
York : Banks. — (Eboracum choral series ; 57a)
Set 1. — 1976. — 7p ; 8vo.
Contents: 1: Carol for Christmas Eve, 'Dureau la durée' - 2: The shepherds
carol, 'Voici la nouvelle' - 3: Will that time return again?.
Unpriced

(B76-50447)

Set 2. — 1976. — 6p ; 8vo.
Contents: 1: The journey of the wise men, 'Voici la Noel' - 2: Carol of the
wise men - 3: Sing praises, 'Quand Dieu naquit à Noël'.
Unpriced

(B76-50448)

FEZDW — Unaccompanied voices. Songs, etc
Lees, Heath
Iona boat song, (For a dead king) : traditional Island air /
arranged for unaccompanied female choir, S.S.A. by Heath Lees ;
words by Hugh S. Roberton. — Wendover : Roberton, 1976. —
4p ; 8vo.
Duration 2 1/2 min. — Staff & tonic sol-fa notation.
£0.10

(B76-50090)

Lyell, Margaret
Love in May : for 4-part female voice choir unaccompanied / [by]
Margaret Lyell ; words anonymous. — Wendover : Roberton,
1976. — 8p ; 8vo. — (Roberton female choir series)
Staff & tonic sol-fa notation.
Unpriced

(B76-50820)

Maconchy, Elizabeth
Two epitaphs : S.S.A. / [by] Elizabeth Maconchy. — London :
Chester, 1976. — 4p ; 8vo.
Contents: 1: Our life is nothing but a winter's day (Quarles) - 2: as the tree
falls.
Unpriced

(B76-50821)

FLDGS — Treble voices. Anglican liturgy. Communion
Rose, Bernard
Missa : Voces choristarum, series 3 : for treble voices with organ /
music by Bernard Rose. — Wendover : Roberton, 1976. — 10p ;
8vo.
Duration 7 min.
£0.20

(B76-50822)

FLDH — Treble voices. Motets, Anthems, Hymns, etc
Schubert, Franz
[Des Tages Weihe. D.763. *arr*]. Where thou reignest / [by] Franz
Schubert ; arranged for three-part treble voices by W.R. Pasfield.
— London : Ashdown, 1976. — 8p ; 8vo.
£0.12

(B76-50091)

FLDP/LEZ — Treble voices. Carols. Advent
Platts, Kenneth
An Advent carol. Opus 25 : for treble voices and piano / [by]
Kenneth Platts ; words, Eleanor Farjeon. — London : Ashdown,
1976. — 4p ; 8vo. — (Ashdown vocal duets ; no.384)
Duration 4 1/2 min.
£0.08

(B76-50092)

FNDW/LC — Mezzo-soprano voices. Spirituals
Hudson, Hazel
The gospel train. (This train is bound for glory) : a quodlibet, for
two mezzo-sopranos and baritone or two baritones / arranged
with optional parts for rhythm instruments by Hazel Hudson. —
London : Ashdown, 1976. — 8p ; 8vo. — (Ashdown vocal duets ;
no.387)
£0.15
Also classified at DW/LC; GNDW

(B76-50449)

G — MALE VOICES
GDE — Religious cantatas
Kagel, Mauricio
Die Mutation : für Männerchor und obligates Klavier / von
Mauricio Kagel. — London : Universal, 1976. — 33p ; 4to.
Based on Prelude 44 from Bach's 'Das wohltemperierte Klavier' and phrases
from Berg's 'Wozzeck'.
Unpriced

(B76-50450)

GDR — Psalms
Head, Michael
Make a joyful noise unto the Lord. Psalm 100 : for 4-part male
voice choir with organ or piano or unaccompanied voices / by
Michael Head. — Wendover : Roberton, 1976. — 11p ; 8vo. —
(Roberton male voice series)
Staff & tonic sol-fa notation.
£0.18
Also classified at GEZDR

(B76-50093)

GDW — Songs, etc
Bacon, Ernst
Bennington riflemen : realized for SA, TB, or two soloists [and
piano] / by Ernst Bacon. — New York ; London : Boosey and
Hawkes, 1976. — 7p ; 8vo.
£0.20
Primary classification FDW

(B76-50079)

Evans, M E
'Pantyfedwen' : i leisiau TTBB / tôn M.E. Evans ; trefn Llifon
Hughes-Jones ; geiriau W. Rhys Nicholas. — Revised ed. —
London : Thames, 1976. — 12p ; 8vo.
Unpriced

(B76-50452)

GE/LDW — With instruments. Songs, etc
Sansom, Clive A
Happiness blues : for S.A.T.B. (or S.S.A., S.A.B., T.T.B.) with
instrumental accompaniment / words and music by Clive A.
Sansom. — London : Paterson, 1975. — 15p ; 8vo.
Duration 3 min.
Unpriced
Primary classification ELDW

(B76-50036)

**GE/NYGNSDW — With strings, keyboard & percussion quartet.
Songs, etc**
Bacon, Ernst
Buttermilk hill : song of 1776, SA, TB or soloist, with instruments
and percussion / realized by Ernst Bacon. — New York ;
[London] : Boosey and Hawkes, 1976. — 6p ; 8vo.
£0.20
Primary classification FE/NYGNSDW

(B76-50087)

GE/TSDW/LC/AY — With guitar. Spirituals. Collections
Spirituals reborn / compiled, edited and arranged by Michael Paget.
— Cambridge : Cambridge University Press.
Melody and guitar edition. Part 1 : for male and female voices, with chords
for piano and guitar and additional parts for voices. — 1976. — 56p ; 8vo.
List of sound discs: p.55.
ISBN 0-521-08714-7 : £1.00
Primary classification FE/TSDW/LC/AY
(B76-50443)

Melody and guitar edition. Part 2 : for male and female voices, with chords
for piano and guitar and additional parts for voices. — 1976. — 64p ; 8vo.
List of sound discs: p.63.
ISBN 0-521-21332-0 : £1.00
Primary classification FE/TSDW/LC/AY
(B76-50444)

GEZDH — Unaccompanied voices. Motets, Anthems, Hymns, etc
Burtch, Mervyn
Epilogue : for four-part male voice choir unaccompanied / music
by Mervyn Burtch ; words by David Walters. — Wendover :
Roberton, 1976. — 4p ; 8vo. — (Roberton male voice series)
£0.10
(B76-50823)

GEZDP/LF — Unaccompanied voices. Carols. Christmas
Wilkinson, Stephen
Consider well : Irish melody / arranged for unaccompanied male
voice choir with optional soprano solo by Stephen Wilkinson ;
words, partly traditional and partly revised, by W.H. Gratton
Flood. — Wendover : Roberton, 1976. — 12p ; 8vo.
The publisher has corrected a printing error on page 12. — Duration 3 min.
£0.18
(B76-50094)

GEZDR — Unaccompanied voices. Psalms
Head, Michael
I will lift up mine eyes : Psalm 121, for 4-part male voice choir
with optional organ or piano / by Michael Head. — Wendover :
Roberton, 1976. — 7p ; 8vo. — (Roberton male voice series)
£0.14
(B76-50095)

Head, Michael
Make a joyful noise unto the Lord. Psalm 100 : for 4-part male
voice choir with organ or piano or unaccompanied voices / by
Michael Head. — Wendover : Roberton, 1976. — 11p ; 8vo. —
(Roberton male voice series)
Staff & tonic sol-fa notation.
£0.18
Primary classification GDR
(B76-50093)

GEZDW — Unaccompanied voices. Songs, etc
Liddell, Claire
I'll ay ca' in by yon toon : old Scottish air / arranged for 3-part
male voice choir unaccompanied by Claire Liddell ; words by
Robert Burns. — Wendover : Roberton, 1976. — 4p ; 8vo.
Staff & tonic sol-fa notation.
£0.10
(B76-50096)

Nelson, Havelock
The lark in the clear air : Irish traditional air / arr. T.T.B.B.
(unacc.) Havelock Nelson ; words by Sir Samuel Ferguson. —
York : Banks, 1976. — 4p ; 8vo. — (Eboracum choral series ; 53)
Unpriced
(B76-50824)

**GEZDW/AYT — Unaccompanied voices. Songs, etc. Collections.
United States**
Barbershop memories : songs / compiled and arranged for male
voices by Hugo Frey. — London : Robbins Music : EMI, 1975.
— 32p ; 4to.
Unpriced
(B76-50097)

GNDW — Baritone voices. Spirituals
Hudson, Hazel
The gospel train. (This train is bound for glory) : a quodlibet, for
two mezzo-sopranos and baritone or two baritones / arranged
with optional parts for rhythm instruments by Hazel Hudson. —
London : Ashdown, 1976. — 8p ; 8vo. — (Ashdown vocal duets ;
no.387)
£0.15
Primary classification FNDW/LC
(B76-50449)

J — VOICES IN UNISON
JDACN — Children's musical plays. Voice parts
Walker, Chris
[The wind on the heath. *Voice part*]. The wind on the heath :
children's musical play / music by Chris Walker ... [et al.] ;
co-ordinated by Anthony Masters ; lyrics by Julie Higgins ... [et
al.]. — London : Dobson, 1975. — 48p ; 8vo. — (Event operas ;
no.2)
ISBN 0-234-77245-x : Unpriced
(B76-50098)

**JDACN/LF — Religious children's musical plays. Christmas. Voice
parts**
Hoskins, Graham
[The Jesus file. *Voice part*]. The Jesus file : a musical nativity /
[by] Graham Hoskins ; co-ordinated by Anthony Masters ; lyrics
by Anthony Masters and Julie Higgins. — London : Dobson,
1975. — 48p ; 8vo. — (Event operas ; no.1)
ISBN 0-234-77244-1 : Unpriced
(B76-50099)

JDG — Roman liturgy. Ordinary of the Mass
Tamblyn, William
New community mass / by William Tamblyn. — London :
Chiswick Music, 1975. — 6p ; 4to.
For voices in unison.
Unpriced
(B76-50100)

JDGK — Roman liturgy. Proper of the Mass
Roman Catholic Church. *Liturgy and ritual*
[Missal. Responses. English]. Sung responses at Mass : music and
English translation of the Rite of Mass. — London : Incorporated
Catholic Truth Society, 1976. — 4p ; 4to.
Unpriced
(B76-50101)

JDGS — Anglican liturgy. Communion
Ellis, Martin
Communion service, series 3 (including two Communion hymns) :
SATB (or unison) / by Martin Ellis. — York : Banks, 1976. —
12p ; 8vo. — (Eboracum choral series ; 19)
Unpriced
Primary classification DGS
(B76-50376)

Mathias, William
Communion service, series 3 : for congregational use with optional
S.A.T.B. choir / [by] William Mathias. — London : Oxford
University Press, 1976. — 8vo. — (Oxford church services ;
S.611)
Score (11p.) & congregational part.
ISBN 0-19-351652-7 : Unpriced
(B76-50453)

JDM — Hymns
Wuorinnen, Charles
Mannheim 87, 87, 87 : for unison chorus and organ / [by] Charles
Wuorinen ; text from Episcopal Hymnal. -- New York ; London :
Peters, 1975. — 2p ; 8vo.
Duration 2 min.
Unpriced
(B76-50825)

JDM/AY — Hymns. Collections
Fresh sounds / compiled by Betty Pulkingham and Jeanne Harper.
— London : Hodder and Stoughton, 1976. — 192p ; 8vo.
Hymns. — A companion volume to 'Sound of Living Waters' - Index.
ISBN 0-340-20622-5 : Unpriced
(B76-50826)

Ten folk songs on the gospel and life. — London : Weinberger,
1975. — 16p ; 8vo.
Unpriced
(B76-50102)

JDP — Carols
Davies, Laurence Hector
Gather gladness from the skies : spring carol, unison or SATB /
music by Laurence H. Davies ; words by Gerard Manley Hopkins.
— London : Ashdown, 1975. — 3p ; 8vo. — (Unison songs ;
no.101)
£0.08
Also classified at DP
(B76-50103)

JDP/LF — Carols. Christmas
Balent, Andrew
What Child is this? : Old English melody / arranged for unison or
two-part chorus and piano with optional flute by Andrew Balent,
words by William Chatterton Dix. — New York : Warner ;
[London] : [Blossom], 1976. — 7p ; 8vo.
Carol.
Unpriced
Also classified at FDP/LF
(B76-50827)

Holder, Ray
Wassailing / music by Ray Holder ; words by Stella Ross. —
London : Thames Music, 1975. — [4]p ; 8vo.
Carol. — Voices in unison.
Unpriced
(B76-50454)

Rocherolle, Eugénie R
Christmas lullaby : unison, two part or SSA chorus and piano /
[by] Eugénie R. Rocherolle. — New York : Warner ; [London] :
[Blossom], 1976. — 7p ; 8vo.
Unpriced
Also classified at FDP/LF

(B76-50455)

JDP/LF/AY — Carols. Christmas. Collections
Favorite Christmas carols / selected and arranged with piano
accompaniment and guitar chords by Charles J.F. Cofone. — New
York : Dover ; London : Collier Macmillan, 1975. — 79p ; 4to.
ISBN 0-486-20445-6 : £1.30

(B76-50104)

JDW/AY — Songs, etc. Collections
Saloon bar favourites. — London : Chappell, 1976. — 40p ; 8vo.
Songs for voices in unison.
Unpriced

(B76-50456)

JDW/G/PP/AY — Folk songs. Pentatonic music. Collections
Second pentatonic song book / edited and arranged by Brian
Brocklehurst. — London : Schott, 1976. — 83p ; 8vo.
Piano ed. (83p.) & melody ed. (460.).
Unpriced

(B76-50828)

JDW/JM — Songs. Incidental music
Roe, Betty
[The barnstormers. *Selections*]. The barnstormers / music by Betty
Roe ; songs from the play for children by Marian Lines. —
London : Thames, 1976. — 12p ; 8vo.
Unpriced

(B76-50457)

JE/LPLTSDW/G/AYD — With instrument & guitar. Folk songs.
Collections. England
Englisches Folksong-Büchlein : die schönsten Songs und Balladen,
für Singstimme, Melodieinstrumente und Gitarrenbegleitung /
herausgegeben von Klaus Buhé ; Linolschnitte von Jutta
Lamprecht. — Wilhmshaven : Heinrichshofen ; [London] :
[Peters], 1976. — 32p ; 16mo.
Unpriced

(B76-50458)

JE/LPLTSDW/G/AYDL — With instrument & guitar. Folk songs.
Collections. Scotland
Schottisches Balladen-Büchlein : die schönsten schottischen
Balladen, für Singstimme, Melodieinstrumente und Gitarre /
herausgegeben von Klaus Buhé ; Linolschnitte von Jutta
Lamprecht. — Wilhemshaven : Heinrichstofen ; [London] :
[Peters], 1976. — 32p ; 16mo.
Unpriced

(B76-50459)

JE/LPLTSDW/G/AYDM — With instrument & guitar. Folk songs.
Collections. Ireland
Irisches Folksong-Büchlein : die schönsten irischen Lieder und
Balladen, für Singstimme, Melodieinstrumente (Blockflöte) und
Gitarrenbegleitung / herausgegeben von Klaus Buhé ;
Linotschnitte von Jutta Lamprecht. — Wilhemshaven :
Heinrichshoten ; [London] : [Peters], 1976. — 32p ; 16mo.
Unpriced

(B76-50460)

JE/TSDP/LF/AY — With guitar. Carols. Christmas. Collections
Happy Christmas for guitar / arranged by Cecil Bolton and Jack
Moore. — London : EMI, 1976. — 49p ; 4to.
Unpriced
Primary classification TSPMK/DP/LF/AY

Twenty-four Christmas carols for classical guitar / compiled by Ron
Taylor. — New York ; London : Wise : Music Sales, 1976. —
32p ; 4to.
With words printed separately.
Unpriced
Primary classification TSPMK/DP/LF/AY

JE/TSDW/G/AYD — With guitar. Folk songs. Collections. England
The crystal spring : English folk songs / collected by Cecil Sharp ;
edited by Maud Karpeles, guitar chords by Pat Shaw. —
London : Oxford University Press, 1975. — 152p ; 8vo.
A selection of songs taken from Cecil Sharp's Collection of English Folk
Songs, vols. 1, 2.
ISBN 0-19-330518-6 : £4.95

(B76-50105)

JE/TSDW/G/AYDGH — With guitar. Folk songs. Collections.
Lincolnshire
Yellowbelly ballads : a third selection of Lincolnshire folk-songs, the
majority of them from the collection of Percy Aldridge Grainger /
edited by Patrick O'Shaughnessy ; guitar chords added. —
Lincoln : Lincolnshire and Humberside Arts, 1975. — 88p ; 8vo.
Unpriced

(B76-50829)

JEZDW/G/AYC — Unaccompanied voices. Folk songs. Collections.
Great Britain
Folk song : music arranged by John and Susanne Bailey, text by
John Bailey. — London : SCM Press, 1976. — 47p : ill ; 8vo. —
(Probe, no.13)
With a select list of books and records.
ISBN 0-334-00492-6 : Unpriced

(B76-50106)

JFDP/LF — Female voices, Children's voices. Carols. Christmas
Rutter, John
[Donkey carol. *arr*]. Donkey carol / words and music by John
Rutter ; shortened version with reduced accompaniment arranged
and fingered by Kenneth Pont. — London : Oxford University
Press, 1976. — 4p ; 8vo. — (Oxford choral songs ; U 152)
ISBN 0-19-342052-x : Unpriced

(B76-50461)

Verrall, Pamela Motley
The organ-grinder's carol. (When Jesus Christ was born) :
unison / words and music by Pamela Verrall. — London :
Leonard, Gould and Bolttler, 1975. — 3p ; 8vo. — (Library of
unison and part-songs for schools ; no.112)
Unpriced

(B76-50107)

Verrall, Pamela Motley
Peter Piper's carol : calypso style, [unison] / words and music by
Pamela Verrall. — London : Leonard, Gould and Bolttler, 1975.
— 3p ; 8vo. — (Library of unison and part-songs for schools ;
no.111)
For voices in unison.
Unpriced

(B76-50108)

JFDW — Female voices, Children's voices. Songs, etc
Benger, Richard
Sky songs / music by Richard Benger ; words by Mary Dawson.
— London : Edwin Ashdown, 1976. — 10p ; 8vo. — (Unison
songs ; no.102)
Contents: 1: Whizz - 2: Stargazing - 3: The rainbow.
£0.40

(B76-50462)

Clements, John
The scarecrow : for unison voices and piano / music by John
Clements ; words by Michael Franklin. — Sevenoaks : Elkin,
1976. — 4p ; 8vo.
£0.12

(B76-50463)

Longmire, John
Norse cradle song : unison / setting by John Longmire ; words by
Margaret Rose. — London : Leonard, Gould and Bolttler, 1976.
— 4p ; 8vo. — (Leonard, Gould and Bolttler's library of unison
and part-songs for schools ; no.113)
£0.09

(B76-50464)

Parke, Dorothy
[By winding roads. In old Donegal]. In old Donegal, and, The
fairy tree / music by Dorothy Parke ; words by John Irvine. —
Wendover : Roberton, 1975. — 4p ; 8vo.
Voices in unison. — Staff & tonic sol-fa notation.
£0.10

(B76-50465)

Parke, Dorothy
[By winding roads. *Selections*]. Over the hills. The old man from
Kilkenny. If / music by Dorothy Parke ; words by John Irvine.
— Wendover : Roberton, 1975. — 7p ; 8vo.
Staff & solfa notation.
£0.15

(B76-50466)

Parke, Dorothy
[By winding roads. *Selections*]. Three little towns, Blarney / music
by Dorothy Parke ; words by John Irvine. — Wendover :
Roberton, 1975. — 4p ; 8vo.
Staff & tonic solfa notation.
£0.10

(B76-50467)

Parke, Dorothy
[By winding roads. The travellers]. The travellers, and, The fairy
hill / music by Dorothy Parke ; words by John Irvine. —
Wendover : Roberton, 1975. — 4p ; 8vo.
Voices in unison. — Staff & tonic sol-fa notation.
£0.10

(B76-50468)

Parke, Dorothy
[By winding roads. Winds]. Winds, and, In summer time / music
by Dorothy Parke ; words by John Irvine. — Wendover :
Roberton, 1975. — 4p ; 8vo.
Voices in unison. — Staff & tonic sol-fa notation.
£0.20

(B76-50469)

Smith, Pat
Things to sing / [by] Pat Smith and Dorothy Wheatley. —
Leeds : Arnold, 1976. — 4to & obl.4to.
Songs. — Teacher's book (25p.) & Pupil's book (23p.).
ISBN 0-560-02720-6 : Unpriced

(B76-50830)

Williams, Patrick
Some hallucinations : unison song / music by Patrick Williams ;
words by Lewis Carroll. — London : Bosworth, 1976. — 4p ; 8vo.
Unpriced

(B76-50831)

**JFDW/GJ/AY — Female voices, Children's voices. Children's songs.
      Collections**
Tops and tails again : eight children's songs with interchangeable
accompaniments / [by] Anne Mendoza. — London : Oxford
University Press, 1976. — 17p ; obl. 8vo.
ISBN 0-19-330573-9 : Unpriced

(B76-50470)

**JFDW/GK/AY — Female voices, Children's voices. Nursery rhymes.
      Collections**
Perry merry dixy : 106 nursery and infant songs, old and new /
selected, edited and arranged by John Horton, illustrated by Robin
Wiggins. — London : Schott, 1975. — 159p ; 4to.
ISBN 0-901938-08-4 : Unpriced

(B76-50109)

JFDW/GR — Female voices, Children's voices. Action songs
Okki-tokki-unga : action songs for children / chosen by Beatrice
Harrop ; with piano accompaniments, chords for guitar, actions by
Linda Friend and drawings by David McKee. — London : A. and
C. Black, 1976. — [96]p : ill, music ; obl.4to.
Index.
ISBN 0-7136-1685-7 Sp : £2.75
ISBN 0-7136-1684-9 School ed. (non-net) : £2.25

(B76-50832)

JFDW/LF — Female voices, Children's voices. Songs, etc. Christmas
Smith, Pat
Christmas things to sing / [by] Pat Smith and Dorothy Wheatley.
— Leeds : Arnold, 1976. — 4to & obl.4to.
Songs. — Teacher's book (28p.) & Pupil's book (28p.).
ISBN 0-560-02721-4 : Unpriced

(B76-50833)

**JFDW/LFZ — Female voices, Children's voices. Songs, etc. Shrove
      Tuesday**
Carter, Andrew
Pancake Tuesday : unison (or solo) song / [by] Andrew Carter ;
words by Eleanor Farjeon. — York : Banks, 1976. — 4p ; 8vo. —
(Eboracum choral series ; no.32)
Unpriced

(B76-50110)

**JFE/LPDP/LF — Female voices, Children's voices. With instruments
      & piano. Carols. Christmas**
Platts, Kenneth
Songs from the stable : for children's voices and instruments /
[by] Kenneth Platts ; poems by Jean Kenward. — London :
Edwin Ashdown, 1976. — 20p ; 4to.
Carols.
£2.00

(B76-50834)

**JFE/NYFSNSDW — Female voices, Children's voices. With
      recorder, keyboard & percussion quartet. Songs, etc**
Senator, Ronald
Streets of London / [by] Ronald Senator ; words by Eleanor
Farjeon. — London : Boosey and Hawkes, 1976. — 8vo. —
(Tonal perspective series for tuned percussion ; no.15)
For voices, recorder, piano and percussion. — Score (30p.) Chorus score
(11p.) & 3 parts.
£2.20

(B76-50471)

**JFE/NYHSDW/AY — Female voices, Children's voices. With
      recorders & percussion. Songs, etc. Collections**
Music time for Brownies : songs for unison voices and
instruments / compiled by George Adam ; illustrated by
Rosemary Thornton-Jones. — London : Girl Guides Association,
1976. — 32p ; 4to.
£0.65

(B76-50111)

**JFE/NYLDP/LF — Female voices, Children's voices. With keyboard
      & percussion. Carols. Christmas**
Brown, Gerald Edgar
Bohemian bell carol : traditional / arr. by Gerald E. Brown,
words by Huw Lewis, adapted by Gerald E. Brown. — London :
Universal, 1976. — 2p ; 8vo.
For unison voices, percussion and piano.
Unpriced

(B76-50835)

**JFE/TSDM/AY — Female voices, Children's voices. With guitar.
      Hymns. Collections**
Neue Gemeindelieder : neue geistliche Lieder / herausgegeben von
Oskar Gottlieb und Uwe Seidel. — Regensburg : Bosse ;
[London] : [Bärenreiter].
Heft 3. — 1975. — 78p ; 16mo.
£1.66

(B76-50836)

Schulgottesdienst für Grund-und Hauptschulen : für Mittelschulen
und Familiengottesdienst, Lieder und Text. — Regensburg :
Boose ; [London] : [Bärenreiter], 1975. — 64p ; 16mo.
£1.31

(B76-50837)

**JFE/XTPRPDP/LF — Female voices, Children's voices. With chime
      bars & piano. Carols. Christmas**
Brown, Gerald Edgar
Carol for a king / words and music by Gerald E. Brown. —
London : Universal, 1976. — 1p ; 8vo.
With accompaniments for chime bars and piano.
Unpriced

(B76-50838)

JFLDP/LF — Treble voices. Carols. Christmas
Ridout, Alan
Rejoice and sing : sacred songs for Christmas, for treble voices
and piano (or organ) / by Alan Ridout. — London : Chappell,
1976. — 12p ; 8vo.
Unpriced

(B76-50839)

JN — SINGLE VOICES IN COMBINATION
JNAYDW — Vocal octet. Songs, etc
Connolly, Justin
Verse, op.7b : for 8 solo voices / [by] Justin Connolly. —
Sevenoaks : Novello, 1976. — 20p ; 8vo.
£1.00

(B76-50472)

JNAZDX — Vocal sextet. Secular cantatas
Williamson, Malcolm
The musicians of Bremen : for 2 counter-tenors, tenor, 2 baritones
and bass / words and music by Malcolm Williamson. — London :
Weinberger, 1974. — 34p ; 4to.
Unpriced

(B76-50473)

**JNDE/NUNPDX — Vocal trios. With wind, string & keyboard
      septet. Secular cantatas**
Kagel, Mauricio
Kantrimiusik : für Sänger (Sopran, Mezzo-Sopran, Tenor) und
Instrumentalensemble (Klarinette, Trompete, Basstuba, Geige,
Klavier, 2 Gitarristen) / [von] Mauricio Kagel. — London :
Universal, 1975. — viii,164p ; 4to.
Reproduction of composer's autograph.
Unpriced

(B76-50112)

**JNEE/NYEPDX — Vocal duets. With woodwind, string &
      percussion. Secular cantatas**
Kagel, Mauricio
Mare nostrum : Entdeckung, Gefriedung und Konversion des
Mittelmeerraumes durch einen Stamm aus Amazonien, für
Contratenor, Bariton, Flöte, Oboe, Gitarre, Harfe, Violoncello und
Schlagzeug / [von] Mauricio Kagel. — London : Universal, 1975.
— a-h,172p ; 4to.
Facsimile of composer's autograph.
Unpriced

(B76-50113)

**JNGE/SRPLSSDX — Male vocal duet. With cello & double bass.
      Secular cantatas**
Reynolds, Roger
Compass : cello, contra bass, tenor, bass and electronics / [by]
Roger Reynolds ; [words by] Jorge Luis Borges, trans. [from the
Spanish] by Alistair Reid. — New York ; London : Peters, 1975.
— 55p ; obl. fol.
Unpriced

(B76-50114)

JNGEZAZDX — Unaccompanied male sextets. Secular cantatas
Patterson, Paul
Time piece : for 2 altos, tenor, 2 baritones and bass / music by
Paul Patterson ; words by Tim Rose-Price. — London :
Weinberger, 1974. — 16p ; 4to.
Facsimile of composer's autograph.
Unpriced

(B76-50840)

K — VOCAL SOLOS
K/EG/AL — Sight singing. Examinations
London College of Music
Examinations in pianoforte playing and singing sight reading tests : sight singing tests as set throughout 1975. — London : Ashdown, 1976. — 15p ; 4to.
Unpriced
Primary classification Q/EG/AL

(B76-50182)

KADW — Songs, etc. Voice part
Russell, Kay
In the picture / [by] Kay Russell. — Breakish (19 Scullamus, Isle of Skye) : Aquila.
Voice part.
Songbook 1. — 1976. — 23p ; obl.8vo.
ISBN 0-7275-0144-5 : Unpriced

(B76-50841)

KDM — HYMNS. SOLOS
KDM/AY — Collections
Good news : new Christian songs for churches and groups / compiled by John Maynard. — London (12 Portland Rd, S.E.25) : Vanguard Music, 1976. — 34p ; 4to.
Unpriced

(B76-50115)

KDR — PSALMS. SOLOS
Head, Michael
Three psalms for solo voice with organ or piano. — Wendover : Roberton.
No.1 : I will lift up mine eyes : Psalm 121. — 1976. — 11p ; 4to.
Arranged for high or low voice.
£0.40

(B76-50474)

No.2 : Be merciful unto me, O God : Psalm 57. — 1976. — 4to.
High key (10p.), Low key (10p.).
£0.40

(B76-50475)

No.3 : Make a joyful noise unto the Lord : Psalm 100. — 1976. — 4to.
High key (7p.), Low key (7p.).
£0.40

(B76-50476)

Lowe, Augustus
Praise ye the Lord / music by Augustus Lowe ; words from the 148th psalm ; metrical version arr. E. Newgass. — London : Paterson, 1975. — 2p ; 4to.
With an erratum slip inserted which should refer to line 3, bar 1, not bar 2.
Unpriced

(B76-50116)

KDW — SONGS, ETC. SOLOS
Amram, David
[Twelfth night. *Selections : arr*]. Five Shakespeare songs : voice and piano / [by] David Amram. — New York ; London : Peters, 1976. — 16p ; 4to.
Unpriced

(B76-50117)

Beethoven, Ludwig van
[Romance, violin & orchestra, no.1, op.40, G major. *arr*]. Beneficence / [music by] Beethoven ; adaptation by Augustus Lowe ; words by Edgar Newgass. — New York : Fischer ; Romsey (Pinns Farm, West Wellow, Romsey) : Edgar Newgass, 1976. — 3p ; 4to.
Song.
Unpriced

(B76-50118)

Berlin, Irving
[Songs. *Selections : arr*]. The Irving Berlin collection : 16 great songs with facsimile covers. — London : EMI, 1976. — 16 nos ; 4to.
Songs in folder.
Unpriced

(B76-50842)

Brahms, Johannes
Wiegenlied = Lullaby = Berceuse. Op.49, no.4 / [by] Johannes Brahms ; English words by Leslie Minchin. — South Croydon : Lengnick, 1976. — 4p ; 4to.
Text in German, English and French.
£0.30

(B76-50119)

Cavalier songs / by Henry Lawes [et al.] ; edited by Ian Spink. — London : Stainer and Bell, 1976. — 32p ; 8vo.
Selected from volume 32 of Musica Britannica. 'The aim has been to provide a performing edition : consequently features such as prefatory staves, etc. have been dispensed with' - Editor's note.
ISBN 0-85249-325-8 : Unpriced
Primary classification KE/TDW

(B76-50129)

Fanshawe, David
Dance ti thi daddy : traditional original theme song from the BBC TV series 'When the boat comes in' / arranged by David Fanshawe. — Ilford : Chappell, 1976. — 8p ; 4to.
For voice and piano.
Unpriced

(B76-50477)

Gershwin, George
[Songs. *Selections : arr*]. The best of George Gershwin / introduction by Edward Lea. — London : Chappell, 1976. — 143p ; 4to.
Unpriced

(B76-50843)

Hamlisch, Marvin
[A chorus line. *Selections : arr*]. A chorus line : vocal selections / music by Marvin Hamlisch ; lyrics by Edward Kleban. — London : Chappell, 1975. — 96p : ill ; 4to.
Unpriced

(B76-50478)

Irene : song album. — London : EMI, 1976. — 32p ; 4to.
Selections from a musical comedy. — Music by Harry Tierney and others.
Unpriced

(B76-50844)

Jara, Victor
[Songs. *Selections*]. Victor Jara : his life and songs / foreword by Pete Seeger. — London : Elm Tree Books : Essex House Publishing, 1976. — 127p ; 4to.
For voice and guitar.
ISBN 0-241-89520-0 : Unpriced

(B76-50845)

Lehár, Franz
[Zigeunerliebe. *Selections : arr*]. Songs from 'Gipsy love' / [by] Franz Lehár ; original lyrics by A.M. Willner and R. Bodanzky ; English by Adam Carstairs. — London : Glocken, 1976. — 24p ; 4to.
Unpriced

(B76-50479)

Naylor, John
Come away, death : song / music by John Naylor ; edited by Bernard Naylor, words by William Shakespeare. — Wendover : Roberton, 1975. — 7p ; 4to.
For low and high voice, published consecutively in D minor and G minor.
£0.35

(B76-50120)

Purcell, Henry
[Songs. *Selections*]. Songs / [by] Henry Purcell ; edited by Peter Wishart and Maureen Lehane. — London : Galliard : Stainer and Bell.
Book 1. — 1976. — 32p ; 8vo.
Unpriced
ISBN 0-85249-323-1

(B76-50480)

Book 2. — 1976. — 32p ; 8vo.
ISBN 0-85249-323-1 : Unpriced

(B76-50481)

Book 3. — 1976. — 32p ; 8vo.
ISBN 0-85249-383-5 : Unpriced

(B76-50482)

Rodgers, Richard
[Songs. *Selections : arr*]. The best of Rodgers and Hart. — London : Chappell, 1975. — 112p ; 4to.
Unpriced

(B76-50121)

Rorem, Ned
To Jane : music by Ned Rorem / words by Percy B. Shelley. — New York ; [London] : Boosey and Hawkes, 1976. — 4p ; 4to.
Song.
£1.00

(B76-50483)

Rorem, Ned
Where we came / music by Ned Rorem ; words by Jean Garrigue. — New York ; [London] : Boosey and Hawkes, 1976. — 6p ; 4to.
Song.
£1.25

(B76-50484)

Rubbra, Edmund
[Songs. *Selections*]. Four short songs : for medium voice / [by] Edmund Rubbra. — South Croydon : Lengnick, 1976. — 9p ; 4to.
Contents: 1: The mystery. Op.4, no.1 (Hodgson) - 2: Rosa mundi. Op.2 (Taylor) - 3: Cradle song. Op.8, no.1 (Colum) - 4: Orpheus with his lute. Op.8, no.2 (Fletcher) - 'Rosa mundi' has an accompaniment for piano or two violins printed in score. 'The mystery' is unaccompanied.
Unpriced

(B76-50122)

Schubert, Franz
[Songs. *Selections*]. Franz Peter Schubert : his greatest songs, 38 lieder with new singable translations / compilation and English lyrics by Robert Kail. — Carlstadt : Copa ; [London] : [Phoenix Music], 1976. — 143p ; 4to.
Unpriced

(B76-50846)

Schubert, Franz
Die schöne Müllerin. D.795 : für Gesang und Klavier / [von] Franz Schubert ; neue Ausgabe ; herausgegeben von Dietrich Fischer-Dieskau ; musikwissenschaftliche Revision von Elmar Budde. — Frankfurt : Litolff ; London : Peters, 1976. — 8vo.
High voice (55p.), Low voice (63p.).
Unpriced

(B76-50847)

Schubert, Franz
Schwanengesang. D.957 : für Gesang und Klavier / [von] Franz Schubert ; neue Ausgabe ; herausgegeben von Dietrich Fischer-Dieskau ; musikwissenschaftliche Revision von Elmar Budde. — Frankfurt : Litolff ; London : Peters, 1976. — 8vo.
High voice (55p.), Low voice (58p.), Middle voice (55p.).
Unpriced

(B76-50848)

Scott, Anthony
Lullaby / music by Anthony Scott ; words by Alfred, Lord Tennyson. — London : Boosey and Hawkes, 1976. — 3p ; 4to.
Song.
£0.45

(B76-50485)

Stolz, Robert
[Songs. *Selections : arr*]. Songs from White Horse Inn and other favourites / by Robert Stolz. — London : Chappell, 1975. — 43p ; 4to.
Introduction by Edward Lea.
Unpriced

(B76-50486)

Stravinsky, Soulima
Chantefaibles : 10 chansons pour enfants / [de] Soulima Stravinsky ; texte de André Truffert. — New York ; London : Peters, 1975. — 26p ; 4to.
For voice and piano.
Unpriced

(B76-50487)

Vieuxtemps, Henri
[Songs. *Selections*]. Cinq melodies inédités / [de] Henri Vieuxtemps ; revision et adaptation de Pierre Duclos ; texte français de Paul Wachsmann. — Paris ; London : Chappell, 1976. — 28p ; 4to.
Text in French and German. — Contents: 1: Mélancolie = Wehmut (Eichendorff) - 2: Toi = An sie (Flachsland) - 3: Décision = Entschluss (Uhland) - 4: Les Angelots et les cicognes = Von den Engeln und Storchen (Eichendorff) - 5: La Mort du meunier = Der tote Muller (Kerner).
Unpriced

(B76-50123)

Warlock, Peter
The everlasting voices / [by] Peter Warlock ; with an alternative ending by Anthony Ingle and an explanatory note by Fred Tomlinson. — London : Thames, 1975. — [3],p ; 4to.
The winning entry of a competition organized by the Peter Warlock Society in 1974 for a conclusion to a song by Warlock.
Unpriced

(B76-50488)

KDW/AY — Collections
Al Jolson. — London : EMI, 1975. — 64p ; 4to.
Songs.
Unpriced

(B76-50124)

Among your souvenirs : based on the BBC Radio 2 series ; fragrant memories from the Victorian and Edwardian period and a little later. — London : Boosey and Hawkes, 1976. — 64p ; 4to.
Songs and two piano pieces.
Unpriced

(B76-50489)

KDW/AYDM — Collections. Ireland
Song of Ireland : songs / compiled by Peter Foss. — New York ; London : Wise : Music Sales, 1976. — 88p ; 4to.
£2.95

(B76-50849)

KDW/AYT — Collections. United States
The **spirit** of America / compiled and edited by Bill Margaretten. — New York ; [London] : Chappell, 1976. — 111p ; 4to.
Songs.
Unpriced

(B76-50850)

Sunset trail : a collection of songs of the American West with text and illustrations / introduction by Clyde Jeavons. — London : EMI, 1976. — viii,80p ; 4to.
Unpriced

(B76-50851)

KDW/G/AYDL — Folk songs. Collections. Scotland
Auld lang syne : schottische Lieder und Balladen / Satz, Klaus Buhé ; deutscher Text, Christiane Agricola. — Mainz ; London : Schott, 1976. — 48p ; 4to.
£0.45

(B76-50490)

KDW/G/AYXR — Folk songs. Collections. New Zealand
Te Wiata, Inia
Inia Te Wiata's Maori songbook : favourite songs and chants as arranged and recorded by Inia Te Wiata / piano accompaniments by William A. Rea ; with English versions (of texts). — Wellington ; London : A.H. & A.W. Reed, 1975. — 47p : ill, port ; 4to.
ISBN 0-589-00877-3 : Unpriced

(B76-50491)

KDW/GB/AY — Popular songs. Collections
The **Beatles** : the singles collection 1962-1970. — London : Wise, Music Sales, 1976. — 80p : ill ; 4to.
ISBN 0-86001-274-3 : £2.50

(B76-50855)

One hundred hits of the seventies / music edited by Peter Evans. — New York ; London : Wise, Music Sales, 1976. — 363p ; 4to.
Unpriced

(B76-50852)

With Christmas in mind : thirty-seven songs of today / arranged for piano/vocal with guitar chords. — London : Music Sales, 1976. — 109p ; 4to.
ISBN 0-86001-059-7 : £2.95

(B76-50125)

KDW/GB/AYT — Popular songs. Collections. United States
Sinatra, the man and his music / music compilation by Hal Shaper and Peter Foss ; foreword written by Hal Shaper with additional material by Stan Britt and Michael Leitch ; edited by Michael Leitch. — London : Wise : Music Sales, 1975. — 171p ; 4to.
Songs.
Unpriced

(B76-50853)

KDW/GB/AYT(XG101) — Popular songs. Collections. United States, 1800-1900
Popular songs of nineteenth-century America : complete original sheet music for 64 songs / selected with an introduction and notes by Richard Jackson. — New York : Dover Publications ; London : Constable, 1976. — xiv,290p ; 4to.
ISBN 0-486-23270-0 : £4.20

(B76-50854)

KDW/JR — Film songs
Sherman, Richard M
[The slipper and the rose. *Selections: arr*]. The slipper and the rose : the story of Cinderella, an album of songs / music and lyrics by Richard M. Sherman and Robert B. Sherman. — London : Noel Gay Music, 1976. — 66p ; 4to.
From the film.
Unpriced

(B76-50492)

KDW/JR — Films
Cole, Tony
Falling angels : music from the film / words and music by Tony Cole. — Croydon (250 Purley Way, Croydon CR9 4QD) : Valley Music, 1976. — 24p ; 4to.
Songs.
£1.00

(B76-50126)

KDW/JR/AYT — Film songs. Collections. United States
The **Judy** Garland souvenir songbook / compiled and edited by Howard Harnne. — New York ; [London] : Chappell, 1976. — [6],298p ; 4to.
ISBN 0-06-465040-5 : Unpriced

(B76-50856)

KDW/L/AY — Religious songs. Collections
'I'll walk with God' : twenty-five of the most famous religious songs and ballads ever written / arranged for piano vocal - easy organ music [and] compiled by Peter Foss. — London : Wise : Music Sales, 1975. — 59p ; 4to.
Unpriced

(B76-50857)

KDW/LC — Spirituals

Burt, James
Michael, row the boat ashore : traditional / arranged by James Burt. — London : Chappell, 1976. — 5p ; 4to. — (Chappell's evergreen classics)
Unpriced

(B76-50858)

KDX — SECULAR CANTATAS. SOLOS

Antoniou, Theodore
Chorochronos 3 : for voice, tape, pianist or percussion / [by] Theodore Antoniou. — Cassel ; London : Bärenreiter, 1975. — 8p ; obl. fol.
A version of Chorochronos 1. — Multilingual text.
£2.50

(B76-50493)

KE — VOCAL SOLOS WITH ACCOMPANIMENT OTHER THAN KEYBOARD

KE/LNUDW/AY — With instruments (2). Songs, etc. Collections
Four French songs from an English song book (Cambridge, University Library Add.MS.5943, ff 161-173) : for voice with 1 and 2 instruments / edited by Richard Rastall, texts edited and translated by Jane Oakshott. — Lustleigh : Antico, 1976. — 9p ; 4to.
Unpriced

(B76-50859)

KE/MDW — With orchestra. Songs, etc

Handel, George Frideric
[Ottone. *Condensed score. Selections*]. Three ornamented arias / [by] G.F. Handel ; edited by Winton Dean. — London : Oxford University Press, 1976. — 21p ; 8vo.
The editor's realization of the ornamentation is here compared with the vocal urtext. — Contents: 1. Affanni del pensier - 2. Alla fama - 3. Benche mi sia crudele.
ISBN 0-19-345412-2 : Unpriced

(B76-50128)

KE/NYGNSDW — With strings, keyboard & percussion quartet. Songs, etc

Bacon, Ernst
Buttermilk hill : song of 1776, SA, TB or soloist, with instruments and percussion / realized by Ernst Bacon. — New York ; [London] : Boosey and Hawkes, 1976. — 6p ; 8vo.
£0.20
Primary classification FE/NYGNSDW

(B76-50087)

KE/PV — With electronic instruments

Lanza, Alcides
Penetrations VI (1972-II) : for voice, chamber ensemble, lights, electronic music and electronic extensions / [by] Alcides Lanza. — New York ; [London] : Boosey and Hawkes, 1976. — 10p ; obl.fol.
Unpriced

(B76-50860)

KE/TDW — With plucked string instrument. Songs, etc
Cavalier songs / by Henry Lawes [et al.] ; edited by Ian Spink. — London : Stainer and Bell, 1976. — 32p ; 8vo.
Selected from volume 32 of Musica Britannica. 'The aim has been to provide a performing edition : consequently features such as prefatory staves, etc. have been dispensed with' - Editor's note.
ISBN 0-85249-325-8 : Unpriced
Also classified at KDW

(B76-50129)

KE/TSDW — With guitar. Songs, etc
Carrick, Malcolm
Higgle-ty pig-le-ty : 20 songs / by Malcolm Carrick. — London : EMI, 1976. — 20p ; 4to.
Unpriced
Primary classification KEZDW

KE/TSDW/HXJ/AY — With guitar. Raggy songs. Collections
Ragtime guitar : complete instructions and exercises, 37 raggy songs, 23 Scott Joplin rags, the Scott Joplin school of ragtime / transcribed for guitar. — New York ; [London] : Chappell, 1976. — 191p ; 4to.
Unpriced
Also classified at TSPMK/AHXJ; TS/AF

(B76-50130)

KEZ — UNACCOMPANIED VOCAL SOLOS

KEZDW — Songs, etc
Carrick, Malcolm
Higgle-ty pig-le-ty : 20 songs / by Malcolm Carrick. — London : EMI, 1976. — 20p ; 4to.
Unpriced
Also classified at KE/TSDW

(B76-50861)

Clayre, Alasdair
[Songs. *Selections*]. Adam and the beasts and other songs / [by] Alasdair Clayre. — London : Faber and Faber in association with Faber Music, 1976. — 39p ; 8vo.
ISBN 0-571-10012-0 : Unpriced

(B76-50494)

Harding, Mike
Napoleon's retreat from Wigan / [by] Mike Harding ; illustrated by Bill Tidy. — London : EMI Music, 1976. — 52p ; 8vo.
Unpriced

(B76-50495)

KF — FEMALE VOICE, CHILD'S VOICE

KFDW — Songs, etc.
Liddell, Claire
Five Orkney scenes : a song cycle for female voice and piano / music by Claire Liddell ; words by George Mackay Brown. — Wendover : Roberton, 1975. — 16p ; 4to.
Duration 10 min.
Unpriced

(B76-50131)

KFLDW — Soprano voice. Songs, etc
Pert, Morris
Four Japanese verses, Op.2 : for soprano and piano / by Morris Pert. — London : Weinberger, 1976. — 8p ; 4to.
English words.
Unpriced

(B76-50862)

KFLE/NUNSDE — Soprano voice. With wind, string & keyboard quartet. Religious cantatas
Lumsdaine, David
Easter fresco : for piano, flute, horn, harp and piano / [by] David Lumsdaine ; [text from] St John 20. — Sydney ; London : Universal, 1975. — 26p ; 4to.
Duration 12 min. — Text in Latin.
Unpriced

(B76-50132)

KFLE/NUWNSDE/LF — Soprano voice. With bassoon, strings & keyboard quartet. Christmas
Bernhard, Christoph
'Fürchtet euch nicht' : Weihnachtskonzert für Sopran, zwei Violinen, Fagott (Violone) und Basso continuo / [von] Christoph Bernhard ; herausgegeben von Bruno Grusnick. — Cassel ; London : Bärenreiter, 1975. — 4to. — (Concerto vocale)
Score (15p.) & 5 parts.
£3.25

(B76-50496)

KFLE/NVNMDW — Soprano voice. With wind & string nonet. Songs, etc
Blake, David
In praise of Krishna : songs from the Bengali for soprano and nine instruments / [by] David Blake ; translated from the Bengali by Edward C. Dimock, jnr and Denise Levertor. — Sevenoaks : Novello, 1976. — 36p ; 8vo.
Study score. — Duration 24 min.
£2.00

(B76-50863)

KFLE/NVPNSDW — Soprano voice. With woodwind & string quartet. Songs, etc
Ung, Chinary
Tall wind : soprano, flute, oboe, guitar and violoncello / [by] Chinary Ung ; words by E.E. Cummings. — New York ; London : Peters, 1975. — 20p ; 4to.
Duration 6 min.
Unpriced

(B76-50133)

KFLE/PVDX — Soprano voice. With electronic instrument. Secular cantatas
Bennett, Richard Rodney
Nightpiece : for soprano and electronic tape / [by] Richard Rodney Bennett ; [words by] Charles Baudelaire. — London : Universal, 1976. — 11p ; 4to.
Duration 10 1/2 min.
Unpriced

(B76-50497)

KFLE/VRNTDH — Soprano voice. With flute trio. Motets, Anthems, Hymns, etc
Wyner, Yehudi
[Memorial music 1]. Memorial music 1 : Man comes from dust = Ki K'shimcho, and, Memorial music 2 : Lord let me know my end, (Psalm 39, Isaiah 40) : for soprano voice with three flutes / [by] Yehudi Wyner. — New York ; London : Associated Music, 1975. — 9p ; 4to.
Unpriced

(B76-50134)

KFLE/VVPDW — Soprano voice. With clarinet & piano. Songs, etc
Wordsworth, William, *b.1908*
The solitary reaper. Op.96 : for soprano, clarinet and piano / by William Wordsworth ; words by William Wordsworth. — Wendover : Roberton, 1975. — 4to.
Score (15p.) & part.
£0.75

(B76-50135)

KFQE/NYERNSDW — Contralto voice. With flute, strings & percussion quartet. Songs, etc
Crumb, George
Night of the four moons : alto, alto flute, (doubling piccolo), banjo, electric cello and percussion (one player) / [by] George Crumb ; text based on fragments from Federico Garcia Lorca, facsimile printing from the original manuscript by the composer. — New York ; London : Peters, 1974. — 10p ; fol.
Duration 16 min.
Unpriced

(B76-50136)

KFT — HIGH VOICE
KFTDW — Songs, etc
Hoddinott, Alun
Landscapes, Ynys Môn, Op.87 : a song cycle for high voice and piano / [by] Alun Hoddinott ; words by Emyr Humphreys. — London : Oxford University Press, 1976. — 21p ; 4to.
ISBN 0-19-345432-7 : Unpriced

(B76-50864)

Liszt, Franz
[Songs. *Selections*]. Thirty songs : for high voice / [by] Franz Liszt ; edited by Carl Armbruster. — New York : Dover Publications ; London : Constable, 1975. — xii,144p ; 4to.
Texts in English and German. — Bibl.
£2.60

(B76-50498)

KFTE/VVNTQDW — With clarinets (2) & piano. Songs, etc
Walker, Robert
Six songs of Mervyn Peake : for high voice, two clarinets and piano / [by] Robert Walker. — Eastwood : Ramsey ; Wendover : Roberton, 1976. — 4to.
Facsimile of the composer's autograph. — The clarinet parts are printed in score. — Score (36p.) & part.
Unpriced

(B76-50499)

KFV — MIDDLE VOICE
KFVDW — Songs, etc
Binkerd, Gordon
Her silver will. Looking back as Sposalizio : medium voice / [by] Gordon Binkerd, poems by Emily Dickinson. — New York ; [London] : Boosey and Hawkes, 1976. — 3p ; 4to.
£0.75

(B76-50500)

KFVE/MDW — With orchestra. Songs, etc
Antoniou, Theodore
Meli, Op.17 : songs on Sappho's poems, for medium voice and orchestra / [by] Theodore Antoniou. — Cassel ; London : Bärenreiter, 1975. — 17p ; 4to.
£3.50

(B76-50501)

KFVE/VVPDW — With clarinet & piano. Songs, etc
Sargon, Simon
Patterns in blue : medium voice, B flat clarinet and piano / [by] Simon Sargon ; texts by James Agee, Kenneth Patchen and Carl Sandburg. — New York ; London : Boosey and Hawkes, 1976. — 4to.
Score (14p.) & part. — Contents: 1: Cabaret song - 2: Snatch of sliphorn jazz - 3: Lonesome boy blues.
£1.75

(B76-50502)

KG — MALE VOICE
KGHE/SNTPWDE — Tenor voice. With violins (3) & keyboard. Religious cantatas
Hammerschmidt, Andreas
[Musikalischer Andachten, Tl 3. Es danken dir, Gott, die Volker]. Es danken dir, Gott, die Volker : solokantate für Tenor, zwei Violinen und Basso continuo / [von] Andreas Hammerschmidt ; herausgegeben von Pierre Pidoux. — Cassel ; London : Bärenreiter, 1975. — 4to. — (Concerto vocale)
Score (7p.) & 4 parts.
£1.63

(B76-50503)

KGHE/TQDE — Tenor voice. With harp. Religious cantatas
Britten, Benjamin, *Baron Britten*
Canticle 5. The death of Saint Narcissus. Op.89 : for tenor and harp / [by] Benjamin Britten ; poem by T.S. Eliot. — London : Faber Music, 1976. — 15p ; 4to.
Duration 7 min.
Unpriced

(B76-50504)

KGNDW — Baritone voice. Songs, etc
Antoniou, Theodore
Moirologhia for Jani Christou : for bariton [sic] and piano or bariton [sic], piano and instruments / by Theodore Antoniou. — Cassel ; London : Bärenreiter, 1975. — 19p ; fol.
£8.00

(B76-50506)

KGNDX — Baritone voice. Secular cantatas
Křenek, Ernst
Spatlese. Op.218 : in sechs Teilen, für Bariton und Klavier / [von] Ernst Křenek. — Cassel ; London : Bärenreiter, 1975. — 62p ; 4to.
Text by the composer.
£7.50

(B76-50507)

Mathias, William
[Elegy for a prince. Op.59. *Vocal score*]. Elegy for a prince. Op.59 : for baritone and orchestra / [by] William Mathias ; English translation by Anthony Conran from the original Welsh by Gruffudd ab yr Ynad Coch. — London : Oxford University Press, 1976. — 32p ; 8vo.
ISBN 0-19-365582-9 : Unpriced

(B76-50508)

KGXDW — Bass voice. Songs, etc
Amran, David
[Three songs for America. *arr*]. Three songs for America : bass voice and instruments (woodwind quintet and string quintet) / [by] David Amran ; piano reduction by the composer ; words by John F. Kennedy, Martin Luther King and Robert F. Kennedy. — New York ; London : Peters, 1974. — 15p ; 4to.
Duration 8 1/2 min.
Unpriced

(B76-50137)

KGXE/MRDW — Bass voice. With chamber orchestra. Songs, etc
Amran, David
Three songs for America : bass voice and instruments (woodwind quintet and string quintet) / [by] David Amran ; words by John F. Kennedy, Martin Luther King, and Robert F. Kennedy. — New York ; London : Peters, 1974. — 4to.
Score (29p.) & 10 parts. — Duration 8 1/2 min.
Unpriced

(B76-50138)

KHYE/M — With orchestra
Lees, Benjamin
The trumpet of the swan : for narrator and orchestra / [by] Benjamin Lees ; narration by E.B. White, based on his book of the same title. — London : Boosey and Hawkes, 1976. — 30p ; 8vo. — (Hawkes pocket scores ; no 897)
Miniature score. — Duration 17 min.
£1.25

(B76-50509)

LH — DANCES
LH/AYDM — Dances. Collections. Ireland
Ceol rince na hEireann / Breandan Breathnach a chuir in eagar. — Dublin : Oifig an tSolathair.
Cuid 2. — 1976. — xiv,203p ; 4to.
Unpriced

(B76-50865)

LH/G/AYDL — Folk dances. Collections. Scotland
Tunes for the band : 70 folk dance melodies with chord symbols / chosen by Beryl and Roger Marriott. — London : English Folk Dance and Song Society, 1976. — 23p ; 8vo.
ISBN 0-85418-114-8 : Unpriced

(B76-50866)

LN — ENSEMBLES
Wright, Francis
Party time : for instrumental ensemble / [by] Francis Wright. — Leicester : Charnwood Music, 1976. — [2]p ; 8vo. — (Group series ; no.4)
Unpriced

(B76-50510)

LN/XC — Rounds
Crawley, Cliff
Aroundabout Christmas : 16 rounds for voices and/or instruments / set to music by Cliff Crawley. — Oakville : Frederick Harris Music ; [South Croydon] : [Lengnick], 1974. — 8p ; obl. 8vo.
£0.25
Primary classification EZDW/XC/LF

LNHVH — Polkas
Wright, Francis
Pic-a-pic-a-polka : instrumental ensemble / by Francis Wright. —
Leicester : Charnwood Music, 1976. — 2p ; 4to. — (Group
series ; no.1)
Unpriced

(B76-50511)

LNHW — Waltzes
Mayes, Jerry
Joy waltz : instrumental ensemble / by Jerry Mayes ; edited by G.
Romani. — Leicester : Charnwood Music, 1976. — 2p ; 4to. —
(Group series ; no.3)
Unpriced

(B76-50512)

Wright, Francis
Valse des guitares : instrumental ensemble / by Francis Wright.
— Leicester : Charnwood Music, 1976. — 3p ; 4to. — (Group
series ; no.2)
Unpriced

(B76-50513)

LNQ — Sextets
Wright, Francis
Etude barcarolle : for instrumental ensemble / [by] Francis
Wright. — Leicester : Charnwood Music, 1976. — [2]p ; 8vo. —
(Group series ; no.5)
Unpriced

(B76-50514)

LNS/AY — Quartets. Collections
Renaissance works for four instruments / edited by Istvan
Mariassy. — London : Boosey and Hawkes, 1975. — 4to.
Score (15p.) & 7 parts.
£1.75

(B76-50515)

LNS/AYK — Quartets. Collections. Spain
Linoi : clarinet in A and piano / [by] Harrison Birtwistle. —
Lustleigh : Antico, 1976. — 12p ; 4to.
Unpriced
Primary classification EZDU/AYK

LNT — Trios
Bartolino da Padova
[Madrigals. *Selections]*. Three madrigals for voices and/or
instruments / [by] Bartolino da Padova ; edited by Nigel Wilkins.
— Newton Abbott : Antico, 1976. — 4to.
Score (12p.) & 3 parts. — Contents: 1: Qual lege move - 2: Imperial
sedendo - 3: La dolce sere.
Unpriced
Primary classification EZDU

(B76-50426)

MK — ARRANGEMENTS
Chabrier, Emmanuel
[España. *arr]*. España : rhapsody for orchestra / by Emmanuel
Chabrier ; arranged by Anthony Carter. — London : Bosworth,
1976. — 47p ; 4to. — (Series for school and amateur orchestra)
Duration 6 1/2 min.
Unpriced

(B76-50139)

Friend, Howard C
Ceremonial occasion : a tribute to Her Majesty the Queen for the
year of her silver jubilee, 1977 : a selection of famous marches and
songs / arranged by Howard C. Friend. — London : Bosworth,
1976. — 35p ; 4to.
Unpriced

(B76-50867)

MK/AH — Dances
Mozart, Wolfgang Amadeus
[Contredanse no.21, K.535, G major, 'La Bataille'. *arr]*.
Contredanse, 'The battle' / [by] W.A. Mozart ; arranged for
recorders, percussion (tuned and untuned), and piano, with
optional violins and optional cello, by Geoffrey Winters. —
London : Oxford University Press, 1976. — 4to.
Score (9p.) & 5 parts.
ISBN 0-19-357927-8 : Unpriced

(B76-50516)

MK/AHVH — Polkas
Strauss, Johann, *b.1825*
[Unter Donner und Blitz. Op.324. *arr]*. Thunder and lightning =
Unter Donner und Blitz, Op.324 : polka / [by] Johann Strauss ;
arr. by Frank Naylor. — London : Bosworth, 1976. — 13p ; 4to.
— (Series for school and amateur orchestra)
Unpriced

(B76-50517)

MK/AHVQ — Arrangements. Sicilianos
Fauré, Gabriel
[Pelléas et Mélisande. Op.80. Sicilienne. *arr]*. Sicilienne / [by]
Gabriel Fauré ; arranged for orchestra by David Stone. —
London : Boosey and Hawkes, 1975. — 4to. — (Hawkes school
series ; no.103)
Score (20p.) & 22 parts. — Various parts are in duplicate.
£3.95

(B76-50140)

MK/AHW — Waltzes
Strauss, Johann, *b.1825*
[Rosen aus dem Suden. Op.388. *arr]*. Roses from the south.
Op.388 : waltz / [by] Johann Strauss ; arr. for school and amateur
orchestra by Frank Naylor. — London : Bosworth, 1976. — 18p ;
4to.
Duration 2 1/2 min.
Unpriced

(B76-50518)

MK/DM/AY — Arrangements. Hymns. Collections
Fifty hymns for band / arranged by Colin Evans, instrumental
descants by Herbert Sumsion. — London : Oxford University
Press.
Score (27p.) & 17 parts.
Book 2 : General, Passiontide and Easter. — 1975. — 4to.
ISBN 0-19-363060-5 : Unpriced

(B76-50868)

MM — WORKS FOR SYMPHONY ORCHESTRA
MM/T — Variations
Bliss, *Sir* Arthur
Metamorphic variations : for orchestra / [by] Arthur Bliss. —
Sevenoaks : Novello, 1976. — 147p ; 8vo.
Study score.
£3.75

(B76-50141)

MME — Symphonies
Becker, John
Symphony no.3, 'Symphonia brevis' / [by] John Becker. — New
York ; London : Peters, 1975. — 45p ; 4to.
Duration 15 min.
Unpriced

(B76-50142)

Josephs, Wilfred
[Symphony no.5, op.75, 'Pastoral']. Pastoral symphony (1970) /
[by] Wilfred Josephs. — Sevenoaks : Novello, 1975. — 85p ; 4to.
£3.50

(B76-50519)

Kubelík, Rafael
[Symphony in one movement]. Sinfonie in einem Satz für
Orchester / [von] Rafael Kubelík. — Frankfurt : Litolff ;
London : Peters, 1976. — 73p ; 8vo.
Duration 27 min.
Unpriced

(B76-50520)

Mahler, Gustav
[Symphony no.10]. A performing version of the draft for the tenth
symphony / [by] Gustav Mahler ; prepared by Deryck Cooke ; in
collaboration with ... [others]. — New York : Associated Music ;
London : Faber Music, 1976. — xlii,193p ; 4to.
Notes by Deryck Cooke in English and German.
Unpriced

(B76-50521)

Matthews, Colin
[Sonata no.4, orchestra, 'Green and gold and blue and white'].
Fourth sonata, 'Green and gold and blue and white' : for
orchestra / [by] Colin Matthews. — Sevenoaks : Novello, 1976. —
107p ; 8vo.
Duration 28 min. — Study score. — Facsimile of the composer's autograph.
£3.00

(B76-50143)

Mendelssohn, Felix
[Symphony no.3, op.56, A, 'Scottish']. Symphony no.3 (Scotch), A
major, Op.56 / by Felix Mendelssohn-Barthold ; foreword by
Roger Fiske. — London : Eulenburg, 1976. — x,168p ; 8vo. —
(Edition Eulenburg ; no.406)
Miniature score.
Unpriced

(B76-50869)

Mozart, Wolfgang Amadeus
[Symphony, no.34, K.338, C major]. Symphony, C major. K.338
[and] Minuetto, C major. K.409 / [by] Wolfgang Amadeus
Mozart ; edited by Hans F. Redlich and Arthur D. Walker ;
foreword by Hans F. Redlich. — London : Eulenburg, 1976. —
ix,76p ; 8vo. — (Edition Eulenburg ; no.542)
Miniature score.
Unpriced

(B76-50144)

Panufnik, Andrzej
Sinfonia di sfere / [by] Andrzej Panufnik. — London : Boosey
and Hawkes, 1976. — 121p ; fol.
Reproduction of the composer's autograph. — Duration 33 min.
£10.00

(B76-50870)

Schwarz-Schilling, Reinhard
[Symphony, C major]. Symphonie in C für Orchester / [von]
Reinhard Schwarz-Schilling. — Cassel ; London : Bärenreiter,
1976. — 120p ; 8vo. — (Taschpartituren ; 259)
Miniature score.
£6.50

(B76-50522)

MMF — Concertos
Payne, Anthony
[Concerto, orchestra]. Concerto for orchestra / [by] Anthony
Payne. — London : Chester, 1976. — 80p ; 4to.
Duration 20 min.
Unpriced

(B76-50871)

MMG — Suites
Schwarz-Schilling, Reinhard
Partita für Orchester / [von] Reinhard Schwarz-Schilling. —
Cassel ; London : Bärenreiter, 1975. — 96p ; 8vo. —
(Taschenpartituren ; 260)
Miniature score.
£6.00

(B76-50523)

MMH — Dances
Hurd, Michael
Dance diversions / [by] Michael Hurd. — Sevenoaks : Novello,
1975. — 75p ; 4to.
For orchestra.
£3.50

(B76-50145)

MMJ — Miscellaneous works
Berlioz, Hector
Le Carnival Romain : ouverture caractéristique à grande orchestre.
Op.9 / [by] Hector Berlioz ; foreword by John Warrack. —
London : Eulenburg, 1972. — viii,59p ; 8vo.
Miniature score.
Unpriced

(B76-50146)

Davies, Peter Maxwell
Worldes blis : motet for orchestra on a thirteenth century English
monody / [by] Peter Maxwell Davies. — London : Boosey and
Hawkes, 1975. — 151p ; fol.
A facsimile of the composer's autograph.
£10.00

(B76-50147)

Delius, Frederick
Dance rhapsody no.2 / [by] Frederick Delius ; corrected by
Robert Threlfall. — London : Stainer and Bell, 1976. — 33p ;
8vo.
ISBN 0-85249-458-0 : Unpriced

(B76-50872)

Delius, Frederick
Eventyr. Once upon time, after Asbjornsen's folklore / by
Frederick Delius ; corrected by Robert Threlfall. — London :
Stainer and Bell, 1976. — 50p ; 8vo.
Study score.
ISBN 0-85249-398-3 : Unpriced

(B76-50148)

Delius, Frederick
North country sketches / [by] Frederick Delius ; corrected by
Robert Threlfall. — London : Stainer and Bell, 1976. — 76p ;
8vo.
ISBN 0-85249-457-2 : Unpriced

(B76-50873)

Hartmann, Karl Amadeus
[Sinfoniae drammaticae, T1.2]. Symphonische Hymnen : für
grosses Orchester / [von] Karl Amadeus Hartmann. — Mainz ;
London : Schott, 1976. — 188p ; 4to.
Study score, with a preface by Andrew D. McCredie.
£11.00

(B76-50524)

Killmayer, Wilhelm
Nachtgedanken : für Orchester / [von] Wilhelm Killmayer. —
Mainz ; London : Schott, 1976. — 52p ; fol.
Study score. — Duration 15 min.
£7.30

(B76-50149)

Liszt, Franz
[Symphonic poem, no.2. Tasso, lamento e trionfo]. Tasso, lamento
e trionfo / [by] Franz Liszt ; revised and with foreword by
Humphrey Searle. — London : Eulenburg, 1976. — x,92p ; 8vo.
— (Edition Eulenburg ; no.448)
Miniature score.
Unpriced

(B76-50874)

Liszt, Franz
Symphonic poem no.4. Orpheus / [by] Franz Liszt ; foreword by
Humphrey Searle. — London : Eulenburg, 1976. — ix,43p ; 8vo.
— (Edition Eulenburg ; no.450)
Miniature score.
Unpriced

(B76-50525)

Liszt, Franz
[Symphonic poem no.5. Prometheus]. Prometheus / [by] Franz
Liszt ; foreword by Humphrey Searle. — London : Eulenburg,
1976. — ix,76p ; 8vo. — (Edition Eulenburg ; no.451)
Miniature score.
Unpriced

(B76-50526)

Liszt, Franz
Symphonic poem no.7. Festklange / [by] Franz Liszt ; revised
with corrections and foreword by Humphrey Searle. — London :
Eulenburg, 1976. — vi,126p ; 8vo. — (Edition Eulenburg ; no.453)
Miniature score.
Unpriced

(B76-50527)

Liszt, Franz
[Symphonic poem no.8 Héroïde funèbre]. Héroïde funèbre / [by]
Franz Liszt ; revised and with foreword by Humphrey Searle. —
London : Eulenburg, 1976. — xii,56p ; 8vo. — (Edition
Eulenburg ; no.454)
Miniature score.
Unpriced

(B76-50875)

Liszt, Franz
[Symphonic poem, no.9. Hungaria]. Hungaria / [by] Franz Liszt.
— Revised ed. / edited with foreword by Humphrey Searle. —
London : Eulenburg, 1976. — vii,120p ; 8vo. — (Edition
Eulenburg ; no.455)
Miniature score.
Unpriced

(B76-50150)

Liszt, Franz
[Symphonic poem, no.10. Hamlet]. Hamlet / [by] Franz Liszt ;
revised and with foreword by Humphrey Searle. — London :
Eulenburg, 1976. — vi,48p ; 8vo. — (Edition Eulenburg ; no.456)
Miniature score.
Unpriced

(B76-50876)

Liszt, Franz
[Symphonic poem, no.12. Die Ideale]. Die Ideale / [by] Franz
Liszt. — Revised ed. / edited with foreword by Humphrey Searle.
— London : Eulenburg, 1976. — ix,119p ; 8vo. — (Edition
Eulenburg ; no.458)
Miniature score.
Unpriced

(B76-50151)

Liszt, Franz
[Symphonic poem, no.13, 'Von der Wiege bis zum Grabe']. Von
der Wiege bis zum Grabe = From the cradle to the grave :
symphonic poem, no.13 / [by] Franz Liszt ; foreword by
Humphrey Searle. — London : Eulenburg, 1976. — vi,24p ; 8vo.
— (Edition Eulenburg ; no.600)
Miniature score.
Unpriced

(B76-50152)

Liszt, Franz
[Two episodes from Lenau's Faust]. Procession by night, and,
Mephisto waltz / [by] Franz Liszt ; foreword by Robert Collet. —
London : Eulenburg, 1976. — xvii,102p ; 8vo. — (Edition
Eulenburg ; no.1361)
Miniature score.
Unpriced

(B76-50528)

Lombardo, Mario
Drakestail : a symphonic fairy tale for children / by Mario
Lombardo ; narration adapted from a French fairy tale by Adele
Lombardo. — New York ; [London] : Chappell, 1976. — 80p ;
4to.
Unpriced

(B76-50529)

Rossini, Gioacchino Antonio
[Guillaume Tell. Overture]. Overture to the opera 'Guillaume
Tell' / by Gioacchino Rossini ; edited by Percival R. Kirby. —
London : Eulenburg, 1976. — ix,66p ; 8vo. — (Edition
Eulenburg ; no.616)
Miniature score.
Unpriced

(B76-50530)

Schafer, Robert Murray
Son of Heldenleben / [by] Robert Murray Schafer. — Toronto ;
London : Universal, 1976. — 31p ; fol.
For orchestra with tape recorder. — Incorporates material from 'Ein
Heldenleben' by Richard Strauss.
Unpriced

(B76-50531)

Schuller, Gunther
Seven studies on themes of Paul Klee : for orchestra / by Gunther
Schuller. — London : Universal, 1975. — 60p ; 8vo.
Study score.
Unpriced

(B76-50153)

Smetana, Bedřich
[My fatherland. Sárka]. Má vlast : a cycle of symphonic poems /
[by] Bedřich Smetana. — London : Eulenburg.
No.3 : Sarka / foreword by John Clapham. — 1976. — xi,84p ; 8vo. —
(Edition Eulenburg ; no.473)
Miniature score.
Unpriced

(B76-50877)

Stekel, Erich Paul
Ouverture pour une tragedie classique. Opus 9 / [par] Eric-Paul
Stekel. — London : Paterson, 1976. — 46p ; 8vo.
Study score.
£1.50

(B76-50532)

MMK — Arrangements
Boccherini, Luigi
[Quintet, strings, op.30, no.6, in C major. Ritirata. *arr*]. Quattro
versioni originale della 'Ritirata notturna di Madrid' / di L.
Boccherini ; sovrapposte e trascritte per orchestra [di] Luciano
Berio. — London : Universal, 1975. — 36p ; fol.
Unpriced

(B76-50154)

MP — WORKS FOR SOLO INSTRUMENT (S) & ORCHESTRA
MPNVPNSE — Woodwind & string quartet & orchestra. Symphonies
Gál, Hans
Symphony no.4 (Sinfonia concertante) : for flute, clarinet, violin,
violoncello and small orchestra. Op.105 / [by] Hans Gál. —
Hamburg ; London : Simrock, 1975. — 90p ; 8vo.
Study score. — Duration 38 min.
£4.00

(B76-50155)

MPQ — Piano & orchestra
Henze, Hans Werner
Tristan : preludes for piano, electronic tapes and orchestra / [by]
Hans Werner Henze. — Mainz ; London : Schott, 1975. — 176p ;
4to.
Study score.
£11.00

(B76-50156)

MPQF — Piano & orchestra. Concertos
Delius, Frederick
[Concerto, piano, C minor]. Piano concerto / [by] Frederick
Delius ; revised and edited by Sir Thomas Beecham, reprint edited
by Robert Threlfall. — London : Boosey and Hawkes, 1975. —
68p ; 8vo. — (Hawkes pocket scores ; no.895)
Unpriced

(B76-50157)

Mozart, Wolfgang Amadeus
[Concerto, piano, no.12, K.414, A major]. Piano concerto, A
major. K.414 / [by] Wolfgang Amadeus Mozart. — Revised ed. ;
foreword by Paul Badura-Skoda. — London : Eulenburg, 1976. —
xiv,95p ; 8vo. — (Edition Eulenburg ; no.800)
Miniature score.
Unpriced

(B76-50158)

Mozart, Wolfgang Amadeus
[Concerto, piano, no.26, K.537, D major]. Piano concerto, D
major, K.537 / [by] Wolfgang Amadeus Mozart ; foreword by
Friedrich Blume. — London : Eulenburg, 1976. — x,128p ; 8vo.
— (Edition Eulenburg ; no.719)
Miniature score.
Unpriced

(B76-50878)

MPSF — Violin & orchestra. Concertos
Dvořák, Antonín
[Concerto, violin, op.53, A minor]. Violin concerto, A minor.
Op.53 / [by] Antonín Dvořák ; foreword by Roger Fiske. —
London : Eulenburg, 1976. — vii,130p ; 8vo. — (Edition
Eulenburg ; no.751)
Miniature score.
Unpriced

(B76-50533)

Mozart, Wolfgang Amadeus
[Concerto, violin, no.3, K.216, G major]. Concerto, G major, for
violin and orchestra. K.216 / by Wolfgang Amadeus Mozart ;
edited by Rudolf Geber ; foreword by Roger Fiske. — London :
Eulenburg, 1976. — vii,60p ; 8vo. — (Edition Eulenburg ; no.747)
Miniature score.
Unpriced

(B76-50534)

MPSPLSRF — Violin, cello & orchestra. Concertos
Delius, Frederick
[Concerto, violin & cello]. Concerto for violin & violoncello / by
Frederick Delius ; corrected by Robert Threlfall. — London :
Stainer and Bell, 1976. — 55p ; 8vo.
Study score.
ISBN 0-85249-399-1 : Unpriced

(B76-50159)

MPSRF — Cello & orchestra. Concertos
Dvořák, Antonín
[Concerto, cello, op.104, B minor]. Cello concerto, B minor.
Op.104 / [by] Antonín Dvořák ; revised with corrections by Roger
Fiske and Norman Del Mar ; foreword by Roger Fiske. —
London : Eulenburg, 1976. — viii,104p ; 8vo.
Miniature score.
Unpriced

(B76-50535)

Saint-Saëns, Camille
[Concerto, cello, no.1, op.33, A minor]. Concerto no.1, A minor
for violoncello and orchestra. Op.33 / [by] Camille Saint-Saëns ;
foreword by Hans-Hubert Schönzeler. — London : Eulenburg,
1976. — 67p ; 8vo.
Miniature score.
Unpriced

(B76-50160)

MPVR — Flute & orchestra
Antoniou, Theodore
Katharsis : for flute, small orchestra, slide projections and groups
of loudspeakers / [by] Theodore Antoniou ; after T.S. Tolia's
poems with illustrations by Andreou. — Cassel ; London :
Bärenreiter, 1975. — 26p ; 4to.
£4.25

(B76-50536)

Fortner, Wolfgang
Prismen : für Soloinstrumente, (Flöte, Oboe, Klarinette in B,
Harfe, Schlagzeug) und Orchester [von] Wolfgang Fortner. —
Mainz ; London : Schott, 1976. — 61p ; fol.
Study score.
£11.20

(B76-50879)

MPVTE — Oboe & orchestra. Symphonies
Berkeley, *Sir* Lennox
[Sinfonia concertante, oboe & chamber orchestra, op.84]. Sinfonia
concertante for oboe and chamber orchestra. Op.84 / [by] Lennox
Berkeley. — London : Chester, 1976. — 79p ; 8vo.
Miniature score.
Unpriced

(B76-50880)

MPVTF — Oboe & orchestra. Concertos
Baird, Tadeusz
[Concerto, oboe]. Konzert für Oboe und Orchester / [von]
Tadeusz Baird. — Frankfurt : Litolff ; London : Peters, 1975. —
42p ; fol.
Study score.
Unpriced

(B76-50161)

MR — WORKS FOR CHAMBER ORCHESTRA
MR/T — Variations
Hamilton, Iain
Arias : for small orchestra / [by] Iain Hamilton. — London :
Schott, 1975. — 45p ; 8vo.
Miniature score.
Unpriced

(B76-50162)

MRE — Symphonies
Bach, Johann Christian
[Symphony, D major]. Sinfonie, D-Dur / [von] Johann Christian
Bach ; herausgegeben von Walter Lebermann. — Mainz ;
London : Schott, 1976. — 24p ; 4to. — (Concertino ; 9)
£4.00

(B76-50881)

Cambini, Giovanni Giuseppe
[Symphony, D major]. Sinfonie D-dur für Kammerorchester /
[von] Giovanni Cambini. — Zum ersten Mal / herausgegeben von
Bernhard Päuler. — Frankfurt : Litolff ; London : Peters, 1976.
— 56p ; 4to. — (Sinfonietta)
Unpriced

(B76-50882)

MRG — Suites
Britten, Benjamin, *Baron Britten*
Suite on English folk tunes, 'A time there was ...' Op.90 : for
orchestra / [by] Benjamin Britten. — London : Faber Music,
1976. — 57p ; fol.
Duration 14 min. — Founded on tunes published in Playford's 'The dancing
master' - Facsimile of the composer's autograph.
Unpriced

(B76-50163)

NU — WIND, STRINGS & KEYBOARD
NUPNS — Woodwind, strings & keyboard. Quartets
Couperin, François
L'Apothéose de Lulli : for 2 flutes/oboes/violins basse d'archet
and b, c / [by] François Couperin ; edited by Edward
Higginbottom. — London : Musica rara, 1976. — 4to.
Score (40p.) & 3 parts.
Unpriced

(B76-50537)

NURNTF — Flute, strings & keyboard trio. Concertos
Pergolesi, Giovanni Battista
[Concerto, flute, two violins & continuo, D major]. Concerto per il
flauto solo, 2 violini e basso continuo (D-dur) / [von] Battista
Pergolesi, herausgegeben von Herbert Kolbel. — Wilhelmshaven :
Heinrichshofen ; London : Peters, 1975. — 4to.
Score (18p.) & 3 parts. — Although ascribed to Pergolesi in this publication,
this work is now generally regarded as spurious.
Unpriced

(B76-50164)

NUVNT — Clarinet, strings & keyboard. Trios
Hannay, Roger
Fantôme : clarinet in B flat, viola, piano / [by] Roger Hannay. —
New York : Henmar Press : Peters ; London : Peters, 1976. —
22p ; obl.fol.
Duration 12 min.
Unpriced

(B76-50883)

NUXTNT — Horn, strings & keyboard. Trios
Josephs, Wilfred
Trio for horn, violin and piano. Opus 76 / [by] Wilfred Josephs.
— Sevenoaks : Novello, 1975. — 4to.
Score (49p.) & 2 parts. — Duration 18 min.
Unpriced

(B76-50165)

NV — WIND & STRINGS
Bedford, David
With 100 kazoos / [by] David Bedford. — London : Universal,
1975. — 44p ; obl. 4to.
Duration 18 min. — For wind & string ensemble.
Unpriced

(B76-50166)

NVNT — Trios
Schuller, Gunther
[Trio, oboe, horn, viola]. Trio for oboe, horn and viola / [by]
Gunther Schuller. — New York ; London : Associated Music,
1975. — 4to.
Score (15p.) & 3 parts.
Unpriced

(B76-50167)

NVRNT — Flute & strings. Trios
Balada, Leonardo
Tresis : for guitar, flute (or violin) and cello / [by] Leonardo
Balada. — New York ; London : Schirmer, 1975. — 12p ; 4to.
Unpriced
Also classified at RWNT

(B76-50168)

NVTNS — Oboe & strings. Quartets
Tate, Phyllis
The rainbow and the cuckoo : for oboe and string trio / [by]
Phyllis Tate. — London : Oxford University Press, 1976. — 46p ;
8vo.
Facsimile of the composer's autograph. — Duration 18 min.
ISBN 0-19-359024-7 : Unpriced

(B76-50884)

NVTNT — Oboe & strings. Trios
Bennett, Richard Rodney
Quartet, oboe & string trio / [by] Richard Rodney Bennett. —
Sevenoaks : Novello, 1976. — 30p ; 8vo.
£1.70

(B76-50538)

NWNT — Wind & keyboard. Trios
Spiegler, Matthias
[Olor solymaeus. Canzon à 2]. Canzon à 2 for cornetto
(recorder-trumpet), bassoon (cello-rackett), & basso continuo /
[by] Matthias Spiegler ; edited by Curtis Wright and Robert Paul
Block. — London : Musica rara, 1975. — 4to.
Score (9p.) & 3 parts.
Unpriced

(B76-50539)

NWNTE — Trios. Sonatas
Loeillet, Jean Baptiste, *of London*
[Sonata, treble recorder, oboe & continuo, op.4, no.2]. Sonata a tre
con fluto e hautboy : for treble recorder, oboe (or treble II) and
continuo / [by] J.B. Loeillet ; edited and figured bass realised by
Layton Ring. — London : Universal, 1975. — 4to. — (Dolmetsch
recorder series ; no.100)
Score (14p.) & 3 parts.
Unpriced

(B76-50885)

NWPNT — Woodwind & keyboard. Trios
Bevan, Clifford
Trois ésquisses : for flute/piccolo, oboe and harpsichord / [by]
Clifford Bevan. — London : British and Continental : EMI, 1975.
— 4to.
Score (15p.) & 2 parts.
Unpriced

(B76-50169)

NX — STRINGS & KEYBOARD
NXNQ — Sextets
Bassett, Leslie
Sextet, piano and strings / [by] Leslie Bassett. — New York ;
London : Peters, 1975. — 4to
Score (30p.) & 5 parts. — Duration 19 min.
Unpriced

(B76-50170)

NXNRG — Quintets. Suites
Fischer, Johann Caspar Ferdinand
[Le Journal de printemps. Partie 3, 4]. Suiten = Suites for four
strings or wind instruments and basso continuo / [by] Johann
Caspar Ferdinand Fischer ; edited by Waldemar Woehl. —
Cassel ; London : Bärenreiter, 1976. — 4to. — (Hortus musicus ;
227)
Score (32p.) & 7 parts. — Contents: 1: Suite 3 in B flat - 2: Suite 4 in D
minor.
£6.00

(B76-50540)

NXNS — Quartets
Dawe, Margery
Circus scenes : six rhythmic pieces for strings and piano
accompaniment / by Margery Dawe. — London : Cramer, 1976.
— 4to & obl. 8vo.
Score (9p.) & 3 parts.
£0.93
Also classified at SPJ; SQPJ; SRPJ

(B76-50541)

Walton, *Sir* **William**
[Quartet, strings & piano]. Quartet for violin, viola, cello and
piano / by William Walton. — Revised ed. — London : Oxford
University Press, 1976. — 4to.
Score (74p.) & 3 parts.
ISBN 0-19-359414-5 : Unpriced

(B76-50171)

NXNSE — Quartets. Sonatas
Purcell, Henry
[Sonatas, string trio & continuo, no.7-12, Z.796-801]. Sonatas of
three parts, no.7-12 / [by] Henry Purcell ; edited with a foreword
by Roger Fiske. — London : Eulenburg, 1976. — xxi,43p ; 8vo.
— (Edition Eulenburg ; no.1354)
Miniature score.
Unpriced

(B76-50172)

NXNT — Trios
Jenkins, John
[Fantasia, viols (2) & organ, A minor]. Fantasia, suite 5 : for
violin (or treble viol), bass viol (or violoncello) and organ (or
harpsichord) / by John Jenkins ; edited by Christopher Field. —
London : Oxford University Press, 1976. — 4to. — (Musica da
camera ; no.37)
Score (9p.) & 2 parts.
ISBN 0-19-357410-1 : Unpriced

(B76-50886)

NXNTE — Trios. Sonatas
Leclair, Jean Marie, *b.1697*
[Sonata, violins (2) & continuo, op.13. no.1]. Two trio sonatas for
two violins and basso continuo / by Jean Marie Leclair l'aîné ;
edited by Graham Sadler. — London : Oxford University Press,
1976. — 4to. — (Musica da camera ; no.38)
Score (26p.) & 6 parts ; the parts for the ouverture and the sonata are
printed separately.
ISBN 0-19-357612-0 : Unpriced
(B76-50887)

Purcell, Henry
[Works]. The works of Henry Purcell. — Sevenoaks : Novello.
Vol.5 : Twelve sonatas of three parts / edited by Michael Tilmouth. —
1976. — xix,60p ; 8vo.
£10.00
(B76-50173)

NYD — WIND, STRINGS, KEYBOARD & PERCUSSION
NYDPNQ — Woodwind, strings, keyboard & percussion. Sextets
Davies, Peter Maxwell
Ave maris stella / [by] Peter Maxwell Davies. — London : Boosey
and Hawkes, 1976. — 33p ; 4to.
For instrumental sextet. — Facsimile of the composer's manuscript.
£2.50
(B76-50542)

NYE — WIND, STRINGS & PERCUSSION
NYESK/AAY — Recorders, strings & percussion. Arrangements.
Collections
Primary music groups / arranged and compiled by Dick Sadleir. —
London : British and Continental : EMI, 1975. — 35p ; 4to.
For recorders, percussion and guitar. — Includes notes on instruments
employed.
Unpriced
(B76-50174)

NYF — WIND, KEYBOARD & PERCUSSION
NYFNPF — Septets. Concertos
Orff, Carl
Kleines Konzert nach Lautensätzen aus dem 16. Jahrhundert =
Little concerto based on lute pieces from the 16th century : for
flute, oboe, bassoon, trumpet, trombone, harpsichord and
percussion / [by] Carl Orff. — New ed. — Mainz ; London :
Schott, 1975. — 4to.
Score (23p.) & 7 parts.
£9.00
(B76-50175)

NYFVNT — Clarinet, keyboard & percussion. Trios
Finney, Rose Lee
Two acts for three players : clarinet, percussion, piano / [by] Rose
Lee Finney. — New York : Henmar Press : Peters ; London :
Peters, 1975. — 4to.
Score (46p.) & 2 parts.
Unpriced
(B76-50176)

NYG — STRINGS, KEYBOARD & PERCUSSION
McLaughlin, John
John McLaughlin and the Mahavishnu Orchestra. — New York :
Warner-Tamerlane ; [London] : [Blossom], 1976. — 152p ; 4to.
Also contains some vocal pieces.
Unpriced
(B76-50888)

NYH — WIND & PERCUSSION
NYHNT — Trios
Maves, David
Oktoechos : B flat clarinet, horn in F and percussion / [by] David
Maves. — New York : Henmar Press : Peters ; London : Peters,
1975. — 8p ; 4to. — (American music awards series)
Duration 9 min.
Unpriced
(B76-50177)

NYL — KEYBOARD & PERCUSSION
NYLNU — Duets
Lumsdaine, David
Kangaroo hunt : for piano and percussion / [by] David
Lumsdaine. — Sydney ; London : Universal, 1975. — s.sh ; fol.
Two copies.
Unpriced
(B76-50178)

PWP — KEYBOARD SOLOS
PWP/AZ — Collected works of individual composers
Musica Britannica : a national collection of music. — 2nd, revised
ed. — London : Stainer and Bell.
Vol.28 : William Byrd : Keyboard music 2 / transcribed and edited by Alan
Brown. — 1976. — xxii,211p ; fol.
ISBN 0-85249-426-2 : Unpriced
Primary classification C/AYD
(B76-50359)

PWPJ — Miscellaneous works
Bartolino da Padova
[Madrigals. *Selections : arr*]. Three madrigals for keyboard / [by]
Bartolino da Padova ; edited by Stanley Boorman. — Newton
Abbott : Antico, 1976. — 14p ; 4to.
An accompanying volume contains the original madrigals from which these
transcriptions are taken. — Contents: 1: Qual lege move - 2: Imperial
sedendo - 3: La dolce sere.
Unpriced
(B76-50543)

Hook, James
[Guida di musica. *Selections*]. A James Hook album : twenty-two
easy keyboard pieces / edited by Eve Barsham. — Sevenoaks :
Elkin, 1975. — 29p ; 4to.
£0.90
(B76-50179)

Q — PIANO
Q/AC — Tutors
Kirkby-Mason, Barbara
First album for piano / by Barbara Kirkby-Mason. — Revised ed.
— London : Bosworth.
Part 1. — 1976. — 24p ; 4to.
Unpriced
(B76-50889)

Part 3. — 1976. — 23p ; 4to.
Unpriced
(B76-50890)

Phillips, Lois
The little piano book : a new way to start / by Lois Phillips. —
London : Forsyth, 1975. — [2],70p ; obl.8vo.
Keyboard chart inserted.
Unpriced
(B76-50180)

Q/AF — Exercises
Lachert, Piotr
Etudes intelligentes : for beginners at the piano / [by] Piotr
Lachert ; with an introduction by Franzpeter Goebels. — Cassel ;
London : Bärenreiter, 1976. — viii,46p ; 4to.
£5.00
(B76-50544)

Q/AF/AL — Exercises. Examinations
Guildhall School of Music and Drama pianoforte examinations,
scales and broken chords : grade one and grade two. — South
Croydon : Lengnick, 1975. — 10p ; obl.8vo.
£0.50
(B76-50181)

Guildhall School of Music
Examinations, scales and arpeggios for pianoforte playing : grades
3, 4, 5, 6 and 7. — Croydon : Lengnick, 1976. — 23p ; 4to.
£0.95
(B76-50545)

Q/AL — Examinations
Associated Board of the Royal Schools of Music
Pianoforte examinations, 1977. — London : Associated Board of
the Royal Schools of Music.
Grade 1 : Lists A and B (primary). — 1976. — 12p ; 4to. —
£0.50
(B76-50546)

Grade 2 : Lists A and B (elementary). — 1976. — 14p ; 4to. —
£0.50
(B76-50547)

Grade 3 : Lists A and B (transitional). — 1976. — 14p ; 4to. —
£0.50
(B76-50548)

Grade 4 : Lists A and B (lower). — 1976. — 12p ; 4to. —
£0.50
(B76-50549)

Grade 5 : List A (higher). — 1976. — 12p ; 4to. —
£0.50
(B76-50550)

Grade 5 : List B (higher). — 1976. — 11p ; 4to. —
£0.50
(B76-50551)

Grade 6 : List A (intermediate). — 1976. — 14p ; 4to. —
£0.50
(B76-50552)

Grade 6 : List B (intermediate). — 1976. — 15p ; 4to. —
£0.50
(B76-50553)

Grade 7 : List A (advanced). — 1976. — 16p ; 4to. —
£0.50
(B76-50554)

Grade 7 : List B (advanced). — 1976. — 17p ; 4to. —
£0.50

(B76-50555)

London College of Music
Examinations in pianoforte playing. — London : Ashdown.
Grade 1 (primary), Book II. — 1976. — 11p ; 4to. —
£0.50

(B76-50556)

London College of Music
Examinations in pianoforte playing / London College of Music. —
London : Edwin Ashdown.
Grade 2, Book 9. — 1976. — 11p ; 4to. —
Unpriced

(B76-50893)

London College of Music
Introductory examinations in pianoforte playing in three steps. —
London : Ashdown.
Step 2, Book 5. — 1976. — 4p ; 4to. —
£0.30

(B76-50557)

Q/EG/AL — Sight reading. Examinations
London College of Music
Examinations in pianoforte playing and singing sight reading
tests : sight singing tests as set throughout 1975. — London :
Ashdown, 1976. — 15p ; 4to.
Unpriced
Also classified at K/EG/AL

(B76-50182)

QNU — TWO PIANOS, 4 HANDS
Lumsdaine, David
Flights : for 2 pianos / [by] David Lumsdaine. — Sydney ;
London : Universal, 1975. — 11pt ; 4to & obl. 4to.
Unpriced

(B76-50183)

QNUHW — Waltzes
Brahms, Johannes
[Waltzes, piano 2 hands, op.39]. Walzer für Klavier zu zwei
Händen. Opus 39 / [von] Johannes Brahms ; herausgegeben von
Carl Seemann ; musikwissenschaftliche Revision von Kurt
Stephenson. — Frankfurt : Litolff ; London : Peters, 1974. —
19p ; 4to.
Unpriced

(B76-50558)

QNUK/LF — Arrangements. Concertos
Delius, Frederick
[Concerto, piano, C minor. *arr*]. Piano concerto / [by] Frederick
Delius ; edited by Sir Thomas Beecham, reduction for two pianos
by Otto Singer, solo part arranged by Theodor Szántó. —
London : Boosey and Hawkes, 1975. — [4],43p ; 4to.
Revised by Robert Threlfall.
Unpriced

(B76-50184)

Tchaikowsky, André
[Concerto, piano, op.4. *arr*]. Concerto for piano and orchestra,
Op.4 / [by] André Tchaikowsky ; reduction for two pianos. —
London : Weinberger, 1975. — 79p ; 4to.
Unpriced

(B76-50185)

QNV — ONE PIANO, 4 HANDS
O'Brien, Eugene
Ambages : for piano, four hands / [by] Eugene O'Brien. — New
York ; London : Schirmer, 1975. — 23p ; obl. fol.
Unpriced

(B76-50186)

QNV/AZ — Collected works of individual composers
Brahms, Johannes
[Piano music, four hands]. Complete piano works for four hands /
[by] Johannes Brahms ; edited by Eusebius Mandyczewski. —
New York : Dover Publications ; London : Constable, 1976. — [4]
,217p ; 4to.
From 'Johannes Brahms, sämtliche Werke, Ausgabe der Gesellschaft der
Musikfreunde in Wien, Band 12, Werke für Klavier zu vier Händen'. —
Editor's preface and table of contents translated for present edition.
ISBN 0-486-23271-9 : £3.50

(B76-50894)

QP — PIANO SOLOS
QP/AYM — Collections. Russia
Russian masters : for piano. — London : EMI, 1976. — 80p ; 4to.
Some pieces edited and fingered by various editors.
Unpriced

(B76-50895)

QP/AZ — Collected works of individual composers
Brahms, Johannes
[Piano music]. Klavierwerke / [von] Johannes Brahms ;
herausgegeben von Carl Seemann ; Musikwissenschaftliche
Revision von Kurt Stephenson. — Frankfurt : Litolff ; London :
Peters.
Urtext.
Band 1. — 1974. — 92p ; 4to.
Unpriced

(B76-50559)

Band 2. — 1974. — 92p ; 4to.
Unpriced

(B76-50560)

Ireland, John
[Piano music]. The collected piano works of John Ireland /
foreword by Geoffrey Bush. — London : Stainer and Bell.
Vol.1. — 1976. — 81p ; 4to.
ISBN 0-85249-393-2 : Unpriced

(B76-50187)

Vol.2. — 1976. — 71p ; 4to.
ISBN 0-85249-394-0 : Unpriced

(B76-50188)

Vol.3. — 1976. — 67p ; 4to.
ISBN 0-85249-395-9 : Unpriced

(B76-50189)

QP/AZ — Collected works of indivudual composers
Liszt, Franz
[Piano music]. Klavierwerke = Piano works / [by] Franz Liszt.
— Cassel ; London : Bärenreiter.
Vol.8 : Années de pèlerinage 3 / edited by Imre Sulyok, Imre Mezö ;
fingering revised by Kornél Zempléni. — 1975. — xii,47p ; 4to.
£3.00

(B76-50561)

QP/JS — Television
McCabe, John
Couples : theme music from the Thames Television series, for
piano solo / by John McCabe. — Sevenoaks : Novello, 1976. —
3p ; 4to.
Unpriced

(B76-50190)

QP/R — Harmony
Morris, Reginald Owen
Figured harmony at the keyboard / [by] R.O. Morris. —
London : Oxford University Press.
The 1933 ed. published in two parts.
Part 1. — 1976. — 57p ; 4to.
ISBN 0-19-321471-7 : £0.75

(B76-50896)

Part 2. — 1976. — 30p ; 4to.
ISBN 0-19-321472-5 : Unpriced

(B76-50897)

QPE — Sonatas
Bach, Johann Christian
[Sonatas, piano. *Selections*]. Twelve keyboard sonatas / [by] J.C.
Bach ; a facsimile edition with an introduction by Christopher
Hogwood. — London : Oxford University Press.
Set 1, Opus 5. — 1976. — [6],34p ; obl.4to.
Facsimile of the Welchter edition of c.1768.
ISBN 0-19-372222-4 : Unpriced

(B76-50191)

Set 2, Opus 17. — 1976. — [6],41p ; obl.4to.
Facsimile of the Preston edition of c.1785.
ISBN 0-19-372223-2 : Unpriced

(B76-50192)

Schonthal, Ruth
Sonata breve : for piano / [by] Ruth Schonthal. — New York ;
[London] : Oxford University Press, 1976. — 8p ; 4to.
Unpriced

(B76-50193)

Wilson, Robert Barclay
[Sonata, piano]. Sonata for piano / [by] Robert Barclay Wilson. —
London : Cramer, 1975. — 12p ; 4to.
£0.45

(B76-50194)

QPEM — Sonatinas
Howells, Herbert
[Sonatina, piano]. Sonatina for piano / [by] Herbert Howells. —
London : Associated Board of the Royal Schools of Music, 1976.
— 22p ; 4to.
£0.80

(B76-50898)

Winters, Geoffrey
[Sonatina, piano, op.29]. Sonatina for piano. Op.29 / by Geoffrey
Winters. — London : Chappell, 1976. — 15p ; 4to.
Unpriced

(B76-50195)

QPG — Suites
Wolford, Darwin
Suite à la mode : fourteen pieces for piano / [by] Darwin Wolford. — New York ; [London] : Boosey and Hawkes, 1976. — 19p ; 4to.
£2.00

(B76-50562)

QPH — Dances
Debussy, Claude
Danse bohémiénne : piano solo / [by] Claude Debussy ; edited by H. Swarsenski. — London : Peters, 1975. — 6p ; 4to.
Unpriced

(B76-50196)

Mignone, Francisco
[Caixinha de brinquedos. Dança campestre]. Dança campestre / [de] Francisco Mignone. — Rio de Janeiro : Arthur Napoleão ; [London] : [Essex Music], 1976. — 2p ; 4to.
For piano.
Unpriced

(B76-50899)

QPHW — Waltzes
Ferreira, Oscar Augusto
Clube 15 : celébre valsa / de Oscar Augusto Ferriera. — São Paulo : Seresta ; [London] : [Essex Music], 1975. — 5p ; 4to.
Unpriced

(B76-50563)

Mignone, Francisco
Valsa brasileira no.3 / [de] Francisco Mignone. — Rio de Janeiro : Arthur Napoleão ; [London] : [Essex Music], 1976. — 3p ; 4to.
For piano.
Unpriced

(B76-50900)

Nazareth, Ernesto
Helena : valsa, piano / [de] Ernesto Nazareth. — Rio de Janeiro : Arthur Napoleão ; [London] : [Essex Music], 1976. — 4p ; 4to.
Unpriced

(B76-50901)

QPHX/AC — Jazz. Tutors
Bolling, Claude
Cours d'initiation à la musique de jazz par le piano / [par] Claude Bolling. — Paris ; [London] : Chappell, 1976. — 74p ; 4to.
Unpriced

(B76-50197)

QPHXJ/AY — Ragtime. Collections
Ragtime classics : ten piano rags / selected by Charles Wilford. — Sevenoaks : Paxton, 1976. — 36p ; 4to.
£1.25

(B76-50564)

Ragtime rarities : complete original music for 63 piano rags / selected and with an introduction by Trebor Jay Tichenor. — New York : Dover Publications ; London : Constable, 1975. — xiv,305p ; 4to.
ISBN 0-486-23157-7 : £4.55

(B76-50565)

QPJ — Miscellaneous works
Babbitt, Milton
Post-partitions : piano / [by] Milton Babbitt. — New York ; London : Peters, 1975. — 29p ; 4to.
Unpriced

(B76-50198)

Bach, Carl Philipp Emanuel
[Piano music. *Selections*]. Sieben Hauptwerke aus dem Klavierschaften / von Carl Ph. E. Bach ; revidierte Interpretationsausgabe [von] E. Caland und F.P. Goebels. — Wilhemshaven : Heinrichshofen ; [London] : [Peters], 1975. — 48p ; 4to.
Unpriced

(B76-50566)

Bailey, Freda O
[Rooftop ballet]. Rooftop ballet and Underwater ballet : two piano solos / by Freda O. Bailey. — Leeds : Regina Music, 1976. — 4p ; 4to.
Unpriced

(B76-50902)

Binkerd, Gordon
Essays for piano / [by] Gordon Binkerd. — New York ; [London] : Boosey and Hawkes, 1976. — 32p ; 4to.
£4.00

(B76-50567)

Bonner, Stuart
Trinket : a piano solo / [by] Stuart Bonner. — Kowloon : Sonia Archer ; [South Croydon] : [Lengnick], 1976. — 4p ; 4to.
Unpriced

(B76-50903)

Boyd, Anne
Angklung : for solo piano / [by] Anne Boyd. — London : Faber Music, 1976. — 6p ; obl. 4to.
Unpriced

(B76-50199)

Cage, John
Etudes Australes : piano / [by] John Cage. — New York ; [London] : Peters.
Books 1 and 2. — 1975. — 33,[2]p ; fol. —
Unpriced

(B76-50568)

Books 3 and 4. — 1975. — 34,65,[3]p ; fol. —
Unpriced

(B76-50569)

Cooper, Joseph
More hidden melodies : six improvisations for piano / by Joseph Cooper ; cartoons by ffolkes. — Sevenoaks : Novello, 1976. — 28p ; 4to.
£1.00

(B76-50570)

Debussy, Claude
Berceuse héroïque : piano solo / [by] Claude Debussy ; edited by H. Swarsenski. — London : Peters, 1975. — 6p ; 4to.
Unpriced

(B76-50200)

Debussy, Claude
D'un cahier d'esquisses : piano solo / [by] Claude Debussy ; edited by H. Swarsenski. — London : Peters, 1975. — 6p ; 4to.
Unpriced

(B76-50201)

Dench, Chris
Helical : for solo piano / [by] Chris Dench. — London (17 Dempster Rd, S.W.18) : The composer, 1976. — 2 leaves ; obl. fol.
Unpriced

(B76-50202)

Elgar, *Sir* **Edward,** *bart*
[In Smyrna]. In Smyrna, and Skizze : piano / [by] Edward Elgar. — Sevenoaks : Novello, 1976. — 8p ; 4to.
Introduction by Jerrold Northrop Moore.
£0.75

(B76-50203)

Ezell, Helen Ingle
When we went to Liza's house : 6 piano pieces / [by] Helen Ingle Ezell. — New York ; [London] : Oxford University Press, 1976. — 11p ; 4to.
Unpriced

(B76-50904)

Françaix, Jean
[Dix pièces enfantines, piano]. Zehn Stücke für Kinder zum Spielen und Träumen, 'De la musique avant toute chose' / dix pièces enfantines pour le piano ; [par] Jean Françaix. — Mainz ; London : Schott, 1976. — 16p ; 4to.
£2.40

(B76-50905)

Franck, César
[Piano music. *Selections*]. Selected piano compositions / [by] César Franck. — New York : Dover Publications ; London : Constable, 1976. — 4to.
ISBN 0-486-23269-7 : Unpriced

(B76-50906)

Gilbert, Anthony
Little piano pieces. Op.20 / [by] Anthony Gilbert. — London : Schott, 1975. — 11p ; 4to.
The first four of these pieces may be performed along with the String quartet, op.20a, to which they were conceived as decorations of the quartet's text. They work equally well as a group for solo performance. — Duration 6 min.
Unpriced

(B76-50204)

Glazunov, Alexander
Deux prélude-improvisations = Two prelude-improvisations : for piano / [by] Alexander Glazunov. — Frankfurt : Belaieff ; [London] : [Peters], 1976. — 12p ; 4to.
Unpriced

(B76-50571)

Globokar, Vinko
Notes : für einen Pianisten / [von] Vinko Globokar. —
Frankfurt : Litolff ; London : Peters, 1975. — 7ff ; obl.fol.
Reproduction of composer's autograph.
Unpriced

(B76-50205)

Gottschalk, Louis Moreau
Le Bannier. Opus 5 : chanson nègre, piano solo / [by] Louis
Moreau Gottschalk. — London : Peters, 1976. — 7p ; 4to.
Unpriced

(B76-50206)

Greene, Arthur
Seven wild mushrooms and a waltz : easy pieces for prepared
piano / by Arthur Greene. — New York : Galaxy ; [London] :
[Galliard], 1975. — 12p ; 4to.
Unpriced

(B76-50572)

Helps, Robert
Nocturne : piano / [by] Robert Helps. — New York ; London :
Peters, 1975. — 16p ; 4to.
Duration 9 min.
Unpriced

(B76-50207)

Hunt, Reginald
Autumn song : piano solo / by Reginald Hunt. — London :
Ashdown, 1976. — 4p ; 4to.
£0.35

(B76-50208)

Laderman, Ezra
Momenti : for piano solo / [by] Ezra Laderman. — New York ;
London : Oxford University Press, 1976. — 15p ; 4to.
Duration 8 min.
Unpriced

(B76-50209)

Liszt, Franz
Liebestraum no.3, [G.298] / [by] Franz Liszt. — London :
Chappell, 1975. — 4p ; 4to. — (Magic piano silhouettes)
Unpriced

(B76-50573)

Lombardi, Nilson
Cantilena no.2 : piano / de Nilson Lombardi. — Rio de Janeiro :
Arthur Napoleão ; [London] : [Essex Music], 1976. — 3p ; 4to.
Unpriced

(B76-50907)

Lombardi, Nilson
Cantilena no.3 : piano / de Nilson Lombardi. — Rio de Janeiro :
Arthur Napoleão ; [London] : [Essex Music], 1976. — 3p ; 4to.
Unpriced

(B76-50908)

Lombardi, Nilson
Homenagem a Ravel : piano / de Nilson Lombardi. — Rio de
Janeiro : Arthur Napoleão ; [London] : [Essex Music], 1976. —
[2]p ; 4to.
Unpriced

(B76-50909)

Lombardi, Nilson
Sex miniaturas : piano / [de] Nilson Lombardi. — Rio de
Janeiro : Arthur Napoleão ; [London] : [Essex Music], 1976. —
11p ; 4to.
Unpriced

(B76-50910)

Lorenzo Fernandez, Oscar
[Recordações da infância. Na beira do rio]. Na beira do rio / [de]
Oscar Lorenzo Fernandez. — Rio de Janeiro : Arthur Napoleão ;
[London] : [Essex Music], 1976. — 2p ; 4to.
For piano.
Unpriced

(B76-50911)

Mancini, Maurice B
Sea of tranquillity : for pianoforte solo / [by] Maurice B. Mancini.
— Leamington Spa : Anthony Music, 1975. — 7p ; 4to.
Unpriced

(B76-50912)

Mignone, Francisco
- e o piano canta, também página para un álbum / [de] Francisco
Mignone. — Rio de Janeiro : Arthur Napoleão ; [London] :
[Essex Music], 1976. — 2p ; 4to.
For piano.
Unpriced

(B76-50913)

Nazareth, Ernesto
Labirinto : chôro, piano / [de] Ernesto Nazareth. — Rio de
Janeiro : Arthur Napoleão ; [London] : [Essex Music], 1976. —
4p ; 4to.
Unpriced

(B76-50914)

Nazareth, Ernesto
Sarambeque : chôro, piano / [de] Ernesto Nazareth. — Rio de
Janeiro : Arthur Napoleão ; [London] : [Essex Music], 1976. —
3p ; 4to.
Unpriced

(B76-50915)

Parke, Dorothy
Tunetime : six easy pieces for the piano / by Dorothy Parke. —
Wendover : Roberton, 1976. — 8p ; 4to.
Unpriced

(B76-50916)

Pickles, Sydney
Events in tune / by Sydney Pickles. — London : EMI, 1976. —
9p ; 4to.
For piano.
Unpriced

(B76-50917)

Satie, Erik
[Piano music. *Selections*]. Children's pieces : for piano / [by] Erik
Satie. — Sevenoaks : Novello, 1976. — 16p ; 4to.
The English translations of Satie's original texts are by Alix MacSweeney. —
Contents: Menus propos enfantins - Enfantillages pittoresques - Peccadilles
importunes.
£0.60

(B76-50210)

Satie, Erik
[Piano music. *Selections*]. Piano album / [by] Erik Satie ; editor ;
Maurice Rogers. — London : Cramer, 1976. — 75p ; 4to.
Unpriced

(B76-50211)

Satie, Erik
[Selections]. An Erik Satie entertainment : a selection of songs and
piano music / compiled and introduced by Peter Dickinson ;
edited by Desmond Ratcliffe. — Sevenoaks : Novello, 1976. —
43p ; 4to.
Comprises piano music, except for Trois Poèmes d'amour.
Unpriced

(B76-50212)

Satie, Erik
Trois gymnopédies : piano solo / [by] Erik Satie ; edited by Roger
Jonns. — London : Leonard, Gould and Bolttler, 1976. — 8p ;
4to.
£0.45

(B76-50213)

Satie, Erik
[Trois gymnopédies]. Trois gymnopédies, [et] Trois gnossiennes /
[par] Erik Satie. — London : United Music, 1976. — 16p ; 4to.
For piano.
Unpriced

(B76-50214)

Schumann, Robert
[Piano music. *Selections*]. Morçeaux choisis à l'usage des mains
petites de la deuxième année de piano (assez facile) à la moyenne
difficulté / [de] Robert Schumann ; doigtes, annotés, commentés
et interprétés par Jacqueline Robin. — Paris ; [London] :
Chappell, 1976. — 28p ; 4to. — (Le Petit concertiste ; no.1)
With 45 r.p.m. grammophone record (CHA 17520).
Unpriced

(B76-50215)

Sullivan, *Sir* Arthur Seymour
[Piano music. *Selections*]. Piano music / [by] Arthur S. Sullivan ;
edited with an introduction and notes by John Parry and Peter
Joslin. — Ilford : Chappell, 1976. — 55p ; 4to.
Unpriced

(B76-50216)

Tate, Phyllis
Explorations around a troubadour song : for piano solo / [by]
Phyllis Tate. — London : Oxford University Press, 1976. — 47p ;
4to.
ISBN 0-19-373809-0 : Unpriced

(B76-50574)

Tjeknavorian, Loris
Nine miniatures : piano solo based on Armenian folk and dance
melodies / [by] Loris Tjeknavorian. — Eastwood : Basil Ramsey ;
Wendover : Roberton, 1976. — 9p ; 4to.
Unpriced

(B76-50575)

Van Appledorn, Mary Jeanne
[Set of five. Improvisation]. Improvisation : for the piano / [by]
Mary Jeanne van Appledorn. — New York ; [London] : Boosey
and Hawkes, 1976. — 2p ; 4to.
Unpriced

(B76-50576)

Waxman, Donald
Fifty études : for piano / [by] Donald Waxman. — New York :
Galaxy ; London : Galliard.
Book 1. — 1976. — 32p ; 4to. —
Unpriced

(B76-50577)

Book 2. — 1976. — 36p ; 4to. —
Unpriced

(B76-50578)

Book 3 : Lower advanced. — 1976. — 35p ; 4to. —
Unpriced

(B76-50891)

QPK — Arrangements
Beethoven, Ludwig van
[Für Elise. G.173. *arr*]. Für Elise / [by] Beethoven ; arranged for
cornet solo with brass band by Edrich Siebert. — Oxted : Paul,
1976. — 8vo.
Conductor 23 parts. — With several copies of various parts.
Unpriced

(B76-50918)

Beethoven, Ludwig van
[Symphony, no.9, op.125, D major, 'Choral'. Freude, schöner
Gotterfunken. *arr*]. Ode to joy : from 'Choral symphony' / [by] L.
van Beethoven. — London : Chappell, 1975. — 3p ; 4to. —
(Magic piano silhouettes)
Unpriced

(B76-50579)

Burt, James
Londonderry air : traditional / arranged by James Burt. —
London : Chappell, 1976. — 3p ; 4to. — (Chappell's evergreen
classics)
Arranged for piano.
Unpriced

(B76-50919)

Debussy, Claude
[Suite bergamasque. Clair de lune. *arr*]. Clair de lune : piano
solo / by Claude Debussy ; arranged by Frank Naylor. —
London : Bosworth, 1976. — 4p ; 4to.
Unpriced

(B76-50920)

Dvořák, Antonín
[Symphony, no.9, op.95, E minor, 'From the new world'. Largo.
arr]. Largo / [by] Antonín Dvořák. — London : Chappell, 1975.
— 4p ; 4to. — (Magic piano silhouettes)
Arranged for piano.
Unpriced

(B76-50580)

The **Henry** Duke piano arrangements of favourite orchestral
classics. — London : EMI, 1976. — 37p ; 4to.
Unpriced

(B76-50921)

Jeffries, George
[Fantasias à 3, viols & keyboard. *arr*]. Four fantasias / by George
Jeffries ; transcribed for keyboard by Peter Aston. — London :
Chappell, 1976. — 19p ; 4to.
Unpriced

(B76-50581)

Liszt, Franz
[Selections. *arr*]. Liszt / transcribed and simplified by Cyril C.
Dalmaine. — Manchester : Warren and Phillips, 1976. — 30p ;
4to.
For piano.
Unpriced

(B76-50582)

Mahler, Gustav
[Selections. *arr*]. Mahler / transcribed and simplified by Cyril C.
Dalmaine. — Manchester : Warren and Phillips, 1976. — 21p ;
4to.
For piano.
Unpriced

(B76-50583)

Mozart, Wolfgang Amadeus
[Symphony no.40, K.550, G minor. First movement : arr]. Mozart
40. — London : Chappell, 1975. — 5p ; 4to. — (Magic piano
silhouettes)
Arranged for piano.
Unpriced

(B76-50584)

Wagner, Richard
[Selections. *arr*]. Wagner / transcribed and simplified by Cyril C.
Dalmaine. — Manchester : Warren and Phillips, 1976. — 33p ;
4to.
For piano.
Unpriced

(B76-50922)

Whittaker, Anthony F
Theme music : single stave edition for organ, piano, guitar / [by]
Anthony F. Whittaker. — Leamington Spa : Anthony Music,
1976. — 11p ; 8vo.
£0.50
Primary classification TSPMK

QPK/AAY — Arrangements. Collections
Most popular finest piano solos : selected from the greatest
composers of all time / compiled by Robert Monroe. —
Carlstadt : Century Music ; [London] : [Phoenix], 1975. — 128p ;
4to. — (Most popular series ; no.10)
Unpriced

(B76-50217)

The **world** of your 100 best tunes. — London : Chappell, 1976. —
203p ; 4to.
Selected by Alan Keith.
Unpriced

(B76-50923)

QPK/AH/H/AYD — Arrangements. Dances for dancing. Collections.
England
Country dance tunes. Sets 3-8, 10 and 11 / collected and arranged
by Cecil J. Sharp. — London : EP Publishing, 1976. — 202p ;
8vo.
Selected from 'Country dance book' originally published 1911-1922.
ISBN 0-7158-1166-5 : £4.00

(B76-50218)

QPK/AHW/JS — Arrangements. Waltzes. Television
Faris, Alexander
The duchess of Duke Street : theme from the BBC television
serial / [by] Alexander Faris. — London : Chappell, 1976. — 5p ;
4to.
For piano.
Unpriced

(B76-50924)

QPK/DP/LF — Arrangements. Carols. Christmas
Oldfield, Mike
In dulci jubilo / arranged [piano] by Mike Oldfield. — London :
Virgin Music : Chappell, 1976. — 7p ; 4to.
Although the music in this publication is ascribed to Bach, no Bach original
is evident in Mike Oldfield's arrangement.
Unpriced

(B76-50219)

QPK/DW — Arrangements. Songs, etc
Puccini, Giacomo
[Operas. *Selections: arr*]. Puccini / transcribed and simplified by
Cyril C. Dalmaine. — Manchester : Warren and Phillips, 1976. —
25p ; 4to.
For piano.
Unpriced

(B76-50585)

QPK/JR — Arrangements. Films
Williams, John, *b.1932*
[Jaws. *Theme: arr*]. Jaws : theme from the film, piano solo /
[arranged] by John Williams. — Croydon : Leeds Music, 1975. —
3p ; 4to.
£0.30

(B76-50220)

QPK/JS — Arrangements. Television
Young, Peter
[Music for Montreal. *arr*]. Music for Montreal : the original BBC
theme music for the 1976 Olympics / by Peter Young. —
London : Chappell, 1976. — 6p ; 4to.
Arranged for piano.
Unpriced

(B76-50586)

QPLXF — Piano & percussion. Concertos
Genzmer, Harald
[Concerto, piano & percussion]. Konzert für Klavier und
Schlagzeug / [von] Harald Genzmer. — Frankfurt : Litolff ;
London : Peters, 1976. — 4to.
Duration 21 min. — Score (45p.) & part.
£14.50(set of pts)

(B76-50925)

QXPE — Carillon solo. Sonatas
    Peeters, Flor
        [Sonatina, carillon, no.2. Op.46]. Sonatina 2. Opus 46 : carillon /
        [by] Flor Peeters. — New York ; London : Peters, 1975. — 7p ;
        4to.
        Duration 6 1/4 min.
        Unpriced
                                                  (B76-50221)

QXPJ — Carillon solo. Miscellaneous works
    Peeters, Flor
        Serenade for carillon. Opus 61 / [by] Flor Peeters. — New York ;
        London : Peters, 1975. — 61p ; 4to.
        Duration 3 1/2 min.
        Unpriced
                                                  (B76-50222)

R — ORGAN
R/AF — Exercises
    Salles, Annita
        A Tecnica na palma da mão : aproximação de elementos que
        compõem a técnica e evolução do estado moderno de órgão / por
        Annita Salles. — São Paulo : Fermata do Brasil ; [London] :
        [Essex Music], 1976. — 70p ; 4to.
        Unpriced
                                                  (B76-50223)

R/AY — Collections
    Organ books / edited by C.H. Trevor. — London : Oxford
    University Press.
        No.5. — 1975. — 32p ; 4to.
        ISBN 0-19-375847-4 : Unpriced
                                                (B76-50224)

        No.6. — 1975. — 32p ; 4to.
        ISBN 0-19-375848-2 : Unpriced
                                                (B76-50225)

    Short and easy pieces for organ / edited by C.H. Trevor. —
    London : Oxford University Press, 1975. — 24p ; 4to.
    ISBN 0-19-375856-3 : Unpriced
                                                (B76-50226)

R/AYC — Collections. Great Britain
    The **cathedral** organist, 1975-1976. — London : Cramer, 1976. —
    30p ; 4to.
        Contents: Works by Michael Nicholas, Christopher Dearnley, Clifford
        Harker, John Sanders, Peter Hurford, Harry Grindle, Noel Rawsthorne and
        Arthur Wills.
    £2.25
                                                (B76-50926)

R/AZ — Collected works of individual composers
    Nares, James
        [Organ music. *Selections*]. Six fugues with introductory
        voluntaries : for the organ or harpsichord / [by] James Nares ;
        facsimile edition with an introduction by Robin Langley. —
        London : Oxford University Press, 1974. — 19p ; obl.4to.
        ISBN 0-19-375611-0 : Unpriced
                                              (B76-50227)

R/T — Variations
    Schroeder, Hermann
        Variationen über den Tonus peregrinus : für Orgel / [von]
        Hermann Schroeder. — Mainz ; London : Schott, 1975. — 21p ;
        4to.
        £2.25
                                              (B76-50228)

R/X — Canons
    Pachelbel, Johann
        [Canon, violins (3) & continuo, D major. *arr*]. Canon in D :
        variations on a ground bass / [by] Johann Pachelbel ; arranged for
        the organ by Frank E. Brown. — London : Cramer, 1976. — 4p ;
        4to. — (St Martin's organ series ; no.15)
        £0.39
                                              (B76-50587)

RE — Sonatas
    Reubke, Julius
        [Sonata, organ 'The 94th psalm']. The 94th psalm. Sonata for
        organ / [by] Julius Reubke ; edited by Daniel Chorzempa. —
        London : Oxford University Press, 1976. — 37p ; 4to.
        ISBN 0-19-375685-4 : Unpriced
                                              (B76-50229)

RF/LF — Concertos. Christmas
    Genzmer, Harald
        Weihnachtskonzert : für Orgel / [von] Harald Genzmer. —
        Frankfurt : Litolff ; London : Peters, 1975. — 28p ; obl.4to.
        Unpriced
                                              (B76-50230)

RHJN — Chaconnes
    Proctor, Charles
        Chaconne for organ / [by] Charles Proctor. — London :
        Weinberger, 1976. — 25p ; obl. 4to.
        Unpriced
                                              (B76-50588)

RJ — Miscellaneous works
    Ashburnham, George
        'Vienna charm' : waltz : an organ solo / composed by George
        Ashburnham. — Sutton (Effingham Close, Sutton) : Ashburnham
        School of Music, 1976. — 7p ; 4to.
        Unpriced
                                              (B76-50589)

    Baker, Richard Charles
        Chorale prelude on 'Christe sanctorum' : organ / [by] Richard C.
        Baker. — Oakville : Frederick Harris Music ; [South Croydon] :
        [Lengnick], 1974. — 4p ; 4to.
        £0.70
                                              (B76-50927)

    Beeson, Jack
        Old hundredth prelude and doxology : music for organ / [by]
        Jack Beeson. — New York ; [London] : Boosey and Hawkes,
        1976. — 7p ; 4to.
        £1.00
                                              (B76-50928)

    Benjamin, Thomas
        Freu'dich sehr : chorale prelude for organ / by Thomas Benjamin.
        — New York : Galaxy ; [London] : [Galliard], 1976. — 5p ; 4to.
        Unpriced
                                              (B76-50590)

    Camilleri, Charles
        Invocation to the Creator : for organ / [by] Charles Camilleri. —
        Wendover : Roberton, 1976. — 15p ; fol.
        Duration 16 min.
        £1.50
                                              (B76-50591)

    Camilleri, Charles
        Missa mundi : for organ / [by] Charles Camilleri ; registration
        indications by Gillian Weir ; and an introduction by Peter
        Serracino-Inglott. — Sevenoaks : Fairfield Music, 1975. — 68p ;
        4to.
        £2.50
                                              (B76-50231)

    Camilleri, Charles
        Wine of peace : for organ / by Charles Camilleri. — Wendover :
        Roberton, 1976. — 4p ; 4to.
        £0.30
                                              (B76-50929)

    Davies, *Sir* Walford
        [Interlude, organ, C major]. Interlude in C for organ solo / [by]
        Walford Davies. — 1st ed. — Eastwood : Ramsey ; Wendover :
        Roberton, 1976. — 7p ; 4to.
        Unpriced
                                              (B76-50592)

    Hummel, Bertold
        Drei marianische Fresken für Orgel = Three Marian frescoes for
        organ / [by] Bertold Hummel. — Hamburg ; London : Simrock.
        1 : Salve regina. — 1976. — 16p ; obl.4to. —
        £3.10
                                              (B76-50930)

        2 : Ave maris stella. — 1976. — 12p ; obl.4to. —
        £2.50
                                              (B76-50931)

        3 : Regina caeli. — 1976. — 16p ; obl.4to. —
        £3.10
                                              (B76-50932)

    Hunt, William
        Six choral preludes for organ / by William Hunt. — London :
        Cramer, 1975. — 20p ; 4to.
        £0.75
                                              (B76-50933)

    Korn, Peter Jona
        [Preludes, organ, op.55]. Vier Präludien für Orgel. Opus 55 /
        [von] Peter Jona Korn. — Frankfurt : Litolff ; London : Peters,
        1976. — 22p ; obl. 4to.
        Unpriced
                                              (B76-50593)

    Michel, Wilfried
        Trakturen für Orgel (Tonband, Mikrophon,
        Kontaktmikrophone) / [von] Wilfried Michel. — Cassel ;
        London : Bärenreiter, 1976. — 20p ; obl.fol.
        £7.00
                                              (B76-50594)

Popplewell, Richard
Puck's shadow : for organ / [by] Richard Popplewell. — London :
Oxford University Press, 1976. — 7p ; 4to.
Duration 3 min.
ISBN 0-19-375657-9 : Unpriced

(B76-50934)

Routh, Francis
Gloria tibi trinitas, Op.29 : a meditation on the Festival of the
Trinity : organ solo / [by] Francis Routh. — London : Boosey
and Hawkes, 1976. — 20p ; 4to.
£1.40

(B76-50595)

Statham, Heathcote
Two posthumous organ pieces / [by] Heathcote Statham. —
Eastwood : Ramsey ; Wendover : Roberton, 1976. — 11p ; 4to.
Contents: 1: Pastorale - 2 : March.
Unpriced

(B76-50596)

Wills, Arthur
Tongues of fire : for organ / [by] Arthur Wills. — London :
Weinberger, 1976. — 18p ; obl. 4to.
Unpriced

(B76-50597)

RK/DP/LF/AY — Arrangements. Carols. Christmas. Collections
Everybody's favourite Christmas carols : for the first time arranged
for piano vocal-easy organ, 25 of the world's best loved Christmas
carols. — London : Wise : Music Sales, 1975. — 39p ; 4to.
ISBN 0-86001-217-4 : £0.95

(B76-50935)

RK/LF/AY — Arrangements. Concertos. Collections
Four eighteenth century concerto movements for organ with and
without pedals / edited by C.H. Trevor. — London : EMI, 1976.
— 16p ; 4to.
Contents: Introduction and allegro, from concerto no.3 / by John Stanley -
Largo and allegro, from concerto no.6 / by John Stanley - Introduction and
allegro, from concerto no.4 / by Thomas Sanders Dupuis - Minuet, from
concerto no.3 / by Thomas Sanders Dupuis.
Unpriced

(B76-50936)

RPLXF — Organ & percussion. Concertos
Genzmer, Harald
[Concerto, organ & percussion]. Konzert für Orgel und
Schlagzeug / [von] Harald Genzmer. — Frankfurt : Litolff ;
London : Peters, 1976. — obl.4to.
Score (32p.) & part.
Unpriced

(B76-50598)

RPV — ELECTRIC ORGANS
RPVK — Arrangements
Suppé, Franz von
[Dichter und Bauer. Overture. *Selections: arr*]. Poet and peasant
overture : (selections) / by Suppé ; arranged for Hammond organ
by Bobby Fisher. — Scarborough : Fisher and Lane, 1976. —
15p ; 4to.
Unpriced

(B76-50937)

Whittaker, Anthony F
Theme music : single stave edition for organ, piano, guitar / [by]
Anthony F. Whittaker. — Leamington Spa : Anthony Music,
1976. — 11p ; 8vo.
£0.50
Primary classification TSPMK

RPVK/AAY — Arrangements. Collections
Leichte Stücke, grosser Meister : elektronische Orgel /
Arrangements mit Angaben zur Registrierung von Jürgen
Sommer. — Cassel : Nagel ; [London] : [Bärenreiter], 1975. —
16p ; 4to.
£1.50

(B76-50599)

RPVK/AHW — Arrangements. Waltzes
Strauss, Johann, b.1825
[An der schönen blauen Donau. Op.314. *arr*]. The blue Danube /
by Johann Strauss ; arranged for Hammond organ by Bobby
Fisher. — Scarborough : Fisher and Lane, 1976. — 12p ; 4to.
Unpriced

(B76-50938)

RPVK/DP/LF/AY — Arrangements. Carols. Christmas. Collections
Happy Christmas for chord organ / arranged by Cecil Bolton and
Jack Moore. — London : EMI, 1976. — 49p ; 4to.
Unpriced

(B76-50939)

Weinachten an der Heimorgel / Lieder und Spielmusiken in
bearbeitungen von Heinrich Riethmuller. — Hamburg ; London :
Anton J. Benjamin.
Band 1. — 1975. — 26p ; 4to.
£1.90

(B76-50600)

Band 2. — 1975. — 27p ; 4to.
£1.90

(B76-50601)

RPVK/DW — Arrangements. Songs, etc
Offenbach, Jacques
[Les Contes d'Hoffmann. Belle nuit. *arr*]. Barcarolle / by
Offenbach ; arranged for Hammond organ by Bobby Fisher. —
Scarborough : Fisher and Lane, 1976. — 5p ; 4to.
£0.30

(B76-50940)

RPVK/DW/AY — Arrangements. Songs, etc. Collections
An **album** of popular tunes for the pianOrgan and 40 and 60 bass
chord organs / arranged by Jack Moore. — London : EMI, 1976.
— 48p ; 4to.
Unpriced

(B76-50941)

Lustige Lieder : für akkordprogrammierte Orgel 1 Manuel
[bearbeitet von] Willi Draths. — Mainz ; London : Schott, 1976.
— 32p ; obl. 8vo.
£1.75

(B76-50232)

**RPVK/DW/G/AYE — Arrangements. Folk songs. Collections.
Germany**
Mein Heimatland : Volkslieder für elektronische Orgel /
neuauswahl von Willi Draths ; Ausgabe mit Akkordsymbolen,
Tastensymbolen für akkordprogrammierte Orgeln, Fingersätzen,
Registrieranweisange, Registrierschema, Akkordgrifftabelle. —
Mainz ; London : Schott, 1976. — 115p ; 4to & obl.4to.
Unpriced

(B76-50942)

RPVK/DW/G/AYE — Arrangements. Folk songs. Germany
Deutsche Volkslieder : für akkordprogrammierte Orgel, 1 Manuel /
[bearbeitung von] Willi Draths. — Mainz ; London : Schott, 1976.
— 32p ; obl. 8vo.
£1.75

(B76-50233)

RS — ACCORDION
RS/AF — Exercises
Wright, Francis
Forty-eight exercises for accordion / [by] Francis Wright. —
Leicester : Charnwood Music, 1976. — 14p ; 4to.
Unpriced

(B76-50943)

RS/EG — Sight reading
Romani, G
Progressive sight reading for accordion students : a collection of
graded exercises / written and compiled by G. Romani. —
Leicester : Charnwood Music.
Book 1 : Stage 1 to stage 5. — 1976. — 29p ; 4to. —
Unpriced

(B76-50944)

Book 2 : Stage 4 to stage 8. — 1976. — 44p ; 4to. —
Unpriced

(B76-50945)

RSPM — UNACCOMPANIED ACCORDION SOLOS
RSPMH — Dances
Watson, Dennis
Dance of the penguins : elementary accordion solo / [by] Dennis
Watson. — Leicester : Charnwood Music, 1976. — [2]p ; 4to.
Unpriced

(B76-50602)

RSPMHW — Waltzes
Farran, Kenneth G
Joyeux : waltz, accordion solo / by Kenneth G. Farran. —
Leicester : Charnwood Music, 1976. — 2p ; 4to.
Unpriced

(B76-50946)

Saint John, A M
Petite ballerina : accordion solo / [by] A.M. Saint John. —
Leicester : Charnwood Music, 1976. — [2]p ; 4to.
Unpriced

(B76-50603)

RSPMJ — Miscellaneous works
St John, A M
April jaunt : elementary accordion solo / [by] A.M. St John. —
Leicester : Charnwood Music, 1976. — 2p ; 4to.
Unpriced

(B76-50604)

RW — STRING INSTRUMENTS
RWMJ — String orchestra (plucked and unplucked). Miscellaneous works
Kagel, Mauricio
    Musi : für Zupforchester / [von] Mauricio Kagel. — London :
    Universal, 1975. — 13p ; 4to.
    Unpriced

(B76-50234)

RWN — STRING ENSEMBLES
RWNT — Trios
Balada, Leonardo
    Tresis : for guitar, flute (or violin) and cello / [by] Leonardo
    Balada. — New York ; London : Schirmer, 1975. — 12p ; 4to.
    Unpriced
    Primary classification NVRNT

(B76-50168)

RXM — STRING ORCHESTRA
RXM/Y — Fugues
Mozart, Wolfgang Amadeus
    [Adagio and fugue, string orchestra, K.546, C minor]. Adagio and
    fugue for strings, C minor. K.546 / [by] Wolfgang Amadeus
    Mozart ; edited by H.F. Redlich. — Revised ed. — London :
    Eulenburg, 1976. — xi,24p ; 8vo. — (Edition Eulenburg ; no.369)
    Miniature score.
    Unpriced

(B76-50947)

Schwarz-Schilling, Reinhard
    [Quartet, strings, F minor. Introduction and fugue. *arr*].
    Introduktion und Fuge für Streichorchester / [von] Reinhard
    Schwarz-Schilling. — London : Bärenreiter, 1976. — 24p ; 8vo. —
    (Taschenpartituren ; 258)
    Miniature score.
    £2.50

(B76-50605)

RXME — Symphonies
Bach, Carl Philipp Emanuel
    [Symphony, string orchestra, no.1, Wotquenne 182/1, G major].
    Sinfonie Nr.1 für Streicher und Basso continuo, G-dur.
    Wotquenne 182/1 / von Carl Philipp Emanuel Bach ;
    Generalbassaussetzung vom herausgeber. — Zum ersten Mal
    herausgegeben von Traugott Fedtke. — Frankfurt : Litolff ; New
    York ; London : Peters, 1975. — 36p ; 4to.
    Unpriced

(B76-50606)

Bach, Carl Philipp Emanuel
    [Symphony, string orchestra, Wotq.182/2, B flat major]. Sinfonie
    nr.2 : für Streicher und Basso continuo, B-Dur, Wotquenne
    182/2 / [von] Carl Philipp Emanuel Bach ; herausgegeben von
    Traugott Fedkte, Generalbassaussetzung von Herausgeber. —
    Frankfurt : Litolff ; London : Peters, 1976. — 36p ; 4to.
    Unpriced

(B76-50607)

Bach, Carl Philipp Emanuel
    [Symphony, string orchestra, no.3, Wotq.182/3].
    Sinfonie nr.3 für Streicher und Basso continuo, C-dur, Wotquenne
    182/3 / [von] Carl Philipp Emanuel Bach ; herausgegeben von
    Traugott Fedtke, Generalbassaussetzung vom Herausgeber. —
    Frankfurt : Litolff ; London : Peters, 1976. — 34p ; 4to.
    Unpriced

(B76-50948)

Bach, Carl Philipp Emanuel
    [Symphony, string orchestra, no.4, Wotq.182/4].
    Sinfonie nr.4 für Streicher und Basso continuo, A-dur, Wotquenne
    182/4 / [von] Carl Philipp Emanuel Bach ; herausgegeben von
    Traugott Fedtke, Generalbassausetzung vom Herausgeber. —
    Frankfurt : Litolff ; London : Peters, 1976. — 36p ; 4to.
    Unpriced

(B76-50949)

RXMEM — Sinfoniettas
Alwyn, William
    Sinfonietta for strings / [by] William Alwyn. — South Croydon :
    Lengnick, 1974. — 54p ; 4to.
    Incorporating a quotation from Act 1 to Alban Berg's opera 'Lulu'.
    Unpriced

(B76-50608)

RXMF/T — Concertos. Variations
McCabe, John
    Concertante variations on a theme of Nicholas Maw : for string
    orchestra / [by] John McCabe. — Sevenoaks : Novello, 1976. —
    105p ; 8vo.
    Study score. — The theme quotes part of Maw's 'Voice of love'.
    £2.25

(B76-50235)

RXMG — Suites
Platts, Kenneth
    Little suite for strings, Op.26 / [by] Kenneth Platts. — London :
    Edwin Ashdown, 1976. — 11p ; 4to.
    £1.00

(B76-50950)

RXMK — Arrangements
Grieg, Edvard
    [Norwegian folksongs and dances. Op.17. *Selections : arr*]. Three
    Norwegian pieces / [by] Edvard Grieg ; arranged for string
    orchestra by Geoffrey Tomlinson. — Sevenoaks : Novello, 1975.
    — 7p ; 4to.
    Unpriced

(B76-50236)

RXMP — SOLO INSTRUMENT (S) & STRING ORCHESTRA
RXMPNYDNN — String, keyboard & percussion octet & string orchestra
Antoniou, Theodore
    Anthithesen, Op.18a : für Helzbläsinstrumente, Trompete, Harfe,
    Schlagzeug, Streichquartett und zwei Streichorchester / [von]
    Theodore Antoniou. — Cassel ; London : Bärenreiter, 1975. —
    55p ; 4to.
    £8.75

(B76-50609)

RXMPNYHNQF — Wind & percussion sextet & string orchestra. Concertos
Telemann, Georg Philipp
    [Concerto, trumpets (3), oboes (2), timpani & string orchestra, D
    major]. Concerto for 3 clarini (trumpets), timpani, 2 oboes,
    strings, and basso continuo / [by] Georg Philipp Telemann ; ed.
    by R.P. Block. — London : Musica rara, 1976. — 4to. —
    (Seventeenth and eighteenth century sonatas, concerti and
    overtures ; no.98)
    Score (24p.) & 14 parts. — With alternative parts for clarinos in B flat and
    D. The part for cello or double bass or bassoon is in duplicate.
    Unpriced

(B76-50610)

RXMPQRF — Harpsichord & string orchestra. Concertos
Bach, Johann Sebastian
    [Concerto, harpsichord & string orchestra, BWV 1052, F minor].
    Concerto, D minor, for harpsichord and string orchestra. BWV
    1052 / [by] Johann Sebastian Bach ; edited by Arnold Schering ;
    foreword by Roger Fiske. — London : Eulenburg, 1975. — ix,
    66p ; 8vo.
    Miniature score.
    Unpriced

(B76-50237)

RXMPSQ — Viola & string orchestra
Dello Joio, Norman
    Lyric fantasias : for viola solo and string orchestra (or string
    quintet) / [by] Norman dello Joio. — New York ; London :
    Associated Music, 1975. — 24p ; 4to.
    Unpriced

(B76-50238)

RXMPVR — Flute & string orchestra
Musgrave, Thea
    Orfeo Z : an improvisation on a theme for solo flute and 15
    strings / [by] Thea Musgrave. — Sevenoaks : Novello, 1976. —
    35p ; 4to.
    Facsimile of composer's score. — Duration 14 min.
    £2.55

(B76-50611)

RXMPVRF — Flute & string orchestra. Concertos
Molter, Johann Melchior
    [Concerto, flute & string orchestra, G major. H.S.315]. Concerto
    in G major for flute, strings and basso continuo, H.S.315 / [by]
    Johann Melchior Molter ; ed. by D. Lasocki, basso continuo
    realization by R.P. Block. — London : Musica rara, 1975. — 4to.
    Score (22p.) & 6 parts.
    Unpriced

(B76-50612)

RXMPWTNTPWF — Horns (2), keyboard & string orchestra. Concertos
Steffan, Joseph Anton
    [Concerto, horns (2), keyboard & string orchestra, D major].
    Concerto in D major for fortepiano, 2 horns and strings / [by]
    Joseph Anton Steffan ; edited by Howard Picton. — London :
    Oxford University Press, for the University of Hull, 1976. — 4to.
    Cadenza selected by the editor from the composer's '90 Cadenze'. — Score
    (95p.) & 6 parts.
    ISBN 0-19-713421-1 : Unpriced

(B76-50613)

RXNR — Quintets

Dalby, Martin
[Quintet, strings]. String quintet, 1972 / [by] Martin Dalby. —
Sevenoaks : Novello, 1976. — 23p ; 4to.
Duration 15 min.
£1.50

(B76-50614)

Mendelssohn, Felix
[Quintet, strings, no.1, op.18, A major]. String quintet, no.1, A
major. Op.18 / [by] Felix Mendelssohn-Bartholdy. — London :
Eulenburg, 1976. — 73p ; 8vo. — (Edition Eulenburg ; no.134)
Miniature score.
Unpriced

(B76-50239)

RXNS — Quartets

Arnold, Malcolm
[Quartet, strings, no.2, op.118]. String quartet no.2, op.118 / [by]
Malcolm Arnold. — London : Faber Music, 1976. — 60p ; 8vo.
Facsimile of the composer's autograph.
Unpriced

(B76-50615)

Arnold, Malcolm
[Quartet, strings, no.2, op.118]. String quartet, no.2, Op.118 / [by]
Malcolm Arnold. — London : Faber Music, 1976. — 4pt ; 4to.
£2.50

(B76-50951)

Babbitt, Milton
[Quartet, strings, no.4]. String quartet, no.4 / [by] Milton Babbitt.
— New York ; London : Peters, 1976. — 73p ; 4to.
Unpriced

(B76-50952)

Borodin, Aleksandr Porfirevich
[Quartet, strings, no.1, A major]. String quartet no.1, A major /
[by] Alexander Borodin ; foreword by David Brown. — London :
Eulenburg, 1976. — v,61p ; 8vo. — (Edition Eulenburg ; no.219)
Miniature score.
Unpriced

(B76-50953)

Crosse, Gordon
Studies for string quartet. Op,34 / [by] Gordon Crosse. —
London : Oxford University Press.
Set 1. — 1976. — 12p ; obl.8vo. —
ISBN 0-19-355972-2 : Unpriced

(B76-50954)

De Smet, Robin
King Charles' pleasure : a fantasy in the olden style for string trio
(or viols) / by Robin de Smet. — London : British and
Continental, 1976. — 4to.
Score (4p.) & 4 parts. — Duration 2 1/2 min.
Unpriced

(B76-50616)

Gilbert, Anthony
[Quartet, strings, op.20a]. String quartet, Op.20a / [by] Anthony
Gilbert. — London : Schott, 1976. — 25p ; 8vo.
Miniature score.
Unpriced

(B76-50617)

Holliger, Heinz
[Quartet, strings]. Streichquartett (1973) / [von] Heinz Holliger.
— Mainz ; London : Schott, 1974. — 44p ; fol.
Study score.
Unpriced

(B76-50955)

Ligeti, György
[Quartet, strings, no.2]. String quartet no.2 / [by] György Ligeti.
— Mainz ; London : Schott, 1976. — 31p ; 4to.
£4.50

(B76-50618)

Luening, Otto
[Quartet, strings, no.2]. String quartet no.2 / [by] Otto Luening.
— New York ; London : Peters, 1976. — 20p ; 4to.
Unpriced

(B76-50956)

McCabe, John
[Quartet, strings, no.2]. String quartet no.2 / [by] John McCabe.
— Sevenoaks : Novello, 1975. — 32p ; 8vo.
A facsimile of the composer's autograph.
£1.50

(B76-50240)

Mandnell, John
[Quartet, strings (1970)]. String quartet (1970) / [by] John
Mandnell. — Sevenoaks : Novello, 1975. — 36p ; 8vo.
Duration 18 min.
£1.50

(B76-50241)

Shifrin, Seymour
[Quartet, strings, no.3]. String quartet, no.3 / [by] Seymour
Shifrin. — New York ; London : Peters, 1974. — 27p ; 4to.
Duration 13 min.
Unpriced

(B76-50957)

Simpson, Robert
[Quartet, strings, no.4]. Quartet n.4 (1973) : first violin, second
violin, viola, cello / [by] Robert Simpson. — Croydon : Lengnick,
1976. — 8vo & 4to.
Score ([2],106p.) & 4 parts.
£11.50

(B76-50619)

Slack, Roy
Four play three / by Roy Slack. — London : British and
Continental, 1976. — 4to.
For string quartet. — Score (4p.) & 4 parts.
Unpriced

(B76-50620)

Tircuit, Heuwell
[Quartet, strings, no.3, 'Drama in musica']. String quartet no.3,
'Drama in musica' / [by] Heuwell Tircuit. — New York ;
London : Associated Music, 1975. — 23p ; 4to.
The players comment on the music as it is played and improvised dialogue
may be added.
Unpriced

(B76-50242)

RXNSK/AAY — Quartets. Arrangements. Collections

Easy music for string quartet or string orchestra / edited by Robin
de Smet. — London : British and Continental : EMI, 1976. —
4to.
Works by Byrd, Bach, Haydn and Palestrina. — Score (9p.) & 5 parts.
Unpriced

(B76-50243)

RXNT — Trios

Rhodes, Phillip
[Trio, strings]. Trio for strings : violin, viola, violoncello / [by]
Phillip Rhodes. — New York ; London : Peters, 1974. — 4to. —
(American music awards series)
Score (18p.) & 3 parts. — Duration 9 min.
Unpriced

(B76-50244)

S — VIOLIN
S/AC — Tutors

Sassmannshaus, Egon
Früher Anfang auf der Geige : eine Violinschule für Kinder ab 4
Jahren / von Egon Sassmannshaus ; Illustrationen von Heinz
Lauer. — Regensburg : Bosse ; [Cassel] ; [London] : [Bärenreiter].
Band 1. — 1976. — 65p ; 4to. —
£3.75

(B76-50621)

S/AL — Examinations

Associated Board of the Royal Schools of Music
Violin examinations, 1977 and 1978. — London : Associated
Board of the Royal Schools of Music.
Grade 1 : Lists A and B (primary). — 1976. — 4to.
Score (15p.) & part.
£0.50

(B76-50622)

Grade 2 : Lists A and B (elementary). — 1976. — 4to.
Score (16p.) & part.
£0.50

(B76-50623)

Grade 3 : Lists A and B (transitional). — 1976. — 4to.
Score (15p.) & part.
£0.50

(B76-50624)

Grade 4 : Lists A and B (lower). — 1976. — 4to.
Score (16p.) & part.
£0.50

(B76-50625)

Grade 5 : Lists A and B (higher). — 1976. — 4to.
Score (24p.) & part.
£0.50

(B76-50626)

Grade 6 : Lists A and B (intermediate). — 1976. — 4to.
Score (25p.) & part.
£0.70

(B76-50627)

Grade 7 : Lists A and B (advanced). — 1976. — 4to.
Score (34p.) & part.
£0.70

(B76-50628)

SN — VIOLIN ENSEMBLE
SNTK/AH — Trios. Arrangements. Dances

Handel, George Frideric
[Selections. *arr*]. Kleine Tänze / [von] Georg Friedrich Händel ;
[bearbeitet] für zwei-und drei Violinen (I. Lage) von Unger-Twarz.
— Wilhemshaven : Heinrichshoffen ; London : Peters, 1975. —
15p ; 4to.
Unpriced

(B76-50245)

SNTPW — Violins (2) & keyboard
Couperin, François
L'Apothéose de Corelli : for 2 flutes or oboes or violins and basso continuo / [by] François Couperin ; edited by Edward Higginbottom. — London : Musica rara, 1976. — 4to.
Score (27p.) & 3 parts.
Unpriced
Primary classification VRNTPW

(B76-50676)

SNTPWG — Violins(2) & keyboard. Suites
Leclair, Jean Marie, b.1697
Première récréation de musique, Op.6 : for two violins and basso continuo / [by] Jean-Marie Leclair l'Aîné ; edited by Hugo Ruf. — Cassel ; London : Bärenreiter, 1976. — 4to. — (Hortus musicus ; 225)
Score (39p.) & 3 parts.
£6.00

(B76-50629)

SNTQK/LF — Violins (2) & piano. Arrangements. Concertos
Josephs, Wilfred
Concerto for two violins and small orchestra. Op.69 / by Wilfred Josephs ; piano reduction by the composer. — New York ; [London] : Chappell, 1976. — 4to.
Score (28p.) & 2 parts.
Unpriced

(B76-50630)

SNU — Duets
Haag, Hanno
Acht Duette für Violinen / [von] Hanno Haag. — Wilhemshaven : Heinrichshofen ; London : Peters, 1975. — 7p ; 4to.
Unpriced

(B76-50246)

Rolla, Alessandro
[Duets, violins, nos 1-3]. Drei Duos für zwei Violinen / [von] Alessandro Rolla. — Zum ersten Mal herausgegeben von Ulrich Drüner. — Frankfurt : Litulff ; New York ; London : Peters, 1976. — 2pt ; 4to.
Unpriced

(B76-50631)

SP — VIOLIN & PIANO
SPE — Sonatas
Gates, Keith
Sonata for violin and piano / [by] Keith Gates. — New York : Galaxy ; [London] : [Galliard], 1976. — 4to.
Score (26p,) & part.
Unpriced

(B76-50632)

SPE/AY — Sonatas. Collections
Eighteenth-century violin sonatas / edited and realised by Lionel Salter with bowing revised and fingering added by Jean Harvey. — London : Associated Board of the Royal Schools of Music.
Book 1. — 1975. — 4to.
Score (38p.) & 2 parts.
£1.00

(B76-50247)

Book 2. — 1975. — 4to.
Score (40p.) & 2 parts.
£1.00

(B76-50248)

SPH — Dances
McCabe, John
Maze dances : for violin solo (1973) / [by] John McCabe. — Sevenoaks : Novello, 1976. — 14p ; 4to.
Facsimile of the composer's autograph.
Unpriced

(B76-50958)

SPJ — Miscellaneous works
Babbitt, Milton
Sextets : violin and piano / [by] Milton Babbitt. — New York ; London : Peters, 1975. — 65p ; 4to.
Duration 13 min.
Unpriced

(B76-50249)

Bassett, Leslie
Sounds remembered : violin and piano / [by] Leslie Bassett. — New York ; London : Peters, 1975. — 4to.
Score (28p.) & part. — Duration 15 min.
Unpriced

(B76-50250)

Brian, Havergal
Legend : for violin and piano / [by] Havergal Brian. — Chelmsford : Musica Viva, 1976. — 4to.
Score (10p.) & part. — Duration 6 1/2 min.
£2.00

(B76-50633)

Dawe, Margery
Circus scenes : six rhythmic pieces for strings and piano accompaniment / by Margery Dawe. — London : Cramer, 1976. — 4to & obl. 8vo.
Score (9p.) & 3 parts.
£0.93
Primary classification NXNS

(B76-50541)

SPK/AAY — Arrangements. Collections
World's favorite easy violin pieces / edited and produced by Robert Kail. — Carlstadt : Ashley ; [London] : [Phoenix], 1976. — 4to. — (World's favorite series ; no.91)
For violin and piano. — Score (128p.) & part.
Unpriced

(B76-50959)

World's favorite intermediate violin pieces / edited and produced by Robert Kail. — Carlstadt : Ashley ; [London] : [Phoenix], 1976. — 4to. — (World's favourite series ; no.92)
For violin and piano. — Score (127p.) & part.
Unpriced

(B76-50960)

SPK/LF — Arrangements. Concertos
Josephs, Wilfred
[Concerto, violins (2), op.69. arr]. Concerto for two violins and small orchestra. Op.69 / [by] Wilfred Josephs ; piano reduction by the composer. — New York ; [London] : Chappell, 1976. — 4to.
Score (28p.) & part. — The parts for solo violins 1 and 2 printed in score are in duplicate.
Unpriced

(B76-50251)

SPM — UNACCOMPANIED VIOLIN
SPMJ — Miscellaneous works
Globokar, Vinko
Limites : für einen Geiger oder Bratschisten / [von] Vinko Globokar. — Frankfurt : Litolff ; London : Peters, 1975. — 5ff ; obl.fol.
Reproduction of the composer's autograph.
Unpriced

(B76-50252)

Stoker, Richard
Monologue : for solo violin / [by] Richard Stoker. — London : Ashdown, 1976. — 3p ; 4to.
£0.30

(B76-50253)

Watkins, Michael Blake
The wings of night : for violin solo / [by] Michael Blake Watkins ; edited by Yfrah Neaman. — Sevenoaks : Novello, 1976. — 11p ; 4to.
Duration 11 1/2 min.
Unpriced

(B76-50254)

SQP — VIOLA & PIANO
SQPE — Sonatas
Hessenberg, Kurt
[Sonata, viola & piano. Opus 94]. Sonate für Bratsche und Klavier. Opus 94 / [von] Kurt Hessenberg. — Mainz ; London : Schott, 1976. — 4to. — (Viola Bibliothek ; no.45)
Score (35p.) & part.
£5.00

(B76-50634)

Shostakovich, Dmitrii Dmitrievich
Sonata for viola and piano. Op.147 / [by] Dmitri Shostakovich. — London : Anglo-Soviet Music Press : Boosey and Hawkes, 1975. — 4to.
Score (44p.) & part.
£5.00

(B76-50635)

Tircuit, Heuwell
[Sonata, viola & piano, 'Homage to Mahler']. Sonata (Homage to Mahler) : for viola and piano / [by] Heuwell Tircuit. — New York ; London : Associated Music, 1975. — 4to.
Score (22p.) & part. — Based on the viola introduction to Mahler's Symphony no.10.
Unpriced

(B76-50255)

Volkonsky, Andrei
[Sonata, viola & piano]. Sonate für Viola und Klavier / [von] André Volkonsky. — Frankfurt : Belaieff ; [London] : [Peters], 1976. — 4to.
Score (24p.) & part.
Unpriced

(B76-50636)

SQPJ — Miscellaneous works
Dawe, Margery
Circus scenes : six rhythmic pieces for strings and piano
accompaniment / by Margery Dawe. — London : Cramer, 1976.
— 4to & obl. 8vo.
Score (9p.) & 3 parts.
£0.93
Primary classification NXNS

(B76-50541)

SQPK — Arrangements
Rachmaninoff, Sergei
[Romance and scherzo. *arr*]. Romance and scherzo / [by] Serge
Rachmaninov ; arranged for viola or cello and piano by Philip
Clark. — London : Oxford University Press, 1976. — 4to.
Score (16p.) & 2 parts. — These two movements were first published in
their original form as isolated movements for string quartet in 1947.
ISBN 0-19-358441-7 : Unpriced

(B76-50637)

SQPK/LF — Arrangements. Concertos
Graun, Johann Gottlieb
[Concerto, viola & string orchestra, E flat major. *arr*]. Konzert
Es-dur für Viola und Streicher = Concerto E flat major for viola
and strings / [by] Joh. Gottl. Graun ; edited and arranged by
Walter Lebermann. — 1st ed. — Hamburg ; London : Simrock,
1976. — 4to.
Preface by Walter Lebermann. — Score (22p.) & part.
£4.00

(B76-50638)

Hoffmeister, Franz Anton
[Concerto, viola, B flat major. *arr*]. Concerto in B flat for viola
and orchestra / [by] Franz Anton Hoffmeister ; edited as a
reduction for viola and piano by Alison A. Copland, the viola part
edited by Freda Dinn. — London : Schott, 1975. — 4to.
Score (31p.) & part.
Unpriced

(B76-50256)

SR — CELLO
SR/AC — Tutors
Morris, Miriam
The key approach to cello playing / by Miriam Morris. —
London : Chappell, 1976. — 36p ; 4to.
Unpriced

(B76-50639)

Sassmannshaus, Egon
Früher Anfang auf dem Cello : eine Violoncelloschule für Kinder
ab 4 Jahren / [von] Egon Sassmannshaus ; Illustrationen von
Heinz Lauer. — Regensburg : Bosse ; [Cassel] ; [London] :
[Bärenreiter].
Band 1. — 1976. — 65p ; 4to.
£3.75

(B76-50640)

SR/AF — Exercises
Dinn, Freda
A viola method from the third to the first position for individual
and class tuition / [by] Freda Dinn. — London : Schott, 1975. —
4to.
Piano accompaniment (20p.) & viola part (30p.).
ISBN 0-901938-53-x : Unpriced

(B76-50257)

Mainardi, Enrico
Einundzwanzig Studien zur Technik des Violoncellospiels / [von]
Enrico Mainardi. — Mainz ; London : Schott, 1976. — 16p ; 4to.
£2.80

(B76-50961)

SRN — CELLO ENSEMBLE
SRNQ/Y — Sextets. Fugues
Bunting, Christopher
Fugue for 6 cellos on themes by Beethoven / [by] Christopher
Bunting. — London : Oxford University Press, 1976. — 13p ; 8vo.
Duration 4 1/2 min.
ISBN 0-19-355743-6 : Unpriced

(B76-50641)

SRNTK/AAY — Trios. Arrangements. Collections
Six easy pieces for 3 cellos (or violas da gamba) / edited by Robin
de Smet. — London : British and Continental, 1976. — 4to.
Score (8p.) & part.
Unpriced

(B76-50642)

SRNU/AY — Duets. Collections
Sammlung kleiner Stücke für Violoncello = Collection of small
pieces for violoncello : duets and solos from the 18th century /
compiled by Erich Doflein. — Mainz ; London : Schott.
Vol.1 : For beginners. — 1976. — 32p ; 4to.
£2.25
Also classified at SRPMJ

(B76-50643)

SRP — CELLO & PIANO
SRPE — Sonatas
Spinner, Leopold
[Sonatina, cello & piano. Op.26]. Sonatina for violoncello and
piano. Op.26 / [by] Leopold Spinner. — London : Boosey and
Hawkes, 1976. — 4to.
Score (20p.) & part.
£5.00

(B76-50644)

Stout, Alan
[Sonata, cello & piano]. Sonata, violoncello and piano / [by] Alan
Stout. — New York ; London : Peters, 1975. — 25p ; 4to.
Duration 18 min. — Facsimile of the composer's autograph.
Unpriced

(B76-50258)

SRPJ — Miscellaneous works
Dawe, Margery
Circus scenes : six rhythmic pieces for strings and piano
accompaniment / by Margery Dawe. — London : Cramer, 1976.
— 4to & obl. 8vo.
Score (9p.) & 3 parts.
£0.93
Primary classification NXNS

(B76-50541)

Delius, Frederick
Romance for cello and piano / [by] Frederick Delius ; edited by
Robert Threlfall. — First ed. — London : Boosey and Hawkes,
1976. — 4to.
Score (6p.) & part.
£1.00

(B76-50645)

SRPK/AHR — Arrangements. Minuets
Haydn, Joseph
[Quartets, strings. *Selections : arr*]. Two minuets / [by] Joseph
Haydn ; arranged for cello and piano by Watson Forbes. —
London : Oxford University Press, 1975. — 4to.
Score (6p.) & part.
ISBN 0-19-357072-6 : Unpriced

(B76-50259)

SRPLX — CELLO & PERCUSSION
Bergsma, William
Clandestine dialogues : for cello and percussion / [by] William
Bergsma. — New York : Galaxy Music ; [London] : [Stainer and
Bell], 1976. — 4to.
Score (15p.) & part.
Unpriced

(B76-50962)

SRPM — UNACCOMPANIED CELLO
SRPM/T — Variations
Fortner, Wolfgang
Thema und Variationen für Violoncello solo / [von] Wolfgang
Fortner. — Mainz ; London : Schott, 1976. — 7p ; 4to.
£2.00

(B76-50646)

SRPMG — Suites
Britten, Benjamin, *Baron Britten*
[Suite, cello, no.3. Op.87]. Third suite for cello. Op.87 / [by]
Benjamin Britten ; edited by Mstislav Rostropovich. — London :
Faber Music, 1976. — 17p ; 4to.
Unpriced

(B76-50647)

SRPMJ — Miscellaneous works
Gabrielli, Domenico
Sieben Ricercari (1689) : Violoncello solo / [von] Domenico
Gabrielli ; herausgegeben von Dieter Staehelin. — Mainz ;
London : Schott, 1976. — 27p ; 4to. — (Cello Bibliothek ; no.122)
£2.00

(B76-50260)

Kagel, Mauricio
Siegfriedp' : für Violoncello / [von] Mauricio Kagel. — London :
Universal, 1976. — 10p ; 4to.
Unpriced

(B76-50648)

Sammlung kleiner Stücke für Violoncello = Collection of small
pieces for violoncello : duets and solos from the 18th century /
compiled by Erich Doflein. — Mainz ; London : Schott.
Vol.1 : For beginners. — 1976. — 32p ; 4to.
£2.25
Primary classification SRNU/AY

(B76-50643)

SSN — DOUBLE BASS ENSEMBLE
SSNN — Octets
Drew, Lucas
Sound study : for eight double basses / [by] Lucas Drew. — New York ; London : Schirmer, 1975. — 4to.
Score (4p.) & 8 parts. — The parts for 1st and 2nd, 3rd and 4th, 5th and 6th and 7th and 8th double basses are printed severally in score and are in duplicate.
Unpriced

(B76-50261)

STN — VIOL CONSORT
STNQR — Viol & organ septet
Jenkins, John
[Viol consort music]. Consort music for viols in six parts / [by] John Jenkins ; Richard Nicholson and Andrew Ashbee. — London : Faber Music for the Viola da Gamba Society of Great Britain, 1976. — 4to.
Score (122p.) & 7 parts.
Unpriced

(B76-50963)

STNSG — Quartets. Suites
Locke, Matthew
Consort of four parts / [by] Matthew Locke ; edited with a foreword by Michael Tilmouth. — London : Eulenburg, 1976. — x,41p ; 8vo. — (Edition Eulenburg ; no.1356)
Intended for a viol consort. — Miniature score.
Unpriced

(B76-50964)

STNTG — Trios. Suites
Locke, Matthew
The flat consort for my Cousin Kemble / by Matthew Locke ; edited with a foreword by Michael Tilmouth. — London : Eulenburg, 1976. — xii,40p ; 8vo. — (Edition Eulenburg ; no.1357)
Intended for viol consort. — Miniature score.
Unpriced

(B76-50965)

STPM — UNACCOMPANIED VIOL
TNT — Plucked string instruments. Trios
Henze, Hans Werner
Carillon, Récitatif, Masque : Trio für Mandoline, Gitarre und Harfe [von] Hans Werner Henze. — Mainz ; London : Schott, 1976. — 4to.
Score (15p.) & 2 parts.
£3.50

(B76-50649)

TPMK/AAY — Arrangements. Collections
Music from the student repertoire. — London : Musical New Services.
Series 1 : For first and second year students / arranged for guitar by John Mills. — 1974. — 28p ; 4to.
Unpriced

(B76-50966)
Series 2 : For first and second year students / arranged for guitar by John Mills. — 1975. — 36p ; 4to.
Unpriced

(B76-50967)
Series 3 : 'A new varietie of lute lessons' : music for the first three years selected from English and continental master lutenists of the sixteenth century / edited from original sources with an introduction by Anthony Rooley. — 1975. — 36p ; 4to.
Lute tablature.
Unpriced

(B76-50968)

TPMK/DW/AY — Arrangements. Songs, etc. Collections
Seven chords and fifty songs : with photo-chord positions and bigrams for guitar, mandolin, banjo and ukulele / arranged by John Gaunt. — Croydon : Belwin Mills Music, 1975. — 79p ; obl. 8vo.
Unpriced

(B76-50264)

TQN — HARP ENSEMBLE
TQNS — Quartets
Chiti, Gian Paolo
Breakers : for 4 harps / [by] Gian Paolo Chiti. — New York ; [London] : Chappell, 1976. — 23p ; 4to.
Four copies.
Unpriced

(B76-50969)

TQPM — UNACCOMPANIED HARP
TQPMJ — Miscellaneous works
Capanna, Robert
Phorminx : for solo harp / [by] Robert Capanna. — New York ; London : Schirmer, 1975. — 8p ; 4to.
Unpriced

(B76-50265)

Pitfield, Thomas Baron
Eleven miniatures for harp / [by] Thomas B. Pitfield. — London : Peters, 1976. — 10p ; 4to.
Unpriced

(B76-50970)

Rorem, Ned
Sky music : ten pieces for solo harp / [by] Ned Rorem. — New York ; [London] : Boosey and Hawkes, 1976. — 23p ; 4to.
£2.00

(B76-50650)

TQPMK — Arrangements
Purcell, Henry
[Keyboard music. *Selections : arr]*. Purcell for the harp / transcribed for the harp by Dewey Owens. — New York ; London : Schirmer, 1975. — 24p ; 4to.
Unpriced

(B76-50266)

TS — GUITAR
TS/AC — Tutors
Dadi, Marcel
La Méthode de guitare à Dadi / de Marcel Dadi. — Paris : Music Express : Chappell ; [London] : [Chappell], 1974. — 92p ; 4to.
Unpriced

(B76-50267)

Goran, Ulf
Play guitar / by Ulf Goran ; English translation [from the Swedish] by Paul Britten-Austin, illustrations by Sid Jansson. — London : Oxford University Press, 1974. — 49p ; obl. 4to.
With 7" 33 1/3 rpm record (OUP 115).
ISBN 0-19-322210-8 : £1.30

(B76-50651)

Mairants, Ivor
Finger style guitar in theory and practice / by Ivor Mairants. — London : British and Continental : EMI.
Book 1. — 1976. — 40p ; 4to. —
Unpriced

(B76-50971)

Sewell, Penelope
Classical guitar : a complete course / [by] Penelope Sewell ; drawings by Jacqueline Atkinson. — London : Thames.
Book 1. — 1976. — a-f,132p : ill, port ; 4to. —
ISBN 0-905210-04-2 : Unpriced

(B76-50652)

Wangler, Rudolf
Sechs Saiten sehn Finger : Grundlagen und Übunger für Unterricht und Selbststudium des klassischen, spanischen und begleitenden Gitarrenspiels / [von] Rudolf Wangler. — Cassell ; [London] : Bärenreiter, 1976. — 48p ; ill ; obl. 4to.
With two separate leaves of illustrations inserted.
£4.50

(B76-50653)

Wright, Francis
Elementary course for guitar / by Francis Wright. — Leicester : Charnwood Music, 1976. — 18p ; 4to.
Unpriced

(B76-50972)

Wright, Francis
Preparatory course for guitar / by Francis Wright. — Leicester : Charnwood Music, 1976. — 20p ; 4to.
Unpriced

(B76-50973)

Wright, Francis
Primary course for guitar / by Francis Wright. — Leicester :
Charnwood Music, 1976. — 20p ; 4to.
Unpriced

(B76-50974)

TS/AF — Exercises
Kish, Gabriell
Scales and studies for guitar / [by] Gabriell Kish ; foreword by
Aubrey Rolfe. — Oakville : Frederick Harris ; [South Croydon] :
[Lengnick], 1974. — 34p ; 4to.
£1.95

(B76-50975)

Knopf, Bill
Hot licks and fiddle tunes for the bluegrass banjo player : a guide
for improvisation and embellishment, tips on endings and
accompaniment, fiddle tunes in three-finger bluegrass style / by
Bill Knopf. — New York ; [London] : Chappell, 1976. — 71p ;
4to.
Guitar tablature.
Unpriced

(B76-50976)

Mairants, Ivor
Finger style guitar in theory and practice / [by] Ivor Mairants. —
London : British and Continental : EMI.
Book 1 : Basic principles, major and minor scales, chord diagrams and
fingerboard chart. — 1976. — 40p ; 4to. —
Unpriced

(B76-50977)

Book 2 : Instruction for beginners, classical repertoire. — 1976. — 92p ;
4to. —
Unpriced

(B76-50978)

Ragtime guitar : complete instructions and exercises, 37 raggy
songs, 23 Scott Joplin rags, the Scott Joplin school of ragtime /
transcribed for guitar. — New York ; [London] : Chappell, 1976.
— 191p ; 4to.
Unpriced
Primary classification KE/TSDW/HXJ/AY

(B76-50130)

TS/AF/AL — Exercises. Examinations
Guildhall School of Music and Drama : guitar examinations, scales
and arpeggios. — South Croydon : Lengnick, 1975. — 21p ; 4to.
£0.95

(B76-50268)

TS/AY — Collections
Easy modern guitar music : ten pieces by British composers /
edited by Hector Quine. — London : Oxford University Press,
1976. — 17p ; 4to.
ISBN 0-19-358419-0 : Unpriced

(B76-50654)

TS/RC — Chords
Conway, Pat
The pocket book of 288 guitar chords : with fingering chord
arrangements / by Pat Conway ; musical adviser, Kevin Doherty.
— Dublin : International Music, 1976. — 26p ; obl.8vo.
Unpriced

(B76-50269)

Traum, Happy
The guitarist's picture chords / by Happy Traum. — London :
Wise Music Sales, 1975. — 35p ; 4to.
ISBN 0-86001-205-0 : Unpriced

(B76-50270)

TSN — GUITAR ENSEMBLE
TSN/AC — Ensembles. Tutors
Mynall, Frances
Guitar workshop : a course for guitar groups in two parts / by
Frances Mynall and Barry Shaw. — London : Oxford University
Press.
Part 1. — 1976. — 48p ; 4to.
ISBN 0-19-322268-x : Unpriced

(B76-50979)

Part 2. — 1976. — 40p ; 4to.
ISBN 0-19-322269-8 : Unpriced

(B76-50980)

TSNS/T — Quartets. Variations
Croucher, Terence
Three variations on a Japanese theme : for four guitars / by
Terence Croucher. — Leicester (109 St Leonard's Rd, Leicester) :
Clarendon Music, 1974. — 2pt.
Parts for 1st and 3rd and 2nd and 4th guitars are printed in score.
£0.75

(B76-50981)

TSNUK/AAY — Duets. Arrangements. Collections
Seven duos for guitar / arranged by John Gavall. — London :
British and Continental : EMI, 1976. — 16p ; 4to.
Unpriced

(B76-50655)

TSNUK/AEM — Duets. Arrangements. Sonatinas
Beethoven, Ludwig van
[Sonatina, mandoline & piano, Kinsky 43, D minor. *arr*]. Sonatine,
d-moll, für zwei Gitarren / [von] Ludwig van Beethoven ;
bearbeitet von Hans-Dieter Vermeer. — Mainz ; London : Schott,
1975. — 2p ; 4to. — (Gitarren-Archiv ; no.439)
£0.90

(B76-50271)

TSNUK/AH/G/AY — Duets. Arrangements. Folk dances. Collections
Sixteen folk dances / easy arrangements for 2 (3 or more) guitars
by John Gavall. — London : British and Continental : EMI, 1976.
— 20p ; 4to.
Unpriced

(B76-50656)

TSNUK/DM — Duets. Arrangements. Hymns
Bach, Johann Sebastian
[Cantata no.22: Jesus nahm zu sich die Zwölfe. Ertodt' uns durch
dein' Güte. *arr*]. Sanctify us by thy goodness : chorale / [by] J.S.
Bach ; arranged for guitar duet by Hector Quine. — London :
Oxford University Press, 1976. — 5p ; 4to.
ISBN 0-19-355297-3 : Unpriced

(B76-50982)

TSNUK/DW — Duets. Arrangements. Songs, etc
Bach, Johann Sebastian
[Cantata no.208: Was mir behagt. Schafe konnen sicher weiden.
arr]. Sheep may safely graze : aria / [by] J.S. Bach ; arranged for
guitar duet by Hector Quine. — London : Oxford University
Press, 1976. — 5p ; 4to.
ISBN 0-19-355298-1 : Unpriced

(B76-50983)

TSPM — UNACCOMPANIED GUITAR
TSPMH — Dances
Martín, Juan
The exciting sound of flamenco / [by] Juan Martín. — London :
United Music, 1975. — 24p ; 4to.
For guitar. — Staff notation & tablature. — Contents: Mi rumba - Aires
gaditanos (cantinas).
Unpriced

(B76-50984)

TSPMJ — Miscellaneous works
Barrios, Augustin
La Cathedral = The Cathedral : guitar solo / by Augustin
Barrios ; edited and fingered by Ivor Mairants. — London :
British and Continental Music, 1976. — 8p ; 4to.
Unpriced

(B76-50657)

Binge, Ronald
[The watermill. *arr*]. The watermill / [by] Ronald Binge ;
arranged for solo guitar by Hector Quine. — London : Oxford
University Press, 1976. — 4p ; 4to.
ISBN 0-19-355510-7 : Unpriced

(B76-50658)

Croucher, Terence
At the zoo : for guitar / by Terence Croucher. — Leicester (109
St Leonard's Rd, Leicester) : Clarendon Music, 1974. — 8p ; 4to.
£0.75

(B76-50986)

Croucher, Terence
By the sea : for guitar / by Terence Croucher. — Leicester (109
St Leonard's Rd, Leicester) : Clarendon Music, 1974. — 8p ; 4to.
£0.75

(B76-50987)

Croucher, Terence
Divertimento for guitar / by Terence Croucher. — Leicester (109
St Leonard's Rd, Leicester) : Clarendon Music, 1974. — 10p ; 4to.
£1.00

(B76-50988)

Croucher, Terence
In the forest : for guitar / by Terence Croucher. — Leicester (109
St Leonard's Rd, Leicester) : Clarendon Music, 1974. — 8p ; 4to.
£0.75

(B76-50989)

Drabble, L H
Six miniatures : for guitar / [by] L.H. Drabble. — Leicester :
Charnwood Music, 1976. — 3p ; 4to.
Unpriced

(B76-50659)

Peña, Paco
[Toques flamencos. *Selections].* Toques flamencos / [by] Paco
Peña ; collection transcribed by Diana Sainsbury from the album
'Toques flamencos'. — London : Musical New Services, 1976. —
85p ; 4to. — (Music from the student repertoire)
For guitar. — Staff notation & tablature.
Unpriced

(B76-50990)

Qualey, David
Only for guitar : new compositions for solo guitar / by David
Qualey. — London : Scratchwood Music : EMI, 1976. — 44p ;
4to.
Unpriced

(B76-50272)

Searle, Humphrey
Five, Op.61 : for guitar / [by] Humphrey Searle ; edited by Julian
Bream. — London : Faber Music, 1976. — 7p ; 4to. — (Faber
guitar series)
Unpriced

(B76-50991)

TSPMK — Arrangements
Bach, Johann Sebastian
[Selections. *arr].* Bach for the guitar : nine pieces / [by] J.S.
Bach ; arranged for solo guitar by Hector Quine. — London :
Oxford University Press, 1976. — 12p ; 4to.
ISBN 0-19-355300-7 : Unpriced

(B76-50273)

Byrd, William
[Virginals music. *Selections : arr].* Byrd for the guitar : five
pieces / arranged for solo guitar by Nigel North. — London :
Oxford University Press, 1976. — 12p ; 4to. — (Oxford guitar
music)
ISBN 0-19-355800-9 : Unpriced

(B76-50274)

Mudarra, Alonso
[Tres libros de música en cifra para vihuela. Fantasia no.10. *arr].*
Fantasia : das Harfenspiel in der Manier von Ludovico
nachahmend / [von] Alonso Mudarra. Welsh Tantz, 'Wascha
mesa' / [von] Hans Neusidler ; für Gitarre solo, eingerichtet von
Dieter Kreidler. — Mainz ; London : Schott, 1976. — 7p ; 4to. —
(Gitarren-Archiv ; no.441)
£1.00

(B76-50275)

Useful tunes for guitar. — Leicester : Charnwood Music.
No.5 : Hot cross buns : trad. and Auld lang syne : trad. / arr. Rosemary
Wright. — 1974. — 1 sh ; 4to.
Unpriced

Whittaker, Anthony F
Theme music : single stave edition for organ, piano, guitar / [by]
Anthony F. Whittaker. — Leamington Spa : Anthony Music,
1976. — 11p ; 8vo.
£0.50
Also classified at RPVK; QPK

(B76-50992)

TSPMK/AAY — Arrangements. Collections
Another ten for guitar / arranged by Mary Criswick. — London :
Fentone Music : Breitkopf and Härtel, 1975. — 14p ; 4to.
Unpriced

(B76-50276)

Easy favourites : classical guitar / arranged by Philip Moreman. —
London : Chappell, 1976. — 31p ; 4to.
Unpriced

(B76-50660)

TSPMK/AHXJ — Arrangements. Ragtime
Ragtime guitar : complete instructions and exercises, 37 raggy
songs, 23 Scott Joplin rags, the Scott Joplin school of ragtime /
transcribed for guitar. — New York ; [London] : Chappell, 1976.
— 191p ; 4to.
Unpriced
Primary classification KE/TSDW/HXJ/AY

(B76-50130)

TSPMK/DP/LF/AY — Arrangements. Carols. Christmas. Collections
Dancing days : twelve carols for guitar / arranged by Michael
Jessett and Alan Lawrence ; prose translations by Janet Gurney.
— London : Cramer, 1976. — 27p ; 4to.
£1.25

(B76-50993)

Happy Christmas for guitar / arranged by Cecil Bolton and Jack
Moore. — London : EMI, 1976. — 49p ; 4to.
Unpriced
Also classified at JE/TSDP/LF/AY

(B76-50994)

Twenty-four Christmas carols for classical guitar / compiled by Ron
Taylor. — New York ; London : Wise : Music Sales, 1976. —
32p ; 4to.
With words printed separately.
Unpriced
Also classified at JE/TSDP/LF/AY

(B76-50995)

TSPMK/DW/AY — Arrangements. Songs, etc. Collections
Ten for guitar / arranged by Mary Criswick. — London : Fentone
Music : Breitkopf and Härtel, 1975. — 12p ; 4to.
Unpriced

(B76-50277)

The wonderful world of folk : piano, vocal, organ, guitar. —
London : Chappell, 1976. — 40p ; 4to.
Unpriced

(B76-50996)

TTPM — UNACCOMPANIED BANJO
TTV/RC — Tenor banjo. Chords
Conway, Pat
The pocket book of tenor banjo chords : (288 chords with
fingering) / chord arrangements by Pat Conway ; musical adviser,
Kevin Doherty. — Dublin : International Music, 1976. — 26p ;
obl.8vo.
Unpriced

(B76-50278)

TUN — ZITHER ENSEMBLE
TUNS — Quartets
Kagel, Mauricio
Charakterstück : für Zitherquartett / [von] Mauricio Kagel. —
London : Universal, 1976. — 10p ; 4to.
Unpriced

(B76-50661)

TW — LUTE
TW/AY — Collections
Easy lute music / selected, transcribed for guitar and edited by
Adrienne Simpson. — London : Oxford University Press, 1975. —
20p ; 4to. — (Music for the lute ; no.7)
Staff notation & tablature.
ISBN 0-19-358834-x : Unpriced

(B76-50279)

TX — MANDOLIN
TX/RC — Chords
Conway, Pat
The pocket book of mandoline chords : 288 chords with fingering
chord arrangements / by Pat Conway ; musical adviser, Kevin
Doherty. — Dublin : International Music, 1976. — 26p : obl.8vo.
Unpriced

(B76-50280)

UM — WIND BAND
UMJ — Miscellaneous works
Balent, Andrew
Superband meets Mr Boogie / by Andrew Balent. — New York :
Warner ; [London] : [Blossom], 1975. — 4to.
For wind band. — Score (7p.) & 49 parts. — With several copies of various
parts.
Unpriced

(B76-50281)

Wanek, Friedrich K
Vier Grotesken : für 11 Bläser und Schlagzeüg / [von] Friedrich
K. Wanek. — Mainz ; London : Schott, 1976. — 62p ; fol.
Duration 8 min.
£10.50

(B76-50997)

Zehm, Friedrich
Schwierigkeiten und Unfälle mit 1 Choral / [von] Friedrich Zehm.
— Mainz ; London : Schott, 1976. — 20p ; fol.
For wind instruments.
£4.50

(B76-50282)

UMK/AT — Arrangements. Variations
Sweelinck, Jan Pieterzoon
[Mein junges Leben hat ein End]. Variations on 'Mein junges
Leben hat ein End' / by Jan P. Sweelinck ; transcribed for concert
band by Ramon L. Ricker. — New York ; London : Schirmer,
1975. — 19p ; 4to.
Duration 5 min.
Unpriced

(B76-50283)

UMM — MILITARY BAND
UMME — Symphonies
Gillis, Don
Symphony 'X', (Big 'D') / [by] Don Gillis. — New York ;
[London] : Boosey and Hawkes, 1976. — 4to. — (Q.M.B. Edition,
385)
For military band. — Score (60p.) & 72 parts. — With several copies of
various parts.
£0.35

(B76-50662)

UMMGM — Marches
Goldman, Richard Franko
Seaside park : march, symphonic band / [by] Richard Franko
Goldman. — Oceanside ; [London] : Boosey and Hawkes, 1976.
— 8vo.
Condensed score & 52 parts. — With several copies of various parts.
£4.00

(B76-50998)

Washburn, Robert
March-opus '76 / [by] Robert Washburn. — New York ;
[London] : Boosey and Hawkes, 1976. — 4to. — (Q.M.B. edition ;
401)
For military band. — Score (28p.) & 69 parts, with several copies of various
parts.
£12.00

(B76-50999)

UMMJ — Miscellaneous works
Bavicchi, John
Band of the year : Op.66 : overture for concert band / [by] John
Bavicchi. — New York ; [London] : Oxford University Press,
1976. — 4to.
Score (24p.) & 65 parts, with several copies of various parts.
Unpriced

(B76-51000)

Sapieyevski, Jerzy
Morpheus : wind symphony orchestra / [by] Jerzy Sapieyevski. —
New York ; London : Peters, 1975. — 39p ; 4to.
Duration 9 min.
Unpriced

(B76-51001)

Tull, Fisher
Credo for symphonic band / [by] Fisher Tull. — New York ;
[London] : Boosey and Hawkes, 1976. — 4to. — (Q.M.B.
Edition ; no.396)
Score (24p.) & 70 parts.
£15.00

(B76-50663)

Walters, Harold L
Dynamite brass / [by] Harold L. Walters. — Miami : Rubank ;
[Sevenoaks] : [Novello], 1976. — 4to. — (Rubank symphonic band
library ; no.151)
Conductor & 44 parts, with several copies of various parts.
Unpriced

(B76-51002)

Washburn, Robert
Epigon IV / [by] Robert Washburn. — New York ; [London] :
Boosey and Hawkes, 1976. — 4to. — (Q.M.B. edition ; 400)
For military band. — Score (32p.) & 70 parts, with several copies of various
parts.
£15.00

(B76-51004)

Washburn, Robert
Intrada for band / [by] Robert Washburn. — New York ;
[London] : Oxford University Press, 1976. — 4to.
Score (24p.) & 60 parts.
Unpriced

(B76-50284)

Washburn, Robert
Prelude and paragrams / [by] Robert Washburn. — New York ;
[London] : Oxford University Press, 1976. — 4to.
Military band. — Score (32p.) & 56 parts.
Unpriced

(B76-50664)

UMMK/AH — Arrangements. Dances
Mozart, Wolfgang Amadeus
[German dance no.76, K.605, no.3. *arr*]. The sleigh ride / by
W.A. Mozart ; arranged by Leonard Rush. — London : Warner,
1976. — 4to. — (Supersound series for young bands)
Arranged for military band. — Score (5p.) & 49 parts. — With several
copies of various parts.
Unpriced

(B76-51005)

UMMK/AHVH — Arrangements. Polkas
Strauss, Johann, *b.1825*
[Die Fledermaus. Fledermaus - Polka. *arr*]. Polka française / [by]
Johann Strauss ; transcribed for band by Robert O'Brien. — New
York ; [London] : Oxford University Press, 1976. — 4to.
Score (14p.), Condensed score (7p.) & 56 parts. — With several copies of
various parts.
Unpriced

(B76-50665)

UMMK/DW/LC — Arrangements. Spirituals
Balent, Andrew
Got the spirit! / arranged by Andrew Balent. — New York :
Warner ; [London] : [Blossom], 1976. — 4to. — (Supersound
series for young bands)
Spirituals arranged for military band. — Score (7p.) & 49 parts.
Unpriced

(B76-51006)

UMP — SOLO INSTRUMENT (S) & WIND BAND
UMPWV — Tuba & military band
Grundman, Clare
Tuba rhapsody : for tuba and symphonic band / [by] Clare
Grundman. — New York ; [London] : Boosey and Hawkes, 1976.
— 4to. — (Q.M.B. Edition ; 399)
Score (52p.) & 75 parts.
£30.00

(B76-51007)

UN — WIND ENSEMBLE
Walker, James
Scherzo, 'Encore for winds' / [by] James Walker. — New York ;
London : Schirmer, 1975. — 4to.
Score (18p.) & 12 parts. — Duration 2 1/2 min.
Unpriced

(B76-50285)

UN/AYE — Collections. Germany
Alte Bläser-Partiten : gesammelt und für den praktischen Gebrauch
herausgegeben von Wilhelm Ehmann. — Cassel ; Basle ; London :
Bärenreiter, 1975. — 38p ; 8vo.
£2.00

(B76-50666)

UNN — Octets
Shewan, Douglas
[Octet, wind instruments]. Wind octet / [by] Douglas Shewan. —
London : Hansen House, 1975. — 4to.
Score (17p.) & 6 parts. The parts for 1st and 2nd flutes, 1st and 2nd oboes
and 1st and 2nd clarinets are printed severally in score.
Unpriced

(B76-50286)

UNNK/CC — Octets. Arrangements. Opera
Mozart, Wolfgang Amadeus
[Die Entführung aus dem Serail. K.384. *arr*]. The abduction from
the Seraglio / [by] Wolfgang Amadeus Mozart ; arranged for 2
oboes, 2 clarinets, 2 horns and 2 bassoons by Johann Nepomuk
Wendt ; [edited by] Himie Voxman. — London : Musica rara,
1975. — 4to.
Score (29p.) & 8 parts.
Unpriced

(B76-50668)

Mozart, Wolfgang Amadeus
[Le Nozze di Figaro. K.492. *arr*]. The marriage of Figaro / [by]
Wolfgang Amadeus Mozart ; arranged for 2 oboes, 2 clarinets, 2
horns and 2 bassoons ; by Johann Nepomuk Wendt ; edited by
Robert Block, Himie Voxman. — London : Musica rara.
Vol.1. — 1975. — 4to.
Score (22p.) & 8 parts.
Unpriced

(B76-50667)

Mozart, Wolfgang Amadeus
[Le Nozze di Figaro. K.492. *arr*]. The marriage of Figaro / [by]
Wolfgang Amadeus Mozart ; arranged for 2 oboes, 2 clarinets, 2
horns and 2 bassoons by Johann Nepomuk Wendt ; edited by
Robert Block, Himie Voxman. — London : Musica rara.
Vol.2. — 1975. — 4to.
Score (28p.) & 8 parts.
Unpriced

(B76-50669)

UNPG — Septets. Suites
Rosetti, Francesco Antonio
Partia für Oboe, 2 Englisch Hörner, 2 Hörner und 2 Fagotte /
[von] Francesco Antonio Rosetti. — Zum ersten Mal /
herausgegeben von Kurt Janetzky. — Cassel ; London :
Bärenreiter, 1976. — 4to.
Score (16p.) & 7 parts.
Unpriced

(B76-51008)

UNR — Quintets
Kelterborn, Rudolf
Kammermusik für fünf Bläser : Flöte (Piccolo), Oboe, Klarinette,
Horn und Fagott / [von] Rudolf Kelterborn. — Cassel ; London :
Bärenreiter, 1974. — 5pt ; fol.
£5.00

(B76-50670)

Mathias, William
[Quintet, wind instruments, op.22]. Quintet for flute, oboe,
clarinet, horn and bassoon. Op.22 / [by] William Mathias. —
London : Oxford University Press, 1976. — 48p ; 8vo.
Miniature score.
ISBN 0-19-357768-2 : £0.18

(B76-50287)

UNR/AZ — Quintets. Collected works of individual composers
Elgar, Sir Edward, bart
[Works, wind quintet]. Music for wind quintet, 2 flutes, oboe,
clarinet, bassoon (or cello) / [by] Edward Elgar ; performing
edition by Richard McNicol. — First ed. — Croydon : Belwin
Mills.
Volume 1 : Six promenades (1878). — 1976. — 4to.
Score (24p.) & 5 parts. — Promenade no.5 was used later by Elgar in his
Severn Suite.
Unpriced

(B76-50671)

Volume 2 : Harmony music 1 and 2. — 1976. — 4to.
Score (27p.) & 5 parts.
Unpriced

(B76-50672)

Volume 3 : Harmony music 3 and 4. — 1976. — 4to.
Score (31p.) & 5 parts. — Harmony music no.3 was left incomplete and is
published in this edition as a fragment.
Unpriced

(B76-50673)

UNRK — Quintets. Arrangements
Mozart, Wolfgang Amadeus
[Quartet, strings, no.17, K.458, B flat major, 'The hunt'. arr].
String quartet in B flat / [by] Mozart ; arranged for wind quintet
by Geoffrey Emerson. — Ampleforth : Emerson, 1976. — 5pt ;
4to.
Unpriced

(B76-51009)

UNT — Trios
Kagel, Mauricio
Atem : für einen Bläser / [von] Mauricio Kagel. — London :
Universal, 1976. — 18ff ; obl. 4to.
At least three wind instruments of the player's choice to be played one after
another or simultaneously.
Unpriced

(B76-50674)

VN — WOODWIND ENSEMBLE
VNS — Quartets
Diemer, Emma Lou
Music for woodwind quartet / [by] Emma Lou Diemer. — New
York ; [London] : Oxford University Press, 1976. — 4to.
Score & 4 parts. — Duration 7 1/2 min.
Unpriced

(B76-51010)

VNSG — Quartets. Suites
Parfrey, Raymond
[Suite, woodwind quartet, no.1]. Suite no.1 for 2 flutes and 2 B
flat clarinets / by Raymond Parfrey. — London : British and
Continental : EMI, 1976. — 7p ; 4to.
Unpriced

(B76-51012)

Parfrey, Raymond
[Suite, woodwind quartet, no.2]. Suite no.2 for 2 flutes and 2 B
flat clarinets / [by] Raymond Parfrey. — London : British and
Continental, 1976. — 7p ; 4to.
Unpriced

(B76-51011)

VNTG — Trios. Suites
Blake, Nicholas
[Suite, oboes (2) & cor anglais, op.6]. Suite. Opus 6, 2 oboes and
cor anglais / [by] Nicholas Blake. — Ampleforth : Emerson, 1976.
— 4to.
Score (9p.) & 3 parts.
Unpriced

(B76-51013)

VR — FLUTE
Bach, Johann Sebastian
[Selections. Flute parts]. Repertoire der Flötenpartien aus dem
Kantaten und Oratorienwerk / [von] Johann Sebastian Bach ;
herausgegeben von Werner Richter. — Frankfurt : Litolff ;
London : Peters.
Band 1 : Kantaten BWV 8-102, Matthaus Passion, Oster-Oratorium. —
1975. — 88p ; 4to.
Unpriced

(B76-50288)

VR/AF — Exercises
Dick, Robert
The other flute : a performance manual of contemporary
techniques / [by] Robert Dick. — London : Oxford University
Press, 1975. — 154p ; 4to.
With 7" 33 1/3 rpm record (OUP 131).
ISBN 0-19-322125-x : £6.75

(B76-51014)

VR/AF/AY — Exercises. Collections
125 easy classical studies for flute : taken from classical flute
methods / edited by Frans Vester. — London : Universal, 1976.
— 55p ; 4to.
Unpriced

(B76-51015)

VRN — FLUTE ENSEMBLE
VRNSQK — Flutes (3) & piano. Arrangements
Massenet, Jules
[La Navarraise. Nocturne. arr]. Nocturne / [by] Massenet ; arr.
for three C flutes with piano accompaniment by Harold L.
Walters. — Miami : Rubank ; [Sevenoaks] : [Novello], 1976. —
4to.
Score (4p.) & part.
Unpriced

(B76-50675)

VRNTH — Trios. Dances
Greaves, Terence
Dance trios : 3 flutes / [by] Terence Greaves. — Ampleforth :
Emerson, 1976. — 8p ; 4to.
Unpriced

(B76-51016)

VRNTPW — Flutes (2) & keyboard
Couperin, François
L'Apothéose de Corelli : for 2 flutes or oboes or violins and basso
continuo / [by] François Couperin ; edited by Edward
Higginbottom. — London : Musica rara, 1976. — 4to.
Score (27p.) & 3 parts.
Unpriced
Also classified at SNTPW

(B76-50676)

VRNUE — Duets. Sonatas
Corrette, Michel
[Sonatas, flute. Op.23]. Sechs Sonaten für zwei Flöten / [von]
Michel Corrette ; herausgegeben von Frank Nagel. —
Wilhemshaven : Heinrichshofen ; [London] : [Peters], 1975. —
28p ; 4to.
Unpriced

(B76-50289)

VRP — FLUTE & PIANO
VRPE — Sonatas
Bach, Johann Sebastian
[Sonatas, flute & continuo. Selections]. Sonatas for flute and basso
continuo / handed down as works by Johann Sebastian Bach ;
edited by Alfred Dürr. — Cassel ; London : Bärenreiter, 1975. —
4to.
Score (40p.) & 2 parts. — Contents: 1 : Sonata in C major for flute and
basso continuo. BWV 1033 - 2: Sonatas in E flat major and G minor for
flute and harpsichord obbligato. BWV 1031, 1020.
£6.00

(B76-50677)

Simpson, Lionel
[Sonata, flute & piano, op.67]. Sonata for flute. Op.67 / [by]
Lionel Simpson. — London : British and Continental : EMI, 1976.
— 4to.
Score (16p.) & part.
Unpriced

(B76-50290)

VRPJ — Miscellaneous works
Baker, Michael
Elegy, Op.21 : for flute and organ / [by] Michael Baker. —
Oakville : Harmuse ; [South Croydon] : [Lengnick], 1975. — 4to.
Score (3p.) & part.
£1.00

(B76-51017)

Kleyn, Howard
La flauta española : flute solo, with piano accompaniment / by
Howard Kleyn. — Kowloon : Sonia Archer ; [South Croydon] :
[Lengnick], 1975. — 4to.
Score (8p.) & 2 parts.
Unpriced
(B76-51018)

Satie, Erik
[Trois gymnopédies. *arr*]. Three gymnopédies : flute (or oboe) and
piano / [by] Erik Satie ; edited by Robin de Smet. — London :
Fentone Music : Breitkopf and Härtel, 1976. — 4to.
Score (8p.) & part.
Unpriced
(B76-50291)

Simpson, Lionel
Silent waters. Opus 72 : for flute and piano / by Lionel Simpson.
— London : EMI, 1976. — 4to.
Score (8p.) & part.
Unpriced
(B76-51019)

Stout, Alan
Music : for flute and harpsichord / [by] Alan Stout. — New
York ; London : Peters, 1976. — 15p ; 4to.
Duration 6 1/2 min. — Facsimile of the composer's autograph.
Unpriced
(B76-51020)

Wilson, Robert Barclay
The apron of flowers : for flute and piano / by Robert Barclay
Wilson. — London : EMI, 1976. — 4to.
Score (4p.) & part.
Unpriced
(B76-51021)

VRPK/AAY — Arrangements. Collections
Classical music for flute and piano / edited and arranged by Peter
Wastall. — London : Boosey and Hawkes, 1976. — 4to. —
(Exploring music)
Score (24p.) & part.
Unpriced
(B76-51022)

Romantic music for flute and piano / edited and arranged by Peter
Wastall. — London : Boosey and Hawkes, 1976. — 4to. —
(Exploring music)
Score (20p.) & part. — Some works for flute unaccompanied.
Unpriced
(B76-51023)

VRPK/AE — Arrangements. Sonatas
Bach, Johann Sebastian
[Sonatas, organ, nos.1-6. S.525-30. *arr*]. Sechs Sonaten nach
B.W.V. 525-530 Six sonatas after B.W.V. 525-530 : for flute and
harpsichord obbligato / [by] Johann Sebastian Bach ; arranged by
Waltraut and Gerhard Kirchner. — Cassel ; London : Bärenreiter.
Score (34p.) & part.
Book 1 : Sonatas 1 and 2. — 1975. — 4to.
£4.50
(B76-50679)

Bach, Johann Sebastian
[Sonatas, organ, nos.1-6. S.525-30. *arr*]. Sechs Sonaten nach
B.W.V. 525-530 = Six sonatas after B.W.V. 525-530 : for flute
and harpsichord obbligato / [by] Johann Sebastian Bach ;
arranged by Waltraut and Gerhard Kirchner. — Cassel ; London :
Bärenreiter.
Score (39p.) & part.
Book 2 : Sonatas 3 and 4. — 1975. — 4to.
£4.50
(B76-50678)

VRPK/DM — Arrangements. Hymns
Bach, Johann Sebastian
[Cantata no.147, 'Herz und Mund und That und Leben'. Wohl
mir dass ich Jesum habe. *arr*]. Jesu, joy of man's desiring / [by]
J.S. Bach ; arranged for flute and piano by Sidney Lawton. —
London : Oxford University Press, 1976. — 4to.
Score (4p.) & part.
ISBN 0-19-355279-5 : Unpriced
(B76-50292)

VRPK/DW/AY — Arrangements. Songs, etc. Collections
Airs from seven lands / arranged for flute and piano by Beryl Price.
— London : Oxford University Press, 1976. — 4to.
Score (8p.) & part.
ISBN 0-19-358304-6 : Unpriced
(B76-51024)

VRPK/LF — Arrangements. Concertos
Danzi, Franz
[Concerto, flute no.2, op.31, D minor. *arr*]. Konzert nr.2, d-moll,
op.31, für Flöte und Orchester / [von] Franz Danzi ;
herausgegeben von Peter Anspacher ; Ausgabe für Flöte und
Klavier. — Wilhemshaven : Heinrichshofen ; [London] :
[Hinrichsen], 1975. — 4to.
Score (27p.) & part.
Unpriced
(B76-50680)

Molter, Johann Melchior
[Concerto, flute & string orchestra, G major. H.S.315]. Concerto
in G major for flute, strings and basso continuo, H.S.315 / [by]
Johann Melchior Molter ; ed. by D. Lasocki, flute and piano
reduction by R.P. Block. — London : Musica rara, 1975. — 4to.
Score (14p.) & part.
Unpriced
(B76-50681)

VRPLTS — FLUTE & GUITAR
VRPLTSK/AHXJ — Arrangements. Ragtime
Joplin, Scott
[The entertainer. *arr*]. The entertainer : an excerpt / [by] Scott
Joplin ; arranged for flute and guitar by Christopher Boydston. —
New York ; London : Schirmer, 1975. — 3p ; 4to.
Two copies. — Printed on one side of the leaf only.
Unpriced
(B76-50293)

VRPLTSK/DW/G/AY — Flute & guitar. Arrangements. Folk songs.
Collections
Folksongs for flute, with guitar chords : 200 favourites / arranged
by Jerry Silverman. — New York ; [London] : Chappell, 1976. —
93p ; 4to.
Unpriced
(B76-51025)

VRPM — UNACCOMPANIED FLUTE
VRPM/T — Variations
Wuorinen, Charles
Flute variations 2 : flute solo / [by] Charles Wuorinen. — New
York ; London : Peters, 1975. — 6p ; 4to.
Duration 7 min.
Unpriced
(B76-51026)

VRPMG — Suites
Tromlitz, Johann George
[Partitas, flute, nos.1-6]. Sechs Partiten für Flöte / [von] Johann
Georg Tromlitz. — Zum ersten Mal herausgegeben von Walter
Lebermann. — Frankfurt : Litolff ; London : Peters, 1976. —
28p ; 4to.
Unpriced
(B76-50682)

VRPMJ — Miscellaneous works
Davies, Peter Maxwell
Two pieces for flute / [by] Peter Maxwell Davies. — London :
Boosey and Hawkes, 1976. — 10p ; 4to.
Contents: Solita - The kestrel paced round the sun.
£2.00
(B76-51027)

Ferneyhough, Brian
Unity capsule : solo flute / [by] Brian Ferneyhough. — London :
Peters, 1975. — 20p ; obl. fol.
Unpriced
(B76-51028)

Knussen, Oliver
Masks. Op.3 ; for solo flute with glass chimes (ad lib.) / [by]
Oliver Knussen. — New York ; London : Schirmer, 1975. —
10p ; 4to.
Unpriced
(B76-50294)

VS — RECORDER
VS/AC — Tutors
Simpson, Kenneth
Music through the recorder : a course in musicianship / by
Kenneth Simpson. — London : Nelson, 1975. — 80p ; 8vo.
ISBN 0-17-436086-x : £1.10
(B76-50295)

Simpson, Kenneth
Music through the recorder : a course in musicianship / by
Kenneth Simpson. — London : Nelson.
Vol.3. — 1976. — 95p ; 8vo. —
ISBN 0-17-436085-1 : £2.25
(B76-50683)

Trapp Family
[Enjoy your recorder]. The Trapp family recorder method : a new complete method of instruction for the recorder, including exercises, revisions, trill charts, ornaments and embellishments, duets, trios and quartets / by the Trapp Family. — New ed. / revised by Edgar Hunt. — London : Schott.
Vol.1. — 1976. — 60p ; 4to.
ISBN 0-901938-50-5 : Unpriced
(B76-50296)

Trapp family
The Trapp family recorder method : a new complete method of instruction for the recorder, including exercises, revisions, trill charts, ornaments and embellishments, duets, trios and quartets. — New ed. / revised by Edgar Hunt. — London : Schott.
Book 1 : Treble sopranino (or bass). — 1976. — 60p ; 4to.
ISBN 0-901938-51-3 : Unpriced
(B76-50297)

VSM — RECORDER BAND
VSMK/DH — Arrangements. Motets, Anthems, Hymns, etc
Lasso, Orlando di
[Continuation du mellange. Passan vostri triomphi. *arr].* Trionto del tempo / [by] Orlando di Lasso ; and, Ecco l'alma beata / [by] Giovanni Croce ; arranged for ten recorders in 2 choirs by Dennis A. Bamforth. — Bury : Tomus, 1976. — 8vo.
Score (24p.) & 9 parts.
Unpriced
(B76-50298)

VSN — RECORDER ENSEMBLE
VSNQH — Sextets. Dances
Allegri, Lorenzo
[Il primo libro delle musiche. Primo ballo]. Suite in 6 parts for 6 recorders / by Lorenzo Allegri. — Haslemere : Dolmetsch ; London : Chappell, 1976. — 4to. — (Dolmetsch library)
Score (7p.) & 6 parts.
Unpriced
(B76-51029)

VSNQK/AHG — Sextets. Arrangements. Dance suites
Bononcini, Giovanni Maria
[Sinfonia, allemande, correnti e sarabande a 5 e 6. Op.5. *Selections : arr].* Two suites a 6 : for 6 recorders / [by] Giovanni Bononcini ; edited and continuo realised by Layton Ring. — London : Universal, 1976. — 4to. — (Dolmetsch recorder series ; no.99)
Score (15p.) & 7 parts with alternative parts for treble recorder I or descant recorder III.
Unpriced
(B76-51030)

VSNRK/DW — Quintets. Arrangements. Songs, etc
Nicolson, Richard
[Songs. *Selections : arr].* Three consort pieces / by Richard Nicolson ; arranged for recorder quintet (D.D.Tr.T.B.) by Denis Bloodworth. — London : Boosey and Hawkes, 1975. — 4to.
Score (9p.) & 5 parts.
£1.50
(B76-50299)

VSNSG — Quartets. Suites
Chedeville, Nicolas
[Amusements champêtres, liv, 1. Suite, woodwind instruments, no.4, G major]. Quatrième suite : for recorder quartet / [by] Nicholas Chedeville. — Haslemere : Dolmetsch ; London : Chappell, 1976. — 4to. — (Dolmetsch library)
Score (16p.) & 4 parts.
Unpriced
(B76-51031)

VSNSQK/AHXJ — Recorders (3) & piano. Arrangements. Ragtime
Joplin, Scott
[The entertainer. *arr].* The entertainer / by Scott Joplin ; arranged for descant, treble, tenor recorders and piano by Brian Davey. — London : Chappell, 1976. — 4to.
Score (7p.) & 3 parts.
Unpriced
(B76-50684)

VSNT — Trios
Hotteterre, Jean
[Pièces pour la muzette. Overture, 'Le festin'. *arr].* Overture 'Le festin' : for descant, treble and bass recorders / by Jean Hotteterre. — Haslemere : Dolmetsch ; London : Chappell, 1976. — 8p ; 4to. — (Dolmetsch library)
Unpriced
(B76-51032)

Johnson, David
[Trio, recorders]. Trio for recorders in eight movements / [by] David Johnson. — Manchester : Forsyth, 1976. — 13p ; 4to.
Unpriced
(B76-51033)

Turner, John
December music : trio for recorders, descant, treble, tenor / [by] John Turner. — Bury : Tomus, 1975. — 8vo.
Score (11p.) & 3 parts.
Unpriced
(B76-50300)

VSNT/T — Trios. Variations
Meech, Michael
Variations on a well-known theme : for recorder trio, descant, treble, tenor / [by] Michael Meech. — Bury : Tomus, 1976. — 8vo.
The theme is 'Ah! vous dirai-je, maman'. — Score (16p.).
£0.70
(B76-51034)

VSNTQK/AHW — Recorders (2) & piano. Arrangements. Waltzes
Strauss, Johann, *b.1825*
[Waltzes. *Selections].* Seven Strauss waltzes : for descant, treble recorders and piano / arranged by Brian Davey. — London : Chappell, 1976. — 4to.
Score (23p.) & 2 parts.
Unpriced
(B76-51035)

VSNU — Duets
Dench, Chris
Reminiscences of Scriabin : for treble and sopranino recorders / [by] Chris Dench ; version without bells from 'E 330 plays'. — London (17 Dempster Rd, S.W.18) : The composer, 1976. — 2 leaves ; obl. fol.
Unpriced
(B76-50301)

Mignone, Francisco
Quatro pecas para 2 flautas doce em do (C) e fa (F) / de Francisco Mignone. — Rio de Janeiro : Arthur Napoleão ; [London] : [Essex Music], 1976. — 7p ; 4to.
Contents: 1: Preludiando - 2: Cantiga de roda - 3: Seresteira - 4: Alegria do matuto.
Unpriced
(B76-51036)

VSP — RECORDER & PIANO
VSPLK — Descant recorder & other instrument. Arrangements
Kleyn, Howard
Chinese suite, no.2. Op.41 / [by] Howard Kleyn. — Kowloon : Sonia Archer ; [South Croydon] : [Lengnick], 1976. — 8vo.
For baritone & piano. — Contents: 1: O dearest - 2: To one unamed (Li Shang Yin) - 3: Monday (Tan Tseng Hsiang).
Unpriced
(B76-51037)

VSPLTS — RECORDER & GUITAR
VSPLTSK/DW/GB/AY — Arrangements. Popular songs. Collections
Popular songs for the recorder : outstanding selections published complete with lyrics and guitar diagrams plus a six page introduction to playing the recorder / arranged for recorder by Clive A. Sansom. — London : Wise : Music Sales, 1975. — 31p ; 4to.
Unpriced
Primary classification VSPMK/DW/GB/AY

VSPLTSK/DW/JR/AY — Arrangements. Film songs. Collections
Film and TV themes for the recorder : outstanding selections published complete with lyrics and guitar diagrams plus a six page introduction to playing the recorder / arranged for recorder by Clive A. Sansom. — London : Wise : Music Sales, 1976. — 32p ; 4to.
Unpriced
Primary classification VSPMK/DW/JR/AY

VSPM — UNACCOMPANIED RECORDER
VSPMK/DW/GB/AY — Arrangements. Popular songs. Collections
Popular songs for the recorder : outstanding selections published complete with lyrics and guitar diagrams plus a six page introduction to playing the recorder / arranged for recorder by Clive A. Sansom. — London : Wise : Music Sales, 1975. — 31p ; 4to.
Unpriced
Also classified at VSPLTSK/DW/GB/AY
(B76-51038)

VSPMK/DW/JR/AY — Arrangements. Film songs. Collections
Film and TV themes for the recorder : outstanding selections published complete with lyrics and guitar diagrams plus a six page introduction to playing the recorder / arranged for recorder by Clive A. Sansom. — London : Wise : Music Sales, 1976. — 32p ; 4to.
Unpriced
Also classified at VSPLTSK/DW/JR/AY
(B76-51039)

VSR — DESCANT RECORDER
VSRNU/AY — Duets. Collections
Terpsichore : die Tänze der Barockzeit, für zwei
Sopranblockflöten / herausgegeben von Gertrud Keller ; mit
Spielhinweisen von Jacques Martin Hotteterre. — Wilhemshaven :
Noetzel ; London : Peters, 1975. — 32p ; 4to.
With a separate leaf headed 'Trillertabelle für Sopranblockflöten' inserted.
Unpriced

(B76-50302)

VSRNUK/AAY — Duets. Arrangements. Collections
Kleine Stücke, grosser Meister : für zwei Sopranblockflöten /
ausgewählt von Ulrika Emden. — Wilhemshaven : Noetzel ;
London : Peters, 1975. — 31p ; obl.8vo.
Unpriced

(B76-50303)

VSRNUK/AH/AY — Duets. Arrangements. Dances. Collections
Kleine Tänze, grosser Meister : für zwei Sopranblockflöten /
ausgewählt von Ulrika Emden. — Wilhemshaven : Noetzel ;
London : Peters, 1975. — 32p ; obl.8vo.
Unpriced

(B76-50304)

VSRNUK/DP/LF/AYE — Descant recorder. Duets. Arrangements.
Carols. Christmas. Collections
Weinachtslieder in leichten Sätzen : für zwei Sopranflöten / 21
ausgewählte Lieder in Sätzen von Liselotte Böhn. — Cassel :
Nagel ; [London] : [Bärenreiter], 1975. — 23p ; obl. 8vo.
£1.25

(B76-50685)

VSRNUK/DW/G/AYE — Descant recorder. Duets. Arrangements.
Folk songs. Collections. Germany
Volkslieder in leichten Sätzen : für zwei Sopranflöten / 20
ausgewählte Lieder in Sätzen von Liselotte Böhn. — Cassel :
Nagel ; [London] : [Bärenreiter], 1975. — 24p ; obl. 8vo.
£1.25

(B76-50686)

VSRNUK/DW/GJ/AYE — Descant recorder. Duets. Arrangements.
Children's songs. Collections. Germany
Kinderlieder in leichten Sätzen : für zwei Sopranflöten / 27
ausgewählte Lieder in Sätzen von Liselotte Böhn. — Cassel :
Nagel ; [London] : [Bärenreiter], 1975. — 24p ; obl.8vo.
£1.25

(B76-50687)

VSRPJ — Miscellaneous works
Turner, John
Four diversions : for descant recorder and piano / [by] John
Turner. — Manchester : Forsyth, 1976. — 4to.
Score (12p.) & part.
Unpriced

(B76-51040)

VSRPK/AAY — Arrangements. Collections
Recorder music for beginners / edited by Czidra Laszlo. —
London : Boosey and Hawkes, 1976. — 4to.
For descant recorder and piano.
£1.25

(B76-51041)

VSRPLK/AAY — Descant recorder & instrument. Arrangements.
Collections
Play and sing : a third book for descant recorder and/or other
instruments / [by] Richard Addison. — Edinburgh : Holmes
McDougall, 1975. — 32p ; 4to.
Unpriced

(B76-51042)

VSRPLTSK — Descant recorder & guitar. Arrangements
Ten traditional melodies : easy duos for descant recorder and
guitar / arranged by John Gavall. — Croydon : Ricordi, 1976. —
12p ; 4to.
£0.95

(B76-50688)

VSRPMK/AAY — Arrangements. Collections
Play and sing : for descant recorder and-or other instruments /
[compiled by] Richard Addison. — Edinburgh :
Holmes-McDougall.
3rd book. — 1976. — 32p ; 4to.
Notebook format.
ISBN 0-7157-0848-1 : £1.05

(B76-51043)

VSS — TREBLE RECORDER
VSSNU — Duets
Dolci, Amico
Nuovo ricercare 4 a due voci : für zwei Altblockflöten / [von]
Amico Dolci. — Wilhemshaven : Heinrichshofen ; [London] :
[Peters], 1975. — 11p ; 4to.
Unpriced

(B76-50305)

Giamberti, Giuseppe
[Duo tessuti con diversi solfeggiamenti. *Selections*]. Duetti per due
strumenti, soprani e tenori / [di] Giuseppe Giamberti ; a cura di
Giancarlo Rostirolla. — Wilhemshaven : Heinrichshofen ;
[London] : [Peters], 1975. — 18p ; 4to. — (Armonia strumentale ;
no.1)
Unpriced

(B76-50689)

VSSNUG — Duets. Suites
Aubert, Jacques
Les Petits concerts. Opus 16 : leichte Duos für Altblockflöten
(Querflöten, Oboen, Violinen oder andere Melodieninstrumente) /
von Jacques Aubert ; herausgegeben von Jost Harf. —
Wilhemshaven : Heinrichshofen ; London : Peters.
Concerts 1-3. — 1975. — 17p ; 4to.
Unpriced

(B76-50306)

Concerts 4-6. — 1975. — 15p ; 4to.
Unpriced

(B76-50307)

VSSPK/AAY — Treble recorder & piano. Arrangements. Collections
Thirty-one pieces of the 16th-18th centuries : for treble recorder and
piano / edited and arranged by Carl Dolmetsch. — London :
Universal, 1976. — 4to. — (Dolmetsch recorder series ; no.99)
Score (20p.) & part.
Unpriced

(B76-50690)

VSSPMJ — Unaccompanied treble recorder. Miscellaneous works
Dolci, Amico
Nuovo ricercare 5 : für Altblockflöte / [von] Amico Dolci. —
Wilhemshaven : Heinrichshofen ; [London] : [Peters], 1975. —
11p ; 4to.
Unpriced

(B76-50308)

VT — OBOE
VT/AC — Tutors
Rothwell, Evelyn
The oboist's companion / [by] Evelyn Rothwell. — London :
Oxford University Press.
Vol.2. — 1976. — 139p ; 4to. —
ISBN 0-19-322336-8 : Unpriced

(B76-50691)

VTP — OBOE & PIANO
VTPJ — Miscellaneous works
Mamlok, Ursula
Five capriccios : oboe and piano / [by] Ursula Mamlok. — New
York ; London : Peters, 1975. — 7p ; 4to.
Unpriced

(B76-50309)

Tull, Fisher
Fantasy on L'Homme armé : oboe and piano / [by] Fisher Tull.
— New York ; London : Boosey and Hawkes, 1976. — 4to.
Score (12p.) & part.
£1.25

(B76-50692)

VTPK — Arrangements
Couperin, François
[Pièces de clavecin, livre 3, ordre 13. Les Roseaux. *arr*]. Les
Roseaux = The reeds / [by] François Couperin ; arranged for
oboe and piano by Julia Randall. — London : Oxford University
Press, 1976. — 4to.
Score (4p.) & part.
ISBN 0-19-355910-2 : Unpriced

(B76-50310)

Rameau, Jean Philippe
[Les Indes galantes. *Selections : arr*]. Four oboe melodies / [by]
J.P. Rameau ; arranged for oboe and piano by Lionel Lethbridge.
— London : Oxford University Press, 1976. — 4to.
Score (10p.) & part.
ISBN 0-19-358461-1 : Unpriced

(B76-50311)

VTPK/AAY — Arrangements. Collections
The young horn-player : a series of graded arrangements for horn in
F and piano / arranged by Sidney M. Lawton. — London :
Oxford University Press.
Score (21p.) & part.
Vol.1. — 1975. — 4to.
ISBN 0-19-357459-4 : Unpriced

(B76-50312)

Vol.2. — 1975. — 4to.
ISBN 0-19-357461-6 : Unpriced

(B76-50313)

Vol.3. — 1975. — 4to.
ISBN 0-19-357463-2 : Unpriced

(B76-50314)

VTPM — UNACCOMPANIED OBOE
VTPMJ — Miscellaneous works
   Overton, David
      Moods 1 : for unaccompanied solo oboe / by David Overton. —
      London : Paterson, 1976. — 7p ; 4to.
      Unpriced
                                                                (B76-50315)

VTPMK/AAY — Arrangements. Collections
      A tune book for oboe / compiled by Evelyn Rothwell. — London :
      Oxford University Press, 1976. — 48p ; 4to.
         Contents: Part I: Folk songs, dances and traditional tunes - Part II: Rounds.
         ISBN 0-19-358667-3 : Unpriced
                                                                (B76-51044)

VUN — SAXOPHONE ENSEMBLE
VUNS — Quartets
   Howland, Russell
      [Quartet, saxophones no.2]. Saxophone quartet no.2 / [by] Russell
      Howland. — New York ; London : Schirmer, 1975. — 27p ; 4to.
      Unpriced
                                                                (B76-50316)

   Patterson, Paul
      Diversions : for saxophone quartet / [by] Pauk Patterson. —
      London : Weinberger, 1976. — 21p ; 8vo.
      Reproduction of the composer's manuscript.
      Unpriced
                                                                (B76-50693)

   Rushby-Smith, John
      [Quartet, saxophones]. Saxophone quartet / [by] John
      Rushby-Smith. — London : Simrock, 1976. — 4to.
         Score (26p.) & 4 parts. — Contents: 1: Allegretto - 2: Scherzo - 3: Adagio -
         4: Finale.
         £4.50
                                                                (B76-50694)

VUNSK/DW — Quartets. Arrangements. Songs, etc
   Harvey, Paul
      The Agincourt song : traditional, 1415 / arranged for saxophone
      quartet by Paul Harvey. — Sevenoaks : Novello, 1976. — 8p ;
      4to.
         Duration 2 min.
         £0.50
                                                                (B76-50695)

VUNT — Trios
   Taylor, Paul Arden
      Bach goes to sea : saxophone trio (S.A.B.) / [by] Paul Arden
      Taylor. — Ampleforth : Emerson, 1976. — 3pt ; 4to.
      Unpriced
                                                                (B76-50696)

VUS — ALTO SAXOPHONE
VUSNS — Quartets
   Cordell, Frank
      Gestures : saxophone quartet / [by] Frank Cordell. —
      Ampleforth : Emerson, 1976. — 4to.
         Score (9p.) & 4 parts.
         Unpriced
                                                                (B76-51045)

VUSPK — Arrangements
   Jacob, Gordon
      [Miscellanies. arr]. Miscellanies : seven pieces for alto saxophone
      and wind orchestra / [by] Gordon Jacob. — Ampleforth :
      Emerson, 1976. — 4to.
         Score (29p.) & part.
         £2.50
                                                                (B76-51046)

VUSPMJ — Miscellaneous works
   Camilleri, Charles
      Fantasia concertante no.6 : for solo E flat alto saxophone / [by]
      Charles Camilleri. — Eastwood : Basil Ramsey ; Wendover :
      Roberton, 1976. — 11p ; 4to.
         £1.50
                                                                (B76-50697)

VV — CLARINET
VV/AF/AY — Exercises. Collections
      Fifty classical studies for clarinet / edited by Pamela Weston. —
      London : Fentone Music, 1976. — 47p ; 4to.
      Unpriced
                                                                (B76-50698)

VVN — CLARINET ENSEMBLE
VVNSQK — Clarinets (3) & piano. Arrangements
   Massenet, Jules
      [La Navarraise. Nocturne. arr]. Nocturne / [by] J. Massenet ; arr.
      for three B flat clarinets with piano accompaniment by Harold L.
      Walters. — Miami : Rubank ; [Sevenoaks] : [Novello], 1976. —
      4to.
         Score (4p.) & 3 parts.
         Unpriced
                                                                (B76-50699)

VVNTG — Trios. Suites
   Parfrey, Raymond
      [Suite, clarinets (3), no.1]. Suite no.1 for three clarinets / by
      Raymond Parfrey. — London : EMI, 1976. — 7p ; 4to.
      Unpriced
                                                                (B76-51047)

   Parfrey, Raymond
      [Suite, clarinets (3), no.2]. Second suite for 3 clarinets / by
      Raymond Parfrey. — London : EMI, 1976. — 3p ; 4to.
      Unpriced
                                                                (B76-51048)

VVNTK/DW/G/AY — Trios. Arrangements. Folksongs. Collections
      Clarinets in chorus : 14 international folksongs / arranged for
      clarinet trio by Pamela Verrall. — Hamburg ; London : Rahter,
      1976. — 4to.
         Score (18p.) & 3 parts.
         £2.75
                                                                (B76-50700)

VVNU — Duets
   Biber, Heinrich Ignaz Franz
      [Passacaglia, viola, C minor]. Passacaglia, C-moll : für Viola /
      [von] Heinrich Ignaz Franz Biber ; herausgegeben von Walter
      Lebermann. — Frankfurt : Litolff ; New York : a London :
      Peters, 1975. — 13p ; 4to.
      Unpriced
                                                                (B76-50701)

   Gambaro, Giovanni Battista
      [Duets, clarinets, op.10. nos.1-3]. Drei Duos für zwei Klarinetten.
      Opus 10 / [von] Giovanni Battista Gambaro ; herausgegeben von
      Bernhard Päuler. — Frankfurt : Litolff ; New York ; London :
      Peters, 1976. — 2pt ; 4to.
      Unpriced
                                                                (B76-50702)

   Kreutzer, Conradin
      [Duets, clarinets (2), C major]. Duetto für zwei Klarinetten,
      C-dur / [von] Conradin Kreutzer ; herausgegeben von Gyorgy
      Balassa. — Frankfurt : Litolff ; New York ; London : Peters,
      1975. — 13p ; 4to.
      Unpriced
                                                                (B76-50703)

   Zehm, Friedrich
      Klarinetten im Duett : 8 Stücke für 2 Klarinetten gleicher
      Stimmung / [von] Friedrich Zehm. — Mainz ; London : Schott,
      1975. — 12p ; 4to. — (Klarinetten Bibliothek ; no.18)
         £1.75
                                                                (B76-50317)

VVP — CLARINET & PIANO
VVPE — Sonatas
   Hughes, Eric
      Sonata capriccioso : clarinet and piano / [by] Eric Hughes. —
      Ampleforth : Emerson, 1976. — 4to.
         Score (25p.) & part.
         Unpriced
                                                                (B76-51049)

VVPEM — Sonatinas
   Hildemann, Wolfgang
      [Sonatina, clarinet & piano, 'Ritmi dispari']. Ritmi dispari :
      Sonatine für Klarinette in B und Klavier [von] Wolfgang
      Hildemann. — Mainz ; London : Schott, 1976. — 4to. —
      (Klarinetten-Bibliothek ; no.15)
         Score (8p.) & part.
         £1.75
                                                                (B76-50704)

VVPFL — Concertinos
   Genzmer, Harald
      Concertino für Klarinette in B und Klavier / [von] Harald
      Genzmer. — Frankfurt : Litolff ; London : Peters, 1976. — 4to.
         Score (38p.) & part.
         Unpriced
                                                                (B76-50705)

VVPG — Suites
   Noble, John
      Cats : a suite for clarinet and piano / by John Noble. — London :
      Cramer, 1976. — 4to.
         Score (15p.) & part.
         £0.75
                                                                (B76-51050)

VVPK — Arrangements
   Binge, Ronald
      [The watermill. arr]. The watermill / [by] Ronald Binge ;
      arranged for clarinet and piano by Alan Frank. — London :
      Weinberger, 1976. — 4to.
         Score (4p.) & part. — The name of the arranger has been added in
         typewriting.
         Unpriced
                                                                (B76-50706)

VVPK/AAY — Arrangements. Collections
Jack Brymer clarinet series. — London : Weinberger.
For clarinet and piano. — Score (17p.) & part.
Easy book 1. — 1976. — 4to.
Unpriced
(B76-50707)

Moderate book 1. — 1976. — 4to.
Unpriced.
(B76-50708)

Seven romantics / arr. for clarinet and piano by Pamela Verrall. —
London : Cramer, 1976. — 4to.
Score (16p.) & part.
£0.60
(B76-50709)

Six romantic pieces / arranged for clarinet and piano by Gwilym
Beechey. — London : Oxford University Press, 1976. — 4to.
Score & part.
ISBN 0-19-355331-7 : Unpriced
(B76-50318)

VVPK/AW — Arrangements. Rondos
Weber, Carl Maria von, *Freiherr*
[Rondo, two pianos, op.60, no.8, in B flat major. *arr*]. Rondo in B
flat. Op.60, no.8 / [by] C.M. von Weber ; arranged for clarinet in
B flat and piano by Gwilym Beechey. — London : Oxford
University Press, 1975. — 4to.
Score (12p.) & part.
ISBN 0-19-359503-6 : Unpriced
(B76-50319)

VVPK/DW — Arrangements. Songs, etc
Rodgers, Richard
[Musical plays. *Selections: arr*]. Rodgers and Hammerstein clarinet
classics / arranged by Robin de Smet. — London : Williamson,
1976. — 4to.
Score (24p.) & part.
Unpriced
(B76-50710)

VVPK/LF — Arrangements. Concertos
Davis, Allan
[Festival concerto, clarinet & small orchestra. *arr*]. Festival
concerto for B flat clarinet and small orchestra / [by] Allan
Davis ; arrangement by the composer for clarinet and piano. —
New York ; London : Oxford University Press, 1974. — 4to.
Score (44p.) & part.
Unpriced
(B76-50711)

VVPM — UNACCOMPANIED CLARINET
VVPMJ — Miscellaneous works
Globokar, Vinko
Rédoublement : für einen Klarinettisten / [von] Vinko Globokar.
— Frankfurt : Litolff ; London : Peters, 1975. — 9ff ; obl.fol.
Reproduction of the composer's autograph.
Unpriced
(B76-50320)

Valbonesi, Ruggero
Five interludes : for clarinet solo / by Ruggero Valbonesi. —
London : British and Continental : EMI, 1976. — 8p ; 4to.
Unpriced
(B76-50321)

VVQ — CLARINET (A)
Birtwistle, Harrison
Linoi : clarinet in A and piano / [by] Harrison Birtwistle. —
London : Universal, 1976. — 1ff ; fol.
Unpriced
(B76-50712)

VVQPMJ — Unaccompanied clarinet (A). Miscellaneous works
Jenni, Donald
Musica della primavera : for solo clarinet [in A] / [by] D. Jenni.
— New York ; London : Associated Music, 1974. — 5p ; 4to.
Unpriced
(B76-50322)

VVU — BASS CLARINET
VVUPMJ — Unaccompanied bass clarinet. Miscellaneous works
Globokar, Vinko
Voix instrumentalisée : für einen Bassklarinettisten / [von] Vinko
Globokar. — Frankfurt : Litolff ; London : Peters, 1975. — 4ff ;
obl.fol.
Reproduction of the composer's autograph.
Unpriced
(B76-50323)

VWN — BASSOON ENSEMBLE
VWNTG — Trios. Suites
Hartley, Geoffrey
Suite for 3 bassoons / [by] Geoffrey Hartley. — Ampleforth :
Emerson, 1976. — 3pt ; 4to.
Unpriced
(B76-50713)

VWP — BASSOON & PIANO
VWPJ — Miscellaneous works
Burness, John
Four easy pieces : for bassoon / by John Burness. — London :
Paterson, 1976. — 4to.
For bassoon and piano. — Score (4p.) & part.
Unpriced
(B76-51051)

VWPK/LF — Arrangements. Concertos
Français, Jean
[Concerto, bassoon: arr]. Concerto pour contrebasse et orchestre /
[par] Jean Français ; reduction pour contre basse et piano par
Henning Brauel. — Mainz ; London : Schott, 1976. — 4to.
Score (27p.) & part.
£7.00
(B76-51052)

VWPM — UNACCOMPANIED BASSOON
VWPM/T — Variations
Burness, John
Variations for solo bassoon / by John Burness. — London :
Paterson, 1976. — 5p ; 4to.
Unpriced
(B76-50714)

Weait, Christopher
[Variations, bassoon]. Variations for solo bassoon / [by]
Christopher Weait. — Oakville : Harmuse ; [South Croydon] :
[Lengnick], 1975. — 5p ; 4to.
£1.25
(B76-51053)

VX — MOUTH ORGAN
VX/AC — Tutors
Schackner, Alan Blackie
Blues harp and marine band / by Alan Blackie Schackner. —
New York : Warner ; [London] : [Blossom], 1976. — 48p ; 4to.
A tutor for mouth organ.
Unpriced
(B76-51054)

VY — BAGPIPES
VY/AY — Collections
Ross's collection of pipe music / by William Ross ; with a new
foreword by Seamus MacNeill. — Wakefield : E.P., 1976. — [8],x,
254p ; 4to.
Includes original forewords by Willeam Ross and Norman Macleod.
ISBN 0-7158-1201-7 : £6.95
(B76-51055)

VYQ/AC — Northumbrian bag-pipes. Tutors
Fenwick, J W
Instruction book for the Northumbrian small-pipes / by J.W.
Fenwick. — 3rd ed. — Monkseaton (5 Denebank, Monkseaton) :
Northumbrian Pipers' Society, 1974. — [1],24p ; 4to.
ISBN 0-902510-01-0 : Unpriced
(B76-50715)

VYQPMJ — Unaccompanied Northumbrian bag-pipes. Miscellaneous
works
The **Charlton** memorial tune book : a collection of tunes for the
Northumbrian small-pipes and the fiddle / collected and edited by
Alan Hall and W.J. Stafford for the Northumbrian Pipers' Society.
— Monkseaton (5 Denebank, Monkseaton) : Northumbrian
Pipers' Society, 1974. — [4],64p ; obl.8vo.
ISBN 0-902510-03-7 : Unpriced
(B76-50716)

W — BRASS WIND INSTRUMENTS
W/AC — Tutors
Ridgeon, John
Brass for beginners / [by] John Ridgeon. — London : Boosey and
Hawkes, 1976. — vi,54p ; 4to.
£2.00
(B76-50717)

W/EH/AF — Embouchure. Exercises
Ridgeon, John
How brass players do it : a book of lip building and flexibility
exercises / [by] John Ridgeon. — Croydon : Belwin Mills, 1976.
— 38p ; 4to.
Unpriced
(B76-50718)

WM — BRASS BAND
WM/AY — Collections
Salvation Army Brass Band Journal (Festival series). — London :
Salvationist Publishing and Supplies.
Nos.369-372 : On parade : march / by Eilev Herikstad. We are an army :
selection / by Robert Redhead. Radiant pathway : duet, for basses E flat
and B flat / by Leslie Condon. Thou must leave thy lowly dwelling / by
Hector Berlioz ; arr. Ray Steadman-Allen. — 1975. — 65p ; obl. 8vo.
Unpriced
(B76-50719)

Nos.373-376 : Happy in the fight : cornet duet / by Ray Steadman-Allen. Marche militaire française / by C. Saint-Saëns. Towards the victory : prelude and fugue / by Kenneth Downie. The word of grace : trombone solo / by Norman Bearcroft. — 1976. — 73p ; obl. 8vo. — Unpriced

(B76-50720)

Salvation Army Brass Band Journal (General series). — London : Salvationist Publishing and Supplies.
Nos.1673-1676 : Guardian of our way : selection / by James Curnow. Sparkling slides : trombone foursome / by Ray Steadman-Allen. O God of Bethel / transcription by Charles Skinner. Atlanta Temple : march / by Edwin S. Stanyon. — 1975. — 39p ; obl. 4to. — Unpriced

(B76-50721)

Salvation Army Brass Band Journal (Triumph series). — London : Salvationist Publishing and Supplies.
Nos.789-792 : Schaffhausen march / by Eilir Herikstad. Healing waters : selection / by Leslie Condon. The pilgrim band : meditation / by Derek Jordan. Ilford young people : march / by W.J. Hopkins. — 1975. — 38p ; obl. 8vo. — Unpriced

(B76-50722)

Nos.793-796 : Young campaigners : march / by Erik Silfverberg. A Scottish suite / by Michael Kenyon. Emmaus : hymn tune arrangements / by Robert Schramm. Consistency : cornet solo / by John Birch. — 1976. — 48p ; obl. 8vo. — Unpriced

(B76-50723)

Nos.797-800 : Bound for Canaan's shore : march / by Bruce Broughton. The golden rule : suite / by Philip Catelinet. Melcombe : hymn tune arrangement / by David Greenthorne. The decisive step : meditation / by Paul Marti. — 1976. — 34p ; obl. 8vo. — Unpriced

(B76-50724)

WMEM — Sinfoniettas
Ball, Eric
Sinfonietta for brass band 'The wayfarer' / [by] Eric Ball. — London : Boosey and Hawkes, 1976. — obl. 8vo & 8vo. — (Boosey and Hawkes brass band series ; no.924)
Score (41p.), Conductor (17p.) & 26 parts. — With several copies of various parts.
£8.00

(B76-50725)

WMGN — Fanfares
Golland, John
Fanfare for youth, Op.39, no.1 / [by] John Golland. — London : EMI, 1976. — 8vo.
For brass band. — Score (2p.) & 26 parts, with several copies of various parts.
Unpriced

(B76-51056)

WMH — Dances
Heath, Reginald
Dance caprice / [by] Reginald Heath. — Watford : R. Smith, 1976. — 8vo.
For brass band. — Conductor & 25 parts.
Unpriced

(B76-51057)

Lear, W Hogarth
Hogarth's hoe-down : for brass band / [by] W. Hogarth Lear. — London : Chester Music, 1976. — 4to. — (Just brass ; no.1BB)
Piano conductor (8p.) & 25 parts, with several copies of various parts.
Unpriced

(B76-51058)

WMHVKK — Rumbas
Slack, Roy
Rumba : for brass band / [by] Roy Slack. — London : EMI, 1976. — 8vo.
Conductor (1p.) & 25 parts.
Unpriced

(B76-50726)

WMJ — Miscellaneous works
Golland, John
Fives and threes : brass band / [by] John Golland. — London : British and Continental : EMI, 1976. — 8vo.
Short score (4p.) & 10 parts.
Unpriced

(B76-50324)

Gregson, Edward
A Swedish march, and, Fanfare / by Edward Gregson. — Watford : R. Smith, 1976. — 16p ; obl.4to.
For brass band. — Duration 4 min.
Unpriced

(B76-51059)

Howarth, Elgar
Parade : for brass band / [by] Elgar Howarth. — London : Chester Music, 1976. — 4to. — (Just brass ; no.6 BB)
Piano conductor (8p.) & 25 parts, various parts are in duplicate.
Unpriced

(B76-51060)

Kelly, Bryan
Andalucia : for brass band / [by] Bryan Kelly. — Sevenoaks : Paxton, 1976. — 32p ; obl.4to.
Duration 6 min.
Unpriced

(B76-51061)

Kenny, Terry A
The Mexican trot / [by] T.A. Kenny. — London : Studio Music, 1976. — 8vo.
For brass band. — Conductor (3p.) & 24 parts. — With several copies of various parts.
Unpriced

(B76-50727)

Lane, Philip
A spring overture / by Philip Lane. — Watford : R. Smith, 1976. — 30p ; obl. 4to.
For brass band. — Duration 9 min.
Unpriced

(B76-51062)

Lear, W Hogarth
Barney's tune : for brass band / [by] W. Hogarth Lear. — London : Chester Music, 1976. — 4to. — (Just brass ; no.2BB)
Piano conductor (6p.) & 33 parts, with several copies of various parts.
Unpriced

(B76-51063)

Lear, W Hogarth
Paris le soir : for brass band / [by] W. Hogarth Lear. — London : Chester Music, 1976. — 4to. — (Just brass ; no.5 BB)
Piano conductor (7p.) & 25 parts, with several copies of various parts.
Unpriced

(B76-51064)

Lear, W Hogarth
Red sky at night : for brass band / [by] W. Hogarth Lear. — London : Chester Music, 1976. — 4to. — (Just brass ; no.7BB)
Piano conductor (7p.) & 25 parts, with several copies of various parts.
Unpriced

(B76-51065)

Noble, Harold
Tintern Abbey : elegy for brass band / [by] Harold Noble. — London : Studio Music, 1976. — 8vo.
Conductor (4p.) & 26 parts.
Unpriced

(B76-50728)

Sansom, Clive A
Sentimental mood / by Clive A. Sansom. — London : Studio Music, 1976. — 8vo.
For brass band. — Conductor & 23 parts - With several copies of various parts.
Unpriced

(B76-51066)

Siebert, Edrich
Seven league boots / by Edrich Siebert. — London : Studio Music, 1976. — 8vo.
For brass band. — Conductor (2p.) & 24 parts.
Unpriced

(B76-51067)

Sparke, Philip
Concert prelude / by Philip Sparke. — Watford : R. Smith, 1976. — 19p ; obl.4to.
For brass band.
Unpriced

(B76-51068)

Wood, Gareth
Tombstone-Arizona : a concert overture for brass band / [by] Gareth Wood. — Watford : R. Smith, 1976. — 40p ; obl. 4to.
Unpriced

(B76-50729)

WMK — Arrangements
Bach, Johann Sebastian
[Toccata, organ, S.565, D minor. *arr*]. Toccata in D minor / [by] J.S. Bach ; adapted for brass band by Edrich Siebert. — London : Studio Music, 1976. — 8vo.
Conductor & 24 parts. — With several copies of various parts.
Unpriced

(B76-50730)

Barratt, Bob
The piper in the meadow / adapted by Bob Barratt and Edrich Siebert. — London : Ambleside Music, 1976. — 8vo.
The tune appeared originally in the Hibernian Magazine February 1796. — Arranged for brass band. — Conductor (2p.) & 23 parts, with several copies of various parts.
Unpriced

(B76-51069)

Delius, Frederick
[On hearing the first cuckoo in spring. *arr*]. On hearing the first cuckoo in spring / [by] Frederick Delius ; arranged for brass band by Peter Warlock ; the part for flugel horn added by Elgar Howarth. — London : Oxford University Press, 1976. — 20p ; 4to.
Score (20p.). — Duration 4 min.
ISBN 0-19-362813-9 : Unpriced

(B76-50731)

Horovitz, Joseph
[Music hall suite. *Selections : arr*]. Three pieces / [by] Joseph Horovitz ; scored for brass band by Bram Gay. — Sevenoaks : Novello, 1975. — 41p ; 4to.
£2.50

(B76-50325)

MacCunn, Hamish
[The land of the mountain and the flood. Op.3. *arr*]. The land of the mountain and the flood : concert overture, Opus 3 / arranged for brass band by Glyn Bragg. — Sevenoaks : Paxton, 1976. — 40p ; obl.4to.
£2.00

(B76-51070)

Newsome, Roy
Mountains o' Mourne / arranged by Roy Newsome. — London : Keith Prowse : EMI, 1976. — 8vo.
For brass band - Conductor (2p.) & 25 parts - With several copies of various parts.
Unpriced

(B76-51071)

Waterworth, R
[Three gifts. *arr*]. Three gifts : trio for trombones / [by] R. Waterworth ; arranged for brass band by Edrich Siebert. — Hamburg ; London : D. Rahter, 1976. — 8vo.
Conductor (2p.) & 19 parts. — Conductor in triplicate.
£2.75

(B76-50732)

WMK/AAY — Arrangements. Collections
Further progressive steps / compiled by Ronald Hanmer. — Watford : R. Smith, 1976. — 52p ; 4to. — (Strand wind series)
For brass band.
Unpriced

(B76-50326)

WMK/AGM — Arrangements. Marches
Kennedy, James
[The St John march. *arr*]. The St John march / [by] James Kennedy ; arranged for brass band by James Howe. — London : Studio Music, 1975. — 8vo.
Conductor & 24 parts. — With several copies of various parts.
Unpriced

(B76-50327)

Prokofiev, Sergei
[The love of three oranges. March. *arr*]. March / by Serge Prokofieff ; arranged for brass and percussion by Fisher Tull. — New York ; London : Boosey and Hawkes, 1976. — 4to.
Score (5p.) & 13 parts.
£5.00

(B76-50733)

WMK/AY(XDXT46) — Arrangements. Collections, 1558-1603
Music from the Elizabethan court / arranged for brass band by Elgar Howarth. — Sevenoaks : Paxton, 1976. — 48p ; obl.4to.
Contents: The Earle of Oxford's marche, by William Byrd - Pavane, 'St Thomas Wake', by John Bull - Galliard, by John Bull - The King's hunting jigg, by John Bull.
£2.55

(B76-51072)

WMK/CM — Arrangements. Musical plays
Sherman, Richard M
[The slipper and the rose. *Selections : arr*]. The slipper and the rose. The story of Cinderella / music by Richard M. Sherman and Robert B. Sherman ; brass band arrangement by Edrich Siebert. — London : Noel Gay Music, 1976. — 4to.
A selection from the musical play. — Conductor & 24 parts. — With several copies of various parts.
Unpriced

(B76-50328)

WMK/DW — Arrangements. Songs, etc
Denza, Luigi
[Funiculi, funicula. *arr*]. Funiculi - finicula [sic] / [by] Luigi Denza ; arranged by Edrich Siebert. — Oxted (8 Hurst Green Close, Hurst Green, Oxted) : Paul, 1976. — obl.8vo.
For brass band. — Conductor & 24 parts. — With several copies of various parts.
Unpriced

(B76-50734)

Monckton, Lionel
[Songs. *Selections : arr*]. Lionel Monckton memories / arranged by Ronald Hanmer. — London : Studio Music, 1976. — 8vo.
For brass band - Conductor (8p.) & 25 parts.
Unpriced

(B76-51073)

Parry, *Sir* **Charles Hubert**
[And did those feet in ancient time. *arr*]. Jerusalem / music by C. Hubert Parry ; arranged for brass band by Ronald Hanmer. — London : Studio Music, 1976. — 8vo.
Conductor & 25 parts. — With several copies of various parts.
Unpriced

(B76-51074)

WMP — SOLO INSTRUMENT (S) & BRASS BAND
WMPWR/T — Cornet & brass band. Variations
Boddington, Stanley H
Silver threads among the gold : cornet solo / by Stanley H. Boddington. — London : Studio Music, 1976. — 8vo.
Conductor (3p.) & 26 parts. — Variations on the song by H.P. Danks.
Unpriced

(B76-50735)

WMPWRNT — Cornets (3) & brass band
Lear, W Hogarth
Chinese take away : for cornet trio and brass band / [by] W. Hogarth Lear. — London : Chester Music, 1976. — 4to. — (Just brass ; no.4 BB)
Piano conductor (12p.) & 25 parts, with several copies of various parts.
Unpriced

(B76-51075)

WMPWUNU — Trombones (2) & brass band
New, Derek
Hill-billy holiday : trombone duet / [by] Derek New. — London : Studio Music, 1976. — 8vo.
Conductor (2p.) & 24 parts - With several copies of various parts.
Unpriced

(B76-51076)

WMPWWK/DW — Euphonium & brass band. Arrangements. Songs, etc
Boddington, Stanley H
Believe me, if all those endearing young charms : euphonium solo / arranged by Stanley H. Boddington. — London : Studio Music, 1976. — 8vo.
Conductor (4p.) & 26 parts. — With several copies of various parts.
Unpriced

(B76-50736)

Foster, Stephen
[Jennie with the light brown hair. *arr*]. Jeanie with the light brown hair / [by] Stephen Foster ; arranged for euphonium solo and small band (excluding cornets and BB flat tubas) [by] Elgar Howarth. — London : Chester Music, 1976. — 4to. — (Just brass ; no.3 BB)
Piano conductor (3p.) & 12 parts, the parts for 1st and 2nd trombones, printed in score, are in duplicate.
Unpriced

(B76-51077)

WN — BRASS ENSEMBLE
Massaino, Tiburtio
Canzon trigesimaquinta : for four antiphonal brass choirs / [by] Tiburtio Massaino ; arranged by Daniel S. Augustine. — New York ; London : Schirmer, 1975. — 4to.
Score (14p.) & 17 parts.
Unpriced

(B76-50329)

WNK/AHXJ — Arrangements. Ragtime
Joplin, Scott
[The strenuous life. *arr*]. The strenuous life : a ragtime two-step / [by] Scott Joplin ; arranged for brass ensemble (4 B flat trumpets, 4 trombones, baritone, tuba) by Carl H. Kandel. — New York ; London : Schirmer, 1975. — 4to.
Score (9p.) & 11 parts.
Unpriced

(B76-50330)

WNK/DJ — Arrangements. Motets
Handl, Jacob
[Secundus tomus musici operis. Alleluia. In resurrectione tua. *arr*]. In resurrectione tua Christe / [by] Jacobus Gallus ; transcribed for two brass choirs by Carl H. Kandel. — New York ; London : Associated Music, 1975. — 4to.
Score (7p.) & 12 parts.
Unpriced

(B76-50331)

WNPG — Septets. Suites
Dodgson, Stephen
Suite for brass septet / [by] Stephen Dodgson. — London : Chester, 1976. — 4to. — (Just brass ; no.15)
Score in C (23pt.) & 7 parts.
Unpriced

(B76-50737)

WNQ — Sextets
Premru, Raymond
Music from Harter Fell : for brass sextet / [by] Raymond Premru. — London : Chester, 1976. — 4to. — (Just brass ; no.14)
Score (18p.) & 6 parts.
Unpriced

(B76-50738)

WNR — Quintets
Burrell, Howard
Festive occasion : for brass quintet / [by] Howard Burrell. — London : Chester : Hansen, 1975. — 4to.
Score (16p.) & 5 parts.
Unpriced

(B76-51078)

Ghent, Emmanuel
Dithyrambos : for brass quintet / [by] Emmanuel Ghent. — New York ; [London] : Oxford University Press, 1976. — 26p ; 4to.
Duration 17 1/2 min.
Unpriced

(B76-50332)

Henze, Hans Werner
[Der langwierige Weg in die Wohnung der Natascha Ungeheur. *Selections*]. Fragmente aus einer Show : Sätze für Blechquintett / [von] Hans Werner Henze. — Mainz ; London : Schott, 1976. — 18p ; 4to.
£2.25

(B76-50739)

London, Edwin
[Quintet, brass instruments]. Brass quintet : 2 trumpets in C, horn in F, trombone, tuba / [by] Edwin London. — New York : Henmar Press : Peters ; London : Peters, 1975. — 4to.
Score (41p.) & 5 parts. — Duration 14 min.
Unpriced

(B76-50333)

WNRK/AH — Quintets. Arrangements. Dances
Holborne, Antony
[Pavans, galiards, almains and other short airs. *Selections : arr*]. Suite of Elizabethan dances / [by] Antony Holborne ; arranged for brass quintet by Gerard R. Schwarz. — New York ; London : Schirmer, 1975. — 4to.
Score (20p.) & 5 parts.
Unpriced

(B76-50334)

WNRK/AH/AYD(XD101) — Quintets. Arrangements. Dances.
Collections. England, 1500-1600
English dances of the 16th century / arranged for brass ensemble by Elgar Howarth. — Sevenoaks : Novello, 1976. — 12p ; 8vo.
Duration 15 min. (complete).
£0.75

(B76-51079)

WNRK/DW — Quintets, Arrangements. Songs, etc
Iveson, John
Frère Jacques / arranged for brass quintet by John Iveson. — London : Chester : Hansen, 1976. — 4to. — (Just brass ; no.12)
Score (5p.) & 6 parts, with alternative parts for horn or trombone.
Unpriced

(B76-51080)

WNS — Quartets
Gabrieli, Giovanni
Canzon a 4, no.2 (1608) : for brass quartet / [by] Giovanni Gabrieli ; edited by Philip Jones. — London : Chester : Hansen, 1976. — 4to. — (Just brass ; no.13)
No.2 from Alessandro Raverii's collection published in 1608. — Score (4p.) & 5 parts, with an alternative part for trombone.
Unpriced

(B76-51081)

Hughes, Eric
Prelude and scherzo : for brass quartet (2 B flat cornets, E flat horn and euphonium) / [by] Eric Hughes. — London : Studio Music, 1976. — 8vo.
Score (15p.) & 4 parts.
Unpriced

(B76-51082)

Simpson, Lionel
[Quartet, brass instruments, no.2]. Brass quartet no.2, Opus 106, [sic] / by Lionel Simpson. — London : British and Continental, 1976. — 8vo.
Opus 106 is also allocated to the composer's 'Allegro for piano and recorder. — Score (3p.) & 6 parts, alternative parts for horn in F and E flat and for euphonium in treble and bass clefs.
Unpriced

(B76-51083)

WNSG — Quartets. Suites
Stephen, John
Play suite : seven simple quartets for beginner brass ensemble / by John Stephen. — London : British and Continental : EMI, 1975. — 8vo.
Score (4p.) & 9 parts.
Unpriced

(B76-50335)

WNSGM — Quartets. Marches
Parrott, Ian
Fanfare and march : for brass quartet / [by] Ian Parrott. — London : EMI, 1976. — 4to.
Score (4p.) & 4 parts. — Duration 4 1/4 min.
Unpriced

(B76-50740)

WNSK — Quartets. Arrangements
Haydn, Joseph
[Quartets, strings, ops.64, 77. *Selections: arr*]. Quartet no.3 on themes from Haydn / transcribed by Edrich Siebert. — London : Studio Music, 1976. — 8vo.
For brass quartet. — Score (12p.) & 4 parts.
Unpriced

(B76-50741)

Mozart, Wolfgang Amadeus
[Quartets, strings, nos.14, 16, K.387, 428. *Selections : arr*]. Quartet no.2 on themes from Mozart / transcribed by Edrich Siebert. — London : Studio Music, 1976. — 8vo.
For brass quartet. — Score (12p.) & 4 parts.
Unpriced

(B76-50742)

WPM — UNACCOMPANIED BRASS INSTRUMENT
WPMJ — Miscellaneous works
Globokar, Vinko
Echanges : für einen Blechbläser / [von] Vinko Globokar. — Frankfurt : Litolff ; London : Peters, 1975. — 4ff ; obl.fol.
Reproduction of composer's autograph.
Unpriced

(B76-50336)

Globokar, Vinko
Res/as/ex/ins-pirer : für einen Blechbläser / [von] Vinko Globokar. — Frankfurt : Litolff ; London : Peters, 1975. — 6ff ; obl.fol.
Reproduction of the composer's autograph.
Unpriced

(B76-50337)

WRP — CORNET & PIANO
WRPK — Arrangements
Beethoven, Ludwig van
[Für Elise. G.173. *arr*]. Für Elise / [by] Beethoven ; arranged for cornet solo with piano accompaniment by Edrich Siebert. — Oxted : Paul, 1976. — 4to.
Score (8p.) & part.
Unpriced

(B76-51084)

WS — TRUMPET
Purcell, Henry
[Selections. *Trumpet parts*]. Complete trumpet repertoire [of] Henry Purcell / edited by John King. — London : Musica rara, 1975. — 71p ; 4to.
The trumpet parts from Purcell's dramatic, choral and instrumental works.
Unpriced

(B76-50338)

WSP — TRUMPET & PIANO
WSPJ — Miscellaneous works
Konietzny, Heinrich
Collagen 1 & 2 : für Trompete in B und Klavier / [von] Heinrich Konietzny. — Regensburg : Bosse ; [London] : [Bärenreiter], 1975. — 4to.
Score (7p.) & part.
£6.50

(B76-50743)

Slack, Roy
A toye : for trumpet and piano / by Roy Slack. — London : British and Continental : EMI, 1976. — 4to.
Score (4p.) & part.
Unpriced

(B76-50339)

Williams, Christopher
Trumpet excursions : seven easy pieces for trumpet and piano / [by] Christopher Williams. — London : Chappell, 1976. — 4to.
Score (19p.) & part.
Unpriced

(B76-50340)

WSPK/AAY — Arrangements. Collections
The **first** year trumpeter. — London : Ashdown.
Volume 2 : Eight famous melodies for trumpet (or cornet) in B flat and piano / arranged by Robin de Smet. — 1976. — 4to.
Score (30p.) & part.
£1.20

(B76-50341)

Twelve trumpet tunes with piano accompaniment / arranged by Eve Barsham. — London : Oxford University Press, 1976. — 4to.
Score (16p.) & part.
ISBN 0-19-355320-1 : Unpriced

(B76-50744)

WSPK/AGM — Arrangements. Marches
Telemann, Georg Philipp
[Musique héroïque. *arr*]. Heroic music : a suite of twelve marches / [by] Georg Philipp Telemann ; transcribed for trumpet in B flat, or horn in F, or trombone and keyboard by Sidney Lawton. — London : Oxford University Press, 1976. — 4to.
Score (20p.) & 3 parts.
ISBN 0-19-359067-0 : Unpriced

(B76-50342)

WSPK/LF — Arrangements. Concertos
Mudge, Richard
[Concerto, trumpet & string orchestra, no.1, B flat major. *arr*]. Concerto no.1 for trumpet, strings and continuo / by Richard Mudge ; edited and arranged by Gerald Finzi, reduction for trumpet in B flat and piano by John Hampden. — London : Boosey and Hawkes, 1975. — 4to.
Score (14p.) & part.
£1.00

(B76-50343)

WSPLR — TRUMPET & PIANO
Farrell, Graham
Two revival preludes : for trumpet and organ / [by] Graham Farrell. — New York : Galaxy ; [London] : Galliard], 1976. — 4to.
Score (27p,) & part. — Contents: 1: Rock of ages - 2: What a friend we have in Jesus.
Unpriced

(B76-50745)

WSPLX — TRUMPET & PERCUSSION
Konietzny, Heinrich
Zwei Miniaturen : für Trompete (B) und Schlagwerk / von Heinrich Konietzny. — Regensburg : Bosse ; [London] : [Barenreiter], 1975. — 7p ; 4to.
£6.00

(B76-50746)

WSPM — UNACCOMPANIED TRUMPET
WSPMJ — Miscellaneous works
Beliebte Volkslieder : für Trompete (Flügelhorn oder Kornett) mit 2, Stimme ad lib., / bearbeitet von Willi Draths. — Mainz ; London : Schott, 1976. — 30p ; obl. 8vo.
£1.75

(B76-50747)

Holzer, Gerhard
Mikro-Kontapunkte Z : für Trompete / [von] Gerhard Holzer. — Frankfurt : Litolff ; London : Peters, 1974. — 65p ; 4to.
Unpriced

(B76-50748)

WTP — HORN & PIANO
WTPK/AAY — Arrangements
A **third** classical and romantic album for horn in F and piano / arranged by Watson Forbes. — London : Oxford University Press, 1976. — 4to.
Score (10p.) & part.
ISBN 0-19-356530-7 : Unpriced

(B76-50749)

WTPK/AAY — Arrangements. Collections
An **album** for the horn : thirteen easy pieces for horn in F and piano / arranged by Nicholas Marshall. — London : Oxford University Press, 1976. — 4to.
Score (21p.) & part.
ISBN 0-19-357745-3 : Unpriced

(B76-50344)

A **second** classical and romantic album for horn in F and piano / arranged by Watson Forbes. — London : Oxford University Press, 1976. — 4to.
Score (13p.) & part.
ISBN 0-19-356528-5 : Unpriced

(B76-50750)

WUN — TROMBONE ENSEMBLE
WUNS — Quartets
Langley, James
Maestoso and allegro for trombone quartet / by James Langley. — London : Studio Music, 1976. — 8vo.
Score (11p.) & 4 parts ; the parts for trombones in B flat are printed on the verso of the parts for concert trombones.
Unpriced

(B76-51085)

WUP — TROMBONE & PIANO
WUPK/LF — Arrangements. Concertos
Orr, Buxton
[Concerto, trombone & brass band. *arr*]. Concerto for trombone and brass band / [by] Buxton Orr ; arranged for trombone and piano by the composer. — Sevenoaks : Novello, 1976. — 4to.
Score (28p.) & part.
£2.55

(B76-51086)

WVP — TUBA & PIANO
WVPK — Arrangements
Grundman, Clare
Tuba rhapsody : tuba solo and piano reduction / [by] Clare Grundman. — New York ; [London] : Boosey and Hawkes, 1976. — 4to.
Score (20p.) & part.
£3.25

(B76-51087)

X — PERCUSSION INSTRUMENTS
X/AC — Tutors
Keune, Eckehardt
Schlaginstrumente = Percussion instruments : a method of instruction / [by] Eckehardt Keune ; translation Percy M. Young. — Cassel ; London : Bärenreiter.
Part 1 : Kleine Trommel = Side drum. — 1975. — 152p ; 4to.
£6.25

(B76-50751)

XM — PERCUSSION BAND
XMPXQR — Conga & percussion band
Fink, Siegfried
Conga negro / [von] Siegfried Fink. — Mainz ; London : Schott, 1976. — 5pt ; 4to. — (A battere ; 24)
Version 1 for conga solo, version 2 for conga and an ensemble of from 2-7 players.
£2.80
Primary classification XQRPMJ

XN — PERCUSSION ENSEMBLE
XNU — Duets
Carey, David
Eight études for two percussionists / [by] David Carey. — New York : Galaxy ; [London] : [Galliard], 1976. — 31p ; obl. 4to.
Unpriced

(B76-50752)

XPM — UNACCOMPANIED PERCUSSION
XPMJ — Miscellaneous works
Hiller, Wilfried
Katalog für Schlagzeug 1 = Catalogue for percussion 1 : 1 player / [by] Wilfried Hiller. — Mainz ; London : Schott, 1976. — 24p ; 4to. — (A battere ; no.22)
£2.00

(B76-50346)

Marco, Tomás
Floreal : música celestial 2, for percussion solo / by Tomás Marco. — Hamburg ; London : Simrock, 1976. — 8p ; 4to & obl, 4to. — (Percussion Studio)
£1.45

(B76-50345)

XPQ — MELODIC PERCUSSION
XPQNSK/AX — Quartets. Arrangements. Canons
Mozart, Wolfgang Amadeus
[Vier Scherzduette, K. Anh. 284 dd. Spiegelkanon. *arr*]. Mirror canon = Spiegelkanon / [by] W.A. Mozart ; arranged for mallet quartet by Stanley Leonard. — Hamburg ; London : Simrock, 1976. — 4to.
Attributed to Mozart. — Score (4p.) & 4 parts. — 'Originally for two instrumentalists, two more parts have been added by the arranger which are also in canon'.
Unpriced

(B76-51088)

XPQNU — Melodic percussion. Duets
Stahmer, Klaus
Musik für Mallets : 14 Duos und Soli für Malleinstrumente (Vibraphon, Marimbaphon, Xylophon, Stabspiele) / [von] Klaus Stahmer. — Mainz ; London : Schott, 1976. — 34p ; 4to. — (A battere ; no.23)
£3.50

(B76-51089)

XQ — DRUM
XQ/AF — Exercises
Fink, Siegfried
Studien für Drums = Studies for drums / [by] Siegfried Fink. — Hamburg ; London : Simrock. — (Percussion Studio)
Vol.1 : Elementary. — 1976. — 31p ; 4to. —
£2.00

(B76-50753)

May, Randy
Gamut : equalizing single strokes, double strokes, and paradiddles around the drum set with simultaneous footwork / [by] Randy May. — New York ; [London] : Chappell, 1976. — 55p ; 4to.
Unpriced

(B76-50754)

Moisy, Heinz von
Sounds and fills : for drumset / by Heinz von Moisy. — Hamburg ; London : Simrock, 1976. — 23p ; 4to. — (Percussion Studio)
£2.50

(B76-50347)

XQN — DRUM ENSEMBLE
XQRPMJ — Unaccompanied conga. Miscellaneous works
Fink, Siegfried
Conga negro / [von] Siegfried Fink. — Mainz ; London : Schott, 1976. — 5pt ; 4to. — (A battere ; 24)
Version 1 for conga solo, version 2 for conga and an ensemble of from 2-7 players.
£2.80
Also classified at XMPXQR

(B76-51090)

XR — TIMPANI
XR/AF — Exercises
Fink, Siegfried
Studien für Pauken = Studies for timpani / [by] Siegfried Fink. — Hamburg ; London : Simrock. — (Percussion Studio)
Vol.1 : Elementary. — 1976. — 63p ; 4to. —
£4.00

(B76-50755)

XS — BELLS
XSQMK — Handbell band. Arrangements
Handel, George Frideric
[Clock music. *arr*]. Ten pieces for a musical clock / [by] George Frideric Handel ; arranged for handbells by Norris L. Stephens. — New York ; London : Schirmer, 1975. — 11p ; 4to.
Unpriced

(B76-50348)

XTQR — XYLOPHONE
XTQRPK/LG — Arrangements. Suites
Carey, David
[Suite, xylophone & orchestra. *arr*]. Suite for xylophone and orchestra : piano reduction / [by] David Carey. — New York : Galaxy ; London : Galliard, 1976. — 4to.
Score (16p.) & part.
Unpriced

(B76-50349)

THE BRITISH CATALOGUE OF MUSIC 69

Composer and Title Index

20 years of British record charts, 1955-1975. *Queen Anne Press. £0.75* ADW/GB/FD(XPQ21/WT) (B76-08789) ISBN 0-362-00263-0

94th psalm. Sonata for organ. (Reubke, Julius). *Oxford University Press. Unpriced* RE (B76-50229) ISBN 0-19-375685-4

125 easy classical studies for flute : taken from classical flute methods. *Universal. Unpriced* VR/AF/AY (B76-51015)

A battere.
- Fink, Siegfried. Conga negro. *Schott. £2.80* XQRPMJ (B76-51090)
- Hiller, Wilfried. Katalog für Schlagzeug 1 = Catalogue for percussion 1 : 1 player. *Schott. £2.00* XPMJ (B76-50346)
- Stahmer, Klaus. Musik für Mallets : 14 Duos und Soli für Malletinstrumente (Vibraphon, Marimbaphon, Xylophon, Stabspiele). *Schott. £3.50* XPQNU (B76-51089)

A Tecnica na palma da mão : aproximação de elementos que compõem a técnica e evolução do estado moderno de órgão. (Salles, Annita). *Fermata do Brasil : Essex Music. Unpriced* R/AF (B76-50223)

ABC of music for actors. (Roe, Betty). *14 Barlby Rd, W10 6AR : Thomas Publishing. £0.30* A/M (B76-05037) ISBN 0-905210-00-x

Abduction from the Seraglio. (Mozart, Wolfgang Amadeus). *Musica rara. Unpriced* UNNK/CC (B76-50668)

Abend : für Doppelvokalquartett, Posaunenquintett, elektrische Orgel und Klavier. (Kagel, Mauricio). *Universal. Unpriced* ENWXUNPDX (B76-50043)

Action rhymes. *Ladybird Books. £0.24* ADW/GR (B76-30340) ISBN 0-7214-0439-1

Activities in music with children under six. (Hope-Brown, Margaret). *Evans Bros. £0.80* A/GR(VH) (B76-04797) ISBN 0-237-29165-7

Adam, George. Music time for Brownies : songs for unison voices and instruments. *Girl Guides Association. £0.65* JFE/NYHSDW/AY (B76-50111)

Adam and the beasts and other songs. (Clayre, Alasdair). *Faber and Faber in association with Faber Music. Unpriced* KEZDW (B76-50494) ISBN 0-571-10012-0

Adam lay y-bounden : S.A. unacc. (Carter, Andrew). *Banks. Unpriced* FEZDP/LF (B76-50445)

Adams, Brian. Three epitaphs : for voices and percussion. (Withams, Eric L). *Boosey and Hawkes. £0.35* FE/XPQDW (B76-50088)

Addison, Joseph. The spacious firmament on high : anthem for SSATTB unaccompanied. (Beaumont, Adrian). *Roberton. £0.18* EZDH (B76-50414)

Addison, Richard.
- Play and sing : a third book for descant recorder and/or other instruments. *Holmes McDougall. Unpriced* VSRPLK/AAY (B76-51042)
- Play and sing : for descant recorder and-or other instruments
- 3rd book. *Holmes-McDougall. £1.05* VSRPMK/AAY (B76-51043) ISBN 0-7157-0848-1

African music oral data : a catalog of field recordings, 1902-1975. (Stone, Ruth M). *Indiana University Press Distributed by Bell. £12.00* BZK/FD(WT) (B76-50759) ISBN 0-253-30262-5

Agay, Denes. The first psalm : for SATB chorus and piano with optional guitar and bass. *Warner : Blossom. Unpriced* DR (B76-50793)

Age of rock'n'roll. *See* Encyclopedia of rock. Vol.1.

Agee, James. Patterns in blue : medium voice, B flat clarinet and piano. (Sargon, Simon). *Boosey and Hawkes. £1.75* KFVE/VVPDW (B76-50502)

Agincourt song : traditional, 1415. (Harvey, Paul). *Novello. £0.50* VUNSK/DW (B76-50695)

Agricola, Christiane. Auld lang syne : schottische Lieder und Balladen. *Schott. £0.45* KDW/G/AYDL (B76-50490)

Ah! vous dirai-je, maman. Variations on a well-known theme : for recorder trio, descant, treble, tenor. (Meech, Michael). *Tomus. £0.70* VSNT/T (B76-51034)

Airs from seven lands. *Oxford University Press. Unpriced* VRPK/DW/AY (B76-51024) ISBN 0-19-358304-6

Aitchison, Martin. Dancing rhymes. *Ladybird Books. £0.24* ADW/H (B76-30341) ISBN 0-7214-0440-5

Akond of Swat : for four-part chorus of mixed voices with baritone solo and piano accompaniment. (Thomson, Virgil). *Schirmer. Unpriced* DW (B76-50032)

Albertson, Chris. Bessie. *Abacus. £1.00* AKDW/HHW/E(P) (B76-31123) ISBN 0-349-10054-3

Album for the horn : thirteen easy pieces for horn in F and piano. *Oxford University Press. Unpriced* WTPK/AAY (B76-50344) ISBN 0-19-357745-3

Album of popular tunes for the pianOrgan and 40 and 60 bass chord organs. *EMI. Unpriced* RPVK/DW/AY (B76-50941)

Aldine paperbacks. Blom, Eric. Everyman's dictionary of music. 5th ed. *Dent. £1.95* A(C) (B76-31911) ISBN 0-460-02151-6

Alexander Wood's the physics of music. (Wood, Alexander). 7th ed. *Chapman and Hall etc.. £5.50* A/B (B76-23699) ISBN 0-412-13250-8

Alkan
- Vol.1: The enigma. (Smith, Ronald). *Kahn and Averill. £3.00* BAO (B76-07533) ISBN 0-900707-39-9

All praises be to the Lord = Gelobet sey der Herr. (Antes, John). *Boosey and Hawkes. £0.30* DH (B76-50378)

All the tunes that ever there were : an introduction to the dulcimer in the British Isles. (Kettlewell, David). *Tisbury, Wilts. : Spoot Books. £3.25* ATWT/B(X) (B76-50758) ISBN 0-9505111-0-2

All this and 10%. (Godbolt, Jim). *Hale. £4.95* AMT(YC/XTA15) (B77-00347) ISBN 0-7091-5841-6

Allegri, Lorenzo. Il primo libro delle musiche. Primo ballo. Suite in 6 parts for 6 recorders. *Dolmetsch : Chappell. Unpriced* VSNQH (B76-51029)

Alleluia! I heard a voice : anthem for SATBB or SSATB. (Weelkes, Thomas). Revised edition. *Oxford University Press. Unpriced* DK (B76-50024) ISBN 0-19-352090-7

Along the sand : SSAA chorus and piano with optional alto. (Rocherolle, Eugénie R). *Warner : Blossom. Unpriced* FDW (B76-50081)

Alpári, Paul. Volksmusikartige Variierungstechnik in den ungarischen Passionen, 15. bis 18. Jahrhundert. (Bárdos, Kornél). *32 Great Titchfield St., W.1 : Bärenreiter. £16.25* ADD/LH(YG/XD301)

Alpári, Tilda. Volksmusikartige Variierungstechnik in den ungarischen Passionen, 15. bis 18. Jahrhundert. (Bárdos, Kornél). *32 Great Titchfield St., W.1 : Bärenreiter. £16.25* ADD/LH(YG/XD301)

Alte Bläser-Partiten : gesammelt und für den praktischen Gebrauch herausgegeben von Wilhelm Ehmann. *Bärenreiter. £2.00* UN/AYE (B76-50666)

Alvin, Juliette. Music for the handicapped child. 2nd ed. *Oxford University Press. £2.75* A(VMX) (B76-25691) ISBN 0-19-314920-6

Alwyn, William. Sinfonietta for strings. *Lengnick. Unpriced* RXMEM (B76-50608)

Ambages : for piano, four hands. (O'Brien, Eugene). *Schirmer. Unpriced* QNV (B76-50186)

American flag. Op.102. *Vocal score.* The American flag. Op.102 : cantata for four-part chorus of mixed voices and alto, tenor and bass soli. (Dvořák, Antonín). *Schirmer. Unpriced* DX (B76-50035)

American music awards series.
- Maves, David. Oktoechos : B flat clarinet, horn in F and percussion. *Henmar Press : Peters : Peters. Unpriced* NYHNT (B76-50177)
- Rhodes, Phillip. Trio, strings. Trio for strings : violin, viola, violoncello. *Peters. Unpriced* RXNT (B76-50244)

America's bicentennial songs from the great sentimental age, 1850-1900, Stephen C. Foster to Charles E. Ives : for unison, two- and four-part vocal ensembles with piano accompaniment. *Schirmer. Unpriced* CB/AYT (B76-50004)

Among your souvenirs : based on the BBC Radio 2 series ; fragrant memories from the Victorian and Edwardian period and a little later. *Boosey and Hawkes. Unpriced* KDW/AY (B76-50489)

Amram, David. Twelfth night. *Selections : arr.* Five Shakespeare songs : voice and piano. *Peters. Unpriced* KDW (B76-50117)

Amran, David.
- Three songs for America. *arr.* Three songs for America : bass voice and instruments (woodwind quintet and string quintet). *Peters. Unpriced* KGXDW (B76-50137)
- Three songs for America : bass voice and instruments (woodwind quintet and string quintet). *Peters. Unpriced* KGXE/MRDW (B76-50138)

Amusements champêtres, liv, 1. Suite, woodwind instruments, no.4, G major. Quatrième suite : for recorder quartet. (Chedeville, Nicolas). *Dolmetsch : Chappell. Unpriced* VSNSG (B76-51031)

An der schönen blauen Donau. Op.314. *arr.* The blue Danube. (Strauss, Johann, *b.1825*). *Fisher and Lane. Unpriced* RPVK/AHW (B76-50938)

An die Nachgeborenen, Op.42 : Kantate für Mezzosopran, Bariton, gemischte Chor und Orchester. (Einem, Gofffried von). *Boosey and Hawkes. £12.50* DE (B76-50777)

An die Nachgeborenen. Op.42. *Vocal score.* An die Nachgeborenen, Op.42 : Kantate für Mezzosopran, Bariton, gemischte Chor und Orchester. (Einem, Gofffried von). *Boosey and Hawkes. £12.50* DE (B76-50777)

And did those feet in ancient time. *arr.* Jerusalem. (Parry, *Sir* Charles Hubert). *Studio Music. Unpriced* WMK/DW (B76-51074)

Andalucia : for brass band. (Kelly, Bryan). *Paxton. Unpriced* WMJ (B76-51061)

Anderton, Barrie. Sonny boy! : the world of Al Jolson. *Jupiter Books. £3.95* AKDW/GB/E(P) (B76-12797) ISBN 0-904041-35-2

Andrews, Frank. 'Sterling'. (Carter, Sydney Horace). *19 Glendale Rd, Bournemouth BH6 4JA : 'Talking Machine Review'. £1.60* A/FE(P/X) (B76-09865) ISBN 0-902338-22-6

Angel voices singing : Christmas carol for four-part chorus of mixed, female or boys' voices with organ or unison voices with piano. (Garden, Edward). *Roberton. £0.15* DP/LF (B76-50789)

Angklung : for solo piano. (Boyd, Anne). *Faber Music. Unpriced* QPJ (B76-50199)

Annand, Herbert Harry. The catalogue of the United States Everlasting Indestructible cylinders, 1908-1913. 2nd ed. *19 Glendale Rd, Bournemouth BH6 4JA : The Talking Machine Review International. £0.45* A/FE(WT) (B76-27984) ISBN 0-902338-21-8

Another ten for guitar. *Fentone Music : Breitkopf and Härtel. Unpriced* TSPMK/AAY (B76-50276)

Anspacher, Peter. Concerto, flute no.2, op.31, D minor. *arr.* Konzert nr.2, d-moll, op.31, für Flöte und Orchester. (Danzi, Franz). *Heinrichshofen : Hinrichsen. Unpriced* VRPK/LF (B76-50680)

Antes, John.
- Die mit Thränen saën. *Vocal score.* Who with weeping soweth = Die mit Thränen saën. *Boosey and Hawkes. £0.30* DH (B76-50377)
- Gelobet sey der Herr. *Vocal score.* All praises be to the Lord = Gelobet sey der Herr. *Boosey and Hawkes. £0.30* DH (B76-50378)
- Gott hat uns angenehm gemacht. *Vocal score.* The Lord has been gracious unto us = Gott hat uns angenehm gemacht. *Boosey and Hawkes. £0.40* DH (B76-50379)
- My heart shall rejoice in His salvation. *Vocal score.* My heart shall rejoice in His salvation. *Boosey and Hawkes. £0.40* DH (B76-50380)
- Sing and rejoice, O daugher of Zion. *Vocal score.* Sing and rejoice, O daughter of Zion. *Boosey and Hawkes. £0.40* DH (B76-50381)
- Unser Seele wartet auf den Herrn. *Vocal score.* Our soul doth wait upon the Lord = Unser Seele wartet auf den Herrn. *Boosey and Hawkes. £0.30* DH (B76-50382)

Anthems for choirs
- Vol.4: Twenty-six anthems for mixed voices by twentieth-century composers. *Oxford University Press. Unpriced* DK/AY (B76-50025) ISBN 0-19-353016-3

Anthithesen, Op.18a : für Helzbläsinstrumente, Trompete, Harfe, Schlagzeug, Streichquartett und zwei Streichorchester. (Antoniou, Theodore). *Bärenreiter. £8.75* RXMPNYDNN (B76-50609)

Anthology of early renaissance music. *Dent. £9.95* C/AY(XCSK76) (B76-50001) ISBN 0-460-04300-5

Antiphonies : for mixed chorus unaccompanied
- No. 1. (Druckman, Jacob). *Boosey and Hawkes. £0.55* EZDW (B76-50429)
- No. 2. (Druckman, Jacob). *Boosey and Hawkes. £0.70* EZDW (B76-50430)
- No. 3. (Druckman, Jacob). *Boosey and Hawkes. £1.00* EZDW (B76-50431)

Antonicek, Theophil. De ratione in musica : Festschrift Erich Schenk, zu 5.Mai 1972. *32 Great Titchfield St., W.1 : Bärenreiter Kassel. £18.00* A(ZC)

Antoniou, Theodore.
- Anthithesen, Op.18a : für Helzbläsinstrumente, Trompete, Harfe, Schlagzeug, Streichquartett und zwei Streichorchester. *Bärenreiter. £8.75* RXMPNYDNN (B76-50609)
- Chorochronos 3 : for voice, tape, pianist or percussion. *Bärenreiter. £2.50* KDX (B76-50493)
- Katharsis : for flute, small orchestra, slide projections and groups of loudspeakers. *Bärenreiter. £4.25* MPVR (B76-50536)
- Meli, Op.17 : songs on Sappho's poems, for medium voice and orchestra. *Bärenreiter. £3.50* KFVE/MDW (B76-50501)
- Moirologhia for Jani Christou : for bariton sic and piano or bariton sic, piano and instruments. *Bärenreiter. £8.00* KGNDW (B76-50506)

Apothéose de Lulli : for 2 flutes/oboes/violins basse d'archet and b, c. (Couperin, François). *Musica rara. Unpriced* NUPNS (B76-50537)

Apple tree : Christmas music from 'The Cambridge hymnal'. *Cambridge University Press. £4.00* DP/LF/AY (B76-50791) ISBN 0-521-21479-3

Applebaum, Stanley. Eleven great cantatas : in full vocal and instrumental score. (Bach, Johann Sebastian). *Dover Publications : Constable. £5.25* EMDE (B76-50797) ISBN 0-486-23268-9

Appledorn, Mary Jeanne van. *See* Van Appledorn, Mary Jeanne.

Appleford, Patrick. Music for series 3 : new Communion hymns, Morning and Evening Prayer. *Weinberger. Unpriced* DM (B76-50390)

Appleyard, Patrick. Golden cross. The Hereford Festival hymn : written for the Hereford Diocesan 13th Centenary Festival, 1976. *Weinberger. £0.05* EZDM (B76-50057)

Aprahamian, Felix.
- Conversations with Olivier Messiaen. (Samuel, Claude). *Stainer and Bell. Unpriced* BMKS (B76-18371)

ISBN 0-85249-308-8

Essays from the world of music : essays from 'The Sunday Times'. (Newman, Ernest). *J. Calder. £6.50* A(D) (B76-34776) ISBN 0-7145-3548-6

More essays from the world of music : essays from the 'Sunday Times'. (Newman, Ernest). *J. Calder. £7.50* A(D) (B76-34777) ISBN 0-7145-3549-4

April jaunt : elementary accordion solo. (St John, A M). *Charnwood Music. Unpriced* RSPMJ (B76-50604)

Apron of flowers : for flute and piano. (Wilson, Robert Barclay). *EMI. Unpriced* VRPJ (B76-51021)

Aquinas, Thomas, *Saint. See* Thomas Aquinas, *Saint.*

Argento, Dominick. Jonah and the whale. *Vocal score.* Jonah and the whale : tenor and bass soli, mixed chorus, narrator and instrumental ensemble. *Boosey and Hawkes. £10.00* DE (B76-50774)

Arias : for small orchestra. (Hamilton, Iain). *Schott. Unpriced* MR/T (B76-50162)

Armbruster, Carl. Thirty songs : for high voice. (Liszt, Franz). *Dover Publications : Constable. £2.60* KFTDW (B76-50498)

Armonia strumentale. Giamberti, Giuseppe. Duo tessuti con diversi solfeggiamenti. *Selections.* Duetti per due strumenti, soprani e tenori. *Heinrichshofen : Peters. Unpriced* VSSNU (B76-50689)

Arnell, Richard. The technique of film music. (Manvell, Roger). Revised and enlarged ed. *Focal Press. £5.00* A/JR (B76-12128) ISBN 0-240-50848-3

Arnold, Malcolm.

Quartet, strings, no.2, op.118. String quartet no.2, op.118. *Faber Music. Unpriced* RXNS (B76-50615)

Quartet, strings, no.2, op.118. String quartet, no.2, Op.118. *Faber Music. £2.50* RXNS (B76-50951)

Arnold Schoenberg. Schoenberg. (Rosen, Charles). *Fontana. £0.75* BSET (B76-34779) ISBN 0-00-633558-6

Arnold Schoenberg. Schoenberg. (Rosen, Charles). *Marion Boyars : Distributed by Calder and Boyars. £4.25* BSET (B76-14361) ISBN 0-7145-2566-9

Aroundabout Christmas : 16 rounds for voices and/or instruments. (Crawley, Cliff). *Frederick Harris Music Lengnick. £0.25* EZDW/XC/LF (B76-50817)

Art of record buying : a list of recommended microgroove recordings

1976. *E.M.G. £5.00* A/FD(WT)

Art of the conductor. Robinson, Paul. Karajan. *Macdonald and Jane's. £3.95* A/EC(P) (B76-35356) ISBN 0-354-04031-6

Art of wind playing. (Weisberg, Arthur). *Schirmer Books : Collier Macmillan. £5.00* AU/E (B76-05041) ISBN 0-02-872800-9

Artman, Ruth. Today is the first day ... (of the rest of my life) : SATB chorus and piano, (optional flute, recorder or harmonica). *Warner : Blossom. Unpriced* DH (B76-50014)

Arts third level course : the development of instruments and their music. Bray, Trevor. Contemporary music, case stuwies II. *Open University Press. £1.60* A(XM76) (B76-50756) ISBN 0-335-00870-4

Arts third level course : the revolutions of 1848. Burrows, Donald. Music and revolution, Verdi. *Open University Press. Unpriced* BVE(N/XHK19) (B76-23700) ISBN 0-335-05059-x

Ashbee, Andrew. Consort music for viols in six parts. (Jenkins, John). *Faber Music for the Viola da Gamba Society of Great Britain. Unpriced* STNQR (B76-50963)

Ashburnham, George.

The story of unique piano tuition. 3rd ed.. *22 Effingham Close, Sutton, Surrey SM2 6AG : Ashburnham School of Music. £1.15* AQ/E(P) (B76-05916) ISBN 0-905329-00-7

'Vienna charm' : waltz : an organ solo. *Effingham Close, Sutton : Ashburnham School of Music. Unpriced* RJ (B76-50589)

Ashburnham School of Music. The story of unique piano tuition. (Ashburnham, George). 3rd ed.. *22 Effingham Close, Sutton, Surrey SM2 6AG : Ashburnham School of Music. £1.15* AQ/E(P) (B76-05916) ISBN 0-905329-00-7

Ashdown vocal duets.

Hudson, Hazel. The gospel train. (This train is bound for glory) : a quodlibet, for two mezzo-sopranos and baritone or two baritones. *Ashdown. £0.15* FNDW/LC (B76-50449)

Hudson, Hazel. Roll the old chariot along (with other things) : a quodlibet. *Ashdown. £0.15* FDW/LC (B76-50440)

Platts, Kenneth. An Advent carol. Opus 25 : for treble voices and piano. *Ashdown. £0.08* FLDP/LEZ (B76-50092)

Assisi, Francis of, *Saint. See* Francis of Assisi, *Saint.*

Associated Board of the Royal Schools of Music.

Eighteenth-century violin sonatas

Book 1. *Associated Board of the Royal Schools of Music. £1.00* SPE/AY (B76-50247)

Book 2. *Associated Board of the Royal Schools of Music. £1.00* SPE/AY (B76-50248)

Pianoforte examinations, 1977

Grade 1: Lists A and B (primary). *Associated Board of the Royal Schools of Music. £0.50* Q/AL (B76-50546)

Grade 2: Lists A and B (elementary). *Associated Board of the Royal Schools of Music. £0.50* Q/AL (B76-50547)

Grade 3: Lists A and B (transitional). *Associated Board of the Royal Schools of Music. £0.50* Q/AL (B76-50548)

Grade 4: Lists A and B (lower). *Associated Board of the Royal Schools of Music. £0.50* Q/AL (B76-50549)

Grade 5: List A (higher). *Associated Board of the Royal Schools of Music. £0.50* Q/AL (B76-50550)

Grade 5: List B (higher). *Associated Board of the Royal Schools of Music. £0.50* Q/AL (B76-50551)

Grade 6: List A (intermediate). *Associated Board of the Royal Schools of Music. £0.50* Q/AL (B76-50552)

Grade 6: List B (intermediate). *Associated Board of the Royal Schools of Music. £0.50* Q/AL (B76-50553)

Grade 7: List A (advanced). *Associated Board of the Royal Schools of Music. £0.50* Q/AL (B76-50554)

Grade 7: List B (advanced). *Associated Board of the Royal Schools of Music. £0.50* Q/AL (B76-50555)

Violin examinations, 1977 and 1978

Grade 1: Lists A and B (primary). *Associated Board of the Royal Schools of Music. £0.50* S/AL (B76-50622)

Grade 2: Lists A and B (elementary). *Associated Board of the Royal Schools of Music. £0.50* S/AL (B76-50623)

Grade 3: Lists A and B (transitional). *Associated Board of the Royal Schools of Music. £0.50* S/AL (B76-50624)

Grade 4: Lists A and B (lower). *Associated Board of the Royal Schools of Music. £0.50* S/AL (B76-50625)

Grade 5: Lists A and B (higher). *Associated Board of the Royal Schools of Music. £0.50* S/AL (B76-50626)

Grade 6: Lists A and B (intermediate). *Associated Board of the Royal Schools of Music. £0.70* S/AL (B76-50627)

Grade 7: Lists A and B (advanced). *Associated Board of the Royal Schools of Music. £0.70* S/AL (B76-50628)

Associated Examining Board for the General Certificate of Education. Report on the music examination in 1974 relating to the proposed single system of examining at 16+. *Wellington House, Aldershot, Hants. GU11 1BQ The Board. £0.50* A(VK/AL) (B76-15048) ISBN 0-901893-07-2

Aston, Peter.

Fantasias à 3, viols & keyboard. *arr.* Four fantasias. (Jeffries, George). *Chappell. Unpriced* QPK (B76-50581)

Make we joye : four carols set to anonymous 15th century texts, for S.A.T.B. *Chappell. Unpriced* EZDP/LF (B76-50807)

The true glory. *Royal School of Church Music. Unpriced* DH (B76-50782)

At the zoo : for guitar. (Croucher, Terence). *109 St Leonard's Rd, Leicester : Clarendon Music. £0.75* TSPMJ (B76-50986)

Ate Domino. *arr.* Cantate Domino, canticum novum. (Buxtehude, Dietrich). *Schirmer. Unpriced* DE (B76-50009)

Atem : für einen Bläser. (Kagel, Mauricio). *Universal. Unpriced* UNT (B76-50674)

Atkinson, Condit. I yield thee praise : for mixed chorus and piano. *Galaxy : Galliard. Unpriced* DH (B76-50383)

Aubert, Jacques.

Les Petits concerts. Opus 16 : leichte Duos für Altblockflöten (Querflöten, Oboen, Violinen oder andere Melodieninstrumente)

Concerts 1-3. *Heinrichshofen : Peters. Unpriced* VSSNUG (B76-50306)

Concerts 4-6. *Heinrichshofen : Peters. Unpriced* VSSNUG (B76-50307)

Auden, Wystan Hugh. Paul Bunyan : an operetta in two acts and a prologue. *38 Russell Sq., WC1B 5DA : Faber Music Limited for Faber. £0.80* BBUACF (B76-10251) ISBN 0-571-10015-5

Augustine, Daniel S. Canzon trigesimaquinta : for four antiphonal brass choirs. (Massaino, Tiburtio). *Schirmer. Unpriced* WN (B76-50329)

Auld lang syne : schottische Lieder und Balladen. *Schott. £0.45* KDW/G/AYDL (B76-50490)

Austin, Paul Britten-. *See* Britten-Austin, Paul.

Autumn song : piano solo. (Hunt, Reginald). *Ashdown. £0.35* QPJ (B76-50208)

Ave Maria : for four-part chorus of mixed voices with piano. (Rossini, Gioacchino Antonio). *Roberton. £0.14* DH (B76-50018)

Ave Maria : für Sopran, gemischten Chor und Streicher. (Donizetti, Gaetano). *Editio musica : Litolff. Unpriced* ERXMDJ (B76-50407)

Ave Maria. *Vocal score.* Ave Maria : für Sopran, gemischten Chor und Streicher. (Donizetti, Gaetano). *Editio musica : Litolff. Unpriced* DJ (B76-50387)

Ave maris stella. (Davies, Peter Maxwell). *Boosey and Hawkes. £2.50* NYDPNQ (B76-50542)

Ave verum corpus : S.A.T.T.B. and organ. (Milani, Francesco). *Oxford University Press. Unpriced* DJ (B76-50022) ISBN 0-19-350357-3

Away he run. *Vocal score.* Away he run : a musical based on the story of the prodigal son. (Fargo, Milford). *Stainer and Bell. Unpriced* CM/L (B76-50764) ISBN 0-85249-315-0

B., T. The maske of flowers. *5 Albert Grove, Leeds LS6 4DA : Boethius Press. £3.20* ACPF (B76-10977) ISBN 0-904263-02-9

Babbitt, Milton.

Post-partitions : piano. *Peters. Unpriced* QPJ (B76-50198)

Quartet, strings, no.4. String quartet, no.4. *Peters. Unpriced* RXNS (B76-50952)

Sextets : violin and piano. *Peters. Unpriced* SPJ (B76-50249)

Babe of Bethlehem : SATB. (Madden, John). *Oxford University Press. Unpriced* DP/LF (B76-50396) ISBN 0-19-343060-6

Babylon's falling : a jazz spiritual, for voices, recorders, guitars (optional) and piano. (Wastall, Peter). *Boosey and Hawkes. £1.75* FE/NWSDW/LC (B76-50083)

Bach, Carl Philipp Emanuel.

Die Israeliten in der Wuste = The Israelites in the wilderness : oratorio for soli, chorus and orchestra. *Eulenburg. Unpriced* EMDD (B76-50037)

Magnificat for soli, chorus and orchestra. *Eulenburg. Unpriced* EMDGKK (B76-50040)

Sieben Hauptwerke aus dem Klavierschaften. *Heinrichshofen : Peters. Unpriced* QPJ (B76-50566)

Symphony, string orchestra , no.3, Wotq.182/3. Sinfonie nr.3 für Streicher und Basso continuo, C-dur, Wotquenne 182/3. *Litolff : Peters. Unpriced* RXME (B76-50948)

Symphony, string orchestra , no.4, Wotq 182/4. Sinfonie nr.4 für Streicher und Basso continuo, A-dur, Wotquenne 182/4. *Litolff : Peters. Unpriced* RXME (B76-50949)

Symphony, string orchestra, no.1, Wotquenne 182/1, G major. Sinfonie Nr.1 für Streicher und Basso continuo, G-dur. Wotquenne 182/1. Zum ersten Mal herausgegeben von Traugott Fedtke. *Litolff : Peters. Unpriced* RXME (B76-50606)

Symphony, string orchestra, Wotg,182/2, B flat major. Sinfonie nr.2 : für Streicher und Basso continuo, B-Dur, Wotquenne 182/2. *Litolff : Peters. Unpriced* RXME (B76-50607)

Versuch über die wahre Art das Clavier zu spielen. *English.* Essay on the true art of playing keyboard instruments. *48 Great Marlborough St., W1V 2BN : Eulenburg Books. £3.00* APW/E (B76-15055) ISBN 0-903873-14-1

Bach, Jan. Dirge for a minstrel : SATB, soprano and tenor soli a cappella. *Associated Music. Unpriced* EZDW (B76-50065)

Bach, Johann Christian.

Sonatas, piano. *Selections.* Twelve keyboard sonatas Set 1, Opus 5. *Oxford University Press. Unpriced* QPE (B76-50191) ISBN 0-19-372222-4

Sonatas, piano. *Selections.* Twelve keyboard sonatas Set 2, Opus 17. *Oxford University Press. Unpriced* QPE (B76-50192) ISBN 0-19-372223-2

Symphony, D major. Sinfonie, D-Dur. *Schott. £4.00* MRE (B76-50881)

Bach, Johann Sebastian.

Cantata no.22: Jesus nahm zu sich die Zwölfe. Ertodt' uns durch dein' Güte. *arr.* Sanctify us by thy goodness : chorale. *Oxford University Press. Unpriced* TSNUK/DM (B76-50982) ISBN 0-19-355297-3

Cantata no.147, 'Herz und Mund und That und Leben'. Wohl mir dass ich Jesum habe. *arr.* Jesu, joy of man's desiring *Oxford University Press. Unpriced* VRPK/DM (B76-50292) ISBN 0-19-355279-5

Cantata no.208: Was mir behagt. Schafe konnen sicher weiden. *arr.* Sheep may safely graze : aria. *Oxford University Press. Unpriced* TSNUK/DW (B76-50983) ISBN 0-19-355298-1

Concerto, harpsichord & string orchestra, BWV 1052, F minor. Concerto, D minor, for harpsichord and string orchestra. BWV 1052. *Eulenburg. Unpriced* RXMPQRF (B76-50237)

Eleven great cantatas : in full vocal and instrumental score. *Dover Publications : Constable. £5.25* EMDE (B76-50797) ISBN 0-486-23268-9

Geistliche Lieder aus Schmelli's Gesangbuch und dem Notenbuch der Anna Magdelena Buch. Jesus ist das schönste Licht. S.474. *arr.* Jesus is the loveliest light. *Roberton. £0.10* EZDM (B76-50420)

St John passion. S.245. Johannes-Passion, BWV 245. *Bärenreiter. £6.50* EMDD/LK (B76-50405)

Selections. *arr.* Bach for the guitar : nine pieces. *Oxford University Press. Unpriced* TSPMK (B76-50273) ISBN 0-19-355300-7

Selections. *Flute parts.* Repertoire der Flötenpartien aus dem Kantaten und Oratorienwerk

Band 1: Kantaten BWV 8-102, Matthaus Passion, Oster-Oratorium. *Litolff : Peters. Unpriced* VR (B76-50288)

Sonatas, flute & continuo. *Selections.* Sonatas for flute and basso continuo. *Bärenreiter. £6.00* VRPE (B76-50677)

Sonatas, organ, nos.1-6. S.525-30. *arr.* Sechs Sonaten nach B.W.V. 525-530 = Six sonatas after B.W.V. 525-530 : for flute and harpsichord obbligato

Book 2: Sonatas 3 and 4. *Bärenreiter. £4.50* VRPK/AE (B76-50678)

Sonatas, organ, nos.1-6. S.525-30. *arr.* Sechs Sonaten nach B.W.V. 525-530 Six sonatas after B.W.V. 525-530 : for flute and harpsichord obbligato

Book 1: Sonatas 1 and 2. *Bärenreiter. £4.50* VRPK/AE (B76-50679)

Toccata, organ, S.565, D minor. *arr.* Toccata in D minor. *Studio Music. Unpriced* WMK (B76-50730)

Bach for the guitar : nine pieces. (Bach, Johann Sebastian). *Oxford University Press. Unpriced* TSPMK (B76-50273) ISBN 0-19-355300-7

Bach goes to sea : saxophone trio (S.A.B.). (Taylor, Paul Arden). *Emerson. Unpriced* VUNT (B76-50696)

Bacon, Ernst.

Bennington riflemen : realized for SA, TB, or two soloist and piano. *Boosey and Hawkes. £0.20* FDW (B76-50079)

Buttermilk hill : song of 1776, SA, TB or soloist, with instruments and percussion. *Boosey and Hawkes. £0.20* FE/NYGNSDW (B76-50087)

Bailey, Freca O. Rooftop ballet. Rooftop ballet and Underwater ballet : two piano solos. *Regina Music. Unpriced* QPJ (B76-50902)

Bailey, John.

Folk song : music arranged by John and Susanne Bailey, text by John Bailey. *SCM Press. Unpriced* JEZDW/G/AYC (B76-50106) ISBN 0-334-00492-6

Folk song : music arranged by John and Susanne Bailey, text by John Bailey. *SCM Press. Unpriced* JEZDW/G/AYC (B76-50106) ISBN 0-334-00492-6

Bailey, Susanne. Folk song : music arranged by John and Susanne Bailey, text by John Bailey. *SCM Press.*

Unpriced JEZDW/G/AYC (B76-50106)
ISBN 0-334-00492-6
Baines, Anthony. Brass instruments : their history and development. *Faber. £12.50* AW/B(X) (B77-00350)
ISBN 0-571-10600-5
Baird, Tadeusz. Concerto, oboe. Konzert für Oboe und Orchester. *Litolff : Peters. Unpriced* MPVTF (B76-50161)
Baker, Jennifer. Four anthems : for mixed chorus. (Tchaikovsky, Peter). *Ramsey : Roberton. Unpriced* EZDGTC (B76-50413)
Baker, Michael. Elegy, Op.21 : for flute and organ. *Harmuse : Lengnick. £1.00* VRPJ (B76-51017)
Baker, Richard, *b.1925.* The magic of music. *Sphere. £0.95* A(X) (B76-29099) ISBN 0-7221-1421-4
Baker, Richard Charles.
Chorale prelude on 'Christe sanctorum' : organ. *Frederick Harris Music : Lengnick. £0.70* RJ (B76-50927)
Three short introits : S.A.T.B. *Frederick Harris Music Lengnick. £0.27* EZDH (B76-50802)
Balada, Leonardo.
Tresis : for guitar, flute (or violin) and cello. *Schirmer. Unpriced* NVRNT (B76-50168)
Voices no.1 : for four-part chorus of mixed voices a cappella. *Schirmer. Unpriced* EZDW (B76-50066)
Balassa, Gyorgy.
Duets, clarinets (2), C major. Duetto für zwei Klarinetten, C-dur. (Kreutzer, Conradin). *Litolff : Peters. Unpriced* VVNU (B76-50703)
Passacaglia, viola, C minor. Passacaglia, C-moll : für Viola. (Biber, Heinrich Ignaz Franz). *Litolff : a London : Peters. Unpriced* VVNU (B76-50701)
Balent, Andrew.
Got the spirit! *Warner : Blossom. Unpriced* UMMK/DW/LC (B76-51006)
Got the spirit! (Balent, Andrew). *Warner : Blossom. Unpriced* UMMK/DW/LC (B76-51006)
Superband meets Mr Boogie. *Warner : Blossom. Unpriced* UMJ (B76-50281)
What Child is this? : Old English melody. *Warner Blossom. Unpriced* JDP/LF (B76-50827)
Ball, Eric. Sinfonietta for brass band 'The wayfarer'. *Boosey and Hawkes. £8.00* WMEM (B76-50725)
Ballad opera.
The medical and legal professions. *Garland. £400.00 the 28 vol. series* ACLM(XFWK61/ZC) (B76-19251)
ISBN 0-8240-0903-7
Topical and nautical operas. *Garland. £400.00 the 28 volume series* ACLM(XFWK61/ZC) (B76-20707)
ISBN 0-8240-0913-4
Ballet, W. Pavane & galliard, 'The Earl of Salisbury'. Pavane. *arr.* The 'Earl of Salisbury' carol. (Byrd, William). *Banks. Unpriced* EZDP/LF (B76-50422)
Ballett, W. Lute book lullaby : for soprano solo and four-part chorus of mixed voices unaccompanied. (Hanson, Geoffrey). *Roberton. £0.10* EZDP/LF (B76-50058)
Bamforth, Dennis A. Continuation du mellagne. Passan vostri triomphi. *arr.* Trionto del tempo / by Orlando di Lasso ; and, Ecco l'alma beata / by Giovanni Croce ; arranged for ten recorders in 2 choirs by Dennis A. Bamforth. (Lasso, Orlando di). *Tomus. Unpriced* VSMK/DH (B76-50298)
Band of the year : Op.66 : overture for concert band. (Bavicchi, John). *Oxford University Press. Unpriced* UMMJ (B76-51000)
Bang. *Choral Score.* Bang! (Rutter, John). *Oxford University Press. Unpriced* DACM (B76-50773)
ISBN 0-19-338051-x
Bangor Cathedral. Monographs. Paul, Leslie Douglas. Music at Bangor Cathedral Church : some historical notes. *The Cathedral Chaplain's House, Glanrafon, Bangor, Caernarvonshire LL57 1LH : Bangor Cathedral. £0.25* AD/LE(YDKPB/X) (B76-24542) ISBN 0-905229-00-2
Bannier. Opus 5 : chanson nègre, piano solo. (Gottschalk, Louis Moreau). *Peters. Unpriced* QPJ (B76-50206)
Barbershop memories : songs. *Robbins Music : EMI. Unpriced* GEZDW/AYT (B76-50097)
Barbirolli, *Lady* Evelyn. *See* Rothwell, Evelyn.
Barcarolle. (Offenbach, Jacques). *Fisher and Lane. £0.30* RPVK/DW (B76-50940)
Bárdos, Kornél. Volksmusikartige Variierungstechnik in den ungarischen Passionen, 15. bis 18. Jahrhundert. *32 Great Titchfield St., W.1 : Bärenreiter. £16.25* ADD/LH(YG/XD301)
Barney's tune : for brass band. (Lear, W Hogarth). *Chester Music. Unpriced* WMJ (B76-51063)
Barnstormers. *Selections.* The barnstormers. (Roe, Betty). *Thames. Unpriced* JDW/JM (B76-50457)
Barratt, Bob. The piper in the meadow. *Ambleside Music. Unpriced* WMK (B76-51069)
Barrett, James Lee. Shenandoah : a musical. (Udell, Peter). *French. £1.25* BGGTACM (B76-06888)
ISBN 0-573-68073-6
Barrios, Augustin. La Cathedral = The Cathedral : guitar solo. *British and Continental Music. Unpriced* TSPMJ (B76-50657)
Bars rest. (Burness, John). *38 Wigmore St., W1H 0EX : Paterson's Publications. £0.50* AVW/E(MN) (B76-09331) ISBN 0-9503608-1-3
Barsham, Eve.
Guida di musica. *Selections.* A James Hook album : twenty-two easy keyboard pieces. (Hook, James). *Elkin. £0.90* PWPJ (B76-50179)
Twelve trumpet tunes with piano accompaniment. *Oxford University Press. Unpriced* WSPK/AAY (B76-50744)
ISBN 0-19-355320-1
Barthold, Kenneth van. *See* Van Barthold, Kenneth.
Bartók, Béla.
Béla Bartók essays. *Faber. £38.50* A/G(D) (B76-36283)
ISBN 0-571-10120-8
Turkish folk music from Asia Minor. *Princeton University Press. £12.20* BZC (B76-36284) ISBN 0-691-09120-x
Bartolino da Padova.
Three madrigals for keyboard. *Antico. Unpriced* PWPJ (B76-50543)
Three madrigals for voices and/or instruments. *Antico. Unpriced* EZDU (B76-50426)
Bassett, Leslie.
Sextet, piano and strings. *Peters. Unpriced* NXNQ (B76-50170)
Sounds remembered : violin and piano. *Peters. Unpriced* SPJ (B76-50250)
Baudelaire, Charles. Nightpiece : for soprano and electronic tape. (Bennett, Richard Rodney). *Universal. Unpriced* KFLE/PVDX (B76-50497)
Bauer, Wilhelm Adolf. Briefe und Afzeichnungen
Band 7: Register. (Mozart, Wolfgang Amadeus). Gesamtuasg. *32 Great Titchfield St., W1P 7AD : Bärenreiter. £37.50* BMS(N)
Bauld, Alison. Van Diemen's land : a choral fantasy for mezzo soprano, bass, 2 tenors, baritones, male speaker and a capella. *Novello. £1.30* EZDX (B76-50818)
Bavicchi, John. Band of the year : Op.66 : overture for concert band. *Oxford University Press. Unpriced* UMMJ (B76-51000)
Baxter, James Reid. The tigers : satirical anti-war opera in a prologue and three acts. (Brian, Havergal). Centennial ed. *7 Gaitside Drive, Aberdeen : Aberdeen Branch of the Havergal Brian Society. £0.40* BBTNAC (B76-30338)
ISBN 0-9505185-0-6
Bazelon, Irwin. Knowing the score : notes on film music. *Van Nostrand Reinhold. £6.25* A/JR (B76-05914)
ISBN 0-442-20594-5
BBC. *See* British Broadcasting Corporation.
Beast of Bettesthorne. (Parry, William Howard). *Chester. Unpriced* CN (B76-50765)
Beatles : the singles collection 1962-1970. *Wise, Music Sales. £2.50* KDW/GB/AY (B76-50855)
ISBN 0-86001-274-3
Beaumont, Adrian. The spacious firmament on high : anthem for SSATTB unaccompanied. *Roberton. £0.18* EZDH (B76-50414)
Beaumont, Joseph. Lift up your heads, Opus 44, no.2 : SATB. (Jackson, Francis). *Oxford University Press. Unpriced* DH (B76-50385) ISBN 0-19-350360-3
Beaumont, William. Cinderella in Salerno. *Vocal score.* Cinderella in Salerno : an opera for schools in three acts based on Rossini's 'La Cenerentola'. (Walker, Raymond). *Novello. £1.70* CN (B76-50766)
Becker, John. Symphony no.3, 'Symphonia brevis'. *Peters. Unpriced* MME (B76-50142)
Beckwith, John, *b.1927.* Contemporary Canadian composers. *Oxford University Press. £11.75* A/D(YSX/XN55/M) (B76-25955) ISBN 0-19-540244-8
Bedford, David.
The golden wine is drunk : for 16 solo voices divided into 2 eight-part choirs of SSAATTBB. *Universal. Unpriced* EZDW (B76-50427)
With 100 kazoos. *Universal. Unpriced* NV (B76-50166)
Beecham, *Sir* Thomas, *bart.*
Concerto, piano, C minor. Piano concerto. (Delius, Frederick). *Boosey and Hawkes. Unpriced* MPQF (B76-50157)
Concerto, piano, C minor. *arr.* Piano concerto. (Delius, Frederick). *Boosey and Hawkes. Unpriced* QNUK/LF (B76-50184)
Beechey, Gwilym.
Rondo, two pianos, op.60, no.8, in B flat major. *arr.* Rondo in B flat. Op.60, no.8. (Weber, Carl Maria von, *Freiherr*). *Oxford University Press. Unpriced* VVPK/AW (B76-50319) ISBN 0-19-359503-6
Six romantic pieces. *Oxford University Press. Unpriced* VVPK/AAY (B76-50318) ISBN 0-19-355331-7
Beeson, Jack. Old hundredth prelude and doxology : music for organ. *Boosey and Hawkes. £1.00* RJ (B76-50928)
Beethoven, Ludwig van.
Fugue for 6 cellos on themes by Beethoven. (Bunting, Christopher). *Oxford University Press. Unpriced* SRNQ/Y (B76-50641) ISBN 0-19-355743-6
Für Elise. G.173. *arr.* Für Elise. *Paul. Unpriced* QPK (B76-50918)
Für Elise. G.173. *arr.* Für Elise. *Paul. Unpriced* WRPK (B76-51084)
Romance, violin & orchestra, no.1, op.40, G major. *arr.* Beneficence. *Fischer; Pinns Farm, West Wellow, Romsey : Edgar New gass. Unpriced* KDW (B76-50118)
Sonatina, mandoline & piano, Kinsky 43, D minor. *arr.* Sonatine, d-moll, für zwei Gitarren. *Schott. £0.90* TSNUK/AEM (B76-50271)
Symphony, no.9, op.125, D major, 'Choral'. Freude, schöner Gotterfunken. *arr.* Ode to joy : from 'Choral symphony'. *Chappell. Unpriced* QPK (B76-50579)
Beethoven : a Victorian tribute based on the papers of Sir George Smart. (Young, Percy Marshall). *Dobson. £5.00* A/EC(P/ZD) (B76-33367) ISBN 0-234-77672-2
Beethoven quartets. (Kerman, Joseph). *Oxford University Press. £6.00* BBJARXNS (B77-00348)
ISBN 0-19-315135-9
Behold, I make all things new : anthem for four-part mixed choir with organ. (Rose, Bernard). *Roberton. £0.15* EZDK (B76-50805)
Behold, I show you a mystery : anthem for SATB and optional organ. (Tomblings, Philip). *St Gregory Publications. Unpriced* EZDK (B76-50056)
Beliebte Volkslieder : für Trompete (Flügelhorn oder Kornett) mit 2, Stimme ad lib.,. *Schott. £1.75* WSPMJ (B76-50747)
Believe me, if all those endearing young charms : euphonium solo. (Boddington, Stanley H). *Studio Music. Unpriced* WMPWWK/DW (B76-50736)
Benade, Arthur Henry. Fundamentals of musical acoustics. *Oxford University Press. £11.50* A/B (B76-25959)
ISBN 0-19-502030-8
Benedictine Nuns. *English Congregation. Stanbrook.* The Stanbrook Abbey hymnal. Revised ed. *Stanbrook Abbey, Callow End, Worcester WR2 4TD : Stanbrook Abbey Music. Unpriced* DM/AY (B76-50786)
Benedictines. *Second Order. See* Benedictine Nuns.
Benediction : for unaccompanied mixed chorus. (Goldsmith, Owen). *Galaxy : Galliard. Unpriced* EZDW (B76-50434)
Beneficence. (Beethoven, Ludwig van). *Fischer; Pinns Farm, West Wellow, Romsey : Edgar New gass. Unpriced* KDW (B76-50118)
Benger, Richard. Sky songs. *Edwin Ashdown. £0.40* JFDW (B76-50462)
Benjamin, Thomas.
Freu'dich sehr : chorale prelude for organ. *Galaxy Galliard. Unpriced* RJ (B76-50590)
Techniques and materials of tonal music : with an introduction to twentieth-century techniques. *Houghton Mifflin. £7.95* A/R (B76-22853) ISBN 0-395-19095-9
Bennett, Michael. Seesaw : a musical. (Fields, Dorothy). *French. £1.25* BCMEACM (B76-06887)
ISBN 0-573-68069-8
Bennett, Richard Rodney.
Nightpiece : for soprano and electronic tape. *Universal. Unpriced* KFLE/PVDX (B76-50497)
Quartet, oboe & string trio. *Novello. £1.70* NVTNT (B76-50538)
Bennett, Robert Russell. The fun and faith of William Billings, American. *Vocal score.* The fun and faith of William Billings, American. *Chappell. Unpriced* DE (B76-50366)
Bennington riflemen : realized for SA, TB, or two soloist and piano. (Bacon, Ernst). *Boosey and Hawkes. £0.20* FDW (B76-50079)
Berceuse. *arr.* You will see an angel tonight. (Ropartz, Joseph Guy). *Galaxy : Galliard. Unpriced* DP/LF (B76-50397)
Berceuse héroïque : piano solo. (Debussy, Claude). *Peters. Unpriced* QPJ (B76-50200)
Berendt, Joachim. The jazz book. *Paladin. £1.50* AMT (B76-33376) ISBN 0-586-08260-3
Bergsagel, John. Early Tudor masses
Volume 2. *Stainer and Bell. Unpriced* EZDG/AYD(XCUE6S) (B76-50049)
ISBN 0-85249-385-1
Bergsma, William. Clandestine dialogues : for cello and percussion. *Galaxy Music : Stainer and Bell. Unpriced* SRPLX (B76-50962)
Berio, Luciano. Quintet, strings, op.30, no.6, in C major. Ritirata. *arr.* Quattro versioni originale della 'Ritirata notturna di Madrid'. (Boccherini, Luigi). *Universal. Unpriced* MMK (B76-50154)
Berkeley, *Sir* Lennox.
The Lord in my shepherd, Op.91, no.1. *Chester. Unpriced* DR (B76-50401)
Sinfonia concertante, oboe & chamber orchestra, op.84. Sinfonia concertante for oboe and chamber orchestra. Op.84. *Chester. Unpriced* MPVTE (B76-50880)
Berlin, Irving. The Irving Berlin collection : 16 great songs with facsimile covers. *EMI. Unpriced* KDW (B76-50842)
Berlioz, Hector.
Le Carnival Romain : ouverture caractéristique à grande orchestre. Op.9. *Eulenburg. Unpriced* MMJ (B76-50146)
Symphonie funébre et triomphale. Op.15. Grande symphonie funébre et triomphale. Op.15. *Eulenburg. Unpriced* EUMMDE (B76-50047)
Te Deum. *Eulenburg. Unpriced* EMDGKHB (B76-50798)
Bernac, Pierre. The interpretation of French song. *Gollancz. £7.50* AKDW/E(YH) (B77-00346)
ISBN 0-575-02207-8
Bernhard, Christoph. 'Fürchtet euch nicht' : Weihnachtskonzert für Sopran, zwei Violinen, Fagott (Violone) und Basso continuo. *Bärenreiter. £3.25* KFLE/NUWNSDE/LF (B76-50496)
Bernstein, Leonard. The unanswered question : six talks at Harvard. *Harvard University Press. £12.75* A (B76-22851) ISBN 0-674-92000-7
Berry, Wallace. Structural functions in music. *Prentice-Hall. £8.40* A/LZ (B76-11503) ISBN 0-13-853903-0
Bessie. (Albertson, Chris). *Abacus. £1.00* AKDW/HHW/E(P) (B76-31123) ISBN 0-349-10054-3
Best of George Gershwin. (Gershwin, George). *Chappell. Unpriced* KDW (B76-50843)
Best of Rodgers and Hart. (Rodgers, Richard). *Chappell. Unpriced* KDW (B76-50121)
Bethell, John. A catalogue of early keyboard instruments : the Benton Fletcher collection. (National Trust). *The Trust. £0.12* APW/B(YDBCF/WJ) (B76-22083)
ISBN 0-7078-0061-7
Bevan, Clifford. Trois ésquisses : for flute/piccolo, oboe and harpsichord. *British and Continental : EMI. Unpriced* NWPNT (B76-50169)
Bevis, Trevor Allen. The Ipswich bellfounders. *36 Great Clarendon St., Oxford : J. Hannon and Co. £2.00* AXS/BC(YDDLI/XEXK300)
Biber, Heinrich Ignaz Franz. Passacaglia, viola, C minor. Passacaglia, C-moll : für Viola. *Litolff : a London : Peters. Unpriced* VVNU (B76-50701)
Bibliography of Russian composers. (Moldon, David). *White Lion Publishers. £15.00* A/D(YM/M/T) (B76-28683)

ISBN 0-7284-0101-0
Biblioteca del Conservatorio di Musica G. Verdi. *MSS (Musica sacra 710).* Dixit Dominus : for SATB soli and chorus, string orchestra and organ continuo. (Scarlatti, Alessandro). *Novello. £1.20* ERXMDGKJ (B76-50046)
Billings, William. The fun and faith of William Billings, American. *Vocal score.* The fun and faith of William Billings, American. (Bennett, Robert Russell). *Chappell. Unpriced* DE (B76-50366)
Bing : the authorised biography. (Thompson, Charles). *Star Books. £0.70* AKDW/GB/E(P) (B76-25963)
ISBN 0-352-39887-6
Binge, Ronald.
The watermill. *arr.* The watermill. *Oxford University Press. Unpriced* TSPMJ (B76-50658)
ISBN 0-19-355510-7
The watermill. *arr.* The watermill. *Weinberger. Unpriced* VVPK (B76-50706)
Binkerd, Gordon.
Essays for piano. *Boosey and Hawkes. £4.00* QPJ (B76-50567)
For the infant Michael : SATB. *Boosey and Hawkes. £0.20* EZDW (B76-50067)
Her silver will. Looking back as Sposalizio : medium voice. *Boosey and Hawkes. £0.75* KFVDW (B76-50500)
Vier kleine Klavierstücke, nos. 3, 4. *arr.* Two Browning choruses : S.A.T.B. unaccompanied. (Liszt, Franz). *Boosey and Hawkes. Unpriced* EZDW (B76-50436)
Bird, George. The Fischer-Dieskau book of Lieder : the texts of over 750 songs in German. *Gollancz : Pan Books. £7.50* AKDW(YE) (B76-33373) ISBN 0-575-01852-6
Bird, John, *b.1941.* Percy Grainger. *Elek. £10.00* BGRT(N) (B76-35350) ISBN 0-236-40004-5
Bird, Richard, *b.1947 (Jan.24).* Musical instruments in colour. (Gammond, Peter). *Blandford Press. £2.60* AL/B (B76-00667) ISBN 0-7137-0628-7
Bird lives! (Russell, Ross). *Quartet Books. £2.25* AMT(P) (B76-31128) ISBN 0-7043-3094-6
Birtwistle, Harrison. Linoi : clarinet in A and piano. *Universal. Unpriced* VVQPJ (B76-50712)
Bishop, John, *b.1931.* The music of Frank Bridge. (Payne, Anthony, *b.1936*). *14 Barlby Rd, W10 6AR : Thames Publishing. £3.20* BBTP (B76-29100)
ISBN 0-905210-02-6
Bizet. (Dean, Winton). 3rd ed.. *Dent. £3.95* BBP (B76-12126) ISBN 0-460-03163-5
Blacking, John. How musical is man? *Faber. £4.95* A(ZF) (B76-22078) ISBN 0-571-10790-7
Blacklock, Robert Shedden. Which song and when : a handbook of selected song titles from 1880 to 1974. *10 Antigua St., Edinburgh EH1 3NH : Bandparts Music Stores Ltd. £0.40* ADW/GB(XL95/WT) (B76-06890)
ISBN 0-9504826-0-9
Blackwood, Brian William. Music and drama
1975-76. (Careers Research and Advisory Centre). *Bateman St., Cambridge CB2 1LZ : Hobsons Press (Cambridge) Ltd for CRAC. £0.85* A(VQ) (B76-04296)
ISBN 0-86021-038-3
Blades, James. Early percussion instruments : from the Middle Ages to the Baroque. *Oxford University Press. £2.95* AX/B(XCG551) (B76-14371)
ISBN 0-19-323176-x
Blake, David. In praise of Krishna : songs from the Bengali for soprano and nine instruments. *Novello. £2.00* KFLE/NVNMDW (B76-50863)
Blake, Nicholas. Suite, oboes (2) & cor anglais, op.6. Suite. Opus 6, 2 oboes and cor anglais. *Emerson. Unpriced* VNTG (B76-51013)
Blattau, Wendelin Müller-. *See* Müller-Blattau, Wendelin.
Blessing and glory : for full chorus of mixed voices with organ. (Boyce, William). *Roberton. £0.14* DK (B76-50388)
Bliss, *Sir* Arthur. Metamorphic variations : for orchestra. *Novello. £3.75* MM/T (B76-50141)
Bliss. (Palmer, Christopher). *Novello. £0.42* BBQ(N) (B76-30335) ISBN 0-85360-064-3
Block, Robert Paul.
Concerto, flute & string orchestra, G major. H.S.315. Concerto in G major for flute, strings and basso continuo, H.S.315. (Molter, Johann Melchior). *Musica rara. Unpriced* RXMPVRF (B76-50612)
Concerto, flute & string orchestra, G major. H.S.315. Concerto in G major for flute, strings and basso continuo, H.S.315. (Molter, Johann Melchior). *Musica rara. Unpriced* VRPK/LF (B76-50681)
Concerto, trumpets (3), oboes (2), timpani & string orchestra, D major. Concerto for 3 clarini (trumpets), timpani, 2 oboes, strings, and basso continuo. (Telemann, Georg Philipp). *Musica rara. Unpriced* RXMPNYHNQF (B76-50610)
Le Nozze di Figaro. K.492. *arr.* The marriage of Figaro Vol.1. (Mozart, Wolfgang Amadeus). *Musica rara. Unpriced* UNNK/CC (B76-50667)
Le Nozze di Figaro. K.492. *arr.* The marriage of Figaro Vol.2. (Mozart, Wolfgang Amadeus). *Musica rara. Unpriced* UNNK/CC (B76-50669)
Olor solymaeus. Canzon à 2. Canzon à 2 for cornetto (recorder-trumpet), bassoon (cello-rackett), & basso continuo. (Spiegler, Matthias). *Musica rara. Unpriced* NWNT (B76-50539)
Blom, Eric.
Everyman's dictionary of music. 5th ed. *Dent. £1.95* A(C) (B76-31911) ISBN 0-460-02151-6
Grove's dictionary of music and musicians. (Grove, *Sir* George). 5th ed. *Macmillan. £75.00(for vols 1-9 and supplementary vol. 10)* A(C) (B76-19247)
ISBN 0-333-00949-5
Bloodworth, Denis. Three consort pieces. (Nicolson, Richard). *Boosey and Hawkes. £1.50* VSNRK/DW (B76-50299)
Blue Danube. (Strauss, Johann, *b.1825*). *Fisher and Lane. Unpriced* RPVK/AHW (B76-50938)
Blues. *Latimer New Dimensions. £5.00* AKDW/HHW (B76-29101) ISBN 0-901539-49-x
Blues harp and marine band. (Schackner, Alan Blackie). *Warner : Blossom. Unpriced* VX/AC (B76-51054)
Blume, Friedrich. Protestant church music : a history. *Gollancz. £15.00* ADGTCW(X) (B76-01876)
ISBN 0-575-01996-4
Blunt, *Sir* Anthony. French art and music since 1500. *Methuen. £1.35* A(YH/X) (B76-50351)
ISBN 0-416-81650-9
Boccherini, Luigi. Quintet, strings, op.30, no.6, in C major. Ritirata. *arr.* Quattro versioni originale della 'Ritirata notturna di Madrid'. *Universal. Unpriced* MMK (B76-50154)
Bodanzky, R. Zigeunerliebe. *Selections : arr.* Songs from 'Gipsy love'. (Lehár, Franz). *Glocken. Unpriced* KDW (B76-50479)
Boddington, Stanley H.
Believe me, if all those endearing young charms : euphonium solo. *Studio Music. Unpriced* WMPWWK/DW (B76-50736)
Silver threads among the gold : cornet solo. *Studio Music. Unpriced* WMPWR/T (B76-50735)
Bodley, Seóirse. Eigse cheol tíre = Irish folk music studies Vol.2 : 1974-1975. *3 Sydenham Rd, Dundrum, Dublin 14 : Folk Music Society of Ireland. £1.00* A/G(YDM) (B76-35799) ISBN 0-905733-00-2
Bohemian bell carol : traditional. (Brown, Gerald Edgar). *Universal. Unpriced* JFE/NYLDP/LF (B76-50835)
Böhn, Liselotte.
Kinderlieder in leichten Sätzen : für zwei Sopranflöten. *Nagel : Bärenreiter. £1.25* VSRNUK/DW/GJ/AYE (B76-50687)
Volkslieder in leichten Sätzen : für zwei Sopranflöten. *Nagel : Bärenreiter. £1.25* VSRNUK/DW/G/AYE (B76-50686)
Weinachtslieder in leichten Sätzen : für zwei Sopranflöten. *Nagel : Bärenreiter. £1.25* VSRNUK/DP/LF/AYE (B76-50685)
Bolling, Claude. Cours d'initiation à la musique de jazz par le piano. *Chappell. Unpriced* QPHX/AC (B76-50197)
Bolton, Cecil.
Happy Christmas for chord organ. *EMI. Unpriced* RPVK/DP/LF/AY (B76-50939)
Happy Christmas for guitar. *EMI. Unpriced* TSPMK/DP/LF/AY (B76-50994)
Bond, Edward. We come to the river = Wir erreichen den Fluss : Handlungen für Musik. (Henze, Hans Werner). *Schott. £39.20* CQC (B76-50767)
Bone pastor, panis vere : SATB unacc. (Harness, Marjorie). *Banks. Unpriced* EZDJ (B76-50055)
Bonner, Stuart. Trinket : a piano solo. *Sonia Archer Lengnick. Unpriced* QPJ (B76-50903)
Bononcini, Giovanni Maria. Sinfonia, allemande, correnti e sarabande a 5 e 6. Op.5. *Selections : arr.* Two suites a 6 : for 6 recorders. *Universal. Unpriced* VSNQK/AHG (B76-51030)
Boorman, Stanley. Three madrigals for keyboard. (Bartolino da Padova). *Antico. Unpriced* PWPJ (B76-50543)
Boosey and Hawkes brass band series. Ball, Eric. Sinfonietta for brass band 'The wayfarer'. *Boosey and Hawkes. £8.00* WMEM (B76-50725)
Borge, Victor. My favorite intermissions. *See* Borge, Victor. My favourite intervals.
Borge, Victor. My favourite intervals. *Sphere. £0.60* A/D(YB/M) (B76-28392) ISBN 0-7221-1779-5
Borges, Jorge Luis. Compass : cello, contra bass, tenor, bass and electronics. (Reynolds, Roger). *Peters. Unpriced* JNGE/SRPLSSDX (B76-50114)
Born to be. (Gordon, Taylor). 1st ed. reprinted. *University of Washington Press. £3.50* AKDW/L/HJ/E(P) (B76-33369) ISBN 0-295-95428-0
Borodin, Aleksandr Porfirevich. Quartet, strings, no.1, A major. String quartet no.1, A major. *Eulenburg. Unpriced* RXNS (B76-50953)
Boustead, Alan. Writing down music. *Oxford University Press. £3.75* A(QU) (B76-14363) ISBN 0-19-317104-x
Bowsher, J M. Alexander Wood's the physics of music. (Wood, Alexander). 7th ed. *Chapman and Hall etc.. £5.50* A/B (B76-23699) ISBN 0-412-13250-8
Boyce, William.
Blessing and glory : for full chorus of mixed voices with organ. *Roberton. £0.14* DK (B76-50388)
Save me, O God : for 4-part chorus of mixed voices with piano or organ. *Roberton. £0.18* DK (B76-50389)
Boyd, Anne. Angklung : for solo piano. *Faber Music. Unpriced* QPJ (B76-50199)
Boydston, Christopher. The entertainer. *arr.* The entertainer : an excerpt. (Joplin, Scott). *Schirmer. Unpriced* VRPLTSK/AHXJ (B76-50293)
Brace, Geoffrey. Listen! music and nature. *Cambridge University Press. £1.60* A/KB (B76-13569)
ISBN 0-521-20706-1
Bragg, Glyn. The land of the mountain and the flood. Op.3. *arr.* The land of the mountain and the flood : concert overture, Opus 3. (MacCunn, Hamish). *Paxton. £2.00* WMK (B76-51070)
Brahms, Johannes.
Complete piano works for four hands. *Dover Publications : Constable. £3.50* QNV/AZ (B76-50894)
ISBN 0-486-23271-9
Klavierwerke
Band 1. *Litolff : Peters. Unpriced* QP/AZ (B76-50559)
Band 2. *Litolff : Peters. Unpriced* QP/AZ (B76-50560)
Waltzes, piano 2 hands, op.39. Walzer für Klavier zu zwei Händen. Opus 39. *Litolff : Peters. Unpriced* QNUHW (B76-50558)
Wiegenlied = Lullaby = Berceuse. Op.49, no.4. *Lengnick. £0.30* KDW (B76-50119)
Brannen, Ann.
E. Humperdinck's 'Hansel and Gretel' : based on E. Humperdinck's opera after the story by the Brothers Grimm. (Isaka, Yoshitaro). *F. Warne. £2.25* BHUACBN (B76-19463) ISBN 0-7232-1835-8
G.A. Rossini's 'William Tell'. (Mizusawa, Hiroshi). *F. Warne. £2.25* BRRACBN (B76-18578)
ISBN 0-7232-1833-1
P. Dukas' 'The sorcerer's apprentice'. (Yangagihara, Ryohei) *F. Warne. £2.25* BDVAMBN (B76-18582)
ISBN 0-7232-1834-x
Brass for beginners. (Ridgeon, John). *Boosey and Hawkes. £2.00* W/AC (B76-50717)
Brass in your school. (Lawrence, Ian). *Oxford University Press. £3.15* AWM(VF/VC) (B76-50355)
ISBN 0-19-318705-1
Brass instruments : their history and development. (Baines, Anthony). *Faber. £12.50* AW/B(X) (B77-00350)
ISBN 0-571-10600-5
Brauel, Henning. Concerto, bassoon: arr. Concerto pour contrebasse et orchestre. (Françaix, Jean). *Schott. £7.00* VWPK/LF (B76-51052)
Bray, Roger. Liber primus sacrarum cantionum. O quam gloriosum. O quam gloriosum : S.S.A.T.B. (Byrd, William). Revised ed. *Oxford University Press. Unpriced* EZDJ (B76-50417) ISBN 0-19-352060-5
Bray, Trevor. Contemporary music, case stuwies II. *Open University Press. £1.60* A(XM76) (B76-50756)
ISBN 0-335-00870-4
Breakers : for 4 harps. (Chiti, Gian Paolo). *Chappell. Unpriced* TQNS (B76-50969)
Bream, Julian. Five, Op.61 : for guitar. (Searle, Humphrey). *Faber Music. Unpriced* TSPMJ (B76-50991)
Breathe on me, breath of God : anthem for 3-part female voice choir unaccompanied. (Lees, Heath). *Roberton. £0.10* FEZDH (B76-50089)
Breathnach, Breandan. Ceol rince na hEireann
Cuid 2. *Oifig an tSolathair. Unpriced* LH/AYDM (B76-50865)
Breathnach, Breandán. Eigse cheol tíre = Irish folk music studies
Vol.2 : 1974-1975. *3 Sydenham Rd, Dundrum, Dublin 14 : Folk Music Society of Ireland. £1.00* A/G(YDM) (B76-35799) ISBN 0-905733-00-2
Brecon service : for mixed voice chorus and organ
No.1: Venite, exultemus Domino. (Hanson, Geoffrey). *Roberton. £0.14* DGM (B76-50370)
No.2 : Benedictus. (Hanson, Geoffrey). *Roberton. £0.22* DGM (B76-50371)
No.3: Te Deum laudamus. (Hanson, Geoffrey). *Roberton. £0.18* DGM (B76-50372)
No.4: Magnificat and Nunc dimittis. (Hanson, Geoffrey). *Robertson. £0.22* DGM (B76-50373)
No.5: Preces and responses. (Hanson, Geoffrey). *Robertson. £0.10* DGM (B76-50374)
Brendel, Alfred. Musical thoughts & afterthoughts. *Robson Books. £5.25* AQ (B76-33377) ISBN 0-903895-43-9
Brian, Havergal.
Legend : for violin and piano. *Musica Viva. £2.00* SPJ (B76-50633)
The tigers : satirical anti-war opera in a prologue and three acts. Centennial ed. *7 Gaitside Drive, Aberdeen : Aberdeen Branch of the Havergal Brian Society. £0.40* BBTNAC (B76-30338) ISBN 0-9505185-0-6
Brian (Havergal) Society. *See* Havergal Brian Society.
Briggs, Noel Currer-. *See* Currer-Briggs, Noel.
British Association of Concert Agents. Composite list of artists showing sole representation, by members of the British Association of Concert Agents, as at January 1, 1976. *c/o The Secretary, 44 Castelnau Gardens, Arundel Terrace, SW13 9DU : The Association. Unpriced* A(M/YC) (B76-15528) ISBN 0-904892-01-8
British Broadcasting Corporation.
Sounds of music. (Taylor, Charles Alfred). *British Broadcasting Corporation. £6.50* A/B (B76-10250)
ISBN 0-563-12228-5
The story of the piano. (Van Barthold, Kenneth). *British Broadcasting Corporation. £3.50* AQ/B(X) (B76-05040)
ISBN 0-563-12580-2
British Federation of Brass Bands. Directory of British brass bands : associations, societies, contests
Vol.1 : 1975-76. *c/o F.H. Bradbury, 47 Hull Rd, York YO1 3JP : British Federation of Brass Bands. £0.50* AWM/E(YC/BC) (B76-01203) ISBN 0-905170-00-8
British Federation of Music Festivals. Year book
1976. *106 Gloucester Place, W1H 3DB : The Federation. £1.00* A(YC/WE/Q) (B76-13568)
ISBN 0-901532-06-1
British music now : a guide to the work of younger composers. *Elek. £6.50* A/D(YC/M) (B76-08493)
ISBN 0-236-30933-1
British music yearbook : a survey and directory with statistics and reference articles
1976. *Bowker. £10.50* A(YC/BC) (B76-20706)
ISBN 0-85935-035-5
Britten, Benjamin.
Paul Bunyan : an operetta in two acts and a prologue. (Auden, Wystan Hugh). *38 Russell Sq., WC1B 5DA : Faber Music Limited for Faber. £0.80* BBUACF (B76-10251) ISBN 0-571-10015-5
Suite on English folk tunes, 'A time there was ...' Op.90 : for orchestra. *Faber Music. Unpriced* MRG (B76-50163)
Britten, Benjamin, *Baron Britten.*
Canticle 5. The death of Saint Narcissus. Op.89 : for tenor and harp. *Faber Music. Unpriced* KGHE/TQDE

(B76-50504)
Suite, cello, no.3. Op.87. Third suite for cello. Op.87. *Faber Music. Unpriced* SRPMG (B76-50647)
Britten-Austin, Paul. Play guitar. (Goran, Ulf). *Oxford University Press. £1.30* TS/AC (B76-50651) ISBN 0-19-322210-8
Brittn, Benjamin, *Baron Britten.* Canticle 5. The death of Saint Narcissus. Op.89 : for tenor and harp. *Faber Music. Unpriced* KGHE/TQDE (B76-50505)
Britton, Dorothy G. Yuzuru. *Vocal score.* Yuzuru = The twilight heron : opera in one act. (Dan, Ikuma). *Boosey and Hawkes. Unpriced* CC (B76-50363)
Brocklehurst, Brian. Second pentatonic song book. *Schott. Unpriced* JDW/G/PP/AY (B76-50828)
Brod, Max. Die Musik Israels. Revidierte Ausg., mit einen zweiten Teil 'Werden und Entwicklung der Musik in Israel'. *32 Great Titchfield St., W.1 : Bärenreiter Kassel. £10.50* A(YVD)
Brody, Elaine. The music guide to Great Britain : England, Scotland, Wales, Ireland. *Hale. £5.50* A(YC/BC) (B76-24539) ISBN 0-7091-5662-6
Brook, Claire. The music guide to Great Britain : England, Scotland, Wales, Ireland. (Brody, Elaine). *Hale. £5.50* A(YC/BC) (B76-24539) ISBN 0-7091-5662-6
Brooke, Stopford A. Let the whole Creation cry : for soprano solo and four-part chorus of mixed voices with organ. (Hanson, Geoffrey). *Roberton. £0.18* DH (B76-50016)
Brown, Alan. Musica Britannica : a national collection of music
Vol.28: William Byrd : Keyboard music 2. 2nd, revised ed. *Stainer and Bell. Unpriced* C/AYD (B76-50359) ISBN 0-85249-426-2
Brown, David. Homo natus de maliere : S.S.A.T.B. (Wilbye, John). *Oxford University Press. Unpriced* EZDH (B76-50054) ISBN 0-19-350352-2
Brown, Frank E. Canon, violins (3) & continuo, D major. *arr.* Canon in D : variations on a ground bass. (Pachelbel, Johann). *Cramer. £0.39* R/X (B76-50587)
Brown, George Mackay. Five Orkney scenes : a song cycle for female voice and piano. (Liddell, Claire). *Roberton. Unpriced* KFDW (B76-50131)
Brown, Gerald Edgar.
Bohemian bell carol : traditional. *Universal. Unpriced* JFE/NYLDP/LF (B76-50835)
Carol for a king. *Universal. Unpriced* JFE/XTPRPDP/LF (B76-50838)
Brown, Howard Mayer.
Embellishing sixteenth-century music. *Oxford University Press. £2.95* A(QM/XD101) (B76-14364) ISBN 0-19-323175-1
Music in the Renaissance. *Prentice-Hall. £8.00* A(XCR181) (B76-26567) ISBN 0-13-608505-9
Brown, Margaret Hope-. *See* Hope-Brown, Margaret.
Browning, Elizabeth Barrett. Vier kleine Klavierstücke, nos. 3, 4. *arr.* Two Browning choruses : S.A.T.B unaccompanied. (Liszt, Franz). *Boosey and Hawkes. Unpriced* EZDW (B76-50436)
Brymer, Jack.
Clarinet. *Macdonald and Jane's. £4.50* AVV/E (B76-36286) ISBN 0-356-08414-0
Jack Brymer clarinet series
Easy book 1. *Weinberger. Unpriced* VVPK/AAY (B76-50707)
Moderate book 1. *Weinberger. Unpriced* VVPK/AAY (B76-50708)
Buckton, David. The story of the piano. (Van Barthold, Kenneth). *British Broadcasting Corporation. £3.50* AQ/B(X) (B76-05040) ISBN 0-563-12580-2
Budde, Elmar.
Die schöne Müllerin. D.795 : für Gesang und Klavier. (Schubert, Franz). *Litolff : Peters. Unpriced* KDW (B76-50847)
Schwanengesang. D.957 : für Gesang und Klavier. (Schubert, Franz). *Litolff : Peters. Unpriced* KDW (B76-50848)
Buhé, Klaus.
Auld lang syne : schottische Lieder und Balladen. *Schott. £0.45* KDW/G/AYDL (B76-50490)
Englisches Folksong-Büchlein : die schönsten Songs und Balladen, für Singstimme, Melodieinstrumente und Gitarrenbegleitung. *Heinrichshofen : Peters. Unpriced* JE/LPLTSDW/G/AYD (B76-50458)
Irisches Folksong-Büchlein : die schönsten irischen Lieder und Balladen, für Singstimme, Melodieinstrumente (Blockflöte) und Gitarrenbegleitung. *Heinrichshoten Peters. Unpriced* JE/LPLTSDW/G/AYDM (B76-50460)
Schottisches Balladen-Büchlein : die schönsten schottischen Balladen, für Singstimme, Melodieinstrumente und Gitarre. *Heinrichstofen : Peters. Unpriced* JE/LPLTSDW/G/AYDL (B76-50459)
Builders. *Vocal score.* The builders : Angevin carol, in a festival setting : for combined mixed and unison choirs, soprano solo and optional instruments. (Davis, William Robert). *Oxford University Press. Unpriced* DP/LF (B76-50788)
Bunting, Christopher. Fugue for 6 cellos on themes by Beethoven. *Oxford University Press. Unpriced* SRNQ/Y (B76-50641) ISBN 0-19-355743-6
Burness, John.
Bars rest. *38 Wigmore St., W1H 0EX : Paterson's Publications. £0.50* AVW/E(MN) (B76-09331) ISBN 0-9503608-1-3
Four easy pieces : for bassoon. *Paterson. Unpriced* VWPJ (B76-51051)
Variations for solo bassoon. *Paterson. Unpriced* VWPM/T (B76-50714)
Burnett, Michael. The poltergoose : for recorder, percussion, voices and piano. *Chester. Unpriced* CQN (B76-50769)
Burns, Robert.
Ae fond kiss : old Highland melody. (Liddell, Claire). *Roberton. £0.14* EZDW (B76-50070)
I'll ay ca' in by yon toon : old Scottish air. (Liddell, Claire). *Roberton. £0.10* GEZDW (B76-50096)
Where are the joys? : traditional Scottish air. (Liddell, Claire). *Roberton. £0.14* EZDW (B76-50072)
Ye banks and braes. (Liddell, Claire). *Roberton. £0.10* EZDW (B76-50073)
Burrell, Howard. Festive occasion : for brass quintet. *Chester : Hansen. Unpriced* WNR (B76-51078)
Burrows, Donald. Music and revolution, Verdi. *Open University Press. Unpriced* BVE(N/XHK19) (B76-23700) ISBN 0-335-05059-x
Burt, James.
Londonderry air : traditional. *Chappell. Unpriced* QPK (B76-50919)
Michael, row the boat ashore : traditional. *Chappell. Unpriced* KDW/LC (B76-50858)
Burtch, Mervyn.
Epilogue : for four-part male voice choir unaccompanied. *Roberton. £0.10* GEZDH (B76-50823)
Three sonnets of John Donne : for four-part choir of mixed voices unaccompanied. *Roberton. £0.28* EZDW (B76-50814)
Burton, Andrew, *b.1916.* Musical instruments from odds and ends. (Burton, John Andrew). *Carousel. £0.45* AY/BC (B76-14366) ISBN 0-552-54096-x
Burton, Ian, *b.1942.* Listen! music and nature. (Brace, Geoffrey). *Cambridge University Press. £1.60* A/KB (B76-13569) ISBN 0-521-20706-1
Burton, John Andrew. Musical instruments from odds and ends. *Carousel. £0.45* AY/BC (B76-14366) ISBN 0-552-54096-x
Bush, Geoffrey.
The collected piano works of John Ireland
Vol.1. (Ireland, John). *Stainer and Bell. Unpriced* QP/AZ (B76-50187) ISBN 0-85249-393-2
Vol.2. (Ireland, John). *Stainer and Bell. Unpriced* QP/AZ (B76-50188) ISBN 0-85249-394-0
Vol.3. (Ireland, John). *Stainer and Bell. Unpriced* QP/AZ (B76-50189) ISBN 0-85249-395-9
Buttermilk hill : song of 1776, SA, TB or soloist, with instruments and percussion. (Bacon, Ernst). *Boosey and Hawkes. £0.20* FE/NYGNSDW (B76-50087)
Buxtehude, Dietrich.
Cantate Domino. *arr.* Cantate Domino, canticum novum. *Schirmer. Unpriced* DE (B76-50009)
In te Domine speravi : Kantate für Sopran, Alt, Bass und Basso continuo. *Litolff : Peters. Unpriced* DE (B76-50010)
By the sea : for guitar. (Croucher, Terence). *109 St Leonard's Rd, Leicester : Clarendon Music. £0.75* TSPMJ (B76-50987)
By winding roads. In old Donegal. In old Donegal, and, The fairy tree. (Parke, Dorothy). *Roberton. £0.10* JFDW (B76-50465)
By winding roads. *Selections.* Over the hills. The old man from Kilkenny. If. (Parke, Dorothy). *Roberton. £0.15* JFDW (B76-50466)
By winding roads. *Selections.* Three little towns, Blarney. (Parke, Dorothy). *Roberton. £0.10* JFDW (B76-50467)
By winding roads. The travellers. The travellers, and, The fairy hill. (Parke, Dorothy). *Roberton. £0.10* JFDW (B76-50468)
By winding roads. Winds. Winds, and, In summer time. (Parke, Dorothy). *Roberton. £0.20* JFDW (B76-50469)
Byrd, William.
Byrd for the guitar : five pieces. *Oxford University Press. Unpriced* TSPMK (B76-50274) ISBN 0-19-355800-9
Liber primus sacrarum cantionum. O quam gloriosum. O quam gloriosum : S.S.A.T.B. Revised ed. *Oxford University Press. Unpriced* EZDJ (B76-50417) ISBN 0-19-352060-5
Musica Britannica : a national collection of music
Vol.28: William Byrd : Keyboard music 2. 2nd, revised ed. *Stainer and Bell. Unpriced* C/AYD (B76-50359) ISBN 0-85249-426-2
Pavane & galliard, 'The Earl of Salisbury'. Pavane. *arr.* The 'Earl of Salisbury' carol. *Banks. Unpriced* EZDP/LF (B76-50422)
Byrd for the guitar : five pieces. (Byrd, William). *Oxford University Press. Unpriced* TSPMK (B76-50274) ISBN 0-19-355800-9
Cage, John.
Études Australes : piano
Books 1 and 2. *Peters. Unpriced* QPJ (B76-50568)
Books 3 and 4. *Peters. Unpriced* QPJ (B76-50569)
Caixinha de brinquedos. Dança campestre. Dança campestre. (Mignone, Francisco). *Arthur Napoleão : Essex Music. Unpriced* QPH (B76-50899)
Caland, Elisabeth. Sieben Hauptwerke aus dem Klavierschaften. (Bach, Carl Philipp Emanuel). *Heinrichshofen : Peters. Unpriced* QPJ (B76-50566)
Callas : prima donna assoluta. (Galatopoulos, Stelios). *W.H. Allen. £7.50* AKFL/E(P) (B76-35800) ISBN 0-491-01518-6
Cambini, Giovanni Giuseppe. Symphony, D major. Sinfonie D-dur für Kammerorchester. Zum ersten Mal. *Litolff : Peters. Unpriced* MRE (B76-50882)
Cambridge hymnal. *See* Apple tree.
Cambridge hymnal. *Choral score.* The Cambridge hymnal : vocal edition. *Cambridge University Press. £1.50* DADM (B76-50008) ISBN 0-521-20398-8
Cambridge University. *See* University of Cambridge.
Camilleri, Charles.
Fantasia concertante no.6 : for solo E flat alto saxophone. *Basil Ramsey : Roberton. £1.50* VUSPMJ (B76-50697)
Invocation to the Creator : for organ. *Roberton. £1.50* RJ (B76-50591)
Missa mundi : for organ. *Fairfield Music. £2.50* RJ (B76-50231)
Wine of peace : for organ. *Roberton. £0.30* RJ (B76-50929)
'Can you hear me, mother?' : Sandy Powell's lifetime of music-hall. (Powell, Sandy). *Jupiter Books. £3.50* A/JV/E(P) (B76-13584) ISBN 0-904041-38-7
Canonic studies. (Ziehn, Bernhard). 1st ed. reprinted. *Kahn and Averill. £4.50* A/RM (B76-35798) ISBN 0-900707-38-0
Canonical studies. Canonic studies. (Ziehn, Bernhard). 1st ed. reprinted. *Kahn and Averill. £4.50* A/RM (B76-35798) ISBN 0-900707-38-0
Cantata for all seasons. *Vocal score.* Cantata for all seasons : for solos and mixed voices with orchestra or organ. (Rooper, Jasper). *Thames. Unpriced* DE (B76-50368)
Cantata on poems of Edward Lear. Half an alphabet. Half an alphabet : canons for chorus, for four-part chorus of mixed voices with piano accompaniment. (Thomson, Virgil). *Schirmer. Unpriced* DW/X (B76-50034)
Cantata on poems of Edward Lear. The Akond of Swat. The Akond of Swat : for four-part chorus of mixed voices with baritone solo and piano accompaniment. (Thomson, Virgil). *Schirmer. Unpriced* DW (B76-50032)
Cantata on poems of Edward Lear. The Jumblies. The Jumblies : for four-part chorus of mixed voices with soprano solo and piano accompaniment. (Thomson, Virgil). *Schirmer. Unpriced* DW (B76-50033)
Canticle 5. The death of Saint Narcissus. Op.89 : for tenor and harp. (Britten, Benjamin, *Baron Britten*). *Faber Music. Unpriced* KGHE/TQDE (B76-50504)
Canticle 5. The death of Saint Narcissus. Op.89 : for tenor and harp. (Brittn, Benjamin, *Baron Britten*). *Faber Music. Unpriced* KGHE/TQDE (B76-50505)
Cantilena no.2 : piano. (Lombardi, Nilson). *Arthur Napoleão : Essex Music. Unpriced* QPJ (B76-50907)
Cantilena no.3 : piano. (Lombardi, Nilson). *Arthur Napoleão : Essex Music. Unpriced* QPJ (B76-50908)
Cantiones sacrae. Hodie Christus natus est. *arr.* Hodie Christus natus est. (Sweelinck, Jan Pieterzoon). *Roberton. £0.15* FEZDJ/LF (B76-50819)
Cantiones sacrae. Te lucis ante terminum. Te lucis ante terminum : festal and ferial tones, S.A.A.T.B. (unacc.). (Tallis, Thomas). *Oxford University Press. Unpriced* EZDGKRM (B76-50052) ISBN 0-19-350356-5
Canzon trigesimaquinta : for four antiphonal brass choirs. (Massaino, Tiburtio). *Schirmer. Unpriced* WN (B76-50329)
Capanna, Robert. Phorminx : for solo harp. *Schirmer. Unpriced* TQPMJ (B76-50265)
Careers Research and Advisory Centre. Music and drama 1975-76. *Bateman St., Cambridge CB2 1LZ : Hobsons Press (Cambridge) Ltd for CRAC. £0.85* A(VQ) (B76-04296) ISBN 0-86021-038-3
Carey, David.
Eight études for two percussionists. *Galaxy : Galliard. Unpriced* XNU (B76-50752)
Suite, xylophone & orchestra. *arr.* Suite for xylophone and orchestra : piano reduction. *Galaxy : Galliard. Unpriced* XTQRPK/LG (B76-50349)
Carillon, Récitatif, Masque : Trio für Mandoline, Gitarre und Harfe von Hans Werner Henze. (Henze, Hans Werner). *Schott. £3.50* TNT (B76-50649)
Carner, Mosco. Puccini : a critical biography. 2nd ed. *Duckworth. £14.00* BPU (B76-22081) ISBN 0-7156-0795-2
Carnival Romain : ouverture caractéristique à grande orchestre. Op.9. (Berlioz, Hector). *Eulenburg. Unpriced* MMJ (B76-50146)
Carol for a king. (Brown, Gerald Edgar). *Universal. Unpriced* JFE/XTPRPDP/LF (B76-50838)
Carol for to sing : 6 new carols for SATB. *Basil Ramsey : Roberton. Unpriced* DP/LF/AY (B76-50400)
Carousel books. Burton, John Andrew. Musical instruments from odds and ends. *Carousel. £0.45* AY/BC (B76-14366) ISBN 0-552-54096-x
Carrick, Malcolm. Higgle-ty pig-le-ty : 20 songs. *EMI. Unpriced* KEZDW (B76-50861)
Carroll, Lewis. Some hallucinations : unison song. (Williams, Patrick). *Bosworth. Unpriced* JFDW (B76-50831)
Carstairs, Adam. Zigeunerliebe. *Selections : arr.* Songs from 'Gipsy love'. (Lehár, Franz). *Glocken. Unpriced* KDW (B76-50479)
Carter, Andrew.
Adam lay y-bounden : S.A. unacc. *Banks. Unpriced* FEZDP/LF (B76-50445)
Ding dong! merrily on high : 16th cent. French tune. *Banks. Unpriced* FEZDP/LF (B76-50446)
Pancake Tuesday : unison (or solo) song. *Banks. Unpriced* JFDW/LFZ (B76-50110)
Sans day carol : Cornish, S.A.T.B. unacc. *Banks. Unpriced* EZDP/LF (B76-50423)
Carter, Anthony. España. *arr.* España : rhapsody for orchestra. (Chabrier, Emmanuel). *Bosworth. Unpriced* MK (B76-50139)
Carter, Sydney Horace. 'Sterling'. *19 Glendale Rd, Bournemouth BH6 4JA : 'Talking Machine Review'. £1.60* A/FE(P/X) (B76-09865) ISBN 0-902338-22-6
Caruso, Enrico. The opera lover's quiz book. (Taylor, Ian, *b.1932*). *Luscombe. £0.95* AC(DE) (B76-15052) ISBN 0-86002-084-3
Caserta, Peggy. Going down with Janis. *Futura Publications. £0.65* AKDW/GB/E(P) (B76-01877) ISBN 0-86007-231-2

Cash, Johnny. Man in black. *Hodder and Stoughton. £3.75* AKDW/GCW/E(P) (B76-22082) ISBN 0-340-20627-6

Catalogue of early keyboard instruments : the Benton Fletcher collection. (National Trust). *The Trust. £0.12* APW/B(YDBCF/WJ) (B76-22083) ISBN 0-7078-0061-7

Catalogue of the Hans Ferdinand Redlich Collection of musical books and scores : (including material on the Second Viennese School). (University of Lancaster. Library). *University Library, Bailrigg, Lancaster LA1 4YH : The University. £3.00* A(T) (B76-31432) ISBN 0-901699-35-7

Catalogue of the United States Everlasting Indestructible cylinders, 1908-1913. (Annand, Herbert Harry). 2nd ed. *19 Glendale Rd, Bournemouth BH6 4JA : The Talking Machine Review International. £0.45* A/FE(WT) (B76-27984) ISBN 0-902338-21-8

Catalogus musicus. Schaefer, Hartmut. Die Notendrucker und Musik verleger in Frankfurt am Main von 1630 bis um 1720 : eine bibliographisch-drucktechnische Untersuchung. *32 Great Titchfield St., W.1 : Bärenreiter. £28.13* A(S/YEF/XWK91)

Cathedral = The Cathedral : guitar solo. (Barrios, Augustin). *British and Continental Music. Unpriced* TSPMJ (B76-50657)

Cathedral organist, 1975-1976. *Cramer. £2.25* R/AYC (B76-50926)

Cats : a suite for clarinet and piano. (Noble, John). *Cramer. £0.75* VVPG (B76-51050)

Cattouse, Nadia. Red and green Christmas. *arr.* Red and green Christmas : for SATB chorus and keyboard. *Galaxy : Galliard. Unpriced* DP/LF (B76-50393)

Cavalier songs. *Stainer and Bell. Unpriced* KE/TDW (B76-50129) ISBN 0-85249-325-8

Cello Bibliothek. Gabrielli, Domenico. Sieben Ricercari (1689) : Violoncello solo. *Schott. £2.00* SRPMJ (B76-50260)

Ceol rince na hEireann
 Cuid 2. *Oifig an tSolathair. Unpriced* LH/AYDM (B76-50865)

Ceremonial occasion : a tribute to Her Majesty the Queen for the year of her silver jubilee, 1977 : a selection of famous marches and songs. (Friend, Howard C). *Bosworth. Unpriced* MK (B76-50867)

Chabrier, Emmanuel. España. *arr.* España : rhapsody for orchestra. *Bosworth. Unpriced* MK (B76-50139)

Chaliapin, Fedor Ivanovich. *See* Shaliapin, Fedor Ivanovich.

Chaliapin : an autobiography. (Shaliapin, Fedor Ivanovich). *White Lion Publishers. £6.50* AKGX/E(P) (B76-07530) ISBN 0-7274-0191-2

Chalker, Bryan. Country music. *Phoebus. £2.50* AKDW/GCW/E(M) (B76-34775) ISBN 0-7026-0015-6

Chant, H. Method splicing
 Part 1: Minor methods. *19 Lonewood Way, Hadlow, Tonbridge, Kent : Press of John Hilton. £2.00* AXSR/E (B76-35807) ISBN 0-900465-06-9

Chantefaibles : 10 chansons pour enfants. (Stravinsky, Soulima). *Peters. Unpriced* KDW (B76-50487)

Chappell, Herbert. The entertainer. *arr.* The entertainer. (Joplin, Scott). *Chappell. Unpriced* EZDW (B76-50068)

Chappell's evergreen classics.
 Burt, James. Londonderry air : traditional. *Chappell. Unpriced* QPK (B76-50919)
 Burt, James. Michael, row the boat ashore : traditional. *Chappell. Unpriced* KDW/LC (B76-50858)

Charakterstück : für Zitherquartett. (Kagel, Mauricio). *Universal. Unpriced* TUNS (B76-50661)

Charles Eliot Norton lectures. Bernstein, Leonard. The unanswered question : six talks at Harvard. *Harvard University Press. £12.75* A (B76-22851) ISBN 0-674-92000-7

Charles Ives and his America. (Rossiter, Frank Raymond). *Gollancz. £8.50* BIV(N) (B76-20007) ISBN 0-575-02103-9

Charlton memorial tune book : a collection of tunes for the Northumbrian small-pipes and the fiddle. *5 Denebank, Monkseaton : Northumbrian Pipers' Society. Unpriced* VYQPMJ (B76-50716) ISBN 0-902510-03-7

Chasin' the Trane : the music and mystique of John Coltrane. (Thomas, J C). *Elm Tree Books. £4.50* AMT(P) (B76-10255) ISBN 0-241-89340-2

Chatterton, Thomas. Dirge for a minstrel : SATB, soprano and tenor soli a cappella. (Bach, Jan). *Associated Music. Unpriced* EZDW (B76-50065)

Chedeville, Nicolas. Amusements champêtres, liv, 1. Suite, woodwind instruments, no.4, G major. Quatrième suite : for recorder quartet. *Dolmetsch : Chappell. Unpriced* VSNSG (B76-51031)

Chelsea College of Science and Technology. Teaching primary science. *See* Teaching primary science.

Chenette, Louis Fred.
 Blessing and glory : for full chorus of mixed voices with organ. (Boyce, William). *Roberton. £0.14* DK (B76-50388)
 Save me, O God : for 4-part chorus of mixed voices with piano or organ. (Boyce, William). *Roberton. £0.18* DK (B76-50389)

Chesterman, Robert. Conversations with conductors : Bruno Walter, Sir Adrian Boult, Leonard Bernstein, Ernest Ansermet, Otto Klemperer, Leopold Stokowski. *Robson Books. £4.50* A/EC(M) (B76-33375) ISBN 0-903895-44-7

Child for today : a carol sequence for SATB and organ. (Wills, Arthur). *Novello. £0.90* DPDE/LF (B76-50792)

Child of God : American folk song for four-part chorus of mixed voices and solo (or soli) unaccompanied. (Terri, Salli). *Roberton. £0.20* EZDW (B76-50816)

Children's pieces : for piano. (Satie, Erik). *Novello. £0.60* QPJ (B76-50210)

Chilton, John. Louis : the Louis Armstrong story, 1900-1971. (Jones, Max). *Mayflower. £0.95* AMT(P) (B76-01204) ISBN 0-583-12710-x

Chinese suite, no.2. Op.41. (Kleyn, Howard). *Sonia Archer : Lengnick. Unpriced* VSPLK (B76-51037)

Chinese take away : for cornet trio and brass band. (Lear, W Hogarth). *Chester Music. Unpriced* WMPWRNT (B76-51075)

Chiti, Gian Paolo. Breakers : for 4 harps. *Chappell. Unpriced* TQNS (B76-50969)

Chivot, Henri. La Fille du tambour major. *Vocal score.* The drum-major's daughter : comic opera in three acts. (Offenbach, Jacques). *Choudens : United Music. Unpriced* CF (B76-50762)

Chopin : his life and times. (Orga, Ateş). *Midas Books. £5.95* BCE(N) (B76-29713) ISBN 0-85936-057-1

Chorale prelude on 'Christe sanctorum' : organ. (Baker, Richard Charles). *Frederick Harris Music : Lengnick. £0.70* RJ (B76-50927)

Chorochronos 3 : for voice, tape, pianist or percussion. (Antoniou, Theodore). *Bärenreiter. £2.50* KDX (B76-50493)

Chorus line. *Selections : arr.* A chorus line : vocal selections. (Hamlisch, Marvin). *Chappell. Unpriced* KDW (B76-50478)

Chorzempa, Daniel. Sonata, organ 'The 94th psalm'. The 94th psalm. Sonata for organ. (Reubke, Julius). *Oxford University Press. Unpriced* RE (B76-50229) ISBN 0-19-375685-4

Christmas lullaby : unison, two part or SSA chorus and piano. (Rocherolle, Eugénie R). *Warner : Blossom. Unpriced* JDP/LF (B76-50455)

Christmas things to sing. (Smith, Pat). *Arnold. Unpriced* JFDW/LF (B76-50833) ISBN 0-560-02721-4

Christus : oratorio for soli, chorus, organ and orchestra. (Liszt, Franz). *Eulenburg. Unpriced* EMDD (B76-50038)

Church bells of Herefordshire : their inscriptions and founders
 Vol.5: Summarised accounts of the bells at the Reformation and the present day and details of bellfounders. (Sharpe, Frederick). *'Derwen', Launton, Oxon. : The author. £3.20* AXSR/B(YDHR) (B76-09332) ISBN 0-9500835-9-3

Church Music Society. Reprints. Wesley, Samuel Sebastian. Magnificat and Nunc dimittis in E. *Oxford University Press. Unpriced* DGPP (B76-50375) ISBN 0-19-395317-x

Cinderella in Salerno. *Vocal score.* Cinderella in Salerno : an opera for schools in three acts based on Rossini's 'La Cenerentola'. (Walker, Raymond). *Novello. £1.70* CN (B76-50766)

Cinq melodies inédites. (Vieuxtemps, Henri). *Chappell. Unpriced* KDW (B76-50123)

Circus scenes : six rhythmic pieces for strings and piano accompaniment. (Dawe, Margery). *Cramer. £0.93* NXNS (B76-50541)

Clair de lune : piano solo. (Debussy, Claude). *Bosworth. Unpriced* QPK (B76-50920)

Clandestine dialogues : for cello and percussion. (Bergsma, William). *Galaxy Music : Stainer and Bell. Unpriced* SRPLX (B76-50962)

Clár amhrán Bhaile na hInse : clár na n-amhrán i mbarúntacht Bhaile na hInse. (Ní Fhlathartaigh Ríonach). *15 Bóthar Ghráinseach an Déin, An Charraig Dhubh, Co. Atha Cliath : An Clóchomhar Tta. £3.50* ADW/G(YDMG/T) (B76-17862) ISBN 0-903758-06-7

Clarinet. (Brymer, Jack). *Macdonald and Jane's. £4.50* AVV/E (B76-36286) ISBN 0-356-08414-0

Clarinet teacher's companion. (Weston, Pamela). *Hale : Distributed to the music trade by Breitkopf and Härtel. £2.00* AVV/E(VC) (B76-14370) ISBN 0-7091-5482-8

Clarinets in chorus : 14 international folksongs. *Rahter. £2.75* VVNTK/DW/G/AY (B76-50700)

Clark, Keith. Metaphysical fragments. Our murmers have their musick too. Our murmers have their musick too : for 4-part chorus of mixed voices unaccompanied. *Roberton. £0.10* EZDW (B76-50428)

Clark, Philip. Romance and scherzo. *arr.* Romance and scherzo. (Rachmaninoff, Sergei). *Oxford University Press. Unpriced* SQPK (B76-50637) ISBN 0-19-358441-7

Clarke, Claudia. The musical experience of the pre-school child. (Moog, Helmut). *48 Great Marlborough St., W1V 2BN : Schott Music. £2.00* A(VCC) (B76-35594) ISBN 0-901938-06-8

Classical guitar : a complete course
 Book 1. (Sewell, Penelope). *Thames. Unpriced* TS/AC (B76-50652) ISBN 0-905210-04-2

Classical music for flute and piano. *Boosey and Hawkes. Unpriced* VRPK/AAY (B76-51022)

Classical style : Haydn, Mozart, Beethoven. (Rosen, Charles). Revised ed. *Faber. £9.00* A(X) (B76-35348) ISBN 0-571-04916-8

Clayre, Alasdair. Adam and the beasts and other songs. *Faber and Faber in association with Faber Music. Unpriced* KEZDW (B76-50494) ISBN 0-571-10012-0

Cleaver, A W T. The theory of change ringing : an introduction. *36 Great Clarendon St., Oxford : J. Hannon and Co. (Publishers) Oxford. £0.60* AXSR/E (B76-35358) ISBN 0-904233-10-3

Clements, John. The scarecrow : for unison voices and piano. *Elkin. £0.12* JFDW (B76-50463)

Clemenza di Tito : Opera seria in zwei Akten : Textbuch italiebisch-deutsch. (Metastasio, Pietro). *32 Great Titchfield St., W1P 7AD : Bärenreiter. £1.13* BMSAC

Cleo and John : a biography of the Dankworths. *Quartet Books. £4.95* AKDW/HJ/E(P) (B76-33371) ISBN 0-7043-2113-0

Cleveland, Philip Jerome. I yield thee praise : for mixed chorus and piano. (Atkinson, Condit). *Galaxy : Galliard. Unpriced* DH (B76-50383)

Clock music. *arr.* Ten pieces for a musical clock. (Handel, George Frideric). *Schirmer. Unpriced* XSQMK (B76-50348)

Clube 15 : celébre valsa. (Ferreira, Oscar Augusto). *Seresta : Essex Music. Unpriced* QPHW (B76-50563)

Clychau'r maes : detholiad o donau. (Edwards, William Llewelyn). *Ruel Uchaf, Bow Street, Dyfed : The composer. Unpriced* DM (B76-50785)

Code of practice for pop concerts : a guide to safety, health and welfare at one day events. (Greater London Council). *G.L.C. £1.50* A/GB(W/Z) (B76-32962) ISBN 0-7168-0732-7

Cofone, Charles J F. Favorite Christmas carols. *Dover : Collier Macmillan. £1.30* JDP/LF/AY (B76-50104) ISBN 0-486-20445-6

Cohen, Yehuda Walter. Werden und Entwicklung der Musik in Israel. Die Musik Israels. (Brod, Max). Revidierte Ausg., mit einen zweiten Teil 'Werden und Entwicklung der Musik in Israel'. *32 Great Titchfield St., W.1 : Bärenreiter Kassel. £10.50* A(YVD)

Coláiste Phádraig, *Má Nuad. See* Maynooth College.

Cole, Tony. Falling angels : music from the film. *250 Purley Way, Croydon CR9 4QD : Valley Music. £1.00* KDW/JR (B76-50126)

Collagen 1 & 2 : für Trompete in B und Klavier. (Konietzny, Heinrich). *Bosse : Bärenreiter. £6.50* WSPJ (B76-50743)

Collier, Graham, *b.1937.* Cleo and John : a biography of the Dankworths. *Quartet Books. £4.95* AKDW/HJ/E(P) (B76-33371) ISBN 0-7043-2113-0

Colville, Thomas. God's world : for unaccompanied mixed chorus, S.S.A.T.B. *Galaxy : Stainer and Bell. Unpriced* EZDH (B76-50803)

Come away, death : song. (Naylor, John). *Roberton. £0.35* KDW (B76-50120)

Come day, go day, God send Sunday : the songs and life story told in his own words, of John Maguire, traditional singer and farmer from Co. Fermanagh. (Maguire, John, *b.1902*). *Routledge and Kegan Paul. £1.50* AKDW/G/E(YDTF/P) (B76-21366) ISBN 0-7100-8388-2

Comparative studies in European social history. Weber, William. Music and the middle class : the social structure of concert life in London, Paris and Vienna. *Croom Helm. £5.95* A(W/YB/XHK19/Z) (B76-32961) ISBN 0-85664-215-0

Compass : cello, contra bass, tenor, bass and electronics. (Reynolds, Roger). *Peters. Unpriced* JNGE/SRPLSSDX (B76-50114)

Complete opera book. *See* Kobbé, Gustave.

Composite list of artists showing sole representation, by members of the British Association of Concert Agents, as at January 1, 1976. (British Association of Concert Agents). *c/o The Secretary, 44 Castelnau Gardens, Arundel Terrace, SW13 9DU : The Association. Unpriced* A(M/YC) (B76-15528) ISBN 0-904892-01-8

Concert prelude. (Sparke, Philip). *R. Smith. Unpriced* WMJ (B76-51068)

Concertante variations on a theme of Nicholas Maw : for string orchestra. (McCabe, John). *Novello. £2.25* RXMF/T (B76-50235)

Concertino. Bach, Johann Christian. Symphony, D major. Sinfonie, D-Dur. *Schott. £4.00* MRE (B76-50881)

Concerto vocale.
 Bernhard, Christoph. 'Fürchtet euch nicht' : Weihnachtskonzert für Sopran, zwei Violinen, Fagott (Violone) und Basso continuo. *Bärenreiter. £3.25* KFLE/NUWNSDE/LF (B76-50496)
 Hammerschmidt, Andreas. Musikalischer Andachten, Tl 3. Es danken dir, Gott, die Volker. Es danken dir, Gott, die Volker : solokantate für Tenor, zwei Violinen und Basso continuo. *Bärenreiter. £1.63* KGHE/SNTPWDE (B76-50503)

Conga negro. (Fink, Siegfried). *Schott. £2.80* XQRPMJ (B76-51090)

Connolly, Justin. Verse, op.7b : for 8 solo voices. *Novello. £1.00* JNAYDW (B76-50472)

Connor, Anthony. Blues. *Latimer New Dimensions. £5.00* AKDW/HHW (B76-29101) ISBN 0-901539-49-x

Conran, Anthony. Elegy for a prince. Op.59. *Vocal score.* Elegy for a prince. Op.59 : for baritone and orchestra. (Mathias, William). *Oxford University Press. Unpriced* KGNDX (B76-50508) ISBN 0-19-365582-9

Consider and hear me, O Lord my God. (Hemingway, Roger). *Novello. £0.12* FDK (B76-50078)

Consider well : Irish melody. (Wilkinson, Stephen). *Roberton. £0.18* GEZDP/LF (B76-50094)

Consort music for viols in six parts. (Jenkins, John). *Faber Music for the Viola da Gamba Society of Great Britain. Unpriced* STNQR (B76-50963)

Contemporary Canadian composers. *Oxford University Press. £11.75* A/D(YSX/XN55/M) (B76-25955) ISBN 0-19-540244-8

Contemporary music, case stuwies II. (Bray, Trevor). *Open University Press. £1.60* A(XM76) (B76-50756) ISBN 0-335-00870-4

Contentment S.A.T. unacc. (Gardner, John). *Oxford University Press. Unpriced* EZDW (B76-50432) ISBN 0-19-343059-2

Contes d'Hoffmann. Belle nuit. *arr.* Barcarolle. (Offenbach, Jacques). *Fisher and Lane. £0.30* RPVK/DW (B76-50940)

Continuation du mellagne. Passan vostri triomphi. *arr.* Trionto del tempo / by Orlando di Lasso ; and, Ecco l'alma beata / by Giovanni Croce ; arranged for ten recorders in 2 choirs by Dennis A. Bamforth. (Lasso, Orlando di). *Tomus. Unpriced* VSMK/DH (B76-50298)

Conversations with conductors : Bruno Walter, Sir Adrian Boult, Leonard Bernstein, Ernest Ansermet, Otto Klemperer, Leopold Stokowski. *Robson Books. £4.50* A/EC(M) (B76-33375) ISBN 0-903895-44-7

Conversations with Olivier Messiaen. (Samuel, Claude). *Stainer and Bell. Unpriced* BMKS (B76-18371) ISBN 0-85249-308-8

Conway, Pat.
The pocket book of 288 guitar chords : with fingering chord arrangements. *International Music. Unpriced* TS/RC (B76-50269)
The pocket book of mandoline chords : 288 chords with fingering chord arrangements. *International Music. Unpriced* TX/RC (B76-50280)
The pocket book of tenor banjo chords : (288 chords with fingering). *International Music. Unpriced* TTV/RC (B76-50278)
Soodlum's selection of Irish ballads with guitar chords
Vol.1. *153 Downpatrick Rd, Dublin 12 : International Music Publications. Unpriced* AKDW/K/G(YDM) (B76-07531) ISBN 0-905326-00-8
Vol.2. *153 Downpatrick Rd, Dublin 12 : International Music Publications. Unpriced* AKDW/K/G(YDM) (B76-07532) ISBN 0-905326-01-6

Cook, Peter, *b.1924*. Hugo Wolf's 'Corregidor' : a study of the opera and its origins. *8 Upper Wimpole St., W.1. : The author. £3.90* BWPAC (B76-05912) ISBN 0-9504360-0-3

Cooke, Deryck. Symphony no.10. A performing version of the draft for the tenth symphony. (Mahler, Gustav). *Associated Music : Faber Music. Unpriced* MME (B76-50521)

Cooper, Joseph. More hidden melodies : six improvisations for piano. *Novello. £1.00* QPJ (B76-50570)

Cooper, Peter, *b.1918*. Style in piano playing. *John Calder Distributed by Calder and Boyars. £6.50* AQ/E (B76-15056) ISBN 0-7145-3512-5

Copland, Alison A. Concerto, viola, B flat major. *arr.* Concerto in B flat for viola and orchestra. (Hoffmeister, Franz Anton). *Schott. Unpriced* SQPK/LF (B76-50256)

Copper, Bob. A song for every season. *Paladin. £1.25* ADW/G(YDCR) (B76-02079) ISBN 0-586-08229-8

Corbett, Jane. Music for GCE 'O' Level 2nd ed., revised. *Barrie and Jenkins. £1.95* A (B76-05035) ISBN 0-214-15676-1

Cordell, Frank. Gestures : saxophone quartet. *Emerson. Unpriced* VUSNS (B76-51045)

Corner, David Gregorius. God is gone up on high : melody from Corner, 1625. (Walmsley, Henry). *Banks. Unpriced* DP/LL (B76-50027)

Corrette, Michel. Sonatas, flute. Op.23. Sechs Sonaten für zwei Flöten. *Heinrichshofen : Peters. Unpriced* VRNUE (B76-50289)

Cotterell, Roger. Jazz now : the Jazz Centre Society guide. *Quartet Books. £1.75* AMT(YC) (B76-27767) ISBN 0-7043-3097-0

Country dance tunes. Sets 3-8, 10 and 11. *EP Publishing. £4.00* QPK/AH/H/AYD (B76-50218) ISBN 0-7158-1166-5

Country music. (Chalker, Bryan). *Phoebus. £2.50* AKDW/GCW/E(M) (B76-34775) ISBN 0-7026-0015-6

Couperin, François.
L'Apothéose de Corelli : for 2 flutes or oboes or violins and basso continuo. *Musica rara. Unpriced* VRNTPW (B76-50676)
L'Apothéose de Lulli : for 2 flutes/oboes/violins basse d'archet and b, c. *Musica rara. Unpriced* NUPNS (B76-50537)
Pièces de clavecin, livre 3, ordre 13. Les Roseaux. *arr.* Les Roseaux = The reeds. *Oxford University Press. Unpriced* VTPK (B76-50310) ISBN 0-19-355910-2

Couples : theme music from the Thames Television series, for piano solo. (McCabe, John). *Novello. Unpriced* QP/JS (B76-50190)

Cours d'initiation à la musique de jazz par le piano. (Bolling, Claude). *Chappell. Unpriced* QPHX/AC (B76-50197)

Covarrubias, Miguel. Born to be. (Gordon, Taylor). 1st ed. reprinted. *University of Washington Press. £3.50* AKDW/L/HJ/E(P) (B76-33369) ISBN 0-295-95428-0

Crabtree, Anthony John. Touches in popular doubles methods. *202 Attenborough La., Beeston, Nottingham NG9 6AL : The author. £1.75* AXSR/E (B76-35805) ISBN 0-904233-11-1

CRAC. *See* Careers Research and Advisory Centre.

Cramer's library of anthems and church music. Curtis, James Gilbert. Jesus by thy wounded feet : for unaccompanied four-part choir. *Cramer. £0.12* EZDH (B76-50415)

Crashaw, Richard.
Jesus by thy wounded feet : for unaccompanied four-part choir. (Curtis, James Gilbert). *Cramer. £0.12* EZDH (B76-50415)
Metaphysical fragments. Our murmers have their musick too. Our murmers have their musick too : for 4-part chorus of mixed voices unaccompanied. (Clark, Keith). *Roberton. £0.10* EZDW (B76-50428)

Crawley, Cliff. Aroundabout Christmas : 16 rounds for voices and/or instruments. *Frederick Harris Music Lengnick. £0.25* EZDW/XC/LF (B76-50817)

Credo for symphonic band. (Tull, Fisher). *Boosey and Hawkes. £15.00* UMMJ (B76-50663)

Criswick, Mary.
Another ten for guitar. *Fentone Music : Breitkopf and Härtel. Unpriced* TSPMK/AAY (B76-50276)
Ten for guitar. *Fentone Music : Breitkopf and Härtel. Unpriced* TSPMK/DW/AY (B76-50277)

Croce, Giovanni. Ecco l'alma beata. Continuation du mellagne. Passan vostri triomphi. *arr.* Trionto del tempo / by Orlando di Lasso ; and, Ecco l'alma beata / by Giovanni Croce ; arranged for ten recorders in 2 choirs by Dennis A. Bamforth. (Lasso, Orlando di). *Tomus. Unpriced* VSMK/DH (B76-50298)

Crosse, Gordon. Studies for string quartet. Op,34
Set 1. *Oxford University Press. Unpriced* RXNS (B76-50954) ISBN 0-19-355972-2

Croucher, Terence.
At the zoo : for guitar. *109 St Leonard's Rd, Leicester : Clarendon Music. £0.75* TSPMJ (B76-50986)
By the sea : for guitar. *109 St Leonard's Rd, Leicester : Clarendon Music. £0.75* TSPMJ (B76-50987)
Divertimento for guitar. *109 St Leonard's Rd, Leicester : Clarendon Music. £1.00* TSPMJ (B76-50988)
In the forest : for guitar. *109 St Leonard's Rd, Leicester : Clarendon Music. £0.75* TSPMJ (B76-50989)
Three variations on a Japanese theme : for four guitars. *109 St Leonard's Rd, Leicester : Clarendon Music. £0.75* TSNS/T (B76-50981)

Crumb, George. Night of the four moons : alto, alto flute, (doubling piccolo), banjo, electric cello and percussion (one player). *Peters. Unpriced* KFQE/NYERNSDW (B76-50136)

Crystal spring : English folk songs. *Oxford University Press. £4.95* JE/TSDW/G/AYD (B76-50105) ISBN 0-19-330518-6

Culshaw, John. Reflections on Wagner's 'Ring'. *Secker and Warburg. £3.50* BWCAC (B76-13571) ISBN 0-436-11801-7

Cumann Cheol Tíre Eireann. *See* Folk Music Society of Ireland.

Cummings, Edward Estlin.
I thank you God : SATB and piano accompaniment. (King, Jeffrey). *Boosey and Hawker. £0.50* DH (B76-50017)
Tall wind : soprano, flute, oboe, guitar and violoncello. (Ung, Chinary). *Peters. Unpriced* KFLE/NVPNSDW (B76-50133)

Cummings, Tony. The sound of Philadelphia. *Eyre Methuen. £2.75* ADW/GB(YTLD/X) (B76-04295) ISBN 0-413-34080-5

Currer-Briggs, Noel. Weber in London, 1826. *Wolff. £1.95* BWL(YDB/XHF) (B76-22852) ISBN 0-85496-403-7

Curtin, Jane. Pretzels : a musical revue. (Forster, John). *French. £1.25* BFNRACP (B76-06889) ISBN 0-573-68071-x

Curtis, James Gilbert. Jesus by thy wounded feet : for unaccompanied four-part choir. *Cramer. £0.12* EZDH (B76-50415)

Curtis, Mira Stella. The folk directory
1976. *The Society. £2.00(£1.00 to members)* A/G(BC) (B76-25961) ISBN 0-85418-111-3

Czidra, Laszlo. Recorder music for beginners. *Boosey and Hawkes. £1.25* VSRPK/AAY (B76-51041)

D., W. The maske of flowers. *5 Albert Grove, Leeds LS6 4DA : Boethius Press. £3.20* ACPF (B76-10977) ISBN 0-904263-02-9

Dadi, Marcel. La Méthode de guitare à Dadi. *Music Express : Chappell : Chappell. Unpriced* TS/AC (B76-50267)

Dakers, Lionel. A handbook of parish music : a working guide for clergy and organists. *Mowbrays. £1.95* A/LD/E (B77-00345) ISBN 0-264-66261-x

Dalby, Martin. Quintet, strings. String quintet, 1972. *Novello. £1.50* RXNR (B76-50614)

Dalmaine, Cyril Carr.
Mahler. (Mahler, Gustav). *Warren and Phillips. Unpriced* QPK (B76-50583)
Puccini. (Puccini, Giacomo). *Warren and Phillips. Unpriced* QPK/DW (B76-50585)
Selections. *arr.* Liszt. (Liszt, Franz). *Warren and Phillips. Unpriced* QPK (B76-50582)
Wagner. (Wagner, Richard). *Warren and Phillips. Unpriced* QPK (B76-50922)

Dan, Ikuma. Yuzuru. *Vocal score.* Yuzuru = The twilight heron : opera in one act. *Boosey and Hawkes. Unpriced* CC (B76-50363)

Dança campestre. (Mignone, Francisco). *Arthur Napoleão Essex Music. Unpriced* QPH (B76-50899)

Dance caprice. (Heath, Reginald). *R. Smith. Unpriced* WMH (B76-51057)

Dance diversions. (Hurd, Michael). *Novello. £3.50* MMH (B76-50145)

Dance of the penguins : elementary accordion solo. (Watson, Dennis). *Charnwood Music. Unpriced* RSPMH (B76-50602)

Dance rhapsody no.2. (Delius, Frederick). *Stainer and Bell. Unpriced* MMJ (B76-50872) ISBN 0-85249-458-0

Dance ti thi daddy : traditional original theme song from the BBC TV series 'When the boat comes in'. (Fanshawe, David). *Chappell. Unpriced* KDW (B76-50477)

Dance trios : 3 flutes. (Greaves, Terence). *Emerson. Unpriced* VRNTH (B76-51016)

Dancing days : twelve carols for guitar. *Cramer. £1.25* TSPMK/DP/LF/AY (B76-50993)

Dancing rhymes. *Ladybird Books. £0.24* ADW/H (B76-30341) ISBN 0-7214-0440-5

Danks, H P. Silver threads among the gold : cornet solo. (Boddington, Stanley H). *Studio Music. Unpriced* WMPWR/T (B76-50735)

Danks, Harry. The viola d'amore. *7 Summit Gardens, Halesowen, West Midlands B63 4SP : Bois de Boulogne. £15.40* ASQQ/B (B76-17084) ISBN 0-900998-15-6

Danse bohémiénne : piano solo. (Debussy, Claude). *Peters. Unpriced* QPH (B76-50196)

Danzi, Franz. Concerto, flute no.2, op.31, D minor. *arr.* Konzert nr.2, d-moll, op.31, für Flöte und Orchester. *Heinrichshofen : Hinrichsen. Unpriced* VRPK/LF (B76-50680)

Dart, Thurston.
Invitation to madrigals
9: for S.S.A.T.B. *Staines and Bell. Unpriced* EZDU/AY (B76-50812) ISBN 0-85249-345-2
9: for S.S.A.T.B. *Stainer and Bell. Unpriced* EZDU/AY (B76-50811) ISBN 0-85249-346-0
Invitation to medieval music
3: Music of the mid-fifteenth century (1). *Stainer and Bell. Unpriced* CB/AY(XCH301) (B76-50362) ISBN 0-85249-316-9

Darvas, Gábor.
Christus : oratorio for soli, chorus, organ and orchestra. (Liszt, Franz). *Eulenburg. Unpriced* EMDD (B76-50038)
Die Israeliten in der Wuste = The Israelites in the wilderness : oratorio for soli, chorus and orchestra. (Bach, Carl Philipp Emanuel). *Eulenburg. Unpriced* EMDD (B76-50037)
Magnificat for soli, chorus and orchestra. (Bach, Carl Philipp Emanuel). *Eulenburg. Unpriced* EMDGKK (B76-50040)

Davey, Brian.
The entertainer. *arr.* The entertainer. (Joplin, Scott). *Chappell. Unpriced* VSNSQK/AHXJ (B76-50684)
Seven Strauss waltzes : for descant, treble recorders and piano. (Strauss, Johann, *b.1825*). *Chappell. Unpriced* VSNTQK/AHW (B76-51035)

David Essex story. (Tremlett, George). *White Lion Publishers. £3.25* AKDW/GB/E(P) (B76-16550) ISBN 0-7274-0113-0

Davies, Laurence Hector.
Gather gladness from the skies : spring carol, unison or SATB. *Ashdown. £0.08* JDP (B76-50103)
Geistliche Lieder aus Schmelli's Gesangbuch und dem Notenbuch der Anna Magdelena Buch. Jesus ist das schönste Licht. S.474. *arr.* Jesus is the loveliest light. (Bach, Johann Sebastian). *Roberton. £0.10* EZDM (B76-50420)

Davies, Peter Maxwell.
Ave maris stella. *Boosey and Hawkes. £2.50* NYDPNQ (B76-50542)
Two pieces for flute. *Boosey and Hawkes. £2.00* VRPMJ (B76-51027)
Worldes blis : motet for orchestra on a thirteenth century English monody. *Boosey and Hawkes. £10.00* MMJ (B76-50147)

Davies, *Sir* Walford. Interlude, organ, C major. Interlude in C for organ solo. 1st ed. *Ramsey : Roberton. Unpriced* RJ (B76-50592)

Davis, Allan. Festival concerto, clarinet & small orchestra. *arr.* Festival concerto for B flat clarinet and small orchestra. *Oxford University Press. Unpriced* VVPK/LF (B76-50711)

Davis, Katherine Kennicot. Berceuse. *arr.* You will see an angel tonight. (Ropartz, Joseph Guy). *Galaxy : Galliard. Unpriced* DP/LF (B76-50397)

Davis, Paul. New life in country music. *Walker. £1.00* AKDW/GC(M) (B76-35353) ISBN 0-85479-591-x

Davis, William Robert.
The builders. *Vocal score.* The builders : Angevin carol, in a festival setting : for combined mixed and unison choirs, soprano solo and optional instruments. *Oxford University Press. Unpriced* DP/LF (B76-50788)
Gloria tibi Domine. A little child there is yborn : Christmas carol, for unaccompanied mixed choir with soprano solo. *Oxford University Press. Unpriced* EZDP/LF (B76-50808)

Dawe, Margery. Circus scenes : six rhythmic pieces for strings and piano accompaniment. *Cramer. £0.93* NXNS (B76-50541)

Dawson, Mary. Mary's dream. (Parfrey, Raymond). *Thames. Unpriced* EZDP/LF (B76-50424)

Dawson, Richard. Sky songs. (Benger, Richard). *Edwin Ashdown. £0.40* JFDW (B76-50462)

Day, James. Vaughan Williams. Revised ed. *Dent. £3.75* BVD (B76-01202) ISBN 0-460-03162-7

Day, Peter. The technique of film music. (Manvell, Roger). Revised and enlarged ed. *Focal Press. £5.00* A/JR (B76-12128) ISBN 0-240-50848-3

De la Motte, Diether. *See* La Motte, Diether de.

De Marne, Denis. Jack the Ripper : a musical play. (Pember, Ron). *French. £0.90* BPEMACM (B76-10909) ISBN 0-573-08042-9

De Smet, Robin.
Easy music for string quartet or string orchestra. *British and Continental : EMI. Unpriced* RXNSK/AAY (B76-50243)
The first year trumpeter
Volume 2: Eight famous melodies for trumpet (or cornet) in B flat and piano. *Ashdown. £1.20* WSPK/AAY (B76-50341)
King Charles' pleasure : a fantasy in the olden style for string trio (or viols). *British and Continental. Unpriced* RXNS (B76-50616)
Rodgers and Hammerstein clarinet classics. (Rodgers, Richard). *Williamson. Unpriced* VVPK/DW (B76-50710)
Six easy pieces for 3 cellos (or violas da gamba). *British and Continental. Unpriced* SRNTK/AAY (B76-50642)
Trois gymnopédies. *arr.* Three gymnopédies : flute (or oboe) and piano. (Satie, Erik). *Fentone Music : Breitkopf and Härtel. Unpriced* VRPJ (B76-50291)

Dean, Winton. Bizet. 3rd ed.. *Dent. £3.95* BBP (B76-12126) ISBN 0-460-03163-5

Dean, Winton. Georges Bizet. *See* Dean, Winton. Bizet.

Dean, Winton.
Ottone. *Condensed score. Selections.* Three ornamented arias. (Handel, George Frideric). *Oxford University Press. Unpriced* KE/MDW (B76-50128) ISBN 0-19-345412-2

The rise of romantic opera. (Dent, Edward Joseph). *Cambridge University Press. £6.50* AC(XG41) (B77-00341) ISBN 0-521-21337-1
Dearmer, Geoffrey. The builders. *Vocal score.* The builders : Angevin carol, in a festival setting : for combined mixed and unison choirs, soprano solo and optional instruments. (Davis, William Robert). *Oxford University Press. Unpriced* DP/LF (B76-50788)
Debussy, Claude.
Berceuse héroïque : piano solo. *Peters. Unpriced* QPJ (B76-50200)
Danse bohémienne : piano solo. *Peters. Unpriced* QPH (B76-50196)
D'un cahier d'esquisses : piano solo. *Peters. Unpriced* QPJ (B76-50201)
Suite bergamasque. Clair de lune. *arr.* Clair de lune : piano solo. *Bosworth. Unpriced* QPK (B76-50920)
December music : trio for recorders, descant, treble, tenor. (Turner, John). *Tomus. Unpriced* VSNT (B76-50300)
Degree course guides. Careers Research and Advisory Centre. Music and drama
1975-76. *Bateman St., Cambridge CB2 1LZ : Hobsons Press (Cambridge) Ltd for CRAC. £0.85* A(VQ) (B76-04296) ISBN 0-86021-038-3
Del Mar, Norman. Concerto, cello, op.104, B minor. Cello concerto, B minor. Op.104. (Dvořák, Antonín). *Eulenburg. Unpriced* MPSRF (B76-50535)
Delius, Frederick.
Concerto, piano, C minor. Piano concerto. *Boosey and Hawkes. Unpriced* MPQF (B76-50157)
Concerto, piano, C minor. *arr.* Piano concerto. *Boosey and Hawkes. Unpriced* QNUK/LF (B76-50184)
Concerto, violin & cello. Concerto for violin & violoncello. *Stainer and Bell. Unpriced* MPSPLSRF (B76-50159) ISBN 0-85249-399-1
Dance rhapsody no.2. *Stainer and Bell. Unpriced* MMJ (B76-50872) ISBN 0-85249-458-0
Eventyr. Once upon time, after Asbjornsen's folklore. *Stainer and Bell. Unpriced* MMJ (B76-50148) ISBN 0-85249-398-3
Fennimore und Gerda = Fennimore and Gerda. *Boosey and Hawkes. £6.50* CQC (B76-50007)
North country sketches. *Stainer and Bell. Unpriced* MMJ (B76-50873) ISBN 0-85249-457-2
On hearing the first cuckoo in spring. *arr.* On hearing the first cuckoo in spring. *Oxford University Press. Unpriced* WMK (B76-50731) ISBN 0-19-362813-9
Romance for cello and piano. First ed. *Boosey and Hawkes. £1.00* SRPJ (B76-50645)
Delius companion. *John Calder : Distributed by Calder and Boyars. £7.50* BDL (B76-17646) ISBN 0-7145-3526-5
Delius : portrait of a cosmopolitan. (Palmer, Christopher). *Duckworth. £9.80* BDL (B76-22079) ISBN 0-7156-0773-1
Delius Society. Warlock and Delius. (Tomlinson, Fred). *14 Barlby Rd, W10 6AR : Thames Publishing for the Peter Warlock Society. £1.50* BDL(Z) (B76-27764) ISBN 0-905210-05-0
Dello Joio, Norman. Lyric fantasias : for viola solo and string orchestra (or string quintet). *Associated Music. Unpriced* RXMPSQ (B76-50238)
Dench, Chris.
Helical : for solo piano. *17 Dempster Rd, S.W.18 : The composer. Unpriced* QPJ (B76-50202)
Reminiscences of Scriabin : for treble and sopranino recorders. *17 Dempster Rd, S.W.18 : The composer. Unpriced* VSNU (B76-50301)
Dennis, Brian. Projects in sound. *Universal Edition. £2.00* AL/E(VG) (B76-22854) ISBN 0-900938-45-5
Dent, Edward Joseph. The rise of romantic opera. *Cambridge University Press. £6.50* AC(XG41) (B77-00341) ISBN 0-521-21337-1
Dent (E.J.) Centenary Committee. E.J. Dent : a centenary memoir. (Radcliffe, Philip). *22 Pheasants Way, Rickmansworth, Herts. : Triad Press for the E.J. Dent Centenary Committee. £1.50* A(VX/P) (B76-20005) ISBN 0-902070-18-5
Denza, Luigi. Funiculi, funicula. *arr.* Funiculi - finicula sic. *8 Hurst Green Close, Hurst Green, Oxted : Paul. Unpriced* WMK/DW (B76-50734)
Deutsch, Babette. For the infant Michael : SATB. (Binkerd, Gordon). *Boosey and Hawkes. £0.20* EZDW (B76-50067)
Deutsch, Otto Erich. Briefe und Afzeichnungen
Band 7: Register. (Mozart, Wolfgang Amadeus). Gesamtuasg. *32 Great Titchfield St., W1P 7AD : Bärenreiter. £37.50* BMS(N)
Deutsche Volkslieder : für akkordprogrammierte Orgel, 1 Manuel. *Schott. £1.75* RPVK/DW/G/AYE (B76-50233)
Deux prélude-improvisations = Two prelude-improvisations : for piano. (Glazunov, Alexander). *Belaieff : Peters. Unpriced* QPJ (B76-50571)
Deverell, Richard. New life in country music. (Davis, Paul). *Walker. £1.00* AKDW/GC(M) (B76-35353) ISBN 0-85479-591-x
Di Lasso, Orlando. *See* Lasso, Orlando di.
Diamond, Dorothy Mary. Musical instruments. *Macdonald Educational for Chelsea College, University of London. £1.50* AL/E(VG) (B76-30110) ISBN 0-356-05077-7
Diamond studs : the life of Jesse James. (Wann, Jim). *French. £1.60* BSHLACM (B77-00344) ISBN 0-573-68076-0
Dichter und Bauer. Overture. *Selections: arr.* Poet and peasant overture : (selections). (Suppé, Franz von). *Fisher and Lane. Unpriced* RPVK (B76-50937)
Dick, Robert. The other flute : a performance manual of contemporary techniques. *Oxford University Press. £6.75* VR/AF (B76-51014) ISBN 0-19-322125-x
Dickie, Murray. Eine Nacht in Venedig. *Vocal score.* A night in Venice. (Korngold, Erich). *Weinberger Unpriced* CF (B76-50364)
Dickinson, Emily. Her silver will. Looking back as Sposalizio : medium voice. (Binkerd, Gordon). *Boosey and Hawkes. £0.75* KFVDW (B76-50500)
Dickinson, Pamela Ingeborg. Music with ESN children : a guide for the classroom teacher. *NFER. £3.65* A(VMWR) (B76-14728) ISBN 0-85633-085-x
Dickinson, Peter. An Erik Satie entertainment : a selection of songs and piano music. (Satie, Erik). *Novello. Unpriced* QPJ (B76-50212)
Dictionary of music and musicians. *See* Grove, *Sir* George.
Did't my Lord deliver Daniel : a jazz spiritual for voices, recorders, guitars (optional) and piano. (Wastall, Peter). *Boosey and Hawkes. £1.75* FE/NWSDW/LC (B76-50084)
Die mit Thränen saën. *Vocal score.* Who with weeping soweth = Die mit Thränen saën. (Antes, John). *Boosey and Hawkes. £0.30* DH (B76-50377)
Diederich, Susanne. Originale Registrieranweisungen in der französischen Orgelmusik des 17. und 18. Jahrhunderts : Beziehungen zwischen Orgelbau und Orgelkomposition im Zeitalter Ludwigs XIV. *32 Great Titchfield St., W.1 : Bärenreiter. £11.00* AR(YH/PU/XE201)
Diemer, Emma Lou. Music for woodwind quartet. *Oxford University Press. Unpriced* VNS (B76-51010)
Dieskau, Dietrich Fischer-. *See* Fischer-Dieskau, Dietrich.
Dimock, Edward C. In praise of Krishna : songs from the Bengali for soprano and nine instruments. (Blake, David). *Novello. £2.00* KFLE/NVNMDW (B76-50863)
Ding dong! merrily on high : 16th cent. French tune. (Carter, Andrew). *Banks. Unpriced* FEZDP/LF (B76-50446)
Dinn, Freda.
Concerto, viola, B flat major. *arr.* Concerto in B flat for viola and orchestra. (Hoffmeister, Franz Anton). *Schott. Unpriced* SQPK/LF (B76-50256)
A viola method from the third to the first position for individual and class tuition. *Schott. Unpriced* SR/AF (B76-50257) ISBN 0-901938-53-x
Directory of British brass bands : associations, societies, contests
Vol.1 : 1975-76. *c/o F.H. Bradbury, 47 Hull Rd, York YO1 3JP : British Federation of Brass Bands. £0.50* AWM/E(YC/BC) (B76-01203) ISBN 0-905170-00-8
Dirge for a minstrel : SATB, soprano and tenor soli a cappella. (Bach, Jan). *Associated Music. Unpriced* EZDW (B76-50065)
Dithyrambos : for brass quintet. (Ghent, Emmanuel). *Oxford University Press. Unpriced* WNR (B76-50332)
Diversions : for saxophone quartet. (Patterson, Paul). *Weinberger. Unpriced* VUNS (B76-50693)
Dix, William Chatterton. What Child is this? : Old English melody. (Balent, Andrew). *Warner : Blossom. Unpriced* JDP/LF (B76-50827)
Dix pièces enfantines, piano. Zehn Stücke für Kinder zum Spielen und Träumen, 'De la musique avant toute chose'. (Françaix, Jean). *Schott. £2.40* QPJ (B76-50905)
Dixit Dominus : for SATB soli and chorus, string orchestra and organ continuo. (Scarlatti, Alessandro). *Novello. £1.20* ERXMDGKJ (B76-50046)
Dodgson, Charles Lutwidge. *See* Carroll, Lewis.
Dodgson, Stephen. Suite for brass septet. *Chester. Unpriced* WNPG (B76-50737)
Doe, Paul. Tallis. 2nd ed. *Oxford University Press. £2.20* BTB (B76-15053) ISBN 0-19-314122-1
Doflein, Erich. Sammlung kleiner Stücke für Violoncello = Collection of small pieces for violoncello : duets and solos from the 18th century
Vol.1: For beginners. *Schott. £2.25* SRNU/AY (B76-50643)
Doherty, Kevin.
The pocket book of 288 guitar chords : with fingering chord arrangements. (Conway, Pat). *International Music. Unpriced* TS/RC (B76-50269)
The pocket book of mandoline chords : 288 chords with fingering chord arrangements. (Conway, Pat). *International Music. Unpriced* TX/RC (B76-50280)
The pocket book of tenor banjo chords : (288 chords with fingering). (Conway, Pat). *International Music. Unpriced* TTV/RC (B76-50278)
Dolci, Amico.
Nuovo ricercare 4 a due voci : für zwei Altblockflöten. *Heinrichshofen : Peters. Unpriced* VSSNU (B76-50305)
Nuovo ricercare 5 : für Altblockflöte. *Heinrichshofen Peters. Unpriced* VSSPMJ (B76-50308)
Dolmetsch, Carl. Thirty-one pieces of the 16th-18th centuries : for treble recorder and piano. *Universal. Unpriced* VSSPK/AAY (B76-50690)
Dolmetsch library.
Allegri, Lorenzo. Il primo libro delle musiche. Primo ballo. Suite in 6 parts for 6 recorders. *Dolmetsch : Chappell. Unpriced* VSNQH (B76-51029)
Chedeville, Nicolas. Amusements champêtres, liv, 1. Suite, woodwind instruments, no.4, G major. Quatrième suite : for recorder quartet. *Dolmetsch : Chappell. Unpriced* VSNSG (B76-51031)
Hotteterre, Jean. Pièces pour la muzette. Overture, 'Le festin'. *arr.* Overture 'Le festin' : for descant, treble and bass recorders. *Dolmetsch : Chappell. Unpriced* VSNT (B76-51032)
Dolmetsch recorder series.
Bononcini, Giovanni Maria. Sinfonia, allemande, correnti e sarabande a 5 e 6. Op.5. *Selections : arr.* Two suites a 6 : for 6 recorders. *Universal. Unpriced* VSNQK/AHG (B76-51030)
Loeillet, Jean Baptiste, *of London.* Sonata, treble recorder, oboe & continuo, op.4, no.2. Sonata a tre con fluto e hautboy for treble recorder, oboe (or treble II) and continuo. *Universal. Unpriced* NWNTE (B76-50885)
Thirty-one pieces of the 16th-18th centuries : for treble recorder and piano. *Universal. Unpriced* VSSPK/AAY (B76-50690)
Donizetti, Gaetano.
Ave Maria : für Sopran, gemischten Chor und Streicher. *Editio musica : Litolff. Unpriced* ERXMDJ (B76-50407)
Ave Maria. *Vocal score.* Ave Maria : für Sopran, gemischten Chor und Streicher. *Editio musica : Litolff. Unpriced* DJ (B76-50387)
Donkey carol. *arr.* Donkey carol. (Rutter, John). *Oxford University Press. Unpriced* JFDP/LF (B76-50461) ISBN 0-19-342052-x
Donkey carol. *Vocal score.* Donkey carol : S.A.T.B. accompanied. (Rutter, John). *Oxford University Press. Unpriced* DP/LF (B76-50398) ISBN 0-19-343055-x
Donne, John. Three sonnets of John Donne : for four-part choir of mixed voices unaccompanied. (Burtch, Mervyn). *Roberton. £0.28* EZDW (B76-50814)
Douglas, Alan. The electronic musical instrument manual : a guide to theory and design. 6th ed. *Pitman. £7.50* ARPV/BC (B76-12801) ISBN 0-273-36193-7
Dowland, John. Lachrimae. 1st ed., reprinted. *5 Albert Grove, Leeds 6 : Boethius Press. £6.60* BDTARWNR (B76-10254) ISBN 0-904263-04-5
Down in yon forest : Advent or Christmas carol for 6-part chorus of mixed voices unaccompanied. (Hanson, Geoffrey). *Roberton. £0.10* EZDP/LEZ (B76-50421)
Downing, David. Future rock. *Panther. £0.60* A/HK(XQK11) (B76-30334) ISBN 0-586-04308-x
Dowson, Ernest. The golden wine is drunk : for 16 solo voices divided into 2 eight-part choirs of SSAATTBB. (Bedford, David). *Universal. Unpriced* EZDW (B76-50427)
Drabble, L.H. Six miniatures : for guitar. *Charnwood Music. Unpriced* TSPMJ (B76-50659)
Drake, *Sir* Francis. The true glory. (Aston, Peter). *Royal School of Church Music. Unpriced* DH (B76-50782)
Drake, Joseph Rodman. The American flag. Op.102. *Vocal score.* The American flag. Op.102 : cantata for four-part chorus of mixed voices and alto, tenor and bass soli. (Dvořák, Antonín). *Schirmer. Unpriced* DX (B76-50035)
Drakestail : a symphonic fairy tale for children. (Lombardo, Mario). *Chappell. Unpriced* MMJ (B76-50529)
Draths, Willi.
Deutsche Volkslieder : für akkordprogrammierte Orgel, 1 Manuel. *Schott. £1.75* RPVK/DW/G/AYE (B76-50233)
Lustige Lieder : für akkordprogrammierte Orgel 1 Manue bearbeitet von Willi Draths. *Schott. £1.75* RPVK/DW/AY (B76-50232)
Mein Heimatland : Volkslieder für elektronische Orgel. *Schott. Unpriced* RPVK/DW/G/AYE (B76-50942)
Draths, William. Beliebte Volkslieder : für Trompete (Flügelhorn oder Kornett) mit 2, Stimme ad lib., *Schott. £1.75* WSPMJ (B76-50747)
Drei marianische Fresken für Orgel = Three Marian frescoes for organ
1: Salve regina. (Hummel, Bertold). *Simrock. £3.10* RJ (B76-50930)
2: Ave maris stella. (Hummel, Bertold). *Simrock. £2.50* RJ (B76-50931)
3: Regina caeli. (Hummel, Bertold). *Simrock. £3.10* RJ (B76-50932)
Drew, Lucas. Sound study : for eight double basses. *Schirmer. Unpriced* SSNN (B76-50261)
Druckman, Jacob.
Antiphonies : for mixed chorus unaccompanied
No. 1. *Boosey and Hawkes. £0.55* EZDW (B76-50429)
No. 2. *Boosey and Hawkes. £0.70* EZDW (B76-50430)
No. 3. *Boosey and Hawkes. £1.00* EZDW (B76-50431)
Drum-major's daughter : comic opera in three acts. (Offenbach, Jacques). *Choudens : United Music. Unpriced* CF (B76-50762)
Drüner, Ulrich. Duets, violins, nos 1-3. Drei Duos für zwei Violinen. (Rolla, Alessandro). Zum ersten Mal herausgegeben von Ulrich Drüner. *Litulff : Peters. Unpriced* SNU (B76-50631)
Dryden, John. A song for St Cecilia's Day. Op.119 : SATB. (Gardner, John). *Oxford University Press. Unpriced* DH (B76-50384) ISBN 0-19-350355-7
Dubey, Matt. Smith : a musical. *French. £1.25* BDUACM (B76-00671) ISBN 0-573-68066-3
Duchess of Duke Street : theme from the BBC television serial. (Faris, Alexander). *Chappell. Unpriced* QPK/AHW/JS (B76-50924)
Duck, Leonard William. Introduction to music. (Library Association. *Public Libraries Group). c/o A.L. Bamber, Divisional Library, Timber St., Chippenham, Wilts. : The Group. £0.40* A(T) (B76-19568) ISBN 0-85365-168-x
Duclos, Pierre. Cinq melodies inédites. (Vieuxtemps, Henri). *Chappell. Unpriced* KDW (B76-50123)
Dukas, Paul. P. Dukas' 'The sorcerer's apprentice'. (Yangagihara, Ryohei). *F. Warne. £2.25* BDVAMBN (B76-18582) ISBN 0-7232-1834-x
Duke, Henry. The Henry Duke piano arrangements of favourite orchestral classics. *EMI. Unpriced* QPK (B76-50921)
D'un cahier d'esquisses : piano solo. (Debussy, Claude). *Peters. Unpriced* QPJ (B76-50201)
Dunand, Frank. Reflections on Wagner's 'Ring'. (Culshaw, John). *Secker and Warburg. £3.50* BWCAC (B76-13571)

ISBN 0-436-11801-7
Dunn, Bernard.
Frederica : operetta in three acts. 10 Rathbone St., W1P 2BJ : Glocken Verlag Ltd. £1.00 BLDACF
Friederike. Vocal score. Frederica : operetta in three acts. (Lehár, Franz). Glocken. Unpriced CF (B76-50761)
Dunn, Paul H. The Osmonds : the official story of the Osmond family. W.H. Allen. £2.95 AKDW/GB/E(P) (B76-00672) ISBN 0-491-01835-5
Dürr, Alfred. Sonatas, flute & continuo. Selections. Sonatas for flute and basso continuo. (Bach, Johann Sebastian). Bärenreiter. £6.00 VRPE (B76-50677)
Duru, Alfred. La Fille du tambour major. Vocal score. The drum-major's daughter : comic opera in three acts. (Offenbach, Jacques). Choudens : United Music. Unpriced CF (B76-50762)
Dvořák, Antonín.
The American flag. Op.102. Vocal score. The American flag. Op.102 : cantata for four-part chorus of mixed voices and alto, tenor and bass soli. Schirmer. Unpriced DX (B76-50035)
Concerto, cello, op.104, B minor. Cello concerto, B minor. Op.104. Eulenburg. Unpriced MPSRF (B76-50535)
Concerto, violin, op.53, A minor. Violin concerto, A minor. Op.53. Eulenburg. Unpriced MPSF (B76-50533)
Symphony, no.9, op.95, E minor, 'From the new world'. Largo. arr. Largo. Chappell. Unpriced QPK (B76-50580)
Dyment, Christopher. Felix Weingartner : recollections & recordings. 22 Pheasants Way, Rickmansworth, Herts. : Triad Press. £5.95 A/EC(P) (B76-17083) ISBN 0-902070-17-7
Dynamite brass. (Walters, Harold L). Rubank : Novello. Unpriced UMMJ (B76-51002)
E. Humperdinck's 'Hansel and Gretel' : based on E. Humperdinck's opera after the story by the Brothers Grimm. (Isaka, Yoshitaro). F. Warne. £2.25 BHUACBN (B76-19463) ISBN 0-7232-1835-8
E o piano canta, também página para un álbum. (Mignone, Francisco). Arthur Napoleão : Essex Music. Unpriced QPJ (B76-50913)
'Earl of Salisbury' carol. (Byrd, William). Banks. Unpriced EZDP/LF (B76-50422)
Early English church music.
Early Tudor masses
Volume 2. Stainer and Bell. Unpriced EZDG/AYD(XCUE6S) (B76-50049) ISBN 0-85249-385-1
Sheppard, John. Masses. Stainer and Bell. Unpriced EZDG (B76-50410) ISBN 0-85249-392-4
Early music reprinted.
Dowland, John. Lachrimae. 1st ed., reprinted. 5 Albert Grove, Leeds 6 : Boethius Press. £6.60 BDTARWNR (B76-10254) ISBN 0-904263-04-5
The maske of flowers. 5 Albert Grove, Leeds LS6 4DA : Boethius Press. £3.20 ACPF (B76-10977) ISBN 0-904263-02-9
Early music series.
Blades, James. Early percussion instruments : from the Middle Ages to the Baroque. Oxford University Press. £2.95 AX/B(XCG551) (B76-14371) ISBN 0-19-323176-x
Brown, Howard Mayer. Embellishing sixteenth-century music. Oxford University Press. £2.95 A(QM/XD101) (B76-14364) ISBN 0-19-323175-1
Montagu, Jeremy. Making early percussion instruments. Oxford University Press. £2.95 AX/BC (B76-14372) ISBN 0-19-323177-8
Early percussion instruments : from the Middle Ages to the Baroque. (Blades, James). Oxford University Press. £2.95 AX/B(XCG551) (B76-14371) ISBN 0-19-323176-x
Early Tudor masses
Volume 2. Stainer and Bell. Unpriced EZDG/AYD(XCUE6S) (B76-50049) ISBN 0-85249-385-1
Eastaugh, Kenneth. Havergal Brian : the making of a composer. Harrap. £10.00 BBTN(N) (B76-33366) ISBN 0-245-52748-6
Easter anthems : SATB and organ. (Middleton, James Roland). Banks. Unpriced DGSKAD/LL (B76-50013)
Easter fresco : for piano, flute, horn, harp and piano. (Lumsdaine, David). Universal. Unpriced KFLE/NUNSDE (B76-50132)
Easy favourites : classical guitar. Chappell. Unpriced TSPMK/AAY (B76-50660)
Easy lute music. Oxford University Press. Unpriced TW/AY (B76-50279) ISBN 0-19-358834-x
Easy modern guitar music : ten pieces by British composers. Oxford University Press. Unpriced TS/AY (B76-50654) ISBN 0-19-358419-0
Easy music for string quartet or string orchestra. British and Continental : EMI. Unpriced RXNSK/AAY (B76-50243)
Eboracum choral series.
Byrd, William. Pavane & galliard, 'The Earl of Salisbury'. Pavane. arr. The 'Earl of Salisbury' carol. Banks. Unpriced EZDP/LF (B76-50422)
Carter, Andrew. Adam lay y-bounden : S.A. unacc. Banks. Unpriced FEZDP/LF (B76-50445)
Carter, Andrew. Ding dong! merrily on high : 16th cent. French tune. Banks. Unpriced FEZDP/LF (B76-50446)
Carter, Andrew. Pancake Tuesday : unison (or solo) song. Banks. Unpriced JFDW/LFZ (B76-50110)
Carter, Andrew. Sans day carol : Cornish, S.A.T.B. unacc. Banks. Unpriced EZDP/LF (B76-50423)
Ellis, Martin. Communion service, series 3 (including two Communion hymns) : SATB (or unison). Banks. Unpriced DGS (B76-50376)
Harness, Marjorie. Bone pastor, panis vere : SATB unacc. Banks. Unpriced EZDJ (B76-50055)
Jackson, Francis. People of Sion : introit for Advent II (Populus Sion), A.T.B. Banks. Unpriced DH (B76-50783)
Jackson, Francis. Two carols arrangements. Banks. Unpriced DP/LF (B76-50395)
Middleton, James Roland. The Easter anthems : SATB and organ. Banks. Unpriced DGSKAD/LL (B76-50013)
Nelson, Havelock. The lark in the clear air : Irish traditional air. Banks. Unpriced GEZDW (B76-50824)
Nelson, Havelock. My God and King! : S.A.T.B. organ or piano. Banks. Unpriced DM (B76-50392)
Six French carols
Set 1. Banks. Unpriced FEZDP/LF/AYH (B76-50447)
Six French carols
Set 2. Banks. Unpriced FEZDP/LF/AYH (B76-50448)
Tunnard, Thomas. Versicles and responses : SATB. Banks. Unpriced EZDGMM (B76-50053)
Walmsley, Henry. God is gone up on high : melody from Corner, 1625. Banks. Unpriced DP/LL (B76-50027)
Échanges : für einen Blechbläser. (Globokar, Vinko). Litolff : Peters. Unpriced WPMJ (B76-50336)
Eddison blues books. Haralambos, Michael. Right on : from blues to soul in Black America. 2 Greycoat Place, SW1P 1SB : Eddison Press Ltd. £2.50 AKDW/HHW/E(M) (B76-20008) ISBN 0-85649-016-4
Edition Eulenburg.
Bach, Carl Philipp Emanuel. Die Israeliten in der Wuste = The Israelites in the wilderness : oratorio for soli, chorus and orchestra. Eulenburg. Unpriced EMDD (B76-50037)
Berlioz, Hector. Symphonie funèbre et triomphale. Op.15. Grande symphonie funèbre et triomphale. Op.15. Eulenburg. Unpriced EUMMDE (B76-50047)
Berlioz, Hector. Te Deum. Eulenburg. Unpriced EMDGKHB (B76-50798)
Borodin, Aleksandr Porfirevich. Quartet, strings, no.1, A major. String quartet no.1, A major. Eulenburg. Unpriced RXNS (B76-50953)
Dvořák, Antonín. Concerto, violin, op.53, A minor. Violin concerto, A minor. Op.53. Eulenburg. Unpriced MPSF (B76-50533)
Haydn, Joseph. Mass, no.7, G major, 'Sancti Nicolai'. Missa Sancti Nicolai. Eulenburg. Unpriced EMDG (B76-50039)
Holst, Gustav. Savitri, Op 25 : an episode from the Mahābharata. Revised ed. Eulenburg. Unpriced CQC (B76-50768)
Liszt, Franz. Christus : oratorio for soli, chorus, organ and orchestra. Eulenburg. Unpriced EMDD (B76-50038)
Liszt, Franz. Symphonic poem, no.2. Tasso, lamento e trionfo. Tasso, lamento e trionfo. Eulenburg. Unpriced MMJ (B76-50874)
Liszt, Franz. Symphonic poem no.4. Orpheus. Eulenburg. Unpriced MMJ (B76-50525)
Liszt, Franz. Symphonic poem no.5. Prometheus. Prometheus. Eulenburg. Unpriced MMJ (B76-50526)
Liszt, Franz. Symphonic poem no.7. Festklange. Eulenburg. Unpriced MMJ (B76-50527)
Liszt, Franz. Symphonic poem no.8 Héroïde funèbre. Héroïde funèbre. Eulenburg. Unpriced MMJ (B76-50875)
Liszt, Franz. Symphonic poem, no.9. Hungaria. Hungaria. Revised ed. Eulenburg. Unpriced MMJ (B76-50150)
Liszt, Franz. Symphonic poem, no.10. Hamlet. Hamlet. Eulenburg. Unpriced MMJ (B76-50876)
Liszt, Franz. Symphonic poem, no.12. Die Ideale. Die Ideale. Revised ed. Eulenburg. Unpriced MMJ (B76-50151)
Liszt, Franz. Symphonic poem, no.13, 'Von der Wiege bis zum Grabe'. Von der Wiege bis zum Grabe = From the cradle to the grave : symphonic poem, no.13. Eulenburg. Unpriced MMJ (B76-50152)
Liszt, Franz. Two episodes from Lenau's Faust. Procession by night, and, Mephisto waltz. Eulenburg. Unpriced MMJ (B76-50528)
Locke, Matthew. Consort of four parts. Eulenburg. Unpriced STNSG (B76-50964)
Locke, Matthew. The flat consort for my Cousin Kemble. Eulenburg. Unpriced STNTG (B76-50965)
Mendelssohn, Felix. Quintet, strings, no.1, op.18, A major. String quintet, no.1, A major. Op.18. Eulenburg. Unpriced RXNR (B76-50239)
Mendelssohn, Felix. Symphony no.3, op.56, A, 'Scottish'. Symphony no.3 (Scotch), A major, Op.56. Eulenburg. Unpriced MME (B76-50869)
Mozart, Wolfgang Amadeus. Adagio and fugue, string orchestra, K.546, C minor. Adagio and fugue for strings, C minor. K.546. Revised ed. Eulenburg. Unpriced RXM/Y (B76-50947)
Mozart, Wolfgang Amadeus. Concerto, piano, no.12, K.414, A major. Piano concerto, A major. K.414. Revised ed. Eulenburg. Unpriced MPQF (B76-50158)
Mozart, Wolfgang Amadeus. Concerto, piano, no.26, K.537, D major. Piano concerto, D major, K.537. Eulenburg. Unpriced MPQF (B76-50878)
Mozart, Wolfgang Amadeus. Concerto, violin, no.3, K.216, G major. Concerto, G major, for violin and orchestra. K.216. Eulenburg. Unpriced MPSF (B76-50534)
Mozart, Wolfgang Amadeus. Symphony, no.34, K.338, C major. Symphony, C major. K.338 and Minuetto, C major. K.409. Eulenburg. Unpriced MME (B76-50144)
Purcell, Henry. Sonatas, string trio & continuo, no.7-12, Z.796-801. Sonatas of three parts, no.7-12. Eulenburg. Unpriced NXNSE (B76-50172)
Rossini, Gioacchino Antonio. Guillaume Tell. Overture. Overture to the opera 'Guillaume Tell'. Eulenburg. Unpriced MMJ (B76-50530)
Smetana, Bedřich. My fatherland. Sárka. Má vlast : a cycle of symphonic poems
No.3: Sarka. Eulenburg. Unpriced MMJ (B76-50877)
Education in action.
Hope-Brown, Margaret. Activities in music with children under six. Evans Bros. £0.80 A/GR(VH) (B76-04797) ISBN 0-237-29165-7
Todd, Dennis. Teaching music-reading in class. Evans Bros. £0.95 A(VF) (B76-06886) ISBN 0-237-29164-9
Edwards, D W. The Lord's Prayer plus two hymn tunes for choir or organ solo. 67 Lang Lane, West Kirby, Wirral, Merseyside : D.W. Edwards. Unpriced DM (B76-50391)
Edwards, Paul Yeats-. See Yeats-Edwards, Paul.
Edwards, Warwick. Lachrimae. (Dowland, John). 1st ed., reprinted. 5 Albert Grove, Leeds 6 : Boethius Press. £6.60 BDTARWNR (B76-10254) ISBN 0-904263-04-5
Edwards, William Llewelyn. Clychau'r maes : detholiad o donau. Ruel Uchaf, Bow Street, Dyfed : The composer. Unpriced DM (B76-50785)
Ehmann, Wilhelm. Alte Bläser-Partiten : gesammelt und für den praktischen Gebrauch herausgegeben von Wilhelm Ehmann. Bärenreiter. £2.00 UN/AYE (B76-50666)
Ehret, Walter. Cantate Domino. arr. Cantate Domino, canticum novum. (Buxtehude, Dietrich). Schirmer. Unpriced DE (B76-50009)
Ehrlich, Cyril. The piano : a history. Dent. £6.95 AQ/B(X) (B76-20709) ISBN 0-460-04246-7
Eibl, Joseph Heinz. Briefe und Afzeichnungen
Band 7: Register. (Mozart, Wolfgang Amadeus). Gesamtuasg. 32 Great Titchfield St., W1P 7AD : Bärenreiter. £37.50 BMS(N)
Eight études for two percussionists. (Carey, David). Galaxy : Galliard. Unpriced XNU (B76-50752)
Eighteenth-century violin sonatas
Book 1. Associated Board of the Royal Schools of Music. £1.00 SPE/AY (B76-50247)
Book 2. Associated Board of the Royal Schools of Music. £1.00 SPE/AY (B76-50248)
Éigse cheol tíre = Irish folk music studies
Vol.2 : 1974-1975. 3 Sydenham Rd, Dundrum, Dublin 14 : Folk Music Society of Ireland. £1.00 A/G(YDM) (B76-35799) ISBN 0-905733-00-2
Einem, Gottfried von. An die Nachgeborenen. Op.42. Vocal score. An die Nachgeborenen, Op.42 : Kantate für Mezzosopran, Bariton, gemischte Chor und Orchester. Boosey and Hawkes. £12.50 DE (B76-50777)
Einem, Gottfried von. An die Nachgeborenen, Op.42 : Kantate für Mezzosopran, Bariton, gemischten Chor und Orchester. Boosey and Hawkes. £8.50 EMDE (B76-50796)
E.J. Dent : a centenary memoir. (Radcliffe, Philip). 22 Pheasants Way, Rickmansworth, Herts. : Triad Press for the E.J. Dent Centenary Committee. £1.50 A(VX/P) (B76-20005) ISBN 0-902070-18-5
E.J. Dent Centenary Committee. See Dent (E.J.) Centenary Committee.
Electric and Musical Industries. World record markets. 3rd ed. 23 Ridgmount St., WC1E 7AH : Henry Melland for EMI. £2.50 A/FD(K) (B76-28828) ISBN 0-9500730-1-6
Electric music : a practical manual for musicians. (Jenkins, John, b.1936). David and Charles. £4.95 APV (B76-33378) ISBN 0-7153-6815-x
Electronic musical instrument manual : a guide to theory and design. (Douglas, Alan). 6th ed. Pitman. £7.50 ARPV/BC (B76-12801) ISBN 0-273-36193-7
Elegy for a prince. Op.59. Vocal score. Elegy for a prince. Op.59 : for baritone and orchestra. (Mathias, William). Oxford University Press. Unpriced KGNDX (B76-50508) ISBN 0-19-365582-9
Elegy, Op.21 : for flute and organ. (Baker, Michael). Harmuse : Lengnick. £1.00 VRPJ (B76-51017)
Elementary course for guitar. (Wright, Francis). Charnwood Music. Unpriced TS/AC (B76-50972)
Eleven miniatures for harp. (Pitfield, Thomas Baron). Peters. Unpriced TQPMJ (B76-50970)
Elgar, Sir Edward, bart.
In Smyrna. In Smyrna, and Skizze : piano. Novello. £0.75 QPJ (B76-50203)
Music for wind quintet, 2 flutes, oboe, clarinet, bassoon (or cello)
Volume 1: Six promenades (1878). First ed. Belwin Mills. Unpriced UNR/AZ (B76-50671)
Volume 2: Harmony music 1 and 2. First ed. Belwin Mills. Unpriced UNR/AZ (B76-50672)
Volume 3: Harmony music 3 and 4. First ed. Belwin Mills. Unpriced UNR/AZ (B76-50673)
Eliot, Thomas Stearns.
Canticle 5. The death of Saint Narcissus. Op.89 : for tenor and harp. (Britten, Benjamin, Baron Britten). Faber Music. Unpriced KGHE/TQDE (B76-50504)
Canticle 5. The death of Saint Narcissus. Op.89 : for tenor and harp. (Brittn, Benjamin, Baron Britten). Faber Music. Unpriced KGHE/TQDE (B76-50505)
Five madrigals : for unaccompanied mixed voices. (Holloway, Robin). Oxford University Press. Unpriced EZDW (B76-50435)
The hollow men : mixed chorus and piano. (Keats, Donald). Boosey and Hawkes. £0.75 DW (B76-50029)
The light invisible. (Wills, Arthur). Weinberger. Unpriced DH (B76-50784)
The river flows, the seasons turn : anthem for S.A.T.B.,

soprano solo and organ. (Frith, Michael). *Oxford University Press. Unpriced* DH (B76-50015)
Ellis, Martin. Communion service, series 3 (including two Communion hymns) : SATB (or unison). *Banks. Unpriced* DGS (B76-50376)
Elton John. (Tatham, Dick). *Octopus Books : Phoebus. £1.99* AKDW/GB/E(P) (B76-28395) ISBN 0-7064-0548-x
Elvin, Laurence. Forster and Andrews : their barrel, chamber and small church organs. *10 Almond Ave., Swanpool, Lincoln : The author. £4.75* AR/B (B76-20009) ISBN 0-9500049-3-6
Elvis. (Jones, Peter, *b.1930*). *Octopus Books. £1.99* AKDW/HK/E(P) (B76-34783) ISBN 0-7064-0550-1
Elvis Presley : an illustrated biography. (Harbinson, William Allen). *Joseph. £5.50* AKDW/HK/E(P) (B76-03356) ISBN 0-7181-1469-8
Embellishing sixteenth-century music. (Brown, Howard Mayer). *Oxford University Press. £2.95* A(QM/XD101) (B76-14364) ISBN 0-19-323175-1
Emden, Ulrika.
Kleine Stücke, grosser Meister : für zwei Sopranblockflöten. *Noetzel : Peters. Unpriced* VSRNUK/AAY (B76-50303)
Kleine Tänze, grosser Meister : für zwei Sopranblockflöten. *Noetzel : Peters. Unpriced* VSRNUK/AH/AY (B76-50304)
Emerson, Geoffrey. Quartet, strings, no.17, K.458, B flat major, 'The hunt'. *arr.* String quartet in B flat. (Mozart, Wolfgang Amadeus). *Emerson. Unpriced* UNRK (B76-51009)
EMG Handmade Gramophones Limited. The art of record buying : a list of recommended microgroove recordings 1976. *E.M.G. £5.00* A/FD(WT)
EMI. *See* Electrical and Musical Industries.
Encyclopedia of folk country and Western music. (Stambler, Irwin). *St Martin's Press : St James Press. £5.00* A/GCW(C) (B76-00666) ISBN 0-900997-24-9
Encyclopedia of opera. *Pitman. £13.50(£10.50 until January 1 1977)* AC(C) (B76-31915) ISBN 0-273-00237-6
Encyclopedia of rock
Vol.1: The age of rock'n'roll. *Panther. £0.95* A/HK(C) (B76-14358) ISBN 0-586-04267-9
Vol.2: From Liverpool to San Francisco. *Panther. £0.95* A/HK(C) (B76-16549) ISBN 0-586-04268-7
Vol.3: The sounds of the seventies. *Panther. £0.95* A/HK(C) (B76-31912) ISBN 0-586-04269-5
Englisches Folksong-Büchlein : die schönsten Songs und Balladen, für Singstimme, Melodieinstrumente und Gitarrenbegleitung. *Heinrichshofen : Peters. Unpriced* JE/LPLTSDW/G/AYD (B76-50458)
English church music : a bibliography. (Yeats-Edwards, Paul). *White Lion Publishers. £15.00* A/LD(T) (B76-50000) ISBN 0-7285-0020-5
English churgh music : essays, reports and reviews 1976. *Addington Place, Croydon CR9 5AD : Royal School of Church Music. £1.50* A/LD(YD/D) (B76-50353) ISBN 0-85402-062-4
English Folk Dance and Song Society.
The folk directory 1976. *The Society. £2.00(£1.00 to members)* A/G(BC) (B76-25961) ISBN 0-85418-111-3
We wunt be druv : songs and stories from Sussex. *Galliard : English Folk Dance and Song Society. £2.80* ADW/G(YDCR) (B76-17456) ISBN 0-85249-307-x
English madrigalists. Nicolson, Richard. Collected madrigals. *Stainer and Bell. Unpriced* EZDU/AZ (B76-50064) ISBN 0-85249-382-7
Enjoy your recorder. The Trapp family recorder method : a new complete method of instruction for the recorder, including exercises, revisions, trill charts, ornaments and embellishments, duets, trios and quartets
Vol.1. (Trapp Family). New ed. *Schott. Unpriced* VS/AC (B76-50296) ISBN 0-901938-50-5
Entertainer. *arr.* The entertainer. (Joplin, Scott). *Chappell. Unpriced* EZDW (B76-50068)
Entertainer. *arr.* The entertainer. (Joplin, Scott). *Chappell. Unpriced* VSNSQK/AHXJ (B76-50684)
Entertainer. *arr.* The entertainer : an excerpt. (Joplin, Scott). *Schirmer. Unpriced* VRPLTSK/AHXJ (B76-50293)
Entertainers. Fisher, John, *b.1945.* George Formby. *Woburn Press. £2.95* AKDW/GB/E(P) (B76-17647) ISBN 0-7130-0144-5
Entführung aus dem Serail. K.384. *arr.* The abduction from the Seraglio. (Mozart, Wolfgang Amadeus). *Musica rara. Unpriced* UNNK/CC (B76-50668)

Epigon IV. (Washburn, Robert). *Boosey and Hawkes. £15.00* UMMJ (B76-51004)
Epilogue : for four-part male voice choir unaccompanied. (Burtch, Mervyn). *Roberton. £0.10* GEZDH (B76-50823)
Eric Clapton : a biography. (Pidgeon, John). *Panther. £0.60* ATS/HK/E(P) (B76-27135) ISBN 0-586-04292-x
Erik Satie entertainment : a selection of songs and piano music. (Satie, Erik). *Novello. Unpriced* QPJ (B76-50212)

Es danken dir, Gott, die Volker : solokantate für Tenor, zwei Violinen und Basso continuo. (Hammerschmidt, Andreas). *Bärenreiter. £1.63* KGHE/SNTPWDE (B76-50503)
España. *arr.* España : rhapsody for orchestra. (Chabrier, Emmanuel). *Bosworth. Unpriced* MK (B76-50139)
Essay on the true art of playing keyboard instruments. (Bach, Carl Philipp Emanuel). *48 Great Marlborough St., W1V 2BN : Eulenburg Books. £3.00* APW/E (B76-15055) ISBN 0-903873-14-1
Essays for piano. (Binkerd, Gordon). *Boosey and Hawkes. £4.00* QPJ (B76-50567)
Essays from the world of music : essays from 'The Sunday Times'. (Newman, Ernest). *J. Calder. £6.50* A(D) (B76-34776) ISBN 0-7145-3548-6
Essays on opera and English music : in honour of Sir Jack Westrup. *Blackwell. £7.00* A(YD/XCE841/D) (B76-15050) ISBN 0-631-15890-1
'Ethode de guitare à Dadi. (Dadi, Marcel). *Music Express : Chappell : Chappell. Unpriced* TS/AC (B76-50267)
'Etude barcarolle : for instrumental ensemble. (Wright, Francis). *Charnwood Music. Unpriced* LNQ (B76-50514)
'Etudes Australes : piano
Books 1 and 2. (Cage, John). *Peters. Unpriced* QPJ (B76-50568)
Books 3 and 4. (Cage, John). *Peters. Unpriced* QPJ (B76-50569)
'Etudes intelligentes : for beginners at the piano. (Lachert, Piotr). *Bärenreiter. £5.00* Q/AF (B76-50544)
Evangeline. *Vocal score.* Evangeline : opera in 3 acts. (Luening, Otto). *Peters. Unpriced* CC (B76-50760)
Evans, Colin. Fifty hymns for band
Book 2: General, Passiontide and Easter. *Oxford University Press. Unpriced* MK/DM/AY (B76-50868) ISBN 0-19-363060-5
Evans, M E. 'Pantyfedwen' : i leisiau TTBB. Revised ed. *Thames. Unpriced* GDW (B76-50452)
Evans, Peter. One hundred hits of the seventies. *Wise, Music Sales. Unpriced* KDW/GB/AY (B76-50852)
Event operas.
Hoskins, Graham. The Jesus file. *Voice part.* The Jesus file : a musical nativity. *Dobson. Unpriced* JDACN/LF (B76-50099) ISBN 0-234-77244-1
Walker, Chris. The wind on the heath. *Voice part.* The wind on the heath : children's musical play. *Dobson. Unpriced* JDACN (B76-50098) ISBN 0-234-77245-x
Events in tune. (Pickles, Sydney). *EMI. Unpriced* QPJ (B76-50917)
Eventyr. Once upon time, after Asbjornsen's folklore. (Delius, Frederick). *Stainer and Bell. Unpriced* MMJ (B76-50148) ISBN 0-85249-398-3
Everlasting voices. (Warlock, Peter). *Thames. Unpriced* KDW (B76-50488)
Everybody's favourite Christmas carols : for the first time arranged for piano vocal-easy organ, 25 of the world's best loved Christmas carols. *Wise : Music Sales. £0.95* RK/DP/LF/AY (B76-50935) ISBN 0-86001-217-4
Everyman's dictionary of music. (Blom, Eric). 5th ed. *Dent. £1.95* A(C) (B76-31911) ISBN 0-460-02151-6
Everyman's reference library. Blom, Eric. Everyman's dictionary of music. 5th ed. *Dent. £1.95* A(C) (B76-31911) ISBN 0-460-02151-6
Examinations in pianoforte playing
Grade 1 (primary), Book II. (London College of Music). *Ashdown. £0.50* Q/AL (B76-50556)
Examinations, scales and arpeggios for pianoforte playing : grades 3, 4, 5, 6 and 7. (Guildhall School of Music). *Lengnick. £0.95* Q/AF/AL (B76-50545)
Exciting sound of flamenco. (Martín, Juan). *United Music. Unpriced* TSPMH (B76-50984)

Explorations around a troubadour song : for piano solo. (Tate, Phyllis). *Oxford University Press. Unpriced* QPJ (B76-50574) ISBN 0-19-373809-0
Exploring music.
Classical music for flute and piano. *Boosey and Hawkes. Unpriced* VRPK/AAY (B76-51022)
Romantic music for flute and piano. *Boosey and Hawkes. Unpriced* VRPK/AAY (B76-51023)
Exploring sound : creative musical projects for teachers. (Tillman, June). *Galliard etc.. £2.50* A/D(VJ) (B76-22855) ISBN 0-85249-310-x
Ezell, Helen Ingle. When we went to Liza's house : 6 piano pieces. *Oxford University Press. Unpriced* QPJ (B76-50904)
Faber guitar series. Searle, Humphrey. Five, Op.61 : for guitar. *Faber Music. Unpriced* TSPMJ (B76-50991)
Falling angels : music from the film. (Cole, Tony). *250 Purley Way, Croydon CR9 4QD : Valley Music. £1.00* KDW/JR (B76-50126)
Famous pianists & their technique. (Gerig, Reginald R). *David and Charles. £8.50* AQ/CY(M) (B76-32593) ISBN 0-7153-7220-3
Fanfare and march : for brass quartet. (Parrott, Ian). *EMI. Unpriced* WNSGM (B76-50740)
Fanfare for youth, Op.39, no.1. (Golland, John). *EMI. Unpriced* WMGN (B76-51056)
Fanshawe, David. Dance ti thi daddy : traditional original theme song from the BBC TV series 'When the boat comes in'. *Chappell. Unpriced* KDW (B76-50477)
Fantasia : das Harfenspiel in der Manier von Ludovico nachahmend / von Alonso Mudarra. Welsh Tantz, 'Wascha mesa' / von Hans Neusidler ; für Gitarre solo, eingerichtet von Dieter Kreidler. (Mudarra, Alonso). *Schott. £1.00* TSPMK (B76-50275)
Fantasia concertante no.6 : for solo E flat alto saxophone. (Camilleri, Charles). *Basil Ramsey : Roberton. £1.50* VUSPMJ (B76-50697)
Fantasia pictorial, stories from famous music.
Isaka, Yoshitaro. E. Humperdinck's 'Hansel and Gretel' : based on E. Humperdinck's opera after the story by the Brothers Grimm. *F. Warne. £2.25* BHUACBN (B76-19463) ISBN 0-7232-1835-8
Mizusawa, Hiroshi. G.A. Rossini's 'William Tell'. *F. Warne. £2.25* BRRACBN (B76-18578) ISBN 0-7232-1833-1
Semba, Taro. M.P. Mussorgsky's 'A night on bare mountain'. *F. Warne. £2.25* BMUAMBN (B76-18581) ISBN 0-7232-1836-6
Yangagihara, Ryohei. P. Dukas' 'The sorcerer's apprentice'. *F. Warne. £2.25* BDVAMBN (B76-18582) ISBN 0-7232-1834-x
Fantasias à 3, viols & keyboard. *arr.* Four fantasias. (Jeffries, George). *Chappell. Unpriced* QPK (B76-50581)
Fantasy on L'Homme armé : oboe and piano. (Tull, Fisher). *Boosey and Hawkes. £1.25* VTPJ (B76-50692)
Fantôme : clarinet in B flat, viola, piano. (Hannay, Roger). *Henmar Press : Peters : Peters. Unpriced* NUVNT (B76-50883)
Fargo, Milford. Away he run. *Vocal score.* Away he run : a musical based on the story of the prodigal son. *Stainer and Bell. Unpriced* CM/L (B76-50764) ISBN 0-85249-315-0
Faris, Alexander. The duchess of Duke Street : theme from the BBC television serial. *Chappell. Unpriced* QPK/AHW/JS (B76-50924)
Farjeon, Eleanor.
An Advent carol. Opus 25 : for treble voices and piano. (Platts, Kenneth). *Ashdown. £0.08* FLDP/LEZ (B76-50092)
Pancake Tuesday : unison (or solo) song. (Carter, Andrew). *Banks. Unpriced* JFDW/LFZ (B76-50110)
People look east : Advent carol, for four-part chorus of mixed voices unaccompanied. (Hanson, Geoffrey). *Roberton. £0.10* EZDP/LEZ (B76-50806)
Streets of London. (Senator, Ronald). *Boosey and Hawkes. £2.20* FE/NYFSNSDW (B76-50471)
Farquharson, W H. Gift of new sight : Christmas anthem, S.A.T.B. (Klusmeier, R T). *Harmuse : Lengnick. £0.21* DP/LF (B76-50790)
Farran, Kenneth G. Joyeux : waltz, accordion solo. *Charnwood Music. Unpriced* RSPMHW (B76-50946)
Farrell, Graham. Two revival preludes : for trumpet and organ. *Galaxy : Galliard. Unpriced* WSPLR (B76-50745)

Fauré, Gabriel. Pelléas et Mélisande. Op.80. Sicilienne. *arr.* Sicilienne. *Boosey and Hawkes. £3.95* MK/AHVQ (B76-50140)
Favorite Christmas carols. *Dover : Collier Macmillan. £1.30* JDP/LF/AY (B76-50104) ISBN 0-486-20445-6
Fedtke, Traugott.
In te Domine speravi : Kantate für Sopran, Alt, Bass und Basso continuo. (Buxtehude, Dietrich). *Litolff : Peters. Unpriced* DE (B76-50010)
Symphony, string orchestra & continuo, no.3, Wotq.182/3. Sinfonie nr.3 für Streicher und Basso continuo, C-dur, Wotquenne 182/3. (Bach, Carl Philipp Emanuel). *Litolff : Peters. Unpriced* RXME (B76-50948)
Symphony, string orchestra & continuo, no.4, Wotq 182/4. Sinfonie nr.4 für Streicher und Basso continuo, A-dur, Wotquenne 182/4. (Bach, Carl Philipp Emanuel). *Litolff : Peters. Unpriced* RXME (B76-50949)
Symphony, string orchestra, no.1, Wotquenne 182/1, G major. Sinfonie Nr.1 für Streicher und Basso continuo, G-dur. Wotquenne 182/1. (Bach, Carl Philipp Emanuel). Zum ersten Mal herausgegeben von Traugott Fedtke. *Litolff : Peters. Unpriced* RXME (B76-50606)
Symphony, string orchestra, Wotg,182/2, B flat major. Sinfonie nr.2 : für Streicher und Basso continuo, B-Dur, Wotquenne 182/2. (Bach, Carl Philipp Emanuel). *Litolff : Peters. Unpriced* RXME (B76-50607)
Feldman, Morton. Voices and instruments. *Universal. Unpriced* ENYHDW (B76-50044)
Felix Weingartner : recollections & recordings. *22 Pheasants Way, Rickmansworth, Herts. : Triad Press. £5.95* A/EC(P) (B76-17083) ISBN 0-902070-17-7
Fellowes, Edmund Horace.
Hosanna to the Son of David : S.S.A.A.T.T.B. (Gibbons, Orlando). *Oxford University Press. Unpriced* EZDK (B76-50418) ISBN 0-19-352078-8
Invitation to madrigals
9: for S.S.A.T.B. *Staines and Bell. Unpriced* EZDU/AY (B76-50812) ISBN 0-85249-345-2
9: for S.S.A.T.B. *Stainer and Bell. Unpriced* EZDU/AY (B76-50811) ISBN 0-85249-346-0
Fenby, Eric. A Delius companion. *John Calder : Distributed by Calder and Boyars. £7.50* BDL (B76-17646) ISBN 0-7145-3526-5
Fennimore und Gerda = Fennimore and Gerda. (Delius, Frederick). *Boosey and Hawkes. £6.50* CQC (B76-50007)
Fenwick, J W. Instruction book for the Northumbrian small-pipes. 3rd ed. *5 Denebank, Monkseaton : Northumbrian Pipers' Society. Unpriced* VYQ/AC (B76-50715) ISBN 0-902510-01-0
Ferguson, Edwin Earle. Messe solennelle. Kyrie. *Vocal score.* Kyrie. (Rossini, Gioacchino Antonio). *Roberton. £0.28* DGB (B76-50778)
Ferguson, Sir Samuel. The lark in the clear air : Irish traditional air. (Nelson, Havelock). *Banks. Unpriced* GEZDW (B76-50824)
Fernandez, Oscar Lorenzo. *See* Lorenzo Fernandez, Oscar.
Ferneyhough, Brian.
Time and motion study III : 16 solo voices with percussion and electronic amplification. *Peters. Unpriced* EPV (B76-50801)
Unity capsule : solo flute. *Peters. Unpriced* VRPMJ (B76-51028)
Ferreira, Oscar Augusto. Clube 15 : celébre valsa. *Seresta Essex Music. Unpriced* QPHW (B76-50563)
Festival concerto, clarinet & small orchestra. *arr.* Festival concerto for B flat clarinet and small orchestra. (Davis, Allan). *Oxford University Press. Unpriced* VVPK/LF (B76-50711)
Festival service book
8: The city : a meditation with words and music. *Royal College of Church Music. Unpriced* DGM (B76-50780)

ISBN 0-85402-064-0
Festive occasion : for brass quintet. (Burrell, Howard). *Chester : Hansen. Unpriced* WNR (B76-51078)
Field, Christopher. Fantasia, viols (2) & organ, A minor. Fantasia, suite 5 : for violin (or treble viol), bass viol (or violoncello) and organ (or harpsichord). (Jenkins, John). *Oxford University Press. Unpriced* NXNT (B76-50886) ISBN 0-19-357410-1
Fielding, Henry. Tom Jones. *Adaptations.* Tom Jones : a comedy for music, based on the novel by Henry Fielding. (Oliver, Stephen). *Novello. £0.85* BOLAC (B76-21365) ISBN 0-85360-063-5
Fields, Dorothy. Seesaw : a musical. *French. £1.25* BCMEACM (B76-06887) ISBN 0-573-68069-8
Fifty classical studies for clarinet. *Fentone Music. Unpriced* VV/AF/AY (B76-50698)
Fifty études : for piano
Book 1. (Waxman, Donald). *Galaxy : Galliard. Unpriced* QPJ (B76-50577)
Book 2. (Waxman, Donald). *Galaxy : Galliard. Unpriced* QPJ (B76-50578)
Fifty études for piano
Book 3: Lower advanced. (Waxman, Donald). *Galaxy Stainer and Bell. Unpriced* Q/AF (B76-50891)
Figured harmony at the keyboard
Part 1. (Morris, Reginald Owen). *Oxford University Press. £0.75* QP/R (B76-50896) ISBN 0-19-321471-7
Part 2. (Morris, Reginald Owen). *Oxford University Press. Unpriced* QP/R (B76-50897) ISBN 0-19-321472-5
Fille du tambour major. *Vocal score.* The drum-major's daughter : comic opera in three acts. (Offenbach, Jacques). *Choudens : United Music. Unpriced* CF (B76-50762)
Film and TV themes for the recorder : outstanding selections published complete with lyrics and guitar diagrams plus a six page introduction to playing the recorder. *Wise : Music Sales. Unpriced* VSPMK/DW/JR/AY (B76-51039)
Fine flowers in the valley : Scottish folk ballad. (Liddell, Claire). *Roberton. £0.14* EZDW (B76-50071)
Finger style guitar in theory and practice
Book 1. (Mairants, Ivor). *British and Continental : EMI. Unpriced* TS/AC (B76-50971)
Book 1: Basic principles, major and minor scales, chord diagrams and fingerboard chart. (Mairants, Ivor). *British and Continental : EMI. Unpriced* TS/AF (B76-50977)
Book 2: Instruction for beginners, classical repertoire. (Mairants, Ivor). *British and Continental : EMI. Unpriced* TS/AF (B76-50978)
Fink, Robert. The language of twentieth century music : a dictionary of terms. *Schirmer Books : Collier Macmillan. £5.50* A(XMA77/C) (B76-05036) ISBN 0-02-870600-5
Fink, Siegfried.
Conga negro. *Schott. £2.80* XQRPMJ (B76-51090)
Studien für Drums = Studies for drums
Vol.1: Elementary. *Simrock. £2.00* XQ/AF (B76-50753)
Studien für Pauken = Studies for timpani
Vol.1: Elementary. *Simrock. £4.00* XR/AF (B76-50755)
Finney, Rose Lee. Two acts for three players : clarinet, percussion, piano. *Henmar Press : Peters : Peters. Unpriced* NYFVNT (B76-50176)
Finzi, Gerald. Concerto, trumpet & string orchestra, no.1, B flat major. *arr.* Concerto no.1 for trumpet, strings and continuo. (Mudge, Richard). *Boosey and Hawkes. £1.00* WSPK/LF (B76-50343)
First album for piano
Part 1. (Kirkby-Mason, Barbara). Revised ed. *Bosworth. Unpriced* Q/AC (B76-50889)
Part 3. (Kirkby-Mason, Barbara). Revised ed. *Bosworth. Unpriced* Q/AC (B76-50890)
First year trumpeter
Volume 2: Eight famous melodies for trumpet (or cornet) in B flat and piano. *Ashdown. £1.20* WSPK/AAY (B76-50341)
Fischer, Jerry Cree. Piano tuning : a simple and accurate method for amateurs. Abridged ed.. *Dover Publication etc. : Constable. £2.10* AQ/P (B76-31127) ISBN 0-486-23267-0
Fischer, Johann Caspar Ferdinand. Le Journal de printemps. Partie 3, 4. Suiten = Suites for four strings or wind instruments and basso continuo. *Bärenreiter. £6.00* NXNRG (B76-50540)
Fischer-Dieskau, Dietrich.
The Fischer-Dieskau book of Lieder : the texts of over 750 songs in German. *Gollancz : Pan Books. £7.50* AKDW(YE) (B76-33373) ISBN 0-575-01852-6
Die schöne Müllerin. D.795 : für Gesang und Klavier. (Schubert, Franz). *Litolff : Peters. Unpriced* KDW (B76-50847)
Schubert : a biographical study of his songs. *Cassell. £5.95* BSFAKDW (B76-33372) ISBN 0-304-29002-5
Schwanengesang. D.957 : für Gesang und Klavier. (Schubert, Franz). *Litolff : Peters. Unpriced* KDW (B76-50848)
Fischer-Dieskau book of Lieder : the texts of over 750 songs in German. *Gollancz : Pan Books. £7.50* AKDW(YE) (B76-33373) ISBN 0-575-01852-6
Fisher, Bobby.
An der schönen blauen Donau. Op.314. *arr.* The blue Danube. (Strauss, Johann, *b.1825*). *Fisher and Lane. Unpriced* RPVK/AHW (B76-50938)
Les Contes d'Hoffmann. Belle nuit. *arr.* Barcarolle. (Offenbach, Jacques). *Fisher and Lane. £0.30* RPVK/DW (B76-50940)
Dichter und Bauer. Overture. *Selections: arr.* Poet and peasant overture : (selections). (Suppé, Franz von). *Fisher and Lane. Unpriced* RPVK (B76-50937)
Fisher, John, *b.1945.* George Formby. *Woburn Press. £2.95* AKDW/GB/E(P) (B76-17647) ISBN 0-7130-0144-5
Fiske, Roger.
Concerto, cello, op.104, B minor. Cello concerto, B minor. Op.104. (Dvořák, Antonín). *Eulenburg. Unpriced* MPSRF (B76-50535)
Sonatas, string trio & continuo, no.7-12, Z.796-801. Sonatas of three parts, no.7-12. (Purcell, Henry). *Eulenburg. Unpriced* NXNSE (B76-50172)
Fitzwilliam Museum. Italian music and the Fitzwilliam : a collection of essays and a catalogue of an exhibition of Italian in the Fitzwilliam Museum in May 1976 on the occasion of four concerts of Italian music. *Fitzwilliam Museum. £1.00* A(YJ/WJ) (B76-26569) ISBN 0-904454-02-9
Five interludes : for clarinet solo. (Valbonesi, Ruggero). *British and Continental : EMI. Unpriced* VVPMJ (B76-50321)
Five madrigals : for unaccompanied mixed voices. (Holloway, Robin). *Oxford University Press. Unpriced* EZDW (B76-50435)
Five, Op.61 : for guitar. (Searle, Humphrey). *Faber Music. Unpriced* TSPMJ (B76-50991)
Five Orkney scenes : a song cycle for female voice and piano. (Liddell, Claire). *Roberton. Unpriced* KFDW (B76-50131)
Five philanders. Contentment. Op.125, no.4. Contentment : S.A.T. unacc. (Gardner, John). *Oxford University Press. Unpriced* EZDW (B76-50432) ISBN 0-19-343059-2
Five philanders. Rejection. Op.125, no.1. Rejection : S.A.T.B. unacc. (Gardner, John). *Oxford University Press. Unpriced* EZDW (B76-50433) ISBN 0-19-343058-4
Five Shakespeare songs : voice and piano. (Amram, David). *Peters. Unpriced* KDW (B76-50117)
Fives and threes : brass band. (Golland, John). *British and Continental : EMI. Unpriced* WMJ (B76-50324)
Flanders, Michael. The wassail of Figgy Duff. *arr.* The wassail of Figgy Duff : for mixed chorus and keyboard, traditional words. *Galaxy : Galliard. Unpriced* DP/LF (B76-50394)
Flat consort for my Cousin Kemble. (Locke, Matthew). *Eulenburg. Unpriced* STNTG (B76-50965)
Flatauer, Susanne. The Wagner family albums, Bayreuth 1876-1976. *Thames and Hudson. £5.95* BWCB(XKR101/EM) (B76-19493) ISBN 0-500-01158-3
Fledermaus. Fledermaus - Polka. *arr.* Polka française. (Strauss, Johann, *b.1825*). *Oxford University Press. Unpriced* UMMK/AHVH (B76-50665)
Fleischer, Leonore. Joni Mitchell. *Flash Books; 78 Newman St., W1P 3LA : Book Sales Ltd. £1.95* AKDW/GB/E(P) (B76-35355) ISBN 0-8256-3907-7
Fleischmann, Aloys. Poet in the suburbs : for unaccompanied mixed voices. *Oxford University Press. Unpriced* EZDX (B76-50077) ISBN 0-19-336108-6
Flights : for 2 pianos. (Lumsdaine, David). *Universal. Unpriced* QNU (B76-50183)
Flood, W H Gratton. Consider well : Irish melody. (Wilkinson, Stephen). *Roberton. £0.18* GEZDP/LF (B76-50094)
Floreal : música celestial 2, for percussion solo. (Marco, Tomás). *Simrock. £1.45* XPMJ (B76-50345)
Flotzinger, Rudolf. De ratione in musica : Festschrift Erich Schenk, zu 5.Mai 1972. *32 Great Titchfield St., W.1 : Bärenreiter Kassel. £18.00* A(ZC)
Flower songs. *Vocal score.* Flower songs : for S(S)A and string orchestra (or piano). (Hurd, Michael). *Novello. £0.50* FDW (B76-50080)
Folk directory
1976. *The Society. £2.00(£1.00 to members)* A/G(BC) (B76-25961) ISBN 0-85418-111-3
Folk Music Society of Ireland. Eigse cheol tíre = Irish folk music studies
Vol.2 : 1974-1975. *3 Sydenham Rd, Dundrum, Dublin 14 : Folk Music Society of Ireland. £1.00* A/G(YDM) (B76-35799) ISBN 0-905733-00-2
Folk song : music arranged by John and Susanne Bailey, text by John Bailey. *SCM Press. Unpriced* JEZDW/G/AYC (B76-50106) ISBN 0-334-00492-6
Folksongs for flute, with guitar chords : 200 favourites. *Chappell. Unpriced* VRPLTSK/DW/G/AY (B76-51025)
Fond kiss : old Highland melody. (Liddell, Claire). *Roberton. £0.14* EZDW (B76-50070)
Fontana modern masters. Rosen, Charles. Schoenberg. *Fontana. £0.75* BSET (B76-34779) ISBN 0-00-633558-6
For gawdsake don't take me! : the songs, ballads, verses, monologues, etc. of the call-up years, 1939-1963. *Hart-Davis, MacGibbon. £2.95* AKDW/KG(YC/XNU25) (B76-50757) ISBN 0-246-10859-2
For the infant Michael : SATB. (Binkerd, Gordon). *Boosey and Hawkes. £0.20* EZDW (B76-50067)
Forbes, Watson.
Quartets, strings. *Selections : arr.* Two minuets. (Haydn, Joseph). *Oxford University Press. Unpriced* SRPK/AHR (B76-50259) ISBN 0-19-357072-6
A second classical and romantic album for horn in F and piano. *Oxford University Press. Unpriced* WTPK/AAY (B76-50750) ISBN 0-19-356528-5
A third classical and romantic album for horn in F and piano. *Oxford University Press. Unpriced* WTPK/AAY (B76-50749) ISBN 0-19-356530-7
Foreman, Lewis.
British music now : a guide to the work of younger composers. *Elek. £6.50* A/D(YC/M) (B76-08493) ISBN 0-236-30933-1
Havergal Brian and the performance of his orchestral music : a history and source book. *14 Barlby Rd, W10 6AR : Thames Publishing. £6.95* BBTN(N) (B76-23704) ISBN 0-905210-01-8
The music of Frank Bridge. (Payne, Anthony, *b.1936*). *14 Barlby Rd, W10 6AR : Thames Publishing. £3.20* BBTP (B76-29100) ISBN 0-905210-02-6
Foreman, Ronald Lewis Edmund. *See* Foreman, Lewis.
Forging of the 'Ring' : Richard Wagner's composition sketches for 'Der Ring des Nibelungen'. (Westernhagen, Curt von). *Cambridge University Press. £7.50* BWAC (B77-00343) ISBN 0-521-21293-6
Forster, John. Pretzels : a musical revue. *French. £1.25* BFNRACP (B76-06889) ISBN 0-573-68071-x
Forster and Andrews : their barrel, chamber and small church organs. (Elvin, Laurence). *10 Almond Ave., Swanpool, Lincoln : The author. £4.75* AR/B (B76-20009) ISBN 0-9500049-3-6
Fortner, Wolfgang.
Prismen : für Soloinstrumente, (Flöte, Oboe, Klarinette in B, Harfe, Schlagzeug) und Orchester von Wolfgang Fortner. *Schott. £11.20* MPVR (B76-50879)
Thema und Variationen für Violoncello solo. *Schott. £2.00* SRPM/T (B76-50646)
Fortune, Nigel. Essays on opera and English music : in honour of Sir Jack Westrup. *Blackwell. £7.00* A(YD/XCE841/D) (B76-15050) ISBN 0-631-15890-1
Forty-eight exercises for accordion. (Wright, Francis). *Charnwood Music. Unpriced* RS/AF (B76-50943)
Foss, Peter.
'I'll walk with God' : twenty-five of the most famous religious songs and ballads ever written. *Wise : Music Sales. Unpriced* KDW/L/AY (B76-50857)
Sinatra, the man and his music. *Wise : Music Sales. Unpriced* KDW/GB/AYT (B76-50853)
Song of Ireland : songs. *Wise : Music Sales. £2.95* KDW/AYDM (B76-50849)
Foster, Stephen. Jennie with the light brown hair. *arr.* Jeanie with the light brown hair. *Chester Music. Unpriced* WMPWWK/DW (B76-51077)
Four diversions : for descant recorder and piano. (Turner, John). *Forsyth. Unpriced* VSRPJ (B76-51040)
Four eighteenth century concerto movements for organ with and without pedals. *EMI. Unpriced* RK/LF/AY (B76-50936)
Four French songs from an English song book (Cambridge, University Library Add.MS.5943, ff 161-173) : for voice with 1 and 2 instruments. *Antico. Unpriced* KE/LNUDW/AY (B76-50859)
Four Japanese verses, Op.2 : for soprano and piano. (Pert, Morris). *Weinberger. Unpriced* KFLDW (B76-50862)
Four oboe melodies. (Rameau, Jean Philippe). *Oxford University Press. Unpriced* VTPK (B76-50311) ISBN 0-19-358461-1
Four play three. (Slack, Roy). *British and Continental. Unpriced* RXNS (B76-50620)
Four short songs : for medium voice. (Rubbra, Edmund). *Lengnick. Unpriced* KDW (B76-50122)
Fourth sonata, 'Green and gold and blue and white' : for orchestra. (Matthews, Colin). *Novello. £3.00* MME (B76-50143)
Fox, Roy. Hollywood, Mayfair, and all that jazz : the Roy Fox story. *Frewin. £4.25* AMT(P) (B76-17648) ISBN 0-85632-171-0
Fragmente aus einer Show : Sätze für Blechquintett. (Henze, Hans Werner). *Schott. £2.25* WNR (B76-50739)
Françaix, Jean.
Concerto, bassoon: arr. Concerto pour contrebasse et orchestre. *Schott. £7.00* VWPK/LF (B76-51052)
Dix pièces enfantines, piano. Zehn Stücke für Kinder zum Spielen und Träumen, 'De la musique avant toute chose'. *Schott. £2.40* QPJ (B76-50905)
Francesco d'Assisi, *Saint. See* Francis of Assisi, *Saint.*
Francis of Assisi, *Saint.* Lord make me an instrument of thy peace. Op.84 : S. solo, S.S.A.A.T.T.B.B. (Joubert, John). *Oxford University Press. Unpriced* DH (B76-50386) ISBN 0-19-350359-x
Franck, César. Selected piano compositions. *Dover Publications : Constable. Unpriced* QPJ (B76-50906) ISBN 0-486-23269-7
Frank, Alan. The watermill. *arr.* The watermill. (Binge, Ronald). *Weinberger. Unpriced* VVPK (B76-50706)
Franklin, J E. The prodigal sister : a new black musical. *French. £1.35* BGSEACM (B76-50357) ISBN 0-573-68075-2
Franklin, Michael. The scarecrow : for unison voices and piano. (Clements, John). *Elkin. £0.12* JFDW (B76-50463)
Fraser, Eric. Der Ring des Nibelungen. *English & German.* The ring. (Wagner, Richard). *Dawson. £15.00* BWCAC (B76-31122) ISBN 0-7129-0698-3
Frederica : operetta in three acts. (Dunn, Bernard). *10 Rathbone St., W1P 2BJ : Glocken Verlag Ltd. £1.00* BLDACF
Frederica : operetta in three acts. (Lehár, Franz). *Glocken. Unpriced* CF (B76-50761)
Freed, Arnold. Gloria. *Vocal score.* Gloria : mixed chorus, brass ensemble, timpani with piano (alternate accompaniment). Revised ed. *Boosey and Hawkes. £0.50* DGC (B76-50779)
Freeman, Bud. If you know of a better life please tell me. *65 Dublin Industrial Estate, Glasnevin, Dublin 11 : Bashall Eaves. £0.80* AMT (B76-31126) ISBN 0-902638-02-5
French art and music since 1500. (Blunt, *Sir* Anthony). *Methuen. £1.35* A(YH/X) (B76-50351) ISBN 0-416-81650-9
French's musical library.
Dubey, Matt. Smith : a musical. *French. £1.25* BDUACM

(B76-00671) ISBN 0-573-68066-3
Fields, Dorothy. Seesaw : a musical. *French. £1.25* BCMEACM (B76-06887) ISBN 0-573-68069-8
Forster, John. Pretzels : a musical revue. *French. £1.25* BFNRACP (B76-06889) ISBN 0-573-68071-x
Stewart, Michael. Mack & Mabel : a musical love story. *French. £1.35* BHKMACM (B76-19250) ISBN 0-573-68074-4
Udell, Peter. Shenandoah : a musical. *French. £1.25* BGGTACM (B76-06888) ISBN 0-573-68073-6
Wann, Jim. Diamond studs : the life of Jesse James. *French. £1.60* BSHLACM (B77-00344) ISBN 0-573-68076-0
Frengh's musical library. Franklin, J E. The prodigal sister : a new black musical. *French. £1.35* BGSEACM (B76-50357) ISBN 0-573-68075-2
Frère Jacques. (Iveson, John). *Chester : Hansen. Unpriced* WNRK/DW (B76-51080)
Fresh sounds. *Hodder and Stoughton. Unpriced* JDM/AY (B76-50826) ISBN 0-340-20622-5
Freu'dich sehr : chorale prelude for organ. (Benjamin, Thomas). *Galaxy : Galliard. Unpriced* RJ (B76-50590)
Frey, Hugo. Barbershop memories : songs. *Robbins Music : EMI. Unpriced* GEZDW/AYT (B76-50097)
Friederike. *See* Herzer, Ludwig.
Friederike. *Vocal score.* Frederica : operetta in three acts. (Lehár, Franz). *Glocken. Unpriced* CF (B76-50761)
Friend, Howard C. Ceremonial occasion : a tribute to Her Majesty the Queen for the year of her silver jubilee, 1977 : a selection of famous marches and songs. *Bosworth. Unpriced* MK (B76-50867)
Friends of Hereford Cathedral. *See* Hereford Cathedral. *Friends of Hereford Cathedral.*
Frith, Michael. The river flows, the seasons turn : anthem for S.A.T.B., soprano solo and organ. *Oxford University Press. Unpriced* DH (B76-50015)
Frith, Simon. Rock file
4. *Panther. £1.25* ADW/GB (B76-25952) ISBN 0-586-04370-5
Frog went a-courtin' : traditional American song, SATBB unaccompanied. (Thomas, Elizabeth). *Roberton. £0.14* EZDW (B76-50075)
From the world of music. Essays from the world of music : essays from 'The Sunday Times'. (Newman, Ernest). *J. Calder. £6.50* A(D) (B76-34776) ISBN 0-7145-3548-6
Frostenson, Anders. Songs and hymns from Sweden. *Stainer and Bell. Unpriced* DM/AYND (B76-50787) ISBN 0-85249-440-8
Froud, Nina. Chaliapin : an autobiography. (Shaliapin, Fedor Ivanovich). *White Lion Publishers. £6.50* AKGX/E(P) (B76-07530) ISBN 0-7274-0191-2
Früher Anfang auf dem Cello : eine Violoncelloschule für Kinder ab 4 Jahren
Band 1. (Sassmannshaus, Egon). *Bosse : Bärenreiter. £3.75* SR/AC (B76-50640)
Früher Anfang auf der Geige : eine Violinschule für Kinder ab 4 Jahren
Band 1. (Sassmannshaus, Egon). *Bosse : Bärenreiter. £3.75* S/AC (B76-50621)
Fugue for 6 cellos on themes by Beethoven. (Bunting, Christopher). *Oxford University Press. Unpriced* SRNQ/Y (B76-50641) ISBN 0-19-355743-6
Fujita, Tamao. G.A. Rossini's 'William Tell'. (Mizusawa, Hiroshi). *F. Warne. £2.25* BRRACBN (B76-18578) ISBN 0-7232-1833-1
Fuller, Dean. Smith : a musical. (Dubey, Matt). *French. £1.25* BDUACM (B76-00671) ISBN 0-573-68066-3
Fun and faith of William Billings, American. *Vocal score.* The fun and faith of William Billings, American. (Bennett, Robert Russell). *Chappell. Unpriced* DE (B76-50366)
Fundamentals of musical acoustics. (Benade, Arthur Henry). *Oxford University Press. £11.50* A/B (B76-25959) ISBN 0-19-502030-8
Funiculi - finicula sic. (Denza, Luigi). *8 Hurst Green Close, Hurst Green, Oxted : Paul. Unpriced* WMK/DW (B76-50734)
Funiculi, funicula. *arr.* Funiculi - finicula sic. (Denza, Luigi). *8 Hurst Green Close, Hurst Green, Oxted : Paul. Unpriced* WMK/DW (B76-50734)
Für Elise. (Beethoven, Ludwig van). *Paul. Unpriced* QPK (B76-50918)
Für Elise. G.173. *arr.* Für Elise. (Beethoven, Ludwig van). *Paul. Unpriced* QPK (B76-50918)
Für Elise. G.173. *arr.* Für Elise. (Beethoven, Ludwig van). *Paul. Unpriced* WRPK (B76-51084)
'Fürchtet euch nicht' : Weihnachtskonzert für Sopran, zwei Violinen, Fagott (Violone) und Basso continuo. (Bernhard, Christoph). *Bärenreiter. £3.25* KFLE/NUWNSDE/LF (B76-50496)
Further progressive steps. *R. Smith. Unpriced* WMK/AAY (B76-50326)
Future rock. (Downing, David). *Panther. £0.60* A/HK(XQK11) (B76-30334) ISBN 0-586-04308-x
G., I. The maske of flowers. *5 Albert Grove, Leeds LS6 4DA : Boethius Press. £3.20* ACPF (B76-10977) ISBN 0-904263-02-9
G.A. Rossini's 'William Tell'. (Mizusawa, Hiroshi). *F. Warne. £2.25* BRRACBN (B76-18578) ISBN 0-7232-1833-1
Gabrieli, Giovanni.
Canzon a 4, no.2 (1608) : for brass quartet. *Chester : Hansen. Unpriced* WNS (B76-51081)
Sacrae symphoniae, bk.2. Hodie completi sunt. Hodie sompleti sunt, Magnificat antiphon for Whit Sunday : double chorus SATB-SATB. *83 Stilehall Gdns, W4 3BT : Chiswick Music. Unpriced* EZDGKH/LN (B76-50051)
Gabrielli, Domenico. Sieben Ricercari (1689) : Violoncello solo. *Schott. £2.00* SRPMJ (B76-50260)
Gàl, Hans. Richard Wagner. *Gollancz. £5.50* BWC (B76-05038) ISBN 0-575-01847-x
Gál, Hans. Symphony no.4 (Sinfonia concertante) : for flute, clarinet, violin, violoncello and small orchestra. Op.105. *Simrock. £4.00* MPNVPNSE (B76-50155)
Galatopoulos, Stelios. Callas : prima donna assoluta. *W.H. Allen. £7.50* AKFL/E(P) (B76-35800) ISBN 0-491-01518-6
Gallus, Jacobus. *See* Handl, Jacob.
Gambaccini, Paul. Paul McCartney in his own words. *78 Newman St., W1P 3LA : Omnibus Press. £1.95* AKDW/GB/E(P) (B76-25962) ISBN 0-8256-3063-0
Gambaro, Giovanni Battista. Duets, clarinets, op.10. nos.1-3. Drei Duos für zwei Klarinetten. Opus 10. *Litolff : Peters. Unpriced* VVNU (B76-50702)
Gammond, Peter.
Musical instruments in colour. *Blandford Press. £2.60* AL/B (B76-00667) ISBN 0-7137-0628-7
Scott Joplin and the ragtime era. *Abacus. £1.25* BJRP(N) (B76-29712) ISBN 0-349-11412-9
Gamut : equalizing single strokes, double strokes, and paradiddles around the drum set with simultaneous footwork. (May, Randy). *Chappell. Unpriced* XQ/AF (B76-50754)
García Lorca, Federico. Night of the four moons : alto, alto flute, (doubling piccolo), banjo, electric cello and percussion (one player). (Crumb, George). *Peters. Unpriced* KFQE/NYERNSDW (B76-50136)
Garden, Edward. Angel voices singing : Christmas carol for four-part chorus of mixed, female or boys' voices with organ or unison voices with piano. *Roberton. £0.15* DP/LF (B76-50789)
Garden, Nicola. Angel voices singing : Christmas carol for four-part chorus of mixed, female or boys' voices with organ or unison voices with piano. (Garden, Edward). *Roberton. £0.15* DP/LF (B76-50789)
Gardner, John.
Five philanders. Contentment. Op.125, no.4. Contentment : S.A.T. unacc. *Oxford University Press. Unpriced* EZDW (B76-50432) ISBN 0-19-343059-2
Five philanders. Rejection. Op.125, no.1. Rejection : S.A.T.B. unacc. *Oxford University Press. Unpriced* EZDW (B76-50433) ISBN 0-19-343058-4
A song for St Cecilia's Day. Op.119 : SATB. *Oxford University Press. Unpriced* DH (B76-50384) ISBN 0-19-350355-7
Garfias, Robert. Music of a thousand autumns : the Tōgaku style of Japanese court music. *University of California Press. £17.45* BZHPAL (B76-19253) ISBN 0-520-01977-6
Garland reference library of the humanities. Whistling, Carl Friedrich. Handbuch der musikalischen Litteratur. 1817 ed. reprinted with the ten supplements, 1818-1827. *Garland; 2 Rugby St., WC1N 3QU : Distributed by George Prior Associated Publishers Ltd. £33.35* A(TC) (B76-04592) ISBN 0-8240-1064-7
Garrett, Georg. Magnificat and Nunc dimittis in E. (Wesley, Samuel Sebastian). *Oxford University Press. Unpriced* DGPP (B76-50375) ISBN 0-19-395317-x
Garrigue, Jean. Where we came. (Rorem, Ned). *Boosey and Hawkes. £1.25* KDW (B76-50484)
Gates, Keith. Sonata for violin and piano. *Galaxy : Galliard. Unpriced* SPE (B76-50632)
Gather gladness from the skies : spring carol, unison or SATB. (Davies, Laurence Hector). *Ashdown. £0.08* JDP (B76-50103)
Gaudeamus : a Leicestershire garland for Europa Cantat 6 for mixed voices a cappella. *Oxford University Press for the British National Committee for Europa Cantat 6. Unpriced* EZDW/AY (B76-50438)
Gaunt, John. Seven chords and fifty songs : with photo-chord positions and bigrams for guitar, mandolin, banjo and ukulele. *Belwin Mills Music. Unpriced* TPMK/DW/AY (B76-50264)
Gavall, John.
Seven duos for guitar. *British and Continental : EMI. Unpriced* TSNUK/AAY (B76-50655)
Sixteen folk dances. *British and Continental : EMI. Unpriced* TSNUK/AH/G/AY (B76-50656)
Ten traditional melodies : easy duos for descant recorder and guitar. *Ricordi. £0.95* VSRPLTSK (B76-50688)
Gay, Bram. Music hall suite. *Selections : arr.* Three pieces. (Horovitz, Joseph). *Novello. £2.50* WMK (B76-50325)
Geistliche Lieder aus Schmelli's Gesangbuch und dem Notenbuch der Anna Magdelena Buch. Jesus ist das schönste Licht. S.474. *arr.* Jesus is the loveliest light. (Bach, Johann Sebastian). *Roberton. £0.10* EZDM (B76-50420)
Gelobet sey der Herr. *Vocal score.* All praises be to the Lord = Gelobet sey der Herr. (Antes, John). *Boosey and Hawkes. £0.30* DH (B76-50378)
Gelston, Anne. The history of the organ in the parish church of St Michael and All Angels, Houghton-le-Spring. *'Lesbury', Hetton Road, Houghton-le-Spring, Co. Durham DH5 8JW : The author. £0.25* AR/B(YDJHH/X) (B76-06891) ISBN 0-9504842-0-2
Genzmer, Harald.
Concertino für Klarinette in B und Klavier. *Litolff : Peters. Unpriced* VVPFL (B76-50705)
Concerto, organ & percussion. Konzert für Orgel und Schlagzeug. *Litolff : Peters. Unpriced* RPLXF (B76-50598)
Concerto, piano & percussion. Konzert für Klavier und Schlagzeug. *Litolff : Peters. £14.50(set of pts)* QPLXF (B76-50925)
Weihnachtskonzert : für Orgel. *Litolff : Peters. Unpriced* RF/LF (B76-50230)
George Formby. (Fisher, John, *b.1945*). *Woburn Press. £2.95* AKDW/GB/E(P) (B76-17647) ISBN 0-7130-0144-5
Georges Bizet. Bizet. (Dean, Winton). 3rd ed.. *Dent. £3.95* BBP (B76-12126) ISBN 0-460-03163-5
Gerber, Rudolf. Concerto, violin, no.3, K.216, G major. Concerto, G major, for violin and orchestra. K.216. (Mozart, Wolfgang Amadeus). *Eulenburg. Unpriced* MPSF (B76-50534)
Gerig, Reginald R. Famous pianists & their technique. *David and Charles. £8.50* AQ/CY(M) (B76-32593) ISBN 0-7153-7220-3
German dance no.76, K.605, no.3. *arr.* The sleigh ride. (Mozart, Wolfgang Amadeus). *Warner. Unpriced* UMMK/AH (B76-51005)
German mass, no.2, G. major. *Vocal score.* Zweite deutsche Messe, 'Hier liegt vor deiner Majestät', für Sopran, Alt, Bass ad libitum (solistisch oder chorisch) und Orgel. (Grünberger, Theodor). *Bosse : Bärenreiter. £8.75* DE (B76-50367)
Germanus *Saint.* Peace on earth to men : SATB. (Tate, Phyllis). *Oxford University Press. Unpriced* DP/LF (B76-50399) ISBN 0-19-343057-6
Gershwin, George. The best of George Gershwin. *Chappell. Unpriced* KDW (B76-50843)
Gesänge zur Feier des heiligen Opfers der Messe. D.872. Zum Sanctus. *arr.* Zum Sanctus : for 4-part chorus of mixed voices with organ or piano. (Schubert, Franz). *Roberton. £0.14* DH (B76-50019)
Gestures : saxophone quartet. (Cordell, Frank). *Emerson. Unpriced* VUSNS (B76-51045)
GGloria tibi trinitas, Op.29 : a meditation on the Festival of the Trinity : organ solo. (Routh, Francis). *Boosey and Hawkes. £1.40* RJ (B76-50595)
Ghent, Emmanuel. Dithyrambos : for brass quintet. *Oxford University Press. Unpriced* WNR (B76-50332)
Giamberti, Giuseppe. Duo tessuti con diversi solfeggiamenti. *Selections.* Duetti per due strumenti, soprani e tenori. *Heinrichshofen : Peters. Unpriced* VSSNU (B76-50689)
Gibbons, Orlando. Hosanna to the Son of David : S.S.A.A.T.T.B. *Oxford University Press. Unpriced* EZDK (B76-50418) ISBN 0-19-352078-8
Gibbs, Douglas. In a stable bare : two Christmas carols for unaccompanied mixed voice choir. *Roberton. £0.15* EZDP/LF (B76-50809)
Gibson, William, *b.1914.* Two for the seesaw. *Adaptations.* Seesaw : a musical. (Fields, Dorothy). *French. £1.25* BCMEACM (B76-06887) ISBN 0-573-68069-8
Gift of new sight : Christmas anthem, S.A.T.B. (Klusmeier, R T). *Harmuse : Lengnick. £0.21* DP/LF (B76-50790)
Gifted young musicians and dancers : report of a Working Group i.e. Working Group on Provision for Children of Exceptional Gifts in Music and Dance set up to consider their general and specialised education. (Working Group on Provision for Children of Exceptional Gifts in Music and Dance). *H.M.S.O. £0.80* A(VMMX/YDL) (B76-24278) ISBN 0-11-491405-2
Gigliotti, Clementine. Music in developmental therapy : a curriculum guide. *University Park Press. £6.25* A(VMWM) (B76-30972) ISBN 0-8391-0895-8
Gilbert, Anthony.
Little piano pieces. Op.20. *Schott. Unpriced* QPJ (B76-50204)
Quartet, strings, op.20a. String quartet, Op.20a. *Schott. Unpriced* RXNS (B76-50617)
Gillett, Charlie. Rock file
4. *Panther. £1.25* ADW/GB (B76-25952) ISBN 0-586-04370-5
Gillis, Don. Symphony 'X', (Big 'D'). *Boosey and Hawkes. £0.35* UMME (B76-50662)
Gillis, Frank J. African music oral data : a catalog of field recordings, 1902-1975. (Stone, Ruth M). *Indiana University Press : Distributed by Bell. £12.00* BZK/FD(WT) (B76-50759) ISBN 0-253-30262-5
Git along, little dogies : songs and songmakers of the American West. (White, John Irwin). *University of Illinois Press. £7.00* AKDW/GNF/E(M) (B76-33374) ISBN 0-252-00327-6
Gitarren-Archiv.
Beethoven, Ludwig van. Sonatina, mandoline & piano, Kinsky 43, D minor. *arr.* Sonatine, d-moll, für zwei Gitarren. *Schott. £0.90* TSNUK/AEM (B76-50271)
Mudarra, Alonso. Tres libros de música en cifra para vihuela. Fantasia no.10. *arr.* Fantasia : das Harfenspiel in der Manier von Ludovico nachahmend / von Alonso Mudarra. Welsh Tantz, 'Wascha mesa' / von Hans Neusidler ; für Gitarre solo, eingerichtet von Dieter Kreidler. *Schott. £1.00* TSPMK (B76-50275)
Gitler, Ira Jazz masters of the Forties. *Collier Books : Collier Macmillan. £1.80* AMT(M/XP10) (B76-12131) ISBN 0-02-060610-9
Glasunow, Alexander. *See* Glazunov, Alexander.
Glazunov, Alexander. Deux prélude-improvisations = Two prelude-improvisations : for piano. *Belaieff : Peters. Unpriced* QPJ (B76-50571)
Globokar, Vinko.
Echanges : für einen Blechbläser. *Litolff : Peters. Unpriced* WPMJ (B76-50336)
Limites : für einen Geiger oder Bratschisten. *Litolff : Peters. Unpriced* SPMJ (B76-50252)
Notes : für einen Pianisten. *Litolff : Peters. Unpriced* QPJ (B76-50205)
Rédoublement : für einen Klarinettisten. *Litolff : Peters. Unpriced* VVPMJ (B76-50320)
Res/as/ex/ins-pirer : für einen Blechbläser. *Litolff : Peters. Unpriced* WPMJ (B76-50337)
Voix instrumentalisée : für einen Bassklarinettisten. *Litolff*

: *Peters. Unpriced* VVUPMJ (B76-50323)
Gloria tibi Domine. A little child there is yborn : Christmas carol, for unaccompanied mixed choir with soprano solo. (Davis, William Robert). *Oxford University Press. Unpriced* EZDP/LF (B76-50808)
God is gone up on high : melody from Corner, 1625. (Walmsley, Henry). *Banks. Unpriced* DP/LL (B76-50027)
Godbolt, Jim. All this and 10%. *Hale. £4.95* AMT(YC/XTA15) (B77-00347) ISBN 0-7091-5841-6
God's world : for unaccompanied mixed chorus, S.S.A.T.B. (Colville, Thomas). *Galaxy : Stainer and Bell. Unpriced* EZDH (B76-50803)
Goebels, Franzpeter. Sieben Hauptwerke aus dem Klavierschaften. (Bach, Carl Philipp Emanuel). *Heinrichshofen : Peters. Unpriced* QPJ (B76-50566)
Goehr, Alexander.
Triptych, no.2. Op.30. Shadowplay, Op.30 : music theatre from book 7 of the Republic of Plato. *Schott. Unpriced* C/JR (B76-50002)
Triptych, no.3. Op.31. Sonata about Jerusalem. Op.31 : cantata. *Schott. Unpriced* C/JR (B76-50003)
Going down with Janis. (Caserta, Peggy). *Futura Publications. £0.65* AKDW/GB/E(P) (B76-01877) ISBN 0-86007-231-2
Golden cross. The Hereford Festival hymn : written for the Hereford Diocesan 13th Centenary Festival, 1976. (Appleyard, Patrick). *Weinberger. £0.05* EZDM (B76-50057)
Golden wine is drunk : for 16 solo voices divided into 2 eight-part choirs of SSAATTBB. (Bedford, David). *Universal. Unpriced* EZDW (B76-50427)
Goldman, Richard Franko. Seaside park : march, symphonic band. *Boosey and Hawkes. £4.00* UMMGM (B76-50998)
Goldsmith, Owen. Benediction : for unaccompanied mixed chorus. *Galaxy : Galliard. Unpriced* EZDW (B76-50434)
Golland, John.
Fanfare for youth, Op.39, no.1. *EMI. Unpriced* WMGN (B76-51056)
Fives and threes : brass band. *British and Continental : EMI. Unpriced* WMJ (B76-50324)
Good companions. *Vocal score.* The good companions : the musical of the novel by J.B. Priestley. (Previn, André). *Chappell. Unpriced* CM (B76-50763)
Good news : new Christian songs for churches and groups. *12 Portland Rd, S.E.25 : Vanguard Music. Unpriced* KDM/AY (B76-50115)
Goodman, Paul.
Little prayers. *Vocal score.* Little prayers : for soprano and baritone solos, mixed chorus, and orchestra. (Rorem, Ned). *Boosey and Hawkes. £6.00* DE (B76-50776)
The poets' requiem. *Vocal score.* The poets' requiem : mixed chorus, soprano solo and orchestra. (Rorem, Ned). *Boosey and Hawkes. £5.00* DX (B76-50404)
Goran, Ulf. Play guitar. *Oxford University Press. £1.30* TS/AC (B76-50651) ISBN 0-19-322210-8
Gordon, Dane. Away he run. *Vocal score.* Away he run : a musical based on the story of the prodigal son. (Fargo, Milford). *Stainer and Bell. Unpriced* CM/L (B76-50764) ISBN 0-85249-315-0
Gordon, Taylor. Born to be. 1st ed. reprinted. *University of Washington Press. £3.50* AKDW/L/HJ/E(P) (B76-33369) ISBN 0-295-95428-0
Goreau, Laurraine. Just Mahalia, baby. *See* Goreau, Laurraine. Mahalia.
Goreau, Laurraine. Mahalia. *Lion Publishing : Aslan. £1.95* AKDW/HJ/L/E(P) (B76-36285) ISBN 0-85648-061-4
Gorky, Maxim. Chaliapin : an autobiography. (Shaliapin, Fedor Ivanovich). *White Lion Publishers. £6.50* AKGX/E(P) (B76-07530) ISBN 0-7274-0191-2
Gospel train : negro spiritual, two-part (with optional recorders). (Johnson, Stuart). *Oxford University Press. Unpriced* FDW/LC (B76-50082) ISBN 0-19-341508-9
Gospel train. (This train is bound for glory) : a quodlibet, for two mezzo-sopranos and baritone or two baritones. (Hudson, Hazel). *Ashdown. £0.15* FNDW/LC (B76-50449)
Got the spirit! (Balent, Andrew). *Warner : Blossom. Unpriced* UMMK/DW/LC (B76-51006)
Gott hat uns angenehm gemacht. *Vocal score.* The Lord has been gracious unto us = Gott hat uns angenehm gemacht. (Antes, John). *Boosey and Hawkes. £0.40* DH (B76-50379)
Gottlied, Oskar. Neue Gemeindelieder : neue geistliche Lieder
Heft 3. *Bosse : Bärenreiter. £1.66* JFE/TSDM/AY (B76-50836)
Gottschalk, Louis Moreau. Le Bannier. Opus 5 : chanson nègre, piano solo. *Peters. Unpriced* QPJ (B76-50206)
Grainger, Percy Aldridge. Yellowbelly ballads : a third selection of Lincolnshire folk-songs, the majority of them from the collection of Percy Aldridge Grainger. *Lincolnshire and Humberside Arts. Unpriced* JE/TSDW/G/AYDGH (B76-50829)
Gramski, Marek. Lwowskie piosenki
Część 5: Zbrodnia i Kara ; oraz uzupelnienia poprzednio wydanych czesci. *Kolo Lwowian. £0.75* ADW/G(YMUL) (B76-05915) ISBN 0-9503005-3-5
Grandsire. (Trollope, J Armiger). 3rd ed. *22 Duke St., Burton Latimer, Kettering, Northants. : Christopher Groome. £2.50* AXSR/E (B76-35806) ISBN 0-904233-09-x
Grandy, Fred. Pretzels : a musical revue. (Forster, John). *French. £1.25* BFNRACP (B76-06889) ISBN 0-573-68071-x
Grant, David. Bang. *Choral Score.* Bang! (Rutter, John). *Oxford University Press. Unpriced* DACM (B76-50773) ISBN 0-19-338051-x
Grant, Micki. The prodigal sister : a new black musical. (Franklin, J E). *French. £1.35* BGSEACM (B76-50357) ISBN 0-573-68075-2
Graun, Johann Gottlieb. Concerto, viola & string orchestra, E flat major. *arr.* Konzert Es-dur für Viola und Streicher = Concerto E flat major for viola and strings. 1st ed. *Simrock. £4.00* SQPK/LF (B76-50638)
Graves, Richard. Pavane & galliard, 'The Earl of Salisbury'. Pavane. *arr.* The 'Earl of Salisbury' carol. (Byrd, William). *Banks. Unpriced* EZDP/LF (B76-50422)
Great Britain. *Scottish Education Department.* Gifted young musicians and dancers : report of a Working Group i.e. Working Group on Provision for Children of Exceptional Gifts in Music and Dance set up to consider their general and specialised education. (Working Group on Provision for Children of Exceptional Gifts in Music and Dance). *H.M.S.O. £0.80* A(VMMX/YDL) (B76-24278) ISBN 0-11-491405-2
Great composers. Walker, Alan, *b.1930.* Schumann. *Faber. £3.25* BSG(N) (B76-21364) ISBN 0-571-10269-7
Greater London Council. Code of practice for pop concerts : a guide to safety, health and welfare at one day events. *G.L.C. £1.50* A/GB(W/Z) (B76-32962) ISBN 0-7168-0732-7
Greatest star. Streisand : an unauthorised biography. (Jordan, René). 1st British ed. *W.H. Allen. £3.95* AKDW/GB/E(P) (B76-11504) ISBN 0-491-01775-8
Greaves, Terence. Dance trios : 3 flutes. *Emerson. Unpriced* VRNTH (B76-51016)
Green, Benny. Swingtime in Tottenham. *Basset Chambers, 27 Bedfordbury, W.C.2 : Lemon Tree Press Ltd. £1.25* AMT(P/XP11) (B76-35803) ISBN 0-904291-11-1
Greenberg, Noah. An anthology of early renaissance music. *Dent. £9.95* C/AY(XCSK76) (B76-50001) ISBN 0-460-04300-5
Greene, Arthur. Seven wild mushrooms and a waltz : easy pieces for prepared piano. *Galaxy : Galliard. Unpriced* QPJ (B76-50572)
Greenfield, Edward. The Penguin stereo record guide. *Penguin. £3.50* A/FF(WT) (B76-03703) ISBN 0-14-046223-6
Greening, Anthony. Hosanna to the Son of David : S.S.A.A.T.T.B. (Gibbons, Orlando). *Oxford University Press. Unpriced* EZDK (B76-50418) ISBN 0-19-352078-8
Gregson, Edward. A Swedish march, and, Fanfare. *R. Smith. Unpriced* WMJ (B76-51059)
Gretz, Susanna. Ten green bottles. *Puffin Books. £0.50* ADW/GJ (B76-14369) ISBN 0-14-050144-4
Grieg, Edvard. Norwegian folksongs and dances. Op.17. *Selections : arr.* Three Norwegian pieces. *Novello. Unpriced* RXMK (B76-50236)
Griffith, Beleta. Music in developmental therapy : a curriculum guide. *University Park Press. £6.25* A(VMWM) (B76-30972) ISBN 0-8391-0895-8
Grimm, Jacob. Hansel und Gretel. *Adaptations.* E. Humperdinck's 'Hansel and Gretel' : based on E. Humperdinck's opera after the story by the Brothers Grimm. (Isaka, Yoshitaro). *F. Warne. £2.25* BHUACBN (B76-19463) ISBN 0-7232-1835-8
Grimm, Wilhelm. E. Humperdinck's 'Hansel and Gretel' : based on E. Humperdinck's opera after the story by the Brothers Grimm. (Isaka, Yoshitaro). *F. Warne. £2.25* BHUACBN (B76-19463) ISBN 0-7232-1835-8
Grimmelshausen, Jakob Christophel von. Trost der Nacht : Chorvariationen für vierstimmigen gemischten Chor a cappella oder mit Flöte und Klavier ad lib. (Reutter, Hermann). *Schott. £5.20* EZDH (B76-50804)
Groome, Christopher. Grandsire. (Trollope, J Armiger). 3rd ed. *22 Duke St., Burton Latimer, Kettering, Northants. : Christopher Groome. £2.50* AXSR/E (B76-35806) ISBN 0-904233-09-x
Grosvenor biographies. Magor, Cliff. The song of a merryman : Ivan Menzies of the D'Oyly Carte Gilbert & Sullivan operas. *Grosvenor Books. £1.00* AKDW/E(P) (B76-19249) ISBN 0-901269-18-2
Group series.
Mayes, Jerry. Joy waltz : instrumental ensemble. *Charnwood Music. Unpriced* LNHW (B76-50512)
Wright, Francis. Etude barcarolle : for instrumental ensemble. *Charnwood Music. Unpriced* LNQ (B76-50514)
Wright, Francis. Party time : for instrumental ensemble. *Charnwood Music. Unpriced* LN (B76-50510)
Wright, Francis. Pic-a-pic-a-polka : instrumental ensemble. *Charnwood Music. Unpriced* LNHVH (B76-50511)
Wright, Francis. Valse des guitares : instrumental ensemble. *Charnwood Music. Unpriced* LNHW (B76-50513)
Grove, *Sir* George. Grove's dictionary of music and musicians. 5th ed. *Macmillan. £75.00(for vols 1-9 and supplementary vol. 10)* A(C) (B76-19247) ISBN 0-333-00949-5
Grove's dictionary of music and musicians. (Grove, *Sir* George). 5th ed. *Macmillan. £75.00(for vols 1-9 and supplementary vol. 10)* A(C) (B76-19247) ISBN 0-333-00949-5
Gruffudd ab yr Ynad Coch. Elegy for a prince. Op.59. *Vocal score.* Elegy for a prince. Op.59 : for baritone and orchestra. (Mathias, William). *Oxford University Press. Unpriced* KGNDX (B76-50508) ISBN 0-19-365582-9
Grünberger, Theodor. German mass, no.2, G. major. *Vocal score.* Zweite deutsche Messe, 'Hier liegt vor deiner Majestät', für Sopran, Alt, Bass ad libitum (solistisch oder chorisch) und Orgel. *Bosse : Bärenreiter. £8.75* DE (B76-50367)
Grundman, Clare.
Tuba rhapsody : for tuba and symphonic band. *Boosey and Hawkes. £30.00* UMPWV (B76-51007)
Tuba rhapsody : tuba solo and piano reduction. *Boosey and Hawkes. £3.25* WVPK (B76-51087)
Grusnick, Bruno. 'Fürchtet euch nicht' : Weihnachtskonzert für Sopran, zwei Violinen, Fagott (Violone) und Basso continuo. (Bernhard, Christoph). *Bärenreiter. £3.25* KFLE/NUWNSDE/LF (B76-50496)
Guida di musica. *Selections.* A James Hook album : twenty-two easy keyboard pieces. (Hook, James). *Elkin. £0.90* PWPJ (B76-50179)
Guidhall School of Music and Drama pianoforte examinations, scales and broken chords : grade one and grade two. *Lengnick. £0.50* Q/AF/AL (B76-50181)
Guildhall School of Music. Examinations, scales and arpeggios for pianoforte playing : grades 3, 4, 5, 6 and 7. *Lengnick. £0.95* Q/AF/AL (B76-50545)
Guildhall School of Music and Drama : guitar examinations, scales and arpeggios. *Lengnick. £0.95* TS/AF/AL (B76-50268)
Guillaume Tell. Overture. Overture to the opera 'Guillaume Tell'. (Rossini, Gioacchino Antonio). *Eulenburg. Unpriced* MMJ (B76-50530)
Guitar workshop : a course for guitar groups in two parts
Part 1. (Mynall, Frances). *Oxford University Press. Unpriced* TSN/AC (B76-50979) ISBN 0-19-322268-x
Part 2. (Mynall, Frances). *Oxford University Press. Unpriced* TSN/AC (B76-50980) ISBN 0-19-322269-8
Guitarist's picture chords. (Traum, Happy). *Wise Music Sales. Unpriced* TS/RC (B76-50270) ISBN 0-86001-205-0
Gurney, Janet. Dancing days : twelve carols for guitar. *Cramer. £1.25* TSPMK/DP/LF/AY (B76-50993)
Gweithdy cerddorol y plant
Llyfr 2: Carolau. *C. Davies. Unpriced* CB/AY (B76-50361) ISBN 0-7154-0188-2
Haag, Hanno. Acht Duette für Violinen. *Heinrichshofen : Peters. Unpriced* SNU (B76-50246)
Hadlock, Richard. Jazz masters of the Twenties. *Collier Books : Collier Macmillan. £1.80* AMT(M/XN10) (B76-12130) ISBN 0-02-060770-9
Hakluyt, Richard. The true glory. (Aston, Peter). *Royal School of Church Music. Unpriced* DH (B76-50782)
Hale, Noel. Point and counterpoint : an account of the founding and first twenty-five years of the Canford Summer School of Music. *250 Purley Way, Croydon CR9 4QD : Belwin Mills Music Limited. £0.80* A(VS/YDFKC/X) (B76-35347) ISBN 0-9503671-3-3
Half an alphabet : canons for chorus, for four-part chorus of mixed voices with piano accompaniment. (Thomson, Virgil). *Schirmer. Unpriced* DW/X (B76-50034)
Hall, Alan. The Charlton memorial tune book : a collection of tunes for the Northumbrian small-pipes and the fiddle. *5 Denebank, Monkseaton : Northumbrian Pipers' Society. Unpriced* VYQPMJ (B76-50716) ISBN 0-902510-03-7
Haltrecht, Montague. The quiet showman : Sir David Webster and the Royal Opera House. *Collins. £6.00* AC(WB/XPD28/P) (B76-03866) ISBN 0-00-211163-2
Hamilton, Iain. Arias : for small orchestra. *Schott. Unpriced* MR/T (B76-50162)
Hamlet. (Liszt, Franz). *Eulenburg. Unpriced* MMJ (B76-50876)
Hamlisch, Marvin. A chorus line. *Selections : arr.* A chorus line : vocal selections. *Chappell. Unpriced* KDW (B76-50478)
Hammerschmidt, Andreas. Musikalischer Andachten, Tl 3. Es danken dir, Gott, die Volker. Es danken dir, Gott, die Volker : solokantate für Tenor, zwei Violinen und Basso continuo. *Bärenreiter. £1.63* KGHE/SNTPWDE (B76-50503)
Hammond, Tom. Hansel and Gretel : a fairy opera in three acts. *48 Great Marlborough St., W1V 2BN : Schott and Co. Ltd. £0.50* BHUAC (B76-18375) ISBN 0-901938-14-9
Hampden, John. Concerto, trumpet & string orchestra, no.1, B flat major. *arr.* Concerto no.1 for trumpet, strings and continuo. (Mudge, Richard). *Boosey and Hawkes. £1.00* WSPK/LF (B76-50343)
Hancock, Gerre. Communion service 'Missa resurrectionis' : based upon the hymn tune 'St Magnus', for mixed choir and organ. *Oxford University Press. Unpriced* DGS (B76-50781)
Hand, Colin. In the beginning. *Vocal score.* In the beginning : a dramatic cantata, for speaker, baritone solo, chancel choir, nave choir and orchestra. *Schott. Unpriced* ENWSDE (B76-50042)
Handbook of parish music : a working guide for clergy and organists. (Dakers, Lionel). *Mowbrays. £1.95* A/LD/E (B77-00345) ISBN 0-264-66261-x
Handbuch der musikalischen Litteratur. (Whistling, Carl Friedrich). 1817 ed. reprinted with the ten supplements, 1818-1827. *Garland; 2 Rugby St., WC1N 3QU Distributed by George Prior Associated Publishers Ltd. £33.35* A(TC) (B76-04592) ISBN 0-8240-1064-7
Handel, George Frideric.
Clock music. *arr.* Ten pieces for a musical clock. *Schirmer. Unpriced* XSQMK (B76-50348)
Kleine Tänze. *Heinrichshoffen : Peters. Unpriced* SNTK/AH (B76-50245)
Ottone. *Condensed score. Selections.* Three ornamented arias. *Oxford University Press. Unpriced* KE/MDW (B76-50128) ISBN 0-19-345412-2
Handl, Jacob. Secundus tomus musici operis. Alleluia. In resurrectione tua. *arr.* In resurrectione tua Christe. *Associated Music. Unpriced* WNK/DJ (B76-50331)
Hanley, James. Chaliapin : an autobiography. (Shaliapin, Fedor Ivanovich). *White Lion Publishers. £6.50* AKGX/E(P) (B76-07530) ISBN 0-7274-0191-2
Hanmer, Ronald.

And did those feet in ancient time. arr. Jerusalem. (Parry, Sir Charles Hubert). Studio Music. Unpriced WMK/DW (B76-51074)
Friederike. Vocal score. Frederica : operetta in three acts. (Lehár, Franz). Glocken. Unpriced CF (B76-50761)
Further progressive steps. R. Smith. Unpriced WMK/AAY (B76-50326)
Lionel Monckton memories. (Monckton, Lionel). Studio Music. Unpriced WMK/DW (B76-51073)
Hannay, Roger. Fantôme : clarinet in B flat, viola, piano. Henmar Press : Peters : Peters. Unpriced NUVNT (B76-50883)
Hannoversche Orgel Christian Vater, 1679-1756. 32 Great Titchfield St., W.1 : Bärenreiter. £13.00 AR/BC(YEH/P)
Hansel and Gretel : a fairy opera in three acts. (Hammond, Tom). 48 Great Marlborough St., W1V 2BN : Schott and Co. Ltd. £0.50 BHUAC (B76-18375) ISBN 0-901938-14-9
Hansel and Gretel : opera in two acts. (Humperdinck, Engelbert). Boosey and Hawkes. £9.00 CC (B76-50005)
Hansel und Gretel. See Grimm, Jacob.
Hänsel und Gretel. See Wette, Adelheid.
Hänsel und Gretel. Vocal score. Hansel and Gretel : opera in two acts. (Humperdinck, Engelbert). Boosey and Hawkes. £9.00 CC (B76-50005)
Hanson, Geoffrey.
Brecon service : for mixed voice chorus and organ
No.1: Venite, exultemus Domino. Roberton. £0.14 DGM (B76-50370)
No.2 : Benedictus. Roberton. £0.22 DGM (B76-50371)
No.3: Te Deum laudamus. Roberton. £0.18 DGM (B76-50372)
No.4: Magnificat and Nunc dimittis. Robertson. £0.22 DGM (B76-50373)
No.5: Preces and responses. Robertson. £0.10 DGM (B76-50374)
Down in yon forest : Advent or Christmas carol for 6-part chorus of mixed voices unaccompanied. Roberton. £0.10 EZDP/LEZ (B76-50421)
Let the whole Creation cry : for soprano solo and four-part chorus of mixed voices with organ. Roberton. £0.18 DH (B76-50016)
Lute book lullaby : for soprano solo and four-part chorus of mixed voices unaccompanied. Roberton. £0.10 EZDP/LF (B76-50058)
People look east : Advent carol, for four-part chorus of mixed voices unaccompanied. Roberton. £0.10 EZDP/LEZ (B76-50806)
Two harvest carols : for four-part chorus of mixed voices unaccompanied. Roberton. £0.10 EZDP/LP (B76-50060)

Happiness blues : for S.A.T.B. (or S.S.A., S.A.B., T.T.B.) with instrumental accompaniment. (Sansom, Clive A). Paterson. Unpriced ELDW (B76-50036)
Happy Christmas for chord organ. EMI. Unpriced RPVK/DP/LF/AY (B76-50939)
Happy Christmas for guitar. EMI. Unpriced TSPMK/DP/LF/AY (B76-50994)
Haralambos, Michael. Right on : from blues to soul in Black America. 2 Greycoat Place, SW1P 1SB : Eddison Press Ltd. £2.50 AKDW/HHW/E(M) (B76-20008) ISBN 0-85649-016-4
Harbinson, William Allen. Elvis Presley : an illustrated biography. Joseph. £5.50 AKDW/HK/E(P) (B76-03356) ISBN 0-7181-1469-8
Harbison, John. Music when soft voices die : SATB (divisi), with keyboard accompaniment. Associated Music. Unpriced DW (B76-50028)
Harding, David. The orchestra. F. Watts. £1.45 AM/B (B76-05039) ISBN 0-85166-558-6
Harding, Mike. Napoleon's retreat from Wigan. EMI Music. Unpriced KEZDW (B76-50495)
Hardy, Phil.
The encyclopedia of rock
Vol.1: The age of rock'n'roll. Panther. £0.95 A/HK(C) (B76-14358) ISBN 0-586-04267-9
Vol.2: From Liverpool to San Francisco. Panther. £0.95 A/HK(C) (B76-16549) ISBN 0-586-04268-7
Vol.3: The sounds of the seventies. Panther. £0.95 A/HK(C) (B76-31912) ISBN 0-586-04269-5
Harewood, George Henry Hubert Lascelles, Earl of. Kobbé's complete opera book. (Kobbé, Gustave). 9th ed. Putnam. £15.00 AC (B76-31916) ISBN 0-370-10020-4
Harf, Jost.
Les Petits concerts. Opus 16 : leichte Duos für Altblockflöten (Querflöten, Oboen, Violinen oder andere Melodieinstrumente)
Concerts 1-3. (Aubert, Jacques). Heinrichshofen : Peters. Unpriced VSSNUG (B76-50306)
Concerts 4-6. (Aubert, Jacques). Heinrichshofen : Peters. Unpriced VSSNUG (B76-50307)
Harman, Alec. Popular Italian madrigals of the sixteenth century : for mixed voices. Oxford University Press. Unpriced EZDU/AYJ (B76-50063) ISBN 0-19-343646-9
Harmonielehre : 1600-1730-1790-1810-1840-1860-1880-1910-1930. (La Motte, Diether de). Bärenreiter etc.. £12.00 A/R(XE331)
Harness, Marjorie. Bone pastor, panis vere : SATB unacc. Banks. Unpriced EZDJ (B76-50055)
Harnne, Howard. The Judy Garland souvenir songbook. Chappell. Unpriced KDW/JR/AYT (B76-50856) ISBN 0-06-465040-5
Harper, Jeanne. Fresh sounds. Hodder and Stoughton. Unpriced JDM/AY (B76-50826) ISBN 0-340-20622-5
Harris sacred choral series.
Baker, Richard Charles. Three short introits : S.A.T.B. Frederick Harris Music : Lengnick. £0.27 EZDH (B76-50802)
Younger, John B. Twas in the moon of wintertime. The Huron carol : old French folk melody. Frederick Harris Music : Lengnick. £0.21 ENYFPNSDP/LF (B76-50799)

Harrop, Beatrice. Okki-tokki-unga : action songs for children. A. and C. Black. £2.75 JFDW/GR (B76-50832) ISBN 0-7136-1685-7
Hart, Lorenz. The best of Rodgers and Hart. (Rodgers, Richard). Chappell. Unpriced KDW (B76-50121)
Hartley, Geoffrey. Suite for 3 bassoons. Emerson Unpriced VWNTG (B76-50713)
Hartmann, Karl Amadeus. Sinfoniae drammaticae, T1.2. Symphonische Hymnen : für grosses Orchester. Schott. £11.00 MMJ (B76-50524)
Hartogs, E. Yuzuru. Vocal score. Yuzuru = The twilight heron : opera in one act. (Dan, Ikuma). Boosey and Hawkes. Unpriced CC (B76-50363)
Harvey, Jean.
Eighteenth-century violin sonatas
Book 1. Associated Board of the Royal Schools of Music. £1.00 SPE/AY (B76-50247)
Book 2. Associated Board of the Royal Schools of Music. £1.00 SPE/AY (B76-50248)
Harvey, Paul. The Agincourt song : traditional, 1415. Novello. £0.50 VUNSK/DW (B76-50695)
Hatch, Edwin. Breathe on me, breath of God : anthem for 3-part female voice choir unaccompanied. (Lees, Heath). Roberton. £0.10 FEZDH (B76-50089)
Hauck, Werner. Vibrato on the violin. Bosworth. £3.00 AS/EV (B76-09329) ISBN 0-900180-71-4
Havergal Brian and his music. (Nettel, Reginald). Dobson. £7.50 BBTN(N) (B76-25956) ISBN 0-234-77861-x
Havergal Brian and the performance of his orchestral music : a history and source book. (Foreman, Lewis). 14 Barlby Rd, W10 6AR : Thames Publishing. £6.95 BBTN(N) (B76-23704) ISBN 0-905210-01-8
Havergal Brian Society. Aberdeen Branch. The tigers : satirical anti-war opera in a prologue and three acts. (Brian, Havergal). Centennial ed. 7 Gaitside Drive, Aberdeen : Aberdeen Branch of the Havergal Brian Society. £0.40 BBTNAC (B76-30338) ISBN 0-9505185-0-6
Havergal Brian : the making of a composer. (Eastaugh, Kenneth). Harrap. £10.00 BBTN(N) (B76-33366) ISBN 0-245-52748-6
Hawkes Pocket Score. Delius, Frederick. Fennimore und Gerda = Fennimore and Gerda. Boosey and Hawkes. £6.50 CQC (B76-50007)
Hawkes pocket scores.
Delius, Frederick. Concerto, piano, C minor. Piano concerto. Boosey and Hawkes. Unpriced MPQF (B76-50157)
Einem, Gottfried von. An die Nachgeborenen, Op.42 : Kantate für Mezzosopran, Bariton, gemischten Chor und Orchester. Boosey and Hawkes. £8.50 EMDE (B76-50796)
Lees, Benjamin. The trumpet of the swan : for narrator and orchestra. Boosey and Hawkes. £1.25 KHYE/M (B76-50509)
Hawkes school series. Fauré, Gabriel. Pelléas et Mélisande. Op.80. Sicilienne. arr. Sicilienne. Boosey and Hawkes. £3.95 MK/AHVQ (B76-50140)
Haydn, Joseph.
Mass, no.7, G major, 'Sancti Nicolai'. Missa Sancti Nicolai. Eulenburg. Unpriced EMDG (B76-50039)
Quartets, strings, ops.64, 77. Selections: arr. Quartet no.3 on themes from Haydn. Studio Music. Unpriced WNSK (B76-50741)
Quartets, strings. Selections : arr. Two minuets. Oxford University Press. Unpriced SRPK/AHR (B75-50259) ISBN 0-19-357072-6
Head, Michael.
I will lift up mine eyes : Psalm 121, for 4-part male voice choir with optional organ or piano. Roberton. £0.14 GEZDR (B76-50095)

Make a joyful noise unto the Lord. Psalm 100 : for 4-part male voice choir with organ or piano or unaccompanied voices. Roberton. £0.18 GDR (B76-50093)
Three psalms for solo voice with organ or piano
No.1: I will lift up mine eyes : Psalm 121. Roberton. £0.40 KDR (B76-50474)
No.2: Be merciful unto me, O God : Psalm 57. Roberton. £0.40 KDR (B76-50475)
No.3: Make a joyful noise unto the Lord : Psalm 100. Roberton. £0.40 KDR (B76-50476)
Heath, Reginald. Dance caprice. R. Smith. Unpriced WMH (B76-51057)
Heavenly archer. (Thackray, Roy). Chester. Unpriced CQN (B76-50365)
Helena : valsa, piano. (Nazareth, Ernesto). Arthur Napoleão : Essex Music. Unpriced QPHW (B76-50901)
Helical : for solo piano. (Dench, Chris). 17 Dempster Rd, S.W.18 : The composer. Unpriced QPJ (B76-50202)
Helps, Robert. Nocturne : piano. Peters. Unpriced QPJ (B76-50207)
Hemingway, Roger. Consider and hear me, O Lord my God. Novello. £0.12 FDK (B76-50078)
Hendra, Tony. Smith : a musical. (Dubey, Matt). French. £1.25 BDUACM (B76-00671) ISBN 0-573-68066-3
Henry Duke piano arrangements of favourite orchestral classics. EMI. Unpriced QPK (B76-50921)
Henze, Hans Werner.
Carillon, Récitatif, Masque : Trio für Mandoline, Gitarre und Harfe von Hans Werner Henze. Schott. £3.50 TNT (B76-50649)
Der langwierige Weg in die Wohnung der Natascha Ungeheur. Selections. Fragmente aus einer Show : Sätze für Blechquintett. Schott. £2.25 WNR (B76-50739)
Tristan : preludes for piano, electronic tapes and orchestra. Schott. £11.00 MPQ (B76-50156)
We come to the river = Wir erreichen den Fluss : Handlungen für Musik. Schott. £39.20 CQC (B76-50767)
Her silver will. Looking back as Sposalizio : medium voice. (Binkerd, Gordon). Boosey and Hawkes. £0.75 KFVDW (B76-50500)
Hereford Cathedral. Friends of Hereford Cathedral. The organists and organs of Hereford Cathedral. (Shaw, Watkins). Friends of Hereford Cathedral Publications Committee. £0.50 AR/B(YDHRHB/X) (B76-35357) ISBN 0-904642-01-1
Hereford Festival hymn : written for the Hereford Diocesan 13th Centenary Festival, 1976. (Appleyard, Patrick). Weinberger. £0.05 EZDM (B76-50057)
Herman, Jerry. Mack & Mabel : a musical love story. (Stewart, Michael). French. £1.35 BHMACM (B76-19250) ISBN 0-573-68074-4
Heroic music : a suite of twelve marches. (Telemann, Georg Philipp). Oxford University Press. Unpriced WSPK/AGM (B76-50342) ISBN 0-19-359067-0
Héroïde funèbre. (Liszt, Franz). Eulenburg. Unpriced MMJ (B76-50875)
Herrick, Robert. Flower songs. Vocal score. Flower songs : for S(S)A and string orchestra (or piano). (Hurd, Michael). Novello. £0.50 FDW (B76-50080)
Herring, Ann King. M.P. Mussorgsky's 'A night on bare mountain'. (Semba, Taro). F. Warne. £2.25 BMUAMBN (B76-18581) ISBN 0-7232-1836-6
Herzer, Ludwig. Friederike. Adaptations. Frederica : operetta in three acts. (Dunn, Bernard). 10 Rathbone St., W1P 2BJ : Glocken Verlag Ltd. £1.00 BLDACF
Heseltine, Philip. Fennimore und Gerda = Fennimore and Gerda. (Delius, Frederick). Boosey and Hawkes. £6.50 CQC (B76-50007)
Heseltine, Philip. For works by this composer under other names see Warlock, Peter.
Heseltine, Philip Arnold. See Warlock, Peter.
Hessenberg, Kurt. Sonata, viola & piano. Opus 94. Sonate für Bratsche und Klavier. Opus 94. Schott. £5.00 SQPE (B76-50634)
Higginbottom, Edward.
L'Apothéose de Corelli : for 2 flutes or oboes or violins and basso continuo. (Couperin, François). Musica rara. Unpriced VRNTPW (B76-50676)
L'Apothéose de Lulli : for 2 flutes/oboes/violins basse d'archet and b, c. (Couperin, François). Musica rara. Unpriced NUPNS (B76-50537)
Higgins, Julie.
The Jesus file. Voice part. The Jesus file : a musical nativity. (Hoskins, Graham). Dobson. Unpriced JDACN/LF (B76-50099) ISBN 0-234-77244-1
The wind on the heath. Voice part. The wind on the heath : children's musical play. (Walker, Chris). Dobson. Unpriced JDACN (B76-50098) ISBN 0-234-77245-x
Higgle-ty pig-le-ty : 20 songs. (Carrick, Malcolm). EMI. Unpriced KEZDW (B76-50861)
Hildemann, Wolfgang. Sonatina, clarinet & piano, 'Ritmi dispari'. Ritmi dispari : Sonatine für Klarinette in B und Klavier von Wolfgang Hildemann. Schott. £1.75 VVPEM (B76-50704)
Hill, Simon R. Cantiones sacrae. Te lucis ante terminum. Te lucis ante terminum : festal and ferial tones, S.A.A.T.B. (unacc.). (Tallis, Thomas). Oxford University Press. Unpriced EZDGKRM (B76-50052) ISBN 0-19-350356-5
Hill-billy holiday : trombone duet. (New, Derek). Studio Music. Unpriced WMPWUNU (B76-51076)
Hiller, Wilfried. Katalog für Schlagzeug 1 = Catalogue for percussion 1 : 1 player. Schott. £2.00 XPMJ (B76-50346)
Hines, Robert S. Salve regina : for 4-part chorus of mixed voices unaccompanied. (Liszt, Franz). Roberton. £0.14 EZDH (B76-50416)
History of the organ in the parish church of St Michael and All Angels, Houghton-le-Spring. (Gelston, Anne). 'Lesbury', Hetton Road, Houghton-le-Spring, Co. Durham DH5 8JW : The author. £0.25 AR/B(YDJHH/X) (B76-06891) ISBN 0-9504842-0-2
Hobhouse, Hermione. London in 1826. Weber in London, 1826. Wolff. £1.95 BWL(YDB/XHF) (B76-22852) ISBN 0-85496-403-7
Hoddinott, Alun.
Landscapes, Ynys Môn, Op.87 : a song cycle for high voice and piano. Oxford University Press. Unpriced KFTDW (B76-50864) ISBN 0-19-345432-7
Two Welsh songs. Oxford University Press. Unpriced DW (B76-50403) ISBN 0-19-343061-4
Hodgson, Julian. Music titles in translation : a checklist of musical compositions. Bingley etc.. £7.50 AB(TCT/WT) (B76-14368) ISBN 0-85157-198-0
Hodie Christus natus est. (Sweelinck, Jan Pieterzoon). Roberton. £0.15 FEZDJ/LF (B76-50819)
Hodie sompleti sunt, Magnificat antiphon for Whit Sunday : double chorus SATB-SATB. (Gabrieli, Giovanni). 83 Stilehall Gdns, W4 3BT : Chiswick Music. Unpriced EZDGKH/LN (B76-50051)
Hoffmeister, Franz Anton. Concerto, viola, B flat major. arr. Concerto in B flat for viola and orchestra. Schott. Unpriced SQPK/LF (B76-50256)
Hofmeister, Friedrich. Handbuch der musikalischen Litteratur. (Whistling, Carl Friedrich). 1817 ed. reprinted with the ten supplements, 1818-1827. Garland; 2 Rugby St., WC1N 3QU : Distributed by George Prior

Associated Publishers Ltd. £33.35 A(TC) (B76-04592) ISBN 0-8240-1064-7
Hogarth's hoe-down : for brass band. (Lear, W Hogarth). *Chester Music. Unpriced* WMH (B76-51058)
Holborne, Antony. Pavans, galiards, almains and other short airs. *Selections : arr.* Suite of Elizabethan dances. *Schirmer. Unpriced* WNRK/AH (B76-50334)
Holbrook, David.
The apple tree : Christmas music from 'The Cambridge hymnal'. *Cambridge University Press. £4.00* DP/LF/AY (B76-50791) ISBN 0-521-21479-3
The Cambridge hymnal. *Choral score.* The Cambridge hymnal : vocal edition. *Cambridge University Press. £1.50* DADM (B76-50008) ISBN 0-521-20398-8
Holder, Ray. Wassailing. *Thames Music. Unpriced* JDP/LF (B76-50454)
Holliger, Heinz. Quartet, strings. Streichquartett (1973). *Schott. Unpriced* RXNS (B76-50955)
Hollow men : mixed chorus and piano. (Keats, Donald). *Boosey and Hawkes. £0.75* DW (B76-50029)
Holloway, Robin. Five madrigals : for unaccompanied mixed voices. *Oxford University Press. Unpriced* EZDW (B76-50435)
Hollywood, Mayfair, and all that jazz : the Roy Fox story. (Fox, Roy). *Frewin. £4.25* AMT(P) (B76-17648) ISBN 0-85632-171-0
Holmes, John. The preces and responses ('for trebles') : S.S.A.T.B. unacc. *Oxford University Press. Unpriced* EZDGMM (B76-50412) ISBN 0-19-351651-9
Holst, Gustav. Savitri, Op 25 : an episode from the Mahābharata. Revised ed. *Eulenburg. Unpriced* CQC (B76-50768)
Holst, Imogen. Savitri, Op 25 : an episode from the Mahābharata. (Holst, Gustav). Revised ed. *Eulenburg. Unpriced* CQC (B76-50768)
Holzer, Gerhard. Mikro-Kontapunkte Z : für Trompete. *Litolff : Peters. Unpriced* WSPMJ (B76-50748)
Homenagem a Ravel : piano. (Lombardi, Nilson). *Arthur Napoleão : Essex Music. Unpriced* QPJ (B76-50909)
Homo natus de maliere : S.S.A.T.B. (Wilbye, John). *Oxford University Press. Unpriced* EZDH (B76-50054) ISBN 0-19-350352-2
Hook, James. Guida di musica. *Selections.* A James Hook album : twenty-two easy keyboard pieces. *Elkin. £0.90* PWPJ (B76-50179)
Hope-Brown, Margaret. Activities in music with children under six. *Evans Bros. £0.80* A/GR(VH) (B76-04797) ISBN 0-237-29165-7
Hopfel, Hans. The exciting sound of flamenco. (Martín, Juan). *United Music. Unpriced* TSPMH (B76-50984)
Hopkins, Gerard Manley.
Antiphonies : for mixed chorus unaccompanied
No. 1. (Druckman, Jacob). *Boosey and Hawkes. £0.55* EZDW (B76-50429)
No. 2. (Druckman, Jacob). *Boosey and Hawkes. £0.70* EZDW (B76-50430)
No. 3. (Druckman, Jacob). *Boosey and Hawkes. £1.00* EZDW (B76-50431)
Gather gladness from the skies : spring carol, unison or SATB. (Davies, Laurence Hector). *Ashdown. £0.08* JDP (B76-50103)
Horniman Museum.
Music and musical instruments in the world of Islam. (Jenkins, Jean). *85 Cromwell Rd, SW7 5BW : World of Islam Festival Publishing Co. Ltd. £1.50* BZCWIAL/B(YDB/WJ) (B76-22080) ISBN 0-905035-12-7
Wind instruments of European art music. *Inner London Education Authority. £0.45* AU/B(YDBL) (B76-21368) ISBN 0-7168-0545-6
Horovitz, Joseph. Music hall suite. *Selections : arr.* Three pieces. *Novello. £2.50* WMK (B76-50325)
Horton, John. Perry merry dixy : 106 nursery and infant songs, old and new. *Schott. Unpriced* JFDW/GK/AY (B76-50109) ISBN 0-901938-08-4
Hortus musicus.
Fischer, Johann Caspar Ferdinand. Le Journal de printemps. Partie 3, 4. Suiten = Suites for four strings or wind instruments and basso continuo. *Bärenreiter. £6.00* NXNRG (B76-50540)
Leclair, Jean Marie, *b.1697.* Première récréation de musique, Op.6 : for two violins and basso continuo. *Bärenreiter. £6.00* SNTPWG (B76-50629)
Horvit, Michael. Techniques and materials of tonal music : with an introduction to twentieth-century techniques. (Benjamin, Thomas). *Houghton Mifflin. £7.95* A/R (B76-22853) ISBN 0-395-19095-9
Hosanna to the Son of David : S.S.A.A.T.T.B. (Gibbons, Orlando). *Oxford University Press. Unpriced* EZDK (B76-50418) ISBN 0-19-352078-8
Hoskins, Graham. The Jesus file. *Voice part.* The Jesus file : a musical nativity. *Dobson. Unpriced* JDACN/LF (B76-50099) ISBN 0-234-77244-1
Hot licks and fiddle tunes for the bluegrass banjo player : a guide for improvisation and embellishment, tips on endings and accompaniment, fiddle tunes in three-finger bluegrass style. (Knopf, Bill). *Chappell. Unpriced* TS/AF (B76-50976)
Hotteterre, Jean. Pièces pour la muzette. Overture, 'Le festin'. *arr.* Overture 'Le festin' : for descant, treble and bass recorders. *Dolmetsch : Chappell. Unpriced* VSNT (B76-51032)
How brass players do it : a book of lip building and flexibility exercises. (Ridgeon, John). *Belwin Mills. Unpriced* W/EH/AF (B76-50718)
How musical is man? (Blacking, John). *Faber. £4.95* A(ZF) (B76-22078) ISBN 0-571-10790-7
Howarth, Elgar.
English dances of the 16th century. *Novello. £0.75* WNRK/AH/AYD(XD101) (B76-51079)
Jennie with the light brown hair. *arr.* Jeanie with the light brown hair. (Foster, Stephen). *Chester Music. Unpriced* WMPWWK/DW (B76-51077)
Music from the Elizabethan court. *Paxton. £2.55* WMK/AY(XDXT46) (B76-51072)
On hearing the first cuckoo in spring. *arr.* On hearing the first cuckoo in spring. (Delius, Frederick). *Oxford University Press. Unpriced* WMK (B76-50731) ISBN 0-19-362813-9
Parade : for brass band. *Chester Music. Unpriced* WMJ (B76-51060)
Howe, James. The St John march. *arr.* The St John march. (Kennedy, James). *Studio Music. Unpriced* WMK/AGM (B76-50327)
Howells, Herbert. Sonatina, piano. Sonatina for piano. *Associated Board of the Royal Schools of Music. £0.80* QPEM (B76-50898)
Howland, Russell. Quartet, saxophones no.2. Saxophone quartet no.2. *Schirmer. Unpriced* VUNS (B76-50316)
Hudson, Hazel.
The gospel train. (This train is bound for glory) : a quodlibet, for two mezzo-sopranos and baritone or two baritones. *Ashdown. £0.15* FNDW/LC (B76-50449)
Roll the old chariot along (with other things) : a quodlibet. *Ashdown. £0.15* FDW/LC (B76-50440)
Hughes, Eric.
Prelude and scherzo : for brass quartet (2 B flat cornets, E flat horn and euphonium). *Studio Music. Unpriced* WNS (B76-51082)
Sonata capriccioso : clarinet and piano. *Emerson. Unpriced* VVPE (B76-51049)
Hughes-Jones, Llifon. 'Pantyfedwen' : i leisiau TTBB. (Evans, M E). Revised ed. *Thames. Unpriced* GDW (B76-50452)
Hugo Wolf's 'Corregidor' : a study of the opera and its origins. (Cook, Peter, *b.1924*). *8 Upper Wimpole St., W.1. : The author. £3.90* BWPAC (B76-05912) ISBN 0-9504360-0-3
Hummel, Bertold.
Drei marianische Fresken für Orgel = Three Marian frescoes for organ
1: Salve regina. *Simrock. £3.10* RJ (B76-50930)
2: Ave maris stella. *Simrock. £2.50* RJ (B76-50931)
3: Regina caeli. *Simrock. £3.10* RJ (B76-50932)
Humperdinck, Engelbert.
E. Humperdinck's 'Hansel and Gretel' : based on E. Humperdinck's opera after the story by the Brothers Grimm. (Isaka, Yoshitaro). *F. Warne. £2.25* BHUACBN (B76-19463) ISBN 0-7232-1835-8
Hansel and Gretel : a fairy opera in three acts. (Hammond, Tom). *48 Great Marlborough St., W1V 2BN : Schott and Co. Ltd. £0.50* BHUAC (B76-18375) ISBN 0-901938-14-9
Hänsel und Gretel. *Vocal score.* Hansel and Gretel : opera in two acts. *Boosey and Hawkes. £9.00* CC (B76-50005)
Humphreys, Emyr. Landscapes, Ynys Môn, Op.87 : a song cycle for high voice and piano. (Hoddinott, Alun). *Oxford University Press. Unpriced* KFTDW (B76-50864) ISBN 0-19-345432-7
Humphries, John, *b.1941.*
Music master
1974. *10 Kingsland High St., E8 2JP : R.P.C. Unpriced* A/FD(WT) (B76-35030) ISBN 0-904520-00-5
1976. *48 Shacklewell La., E8 2EY : John Humphries. £15.00(£22.50 including monthly supplements)* A/FD(WT) (B76-29926) ISBN 0-904520-01-3
Humphris, Frank. Dancing rhymes. *Ladybird Books. £0.24* ADW/H (B76-30341) ISBN 0-7214-0440-5
Hungaria. (Liszt, Franz). Revised ed. *Eulenburg. Unpriced* MMJ (B76-50150)
Hungry for hope. (Lombardo, Maria). *Chappell. Unpriced* DW (B76-50030)
Hungry for hope. *arr.* Hungry for hope. (Lombardo, Maria). *Chappell. Unpriced* DW (B76-50030)
Hunt, Edgar.
Enjoy your recorder. The Trapp family recorder method : a new complete method of instruction for the recorder, including exercises, revisions, trill charts, ornaments and embellishments, duets, trios and quartets
Vol.1. (Trapp Family). New ed. *Schott. Unpriced* VS/AC (B76-50296) ISBN 0-901938-50-5
The Trapp family recorder method : a new complete method of instruction for the recorder, including exercises, revisions, trill charts, ornaments and embellishments, duets, trios and quartets
Book 1: Treble sopranino (or bass). (Trapp family). New ed. *Schott. Unpriced* VS/AC (B76-50297) ISBN 0-901938-51-3
Hunt, Reginald. Autumn song : piano solo. *Ashdown. £0.35* QPJ (B76-50208)
Hunt, William. Six choral preludes for organ. *Cramer. £0.75* RJ (B76-50933)
Huntley, John. The technique of film music. (Manvell, Roger). Revised and enlarged ed. *Focal Press. £5.00* A/JR (B76-12128) ISBN 0-240-50848-3
Huray Peter le. *See* Le Huray, Peter.
Hurd, Michael.
Dance diversions. *Novello. £3.50* MMH (B76-50145)
Flower songs. *Vocal score.* Flower songs : for S(S)A and string orchestra (or piano). *Novello. £0.50* FDW (B76-50080)
Rooster rag : a cantata in popular style for unison voices (with divisions) and piano, with guitar chord symbols. *Novello. £0.50* FDX (B76-50441)
Husler, Frederick. Singing : the physical nature of the vocal organ : a guide to the unlocking of the singing voice. *Hutchinson. £6.50* AB/E (B76-26571) ISBN 0-09-126860-5
Hutchings, Arthur. Mozart : the man, the musician. *Thames and Hudson. £16.00* BMS(N) (B76-34778) ISBN 0-500-01161-3
Hyde, Derek.
Babylon's falling : a jazz spiritual, for voices, recorders, guitars (optional) and piano. (Wastall, Peter). *Boosey and Hawkes. £1.75* FE/NWSDW/LC (B76-50083)
Did't my Lord deliver Daniel : a jazz spiritual for voices, recorders, guitars (optional) and piano. (Wastall, Peter). *Boosey and Hawkes. £1.75* FE/NWSDW/LC (B76-50084)
Joshua fought the battle of Jericho : a jazz spiritual, for voices, recorders, guitars (optional) and piano. (Wastall, Peter). *Boosey and Hawkes. £1.75* FE/NWSDW/LC (B76-50086)
Hymns for choirs. *Oxford University Press. Unpriced* DM/AY (B76-50026) ISBN 0-19-353556-4
I thank you God : SATB and piano accompaniment. (King, Jeffrey). *Boosey and Hawker. £0.50* DH (B76-50017)
I will lift up mine eyes : Psalm 121, for 4-part male voice choir with optional organ or piano. (Head, Michael). *Roberton. £0.14* GEZDR (B76-50095)
I will lift up mine eyes. *Vocal score.* I will lift up mine eyes : SATB. (Rutter, John). *Oxford University Press. Unpriced* DR (B76-50402) ISBN 0-19-350353-0
I yield thee praise : for mixed chorus and piano. (Atkinson, Condit). *Galaxy : Galliard. Unpriced* DH (B76-50383)
Ideale. (Liszt, Franz). Revised ed. *Eulenburg. Unpriced* MMJ (B76-50151)
Ie Nachgeborenen, Op.42 : Kantate für Mezzosopran, Bariton, gemischten Chor und Orchester. (Einem, Gottfried von). *Boosey and Hawkes. £8.50* EMDE (B76-50796)
If you know of a better life please tell me. (Freeman, Bud). *65 Dublin Industrial Estate, Glasnevin, Dublin 11 : Bashall Eaves. £0.80* AMT (B76-31126) ISBN 0-902638-02-5
I.G. *See* G., I.
ILEA. *See* Inner London Education Authority.
Iles, Norman. The pagan carols restored
Vol.1. *381 Marine Rd, Morecambe, Lancs. : The author. £0.50* ADP(YD) (B76-15054) ISBN 0-9500776-4-x
I'll ay ca' in by yon toon : old Scottish air. (Liddell, Claire). *Roberton. £0.10* GEZDW (B76-50096)
'I'll walk with God' : twenty-five of the most famous religious songs and ballads ever written. *Wise : Music Sales. Unpriced* KDW/L/AY (B76-50857)
Improvisation : for the piano. (Van Appledorn, Mary Jeanne). *Boosey and Hawkes. Unpriced* QPJ (B76-50576)
Imre, Laszlo. Eine Nacht in Venedig. *Vocal score.* A night in Venice. (Korngold, Erich). *Weinberger. Unpriced* CF (B76-50364)
In a stable bare : two Christmas carols for unaccompanied mixed voice choir. (Gibbs, Douglas). *Roberton. £0.15* EZDP/LF (B76-50809)
In dulci jubilo. (Oldfield, Mike). *Virgin Music : Chappell. Unpriced* QPK/DP/LF (B76-50219)
In monte Oliveti : responsory, S.A.A.T.B.B. (Lasso, Orlando di). *Chiswick Music. Unpriced* EZDGKH/LHM (B76-50050)
In old Donegal, and, The fairy tree. (Parke, Dorothy). *Roberton. £0.10* JFDW (B76-50465)
In praise of Krishna : songs from the Bengali for soprano and nine instruments. (Blake, David). *Novello. £2.00* KFLE/NVNMDW (B76-50863)
In resurrectione tua Christe. (Handl, Jacob). *Associated Music. Unpriced* WNK/DJ (B76-50331)
In Smyrna. In Smyrna, and Skizze : piano. (Elgar, *Sir* Edward, *bart*). *Novello. £0.75* QPJ (B76-50203)
In te Domine speravi : Kantate für Sopran, Alt, Bass und Basso continuo. (Buxtehude, Dietrich). *Litolff : Peters. Unpriced* DE (B76-50010)
In the beginning. *Vocal score.* In the beginning : a dramatic cantata, for speaker, baritone solo, chancel choir, nave choir and orchestra. (Hand, Colin). *Schott. Unpriced* ENWSDE (B76-50042)
In the forest : for guitar. (Croucher, Terence). *109 St Leonard's Rd, Leicester : Clarendon Music. £0.75* TSPMJ (B76-50989)
In the picture
Songbook 1. (Russell, Kay). *19 Scullamus, Isle of Skye : Aquila. Unpriced* KADW (B76-50841) ISBN 0-7275-0144-5
Inca : a project in sound for young performers. (Odam, George). *Chester. Unpriced* CQN (B76-50770)
Incorporated Society of Musicians. Professional register of private teachers of music
1975-76. *48 Gloucester Place, W1H 3HJ : The Society. £1.00* A(VC/M/BC) (B76-14360) ISBN 0-902900-08-0
Indes galantes. *Selections : arr.* Four oboe melodies. (Rameau, Jean Philippe). *Oxford University Press. Unpriced* VTPK (B76-50311) ISBN 0-19-358461-1
Ingle, Anthony. The everlasting voices. (Warlock, Peter). *Thames. Unpriced* KDW (B76-50488)
Inia Te Wiata's Maori songbook : favourite songs and chants as arranged and recorded by Inia Te Wiata. (Te Wiata, Inia). *A.H. & A.W. Reed. Unpriced* KDW/G/AYXR (B76-50491) ISBN 0-589-00877-3
Inner London Education Authority. Wind instruments of European art music. (Horniman Museum). *Inner London Education Authority. £0.45* AU/B(YDBL) (B76-21368) ISBN 0-7168-0545-6
Instruction book for the Northumbrian small-pipes.

(Fenwick, J W). 3rd ed. *5 Denebank, Monkseaton : Northumbrian Pipers' Society. Unpriced* VYQ/AC (B76-50715) ISBN 0-902510-01-0

Instruments of the Middle Ages and Renaissance. (Munrow, David). *Oxford University Press, Music Department. £3.50* AL/B(XCD801) (B76-18373) ISBN 0-19-321321-4

Integrated violinist. (Whone, Herbert). *Gollancz. £4.75* AS/CY (B76-27768) ISBN 0-575-02148-9

International Association of Music Libraries. Catalogus musicus. *See* Catalogus musicus.

International Musicological Society. Catalogus musicus. *See* Catalogus musicus.

Internationale Stiftung Mozarteum Salzburg. Mozarts italienische Texte mit deutscher Übersetzung. Metastasio, Pietro. La Clemenza di Tito : Opera seria in zwei Akten : Textbuch italiebisch-deutsch. *32 Great Titchfield St., W1P 7AD : Bärenreiter. £1.13* BMSAC

Internationalen Stiftung Mozarteum Salzburg. Briefe und Afzeichnungen

Band 7: Register. (Mozart, Wolfgang Amadeus). Gesamtuasg. *32 Great Titchfield St., W1P 7AD : Bärenreiter. £37.50* BMS(N)

Interpretation of French song. (Bernac, Pierre). *Gollancz. £7.50* AKDW/E(YH) (B77-00346) ISBN 0-575-02207-8

Intrada for band. (Washburn, Robert). *Oxford University Press. Unpriced* UMMJ (B76-50284)

Introduction to music. (Library Association. *Public Libraries Group*). *c/o A.L. Bamber, Divisional Library, Timber St., Chippenham, Wilts. : The Group. £0.40* A(T) (B76-19568) ISBN 0-85365-168-x

Introductory examinations in pianoforte playing in three steps

Step 2, Book 5. (London College of Music). *Ashdown. £0.30* Q/AL (B76-50557)

Invitation to madrigals

9: for S.S.A.T.B. *Staines and Bell. Unpriced* EZDU/AY (B76-50812) ISBN 0-85249-345-2

9: for S.S.A.T.B. *Stainer and Bell. Unpriced* EZDU/AY (B76-50811) ISBN 0-85249-346-0

Invitation to medieval music

3: Music of the mid-fifteenth century (1). *Stainer and Bell. Unpriced* CB/AY(XCH301) (B76-50362) ISBN 0-85249-316-9

Invocation to the Creator : for organ. (Camilleri, Charles). *Roberton. £1.50* RJ (B76-50591)

Iona boat song, (For a dead king) : traditional Island air. (Lees, Heath). *Roberton. £0.10* FEZDW (B76-50090)

Ipswich *(Borough). Council.* A trinity of organs : notes on the history of the organs in three Ipswich public buildings. (Woodward, Michael, *b.1928*). *c/o The Chief Executive, Civic Centre, Civic Drive, Ipswich IP1 2EE : Borough of Ipswich. £0.50* AR/B(YDDLI) (B76-09328) ISBN 0-904023-08-7

Ipswich bellfounders. (Bevis, Trevor Allen). *36 Great Clarendon St., Oxford : J. Hannon and Co. £2.00* AXS/BC(YDDLI/XEXK300)

Ipswich books. Woodward, Michael, *b.1928*. A trinity of organs : notes on the history of the organs in three Ipswich public buildings. *c/o The Chief Executive, Civic Centre, Civic Drive, IP1 2EE : Borough of Ipswich. £0.50* AR/B(YDDLI) (B76-09328) ISBN 0-904023-08-7

Ireland, John.

The collected piano works of John Ireland

Vol.1. *Stainer and Bell. Unpriced* QP/AZ (B76-50187) ISBN 0-85249-393-2

Vol.2. *Stainer and Bell. Unpriced* QP/AZ (B76-50188) ISBN 0-85249-394-0

Vol.3. *Stainer and Bell. Unpriced* QP/AZ (B76-50189) ISBN 0-85249-395-9

Irene : song album. *EMI. Unpriced* KDW (B76-50844)

Irisches Folksong-Büchlein : die schönsten irischen Lieder und Balladen, für Singstimme, Melodieinstrumente (Blockflöte) und Gitarrenbegleitung. *Heinrichshoten Peters. Unpriced* JE/LPLTSDW/G/AYDM (B76-50460)

Irish folk music studies. *See* Eigse cheol tíre.

Irvine, John.

By winding roads. In old Donegal. In old Donegal, and, The fairy tree. (Parke, Dorothy). *Roberton. £0.10* JFDW (B76-50465)

By winding roads. *Selections.* Over the hills. The old man from Kilkenny. If. (Parke, Dorothy). *Roberton. £0.15* JFDW (B76-50466)

By winding roads. *Selections.* Three little towns, Blarney. (Parke, Dorothy). *Roberton. £0.10* JFDW (B76-50467)

By winding roads. The travellers. The travellers, and, The fairy hill. (Parke, Dorothy). *Roberton. £0.10* JFDW (B76-50468)

By winding roads. Winds. Winds, and, In summer time. (Parke, Dorothy). *Roberton. £0.20* JFDW (B76-50469)

Isaka, Yoshitaro. E. Humperdinck's 'Hansel and Gretel' : based on E. Humperdinck's opera after the story by the Brothers Grimm. *F. Warne. £2.25* BHUACBN (B76-19463) ISBN 0-7232-1835-8

Israeliten in der Wuste = The Israelites in the wilderness : oratorio for soli, chorus and orchestra. (Bach, Carl Philipp Emanuel). *Eulenburg. Unpriced* EMDD (B76-50037)

It was a lover and his lass : S.A.T. Bar.B. unacc. (Rutter, John). *Oxford University Press. Unpriced* EZDW (B76-50074) ISBN 0-19-343056-8

Italian music and the Fitzwilliam : a collection of essays and a catalogue of an exhibition of Italian in the Fitzwilliam Museum in May 1976 on the occasion of four concerts of Italian music. *Fitzwilliam Museum. £1.00* A(YJ/WJ) (B76-26569) ISBN 0-904454-02-9

Iveson, John. Frère Jacques. *Chester : Hansen. Unpriced* WNRK/DW (B76-51080)

Jack Brymer clarinet series

Easy book 1. *Weinberger. Unpriced* VVPK/AAY (B76-50707)

Moderate book 1. *Weinberger. Unpriced* VVPK/AAY (B76-50708)

Jack the Ripper : a musical play. (Pember, Ron). *French. £0.90* BPEMACM (B76-10909) ISBN 0-573-08042-9

Jackson, Francis.

Lift up your heads, Opus 44, no.2 : SATB. *Oxford University Press. Unpriced* DH (B76-50385) ISBN 0-19-350360-3

People of Sion : introit for Advent II (Populus Sion), A.T.B. *Banks. Unpriced* DH (B76-50783)

Two carols arrangements. *Banks. Unpriced* DP/LF (B76-50395)

Jackson, Richard. Popular songs of nineteenth-century America : complete original sheet music for 64 songs. *Dover Publications : Constable. £4.20* KDW/GB/AYT(XG101) (B76-50854) ISBN 0-486-23270-0

Jackson-Smith, Stella. The beast of Bettesthorne. (Parry, William Howard). *Chester. Unpriced* CN (B76-50765)

Jacob, Gordon. Miscellanies. *arr.* Miscellanies : seven pieces for alto saxophone and wind orchestra. *Emerson. £2.50* VUSPK (B76-51046)

Jacobs, Arthur. British music yearbook : a survey and directory with statistics and reference articles

1976. *Bowker. £10.50* A(YC/BC) (B76-20706) ISBN 0-85935-035-5

Jacobson, Robert. Reverberations : interviews with the world's leading musicians. *Vision Press. £5.95* AL/E(M) (B76-15049) ISBN 0-85478-453-5

Jagger, Mick. The Rolling Stones file. *78 Newman St., W1P 3LA : Music Sales Ltd. £2.95* AKDW/GB/E(P) (B76-26570) ISBN 0-86001-245-x

Jalapeño : SATB chorus and piano. (Sumerlin, Macon). *Warner : Blossom. Unpriced* DW (B76-50031)

James, Donald. Three carols of the nativity : for S.A.T.B. *Chappell. Unpriced* EZDP/LF (B76-50810)

James Hook album : twenty-two easy keyboard pieces. (Hook, James). *Elkin. £0.90* PWPJ (B76-50179)

Janetzky, Kurt. Partia für Oboe, 2 Englisch Hörner, 2 Hörner und 2 Fagotte. (Rosetti, Francesco Antonio). Zum ersten Mal. *Bärenreiter. Unpriced* UNPG (B76-51008)

Jara, Victor. Victor Jara : his life and songs. *Elm Tree Books : Essex House Publishing. Unpriced* KDW (B76-50845) ISBN 0-241-89520-0

Jasper, Tony.

20 years of British record charts, 1955-1975. *Queen Anne Press. £0.75* ADW/GB/FD(XPQ21/WT) (B76-08789) ISBN 0-362-00263-0

Elton John. (Tatham, Dick). *Octopus Books : Phoebus. £1.99* AKDW/GB/E(P) (B76-28395) ISBN 0-7064-0548-x

The Rolling Stones. *Octopus Books. £1.99* AKDW/GB/E(P) (B76-31917) ISBN 0-7064-0549-8

Jasper Snowdon change ringing series.

Snowdon, Jasper Whitfield. Ropesight : Jasper Whitfield Snowdon's introduction to the art of change ringing, as revised by William Snowdon. *22 Duke St., Burton Latimer, Northants. : C. Groome. £2.50* AXSR/E(XA1935) (B76-35804) ISBN 0-905334-00-0

Trollope, J Armiger. Grandsire. 3rd ed. *22 Duke St., Burton Latimer, Kettering, Northants. : Christopher Groome. £2.50* AXSR/E (B76-35806) ISBN 0-904233-09-x

Jaws. *Theme: arr.* Jaws : theme from the film, piano solo. (Williams, John, *b.1932*). *Leeds Music. £0.30* QPK/JR (B76-50220)

Jaws : theme from the film, piano solo. (Williams, John, *b.1932*). *Leeds Music. £0.30* QPK/JR (B76-50220)

Jazz book. (Berendt, Joachim). *Paladin. £1.50* AMT (B76-33376) ISBN 0-586-08260-3

Jazz Centre Society. Jazz now : the Jazz Centre Society guide. *Quartet Books. £1.75* AMT(YC) (B76-27767) ISBN 0-7043-3097-0

Jazz masters of the Forties. (Gitler, Ira). *Collier Books : Collier Macmillan. £1.80* AMT(M/XP10) (B76-12131) ISBN 0-02-060610-9

Jazz masters of the Twenties. (Hadlock, Richard). *Collier Books : Collier Macmillan. £1.80* AMT(M/XN10) (B76-12130) ISBN 0-02-060770-9

Jazz now : the Jazz Centre Society guide. *Quartet Books. £1.75* AMT(YC) (B76-27767) ISBN 0-7043-3097-0

Jeffries, George. Fantasias à 3, viols & keyboard. *arr.* Four fantasias. *Chappell. Unpriced* QPK (B76-50581)

Jegliches hat seine Zeit : Suite für Männerchor, Sopransolo, Sprecher, in der Fassung für zwei Klaviere, Pauken und Schlagzeug (1 Spieler). (Poos, Heinrich). *Schott. £19.20* ENYLNSDE (B76-50800)

Jenkins, Jean. Music and musical instruments in the world of Islam. *85 Cromwell Rd, SW7 5BW : World of Islam Festival Publishing Co. Ltd. £1.50* BZCWIAL/B(YDB/WJ) (B76-22080) ISBN 0-905035-12-7

Jenkins, John.

Consort music for viols in six parts. *Faber Music for the Viola da Gamba Society of Great Britain. Unpriced* STNQR (B76-50963)

Fantasia, viols (2) & organ, A minor. Fantasia, suite 5 : for violin (or treble viol), bass viol (or violoncello) and organ (or harpsichord). *Oxford University Press. Unpriced* NXNT (B76-50886) ISBN 0-19-357410-1

Jenkins, John, *b.1936.* Electric music : a practical manual for musicians. *David and Charles. £4.95* APV (B76-33378) ISBN 0-7153-6815-x

Jenni, Donald. Musica della primavera : for solo clarinet in A. *Associated Music. Unpriced* VVQPMJ (B76-50322)

Jennie with the light brown hair. *arr.* Jeanie with the light brown hair. (Foster, Stephen). *Chester Music. Unpriced* WMPWWK/DW (B76-51077)

Jergen, A. Eine Nacht in Venedig. *Vocal score.* A night in Venice. (Korngold, Erich). *Weinberger. Unpriced* CF (B76-50364)

Jerusalem. (Parry, *Sir* Charles Hubert). *Studio Music. Unpriced* WMK/DW (B76-51074)

Jessett, Michael. Dancing days : twelve carols for guitar. *Cramer. £1.25* TSPMK/DP/LF/AY (B76-50993)

Jesu, joy of man's desiring. (Bach, Johann Sebastian). *Oxford University Press. Unpriced* VRPK/DM (B76-50292) ISBN 0-19-355279-5

Jesus by thy wounded feet : for unaccompanied four-part choir. (Curtis, James Gilbert). *Cramer. £0.12* EZDH (B76-50415)

Jesus file. *Voice part.* The Jesus file : a musical nativity. (Hoskins, Graham). *Dobson. Unpriced* JDACN/LF (B76-50099) ISBN 0-234-77244-1

Jesus is the loveliest light. (Bach, Johann Sebastian). *Roberton. £0.10* EZDM (B76-50420)

Johannes-Passion, BWV 245. (Bach, Johann Sebastian). *Bärenreiter. £6.50* EMDD/LK (B76-50405)

John, A M St. *See* St John, A M.

John McLaughlin and the Mahavishnu Orchestra. (McLaughlin, John). *Warner-Tamerlane : Blossom. Unpriced* NYG (B76-50888)

Johnson, David. Trio, recorders. Trio for recorders in eight movements. *Forsyth. Unpriced* VSNT (B76-51033)

Johnson, David Sturgess. The organs of the Church of St John : a history. *Mill St., Derby : Church of St John the Evangelist. £0.10* AR/B(YDHWD) (B76-31919) ISBN 0-9505280-0-5

Johnson, Stuart. The gospel train : negro spiritual, two-part (with optional recorders). *Oxford University Press. Unpriced* FDW/LC (B76-50082) ISBN 0-19-341508-9

Joio, Norman dello. *See* Dello Joio, Norman.

Jonah and the whale. *Vocal score.* Jonah and the whale : tenor and bass soli, mixed chorus, narrator and instrumental ensemble. (Argento, Dominick). *Boosey and Hawkes. £10.00* DE (B76-50774)

Jones, E Olwen. Gweithdy cerddorol y plant

Llyfr 2: Carolau. *C. Davies. Unpriced* CB/AY (B76-50361) ISBN 0-7154-0188-2

Jones, Llifon Hughes-. *See* Hughes-Jones, Llifon.

Jones, Max. Louis : the Louis Armstrong story, 1900-1971. *Mayflower. £0.95* AMT(P) (B76-01204) ISBN 0-583-12710-x

Jones, Peter, *b.1930.*

20 years of British record charts, 1955-1975. *Queen Anne Press. £0.75* ADW/GB/FD(XPQ21/WT) (B76-08789) ISBN 0-362-00263-0

Elvis. *Octopus Books. £1.99* AKDW/HK/E(P) (B76-34783) ISBN 0-7064-0550-1

Jones, Philip. Canzon a 4, no.2 (1608) : for brass quartet. (Gabrieli, Giovanni). *Chester : Hansen. Unpriced* WNS (B76-51081)

Joni Mitchell. (Fleischer, Leonore). *Flash Books; 78 Newman St., W1P 3LA : Book Sales Ltd. £1.95* AKDW/GB/E(P) (B76-35355) ISBN 0-8256-3907-7

Jonns, Roger. Trios gymnopédies : piano solo. (Satie, Erik). *Leonard, Gould and Bolttler. £0.45* QPJ (B76-50213)

Joplin, Scott.

The entertainer. *arr.* The entertainer. *Chappell. Unpriced* EZDW (B76-50068)

The entertainer. *arr.* The entertainer. *Chappell. Unpriced* VSNSQK/AHXJ (B76-50684)

The entertainer. *arr.* The entertainer : an excerpt. *Schirmer. Unpriced* VRPLTSK/AHXJ (B76-50293)

The strenuous life. *arr.* The strenuous life : a ragtime two-step. *Schirmer. Unpriced* WNK/AHXJ (B76-50330)

Jordan, René. Greatest star. *See* Jordan, René. Streisand.

Jordan, René. Streisand : an unauthorised biography. 1st British ed. *W.H. Allen. £3.95* AKDW/GB/E(P) (B76-11504) ISBN 0-491-01775-8

Joseph, Jack. Notes on music. *38 Ferndale Rd, Gillingham, Kent : Lindley Press. £0.40* A/M (B76-24540) ISBN 0-9504506-0-x

Josephs, Wilfred.

Concerto for two violins and small orchestra. Op.69. *Chappell. Unpriced* SNTQK/LF (B76-50630)

Concerto, violins (2), op.69. *arr.* Concerto for two violins and small orchestra. Op.69. *Chappell. Unpriced* SPK/LF (B76-50251)

Symphony no.5, op.75, 'Pastoral'. Pastoral symphony (1970). *Novello. £3.50* MME (B76-50519)

Trio for horn, violin and piano. Opus 76. *Novello. Unpriced* NUXTNT (B76-50165)

Joshua fought the battle of Jericho : a jazz spiritual, for voices, recorders, guitars (optional) and piano. (Wastall, Peter). *Boosey and Hawkes. £1.75* FE/NWSDW/LC (B76-50086)

Joslin, Peter. Piano music. *Selections.* Piano music. (Sullivan, *Sir* Arthur Seymour). *Chappell. Unpriced* QPJ (B76-50216)

Joubert, John. Lord make me an instrument of thy peace. Op.84 : S. solo, S.S.A.A.T.T.B.B. *Oxford University Press. Unpriced* DH (B76-50386) ISBN 0-19-350359-x

Journal de printemps. Partie 3, 4. Suiten = Suites for four strings or wind instruments and basso continuo. (Fischer, Johann Caspar Ferdinand). *Bärenreiter. £6.00* NXNRG (B76-50540)

Joy waltz : instrumental ensemble. (Mayes, Jerry). *Charnwood Music. Unpriced* LNHW (B76-50512)
Joyce, James. Five madrigals : for unaccompanied mixed voices. (Holloway, Robin). *Oxford University Press. Unpriced* EZDW (B76-50435)
Joyeux : waltz, accordion solo. (Farran, Kenneth G). *Charnwood Music. Unpriced* RSPMHW (B76-50946)
Judy Garland souvenir songbook. *Chappell. Unpriced* KDW/JR/AYT (B76-50856) ISBN 0-06-465040-5
Jumblies : for four-part chorus of mixed voices with soprano solo and piano accompaniment. (Thomson, Virgil). *Schirmer. Unpriced* DW (B76-50033)
Just brass.
Dodgson, Stephen. Suite for brass septet. *Chester. Unpriced* WNPG (B76-50737)
Foster, Stephen. Jennie with the light brown hair. *arr.* Jeanie with the light brown hair. *Chester Music. Unpriced* WMPWWK/DW (B76-51077)
Gabrieli, Giovanni. Canzon a 4, no.2 (1608) : for brass quartet. *Chester : Hansen. Unpriced* WNS (B76-51081)
Howarth, Elgar. Parade : for brass band. *Chester Music. Unpriced* WMJ (B76-51060)
Iveson, John. Frère Jacques. *Chester : Hansen. Unpriced* WNRK/DW (B76-51080)
Lear, W Hogarth. Barney's tune : for brass band. *Chester Music. Unpriced* WMJ (B76-51063)
Lear, W Hogarth. Chinese take away : for cornet trio and brass band. *Chester Music. Unpriced* WMPWRNT (B76-51075)
Lear, W Hogarth. Hogarth's hoe-down : for brass band. *Chester Music. Unpriced* WMH (B76-51058)
Lear, W Hogarth. Paris le soir : for brass band. *Chester Music. Unpriced* WMJ (B76-51064)
Lear, W Hogarth. Red sky at night : for brass band. *Chester Music. Unpriced* WMJ (B76-51065)
Premru, Raymond. Music from Harter Fell : for brass sextet. *Chester. Unpriced* WNQ (B76-50738)
Just Mahalia, baby. Mahalia. (Goreau, Laurraine). *Lion Publishing : Aslan. £1.95* AKDW/HJ/L/E(P) (B76-36285) ISBN 0-85648-061-4
Kaan, Fred. Songs and hymns from Sweden. *Stainer and Bell. Unpriced* DM/AYND (B76-50787) ISBN 0-85249-440-8
Kagel, Mauricio.
Abend : für Doppelvokalquartett, Posaunenquintett, elektrische Orgel und Klavier. *Universal. Unpriced* ENWXUNPDX (B76-50043)
Atem : für einen Bläser. *Universal. Unpriced* UNT (B76-50674)
Charakterstück : für Zitherquartett. *Universal. Unpriced* TUNS (B76-50661)
Kantrimiusik : für Sänger (Sopran, Mezzo-Sopran, Tenor) und Instrumentalensemble (Klarinette, Trompete, Basstuba, Geige, Klavier, 2 Gitarristen). *Universal. Unpriced* JNDE/NUNPDX (B76-50112)
Mare nostrum : Entdeckung, Gefriedung und Konversion des Mittelmeerraumes durch einen Stamm aus Amazonien, für Contratenor, Bariton, Flöte, Oboe, Gitarre, Harfe, Violoncello und Schlagzeug. *Universal. Unpriced* JNEE/NYEPDX (B76-50113)
Musi : für Zupforchester. *Universal. Unpriced* RWMJ (B76-50234)
Die Mutation : für Männerchor und obligates Klavier. *Universal. Unpriced* GDE (B76-50450)
Siegfriedp' : für Violoncello. *Universal. Unpriced* SRPMJ (B76-50648)
Kahan, Judy. Pretzels : a musical revue. (Forster, John). *French. £1.25* BFNRACP (B76-06889) ISBN 0-573-68071-x
Kail, Robert.
Franz Peter Schubert : his greatest songs, 38 lieder with new singable translations. (Schubert, Franz). *Copa Phoenix Music. Unpriced* KDW (B76-50846)
World's favorite easy violin pieces. *Ashley : Phoenix. Unpriced* SPK/AAY (B76-50959)
World's favorite intermediate violin pieces. *Ashley Phoenix. Unpriced* SPK/AAY (B76-50960)
Kandel, Carl H.
Secundus tomus musici operis. Alleluia. In resurrectione tua. *arr.* In resurrectione tua Christe. (Handl, Jacob). *Associated Music. Unpriced* WNK/DJ (B76-50331)
The strenuous life. *arr.* The strenuous life : a ragtime two-step. (Joplin, Scott). *Schirmer. Unpriced* WNK/AHXJ (B76-50330)
Kangaroo hunt : for piano and percussion. (Lumsdaine, David). *Universal. Unpriced* NYLNU (B76-50178)
Kantrimiusik : für Sänger (Sopran, Mezzo-Sopran, Tenor) und Instrumentalensemble (Klarinette, Trompete, Basstuba, Geige, Klavier, 2 Gitarristen). (Kagel, Mauricio). *Universal. Unpriced* JNDE/NUNPDX (B76-50112)
Kaplan, Abraham. Choral series.
Rossini, Gioacchino Antonio. Ave Maria : for four-part chorus of mixed voices with piano. *Roberton. £0.14* DH (B76-50018)
Schubert, Franz. Gesänge zur Feier des heiligen Opfers der Messe. D.872. Zum Sanctus. *arr.* Zum Sanctus : for 4-part chorus of mixed voices with organ or piano. *Roberton. £0.14* DH (B76-50019)
Karajan. (Robinson, Paul). *Macdonald and Jane's. £3.95* A/EC(P) (B76-35356) ISBN 0-354-04031-6
Karpeles, Maud. The crystal spring : English folk songs. *Oxford University Press. £4.95* JE/TSDW/G/AYD (B76-50105) ISBN 0-19-330518-6
Katalog für Schlagzeug 1 = Catalogue for percussion 1 : 1 player. (Hiller, Wilfried). *Schott. £2.00* XPMJ (B76-50346)
Katharsis : for flute, small orchestra, slide projections and groups of loudspeakers. (Antoniou, Theodore). *Bärenreiter. £4.25* MPVR (B76-50536)
Keats, Donald. The hollow men : mixed chorus and piano. *Boosey and Hawkes. £0.75* DW (B76-50029)
Keith, Alan. The world of your 100 best tunes. *Chappell. Unpriced* QPK/AAY (B76-50923)
Keller, Gertrud. Terpsichore : die Tänze der Barockzeit, für zwei Sopranblockflöten. *Noetzel : Peters. Unpriced* VSRNU/AY (B76-50302)
Kelley, Norman. Hänsel und Gretel. *Vocal score.* Hansel and Gretel : opera in two acts. (Humperdinck, Engelbert). *Boosey and Hawkes. £9.00* CC (B76-50005)
Kelly, Bryan. Andalucia : for brass band. *Paxton. Unpriced* WMJ (B76-51061)
Kelterborn, Rudolf. Kammermusik für fünf Bläser : Flöte (Piccolo), Oboe, Klarinette, Horn und Fagott. *Bärenreiter. £5.00* UNR (B76-50670)
Kendall, Alan, *b.1939.* The tender tyrant, Nadia Boulanger : a life devoted to music : a biography. *Macdonald and Jane's. £5.95* A(VC/P) (B76-29098) ISBN 0-356-08403-5
Kennedy, James. The St John march. *arr.* The St John march. *Studio Music. Unpriced* WMK/AGM (B76-50327)
Kennedy, John Fitzgerald.
Three songs for America. *arr.* Three songs for America : bass voice and instruments (woodwind quintet and string quintet). (Amran, David). *Peters. Unpriced* KGXDW (B76-50137)
Three songs for America : bass voice and instruments (woodwind quintet and string quintet). (Amran, David). *Peters. Unpriced* KGXE/MRDW (B76-50138)
Kennedy, Michael, *b.1926.* Richard Strauss. *Dent. £3.95* BSU (B76-14362) ISBN 0-460-03148-1
Kennedy, Robert Fitzgerald.
Three songs for America. *arr.* Three songs for America : bass voice and instruments (woodwind quintet and string quintet). (Amran, David). *Peters. Unpriced* KGXDW (B76-50137)
Three songs for America : bass voice and instruments (woodwind quintet and string quintet). (Amran, David). *Peters. Unpriced* KGXE/MRDW (B76-50138)
Kenny, Terry A. The Mexican trot. *Studio Music. Unpriced* WMJ (B76-50727)
Kentner, Louis. Piano. *Macdonald and Jane's. £3.95* AQ/B (B76-10253) ISBN 0-356-04713-x
Kenward, Jean. Songs from the stable : for children's voices and instruments. (Platts, Kenneth). *Edwin Ashdown. £2.00* JFE/LPDP/LF (B76-50834)
Kerman, Joseph. The Beethoven quartets. *Oxford University Press. £6.00* BBJARXNS (B77-00348) ISBN 0-19-315135-9
Kettlewell, David. All the tunes that ever there were : an introduction to the dulcimer in the British Isles. *Tisbury, Wilts. : Spoot Books. £3.25* ATWT/B(X) (B76-50758) ISBN 0-9505111-0-2
Keune, Eckehardt. Schlaginstrumente = Percussion instruments : a method of instruction
Part 1: Kleine Trommel = Side drum. *Bärenreiter. £6.25* X/AC (B76-50751)
Key approach to cello playing. (Morris, Miriam). *Chappell. Unpriced* SR/AC (B76-50639)
Killmayer, Wilhelm. Nachtgedanken : für Orchester. *Schott. £7.30* MMJ (B76-50149)
Kinderlieder in leichten Sätzen : für zwei Sopranflöten. *Nagel : Bärenreiter. £1.25* VSRNUK/DW/GJ/AYE (B76-50687)
King, Jeffrey. I thank you God : SATB and piano accompaniment. *Boosey and Hawker. £0.50* DH (B76-50017)
King, John. Complete trumpet repertoire of Henry Purcell. (Purcell, Henry). *Musica rara. Unpriced* WS (B76-50338)
King, Martin Luther.
Three songs for America. *arr.* Three songs for America : bass voice and instruments (woodwind quintet and string quintet). (Amran, David). *Peters. Unpriced* KGXDW (B76-50137)
Three songs for America : bass voice and instruments (woodwind quintet and string quintet). (Amran, David). *Peters. Unpriced* KGXE/MRDW (B76-50138)
King Charles' pleasure : a fantasy in the olden style for string trio (or viols). (De Smet, Robin). *British and Continental. Unpriced* RXNS (B76-50616)
King of glory : a collection of anthems. *Novello. £1.00* DH/AY (B76-50020)
Kinoshita, Junji. Yuzuru. *Vocal score.* Yuzuru = The twilight heron : opera in one act. (Dan, Ikuma). *Boosey and Hawkes. Unpriced* CC (B76-50363)
Kinsella, Thomas. Poet in the suburbs : for unaccompanied mixed voices. (Fleischmann, Aloys). *Oxford University Press. Unpriced* EZDX (B76-50077) ISBN 0-19-336108-6
Kirby, Percival R. Guillaume Tell. Overture. Overture to the opera 'Guillaume Tell'. (Rossini, Gioacchino Antonio). *Eulenburg. Unpriced* MMJ (B76-50530)
Kirchner, Gerhard.
Sonatas, organ, nos.1-6. S.525-30. *arr.* Sechs Sonaten nach B.W.V. 525-530 = Six sonatas after B.W.V. 525-530 : for flute and harpsichord obbligato
Book 2: Sonatas 3 and 4. (Bach, Johann Sebastian). *Bärenreiter. £4.50* VRPK/AE (B76-50678)
Sonatas, organ, nos.1-6. S.525-30. *arr.* Sechs Sonaten nach B.W.V. 525-530 Six sonatas after B.W.V. 525-530 : for flute and harpsichord obbligato
Book 1: Sonatas 1 and 2. (Bach, Johann Sebastian). *Bärenreiter. £4.50* VRPK/AE (B76-50679)
Kirchner, Waltraut.
Sonatas, organ, nos.1-6. S.525-30. *arr.* Sechs Sonaten nach B.W.V. 525-530 = Six sonatas after B.W.V. 525-530 : for flute and harpsichord obbligato
Book 2: Sonatas 3 and 4. (Bach, Johann Sebastian). *Bärenreiter. £4.50* VRPK/AE (B76-50678)
Sonatas, organ, nos.1-6. S.525-30. *arr.* Sechs Sonaten nach B.W.V. 525-530 Six sonatas after B.W.V. 525-530 : for flute and harpsichord obbligato
Book 1: Sonatas 1 and 2. (Bach, Johann Sebastian). *Bärenreiter. £4.50* VRPK/AE (B76-50679)
Kirkby-Mason, Barbara.
First album for piano
Part 1. Revised ed. *Bosworth. Unpriced* Q/AC (B76-50889)
Part 3. Revised ed. *Bosworth. Unpriced* Q/AC (B76-50890)
Kish, Gabriell. Scales and studies for guitar. *Frederick Harris : Lengnick. £1.95* TS/AF (B76-50975)
Kishida, Eriko. E. Humperdinck's 'Hansel and Gretel' : based on E. Humperdinck's opera after the story by the Brothers Grimm. (Isaka, Yoshitaro). *F. Warne. £2.25* BHUACBN (B76-19463) ISBN 0-7232-1835-8
Klarinetten-Bibliothek. Hildemann, Wolfgang. Sonatina, clarinet & piano, 'Ritmi dispari'. Ritmi dispari : Sonatine für Klarinette in B und Klavier von Wolfgang Hildemann. *Schott. £1.75* VVPEM (B76-50704)
Klarinetten Bibliothek. Zehm, Friedrich. Klarinetten im Duett : 8 Stücke für 2 Klarinetten gleicher Stimmung. *Schott. £1.75* VVNU (B76-50317)
Klarinetten im Duett : 8 Stücke für 2 Klarinetten gleicher Stimmung. (Zehm, Friedrich). *Schott. £1.75* VVNU (B76-50317)
Kleban, Edward. A chorus line. *Selections : arr.* A chorus line : vocal selections. (Hamlisch, Marvin). *Chappell. Unpriced* KDW (B76-50478)
Kleine Stücke, grosser Meister : für zwei Sopranblockflöten. *Noetzel : Peters. Unpriced* VSRNUK/AAY (B76-50303)
Kleine Tänze, grosser Meister : für zwei Sopranblockflöten. *Noetzel : Peters. Unpriced* VSRNUK/AH/AY (B76-50304)
Kleines Konzert nach Lautensätzen aus dem 16. Jahrhundert = Little concerto based on lute pieces from the 16th century : for flute, oboe, bassoon, trumpet, trombone, harpsichord and percussion. (Orff, Carl). New ed. *Schott. £9.00* NYFNPF (B76-50175)
Kleinmichel, R. Hänsel und Gretel. *Vocal score.* Hansel and Gretel : opera in two acts. (Humperdinck, Engelbert). *Boosey and Hawkes. £9.00* CC (B76-50005)
Kleyn, Howard.
Chinese suite, no.2. Op.41. *Sonia Archer : Lengnick. Unpriced* VSPLK (B76-51037)
La flauta española : flute solo, with piano accompaniment. *Sonia Archer : Lengnick. Unpriced* VRPJ (B76-51018)
A sheaf of sonnets. Op.36. *Sonia Archer : Lengnick. Unpriced* DW (B76-50795)
Klusmeier, R T. Gift of new sight : Christmas anthem, S.A.T.B. *Harmuse : Lengnick. £0.21* DP/LF (B76-50790)
Knapp, Dan. Going down with Janis. (Caserta, Peggy). *Futura Publications. £0.65* AKDW/GB/E(P) (B76-01877) ISBN 0-86007-231-2
Knapp, John Merrill. The magic of opera. *Hale. £6.50* AC (B76-00668) ISBN 0-7091-5254-x
Knopf, Bill. Hot licks and fiddle tunes for the bluegrass banjo player : a guide for improvisation and embellishment, tips on endings and accompaniment, fiddle tunes in three-finger bluegrass style. *Chappell. Unpriced* TS/AF (B76-50976)
Knowing the score : notes on film music. (Bazelon, Irwin). *Van Nostrand Reinhold. £6.25* A/JR (B76-05914) ISBN 0-442-20594-5
Knussen, Oliver. Masks. Op.3 : for solo flute with glass chimes (ad lib.). *Schirmer. Unpriced* VRPMJ (B76-50294)
Kobbé, Gustave. Kobbé's complete opera book. 9th ed. *Putnam. £15.00* AC (B76-31916) ISBN 0-370-10020-4
Kobbé's complete opera book. (Kobbé, Gustave). 9th ed. *Putnam. £15.00* AC (B76-31916) ISBN 0-370-10020-4
Kolbel, Herbert. Concerto, flute, two violins & continuo, D major. Concerto per il flauto solo, 2 violini e basso continuo (D-dur). (Pergolesi, Giovanni Battista). *Heinrichshofen : Peters. Unpriced* NURNTF (B76-50164)
Konietzny, Heinrich.
Collagen 1 & 2 : für Trompete in B und Klavier. *Bosse Bärenreiter. £6.50* WSPJ (B76-50743)
Zwei Miniaturen : für Trompete (B) und Schlagwerk. *Bosse : Barenreiter. £6.00* WSPLX (B76-50746)
Korn, Peter Jona. Preludes, organ, op.55. Vier Präludien für Orgel. Opus 55. *Litolff : Peters. Unpriced* RJ (B76-50593)
Korngold, Erich. Eine Nacht in Venedig. *Vocal score.* A night in Venice. *Weinberger. Unpriced* CF (B76-50364)
Kraus, Eberhard. German mass, no.2, G. major. *Vocal score.* Zweite deutsche Messe, 'Hier liegt vor deiner Majestät', für Sopran, Alt, Bass ad libitum (solistisch oder chorisch) und Orgel. (Grünberger, Theodor). *Bosse : Bärenreiter. £8.75* DE (B76-50367)
Kreidler, Dieter. Tres libros de música en cifra para vihuela. Fantasia no.10. *arr.* Fantasia : das Harfenspiel in der Manier von Ludovico nachahmend / von Alonso Mudarra. Welsh Tantz, 'Wascha mesa' / von Hans Neusidler ; für Gitarre solo, eingerichtet von Dieter Kreidler. (Mudarra, Alonso). *Schott. £1.00* TSPMK (B76-50275)
Křenek, Ernst. Spatlese. Op.218 : in sechs Teilen, für Bariton und Klavier. *Bärenreiter. £7.50* KGNDX (B76-50507)
Kreuger, Miles. The movie musical from Vitaphone to 42nd Street : as reported in a great fan magazine. *Dover*

Publications etc. : Constable. £4.55 ACM/JR(YT/XNF8) (B76-12805) ISBN 0-486-23154-2
Kreutz, Robert. Spring grass : part song, SATB. *Boosey and Hawkes. Unpriced* EZDW (B76-50069)
Kreutzer, Conradin. Duets, clarinets (2), C major. Duetto für zwei Klarinetten, C-dur. *Litolff : Peters. Unpriced* VVNU (B76-50703)
Kroeger, Karl.
Die mit Thränen saën. *Vocal score.* Who with weeping soweth = Die mit Thränen saën. (Antes, John). *Boosey and Hawkes. £0.30* DH (B76-50377)
Gelobet sey der Herr. *Vocal score.* All praises be to the Lord = Gelobet sey der Herr. (Antes, John). *Boosey and Hawkes. £0.30* DH (B76-50378)
Gott hat uns angenehm gemacht. *Vocal score.* The Lord has been gracious unto us = Gott hat uns angenehm gemacht. (Antes, John). *Boosey and Hawkes. £0.40* DH (B76-50379)
My heart shall rejoice in His salvation. *Vocal score.* My heart shall rejoice in His salvation. (Antes, John). *Boosey and Hawkes. £0.40* DH (B76-50380)
Sing and rejoice, O daugher of Zion. *Vocal score.* Sing and rejoice, O daugher of Zion. (Antes, John). *Boosey and Hawkes. £0.40* DH (B76-50381)
Unser Seele wartet auf den Herrn. *Vocal score.* Our soul doth wait upon the Lord = Unser Seele wartet auf den Herrn. (Antes, John). *Boosey and Hawkes. £0.30* DH (B76-50382)
Kubelík, Rafael.
Mass. Messe für Sopran und Männerchor. *Litolff : Peters. Unpriced* EZDG (B76-50409)
Symphony in one movement. Sinfonie in einem Satz für Orchester. *Litolff : Peters. Unpriced* MME (B76-50520)
La flauta española : flute solo, with piano accompaniment. (Kleyn, Howard). *Sonia Archer : Lengnick. Unpriced* VRPJ (B76-51018)
La Motte, Diether de. Harmonielehre : 1600-1730-1790-1810-1840-1860-1880-1910-1930. *Bärenreiter etc.. £12.00* A/R(XE331)
Labirinto : chôro, piano. (Nazareth, Ernesto). *Arthur Napoleão : Essex Music. Unpriced* QPJ (B76-50914)
Lachert, Piotr. Etudes intelligentes : for beginners at the piano. *Bärenreiter. £5.00* Q/AF (B76-50544)
Lachrimae. (Dowland, John). 1st ed., reprinted. *5 Albert Grove, Leeds 6 : Boethius Press. £6.60* BDTARWNR (B76-10254) ISBN 0-904263-04-5
Laderman, Ezra. Momenti : for piano solo. *Oxford University Press. Unpriced* QPJ (B76-50209)
Laing, Dave.
The encyclopedia of rock
Vol.1: The age of rock'n'roll. *Panther. £0.95* A/HK(C) (B76-14358) ISBN 0-586-04267-9
Vol.2: From Liverpool to San Francisco. *Panther. £0.95* A/HK(C) (B76-16549) ISBN 0-586-04268-7
Vol.3: The sounds of the seventies. *Panther. £0.95* A/HK(C) (B76-31912) ISBN 0-586-04269-5
Lancaster University. *See* University of Lancaster.
Land of the mountain and the flood. Op.3. *arr.* The land of the mountain and the flood : concert overture, Opus 3. (MacCunn, Hamish). *Paxton. £2.00* WMK (B76-51070)
Landon, Grelun. Encyclopedia of folk country and Western music. (Stambler, Irwin). *St Martin's Press : St James Press. £5.00* A/GCW(C) (B76-00666) ISBN 0-900997-24-9
Landon, Howard Chandler Robbins. Mass, no.7, G major, 'Sancti Nicolai'. Missa Sancti Nicolai. (Haydn, Joseph). *Eulenburg. Unpriced* EMDG (B76-50039)
Landscapes, Ynys Môn, Op.87 : a song cycle for high voice and piano. (Hoddinott, Alun). *Oxford University Press. Unpriced* KFTDW (B76-50864) ISBN 0-19-345432-7
Lane, Philip. A spring overture. *R. Smith. Unpriced* WMJ (B76-51062)
Langley, James. Maestoso and allegro for trombone quartet. *Studio Music. Unpriced* WUNS (B76-51085)
Language of twentieth century music : a dictionary of terms. (Fink, Robert). *Schirmer Books : Collier Macmillan. £5.50* A(XMA77/C) (B76-05036) ISBN 0-02-870600-5
Langwierige Weg in die Wohnung der Natascha Ungeheur. *Selections.* Fragmente aus einer Show : Sätze für Blechquintett. (Henze, Hans Werner). *Schott. £2.25* WNR (B76-50739)
Lanza, Alcides. Penetrations VI (1972-II) : for voice, chamber ensemble, lights, electronic music and electronic extensions. *Boosey and Hawkes. Unpriced* KE/PV (B76-50860)
Lark in the clear air : Irish traditional air. (Nelson, Havelock). *Banks. Unpriced* GEZDW (B76-50824)
Lascelles, George Henry Hubert, *Earl of Harewood. See* Harewood, George Henry Hubert Lascelles, *Earl of.*
Lasocki, David.
Concerto, flute & string orchestra, G major. H.S.315. Concerto in G major for flute, strings and basso continuo, H.S.315. (Molter, Johann Melchior). *Musica rara. Unpriced* RXMPVRF (B76-50612)
Concerto, flute & string orchestra, G major. H.S.315. Concerto in G major for flute, strings and basso continuo, H.S.315. (Molter, Johann Melchior). *Musica rara. Unpriced* VRPK/LF (B76-50681)
Lasso, Orlando di.
Continuation du mellagne. Passan vostri triomphi. *arr.* Trionto del tempo / by Orlando di Lasso ; and, Ecco l'alma beata / by Giovanni Croce ; arranged for ten recorders in 2 choirs by Dennis A. Bamforth. *Tomus. Unpriced* VSMK/DH (B76-50298)
Selectissimae cantiones. In monte Oliveti. In monte Oliveti : responsory, S.A.A.T.B.B. *Chiswick Music. Unpriced* EZDGKH/LHM (B76-50050)
Lassus, Orlando di. *See* Lasso, Orlando di.
Lauer, Heinz. Früher Anfang auf dem Cello : eine Violoncelloschule für Kinder ab 4 Jahren
Band 1. (Sassmannshaus, Egon). *Bosse : Bärenreiter. £3.75* SR/AC (B76-50640)
Lawes, Henry. Cavalier songs. *Stainer and Bell. Unpriced* KE/TDW (B76-50129) ISBN 0-85249-325-8
Lawrence, Alan. Dancing days : twelve carols for guitar. *Cramer. £1.25* TSPMK/DP/LF/AY (B76-50993)
Lawrence, Ian. Brass in your school. *Oxford University Press. £3.15* AWM(VF/VC) (B76-50355) ISBN 0-19-318705-1
Lawson-Gould choral series. Clark, Keith. Metaphysical fragments. Our murmers have their musick too. Our murmers have their musick too : for 4-part chorus of mixed voices unaccompanied. *Roberton. £0.10* EZDW (B76-50428)
Lawson-Gould sacred choral series. Rossini, Gioacchino Antonio. Messe solennelle. Kyrie. *Vocal score.* Kyrie. *Roberton. £0.28* DGB (B76-50778)
Lawton, Sidney.
Cantata no.147, 'Herz und Mund und That und Leben'. Wohl mir dass ich Jesum habe. *arr.* Jesu, joy of man's desiring. (Bach, Johann Sebastian). *Oxford University Press. Unpriced* VRPK/DM (B76-50292) ISBN 0-19-355279-5
Musique héroïque. *arr.* Heroic music : a suite of twelve marches. (Telemann, Georg Philipp). *Oxford University Press. Unpriced* WSPK/AGM (B76-50342) ISBN 0-19-359067-0
Lawton, Sidney Maurice.
The young horn-player : a series of graded arrangements for horn in F and piano
Vol.1. *Oxford University Press. Unpriced* VTPK/AAY (B76-50312) ISBN 0-19-357459-4
Vol.2. *Oxford University Press. Unpriced* VTPK/AAY (B76-50313) ISBN 0-19-357461-6
Vol.3. *Oxford University Press. Unpriced* VTPK/AAY (B76-50314) ISBN 0-19-357463-2
Layfield, Kathy. Action rhymes. *Ladybird Books. £0.24* ADW/GR (B76-30340) ISBN 0-7214-0439-1
Layton, Robert.
The Penguin stereo record guide. (Greenfield, Edward). *Penguin. £3.50* A/FF(WT) (B76-03703) ISBN 0-14-046223-6
Sibelius
Vol.1: 1865-1905. (Tawaststjerna, Erik). *Faber. £12.50* BSH(N) (B76-30336) ISBN 0-571-08832-5
Le Huray, Peter. Musica Britannica : a national collection of music
Vol.38: Matthew Locke : anthems and motets. *Stainer and Bell. Unpriced* C/AYD (B76-50360) ISBN 0-85249-397-5
Leabhair thaighde. Ní Fhlathartaigh, Ríonach. Clár amhrán Bhaile na hInse : clár na n-amhrán i mbarúntacht Bhaile na hInse. *15 Bóthar Ghráinseach an Déin, An Charraig Dhubh, Co. Atha Cliath : An Clóchomhar Tta. £3.50* ADW/G(YDMG/T) (B76-17862) ISBN 0-903758-06-7
Léachtaí Cholm Cille VII : an ceol i litríocht la Gaeilge. *Maynooth, Co. Kildare : St Patrick's College. £0.50* A/G(YDM) (B76-34780) ISBN 0-901519-17-0
Lear, Edward.
Cantata on poems of Edward Lear. Half an alphabet. Half an alphabet : canons for chorus, for four-part chorus of mixed voices with piano accompaniment. (Thomson, Virgil). *Schirmer. Unpriced* DW/X (B76-50034)
Cantata on poems of Edward Lear. The Akond of Swat. The Akond of Swat : for four-part chorus of mixed voices with baritone solo and piano accompaniment. (Thomson, Virgil). *Schirmer. Unpriced* DW (B76-50032)
Cantata on poems of Edward Lear. The Jumblies. The Jumblies : for four-part chorus of mixed voices with soprano solo and piano accompaniment. (Thomson, Virgil). *Schirmer. Unpriced* DW (B76-50033)
Lear, W Hogarth.
Barney's tune : for brass band. *Chester Music. Unpriced* WMJ (B76-51063)
Chinese take away : for cornet trio and brass band. *Chester Music. Unpriced* WMPWRNT (B76-51075)
Hogarth's hoe-down : for brass band. *Chester Music. Unpriced* WMH (B76-51058)
Paris le soir : for brass band. *Chester Music. Unpriced* WMJ (B76-51064)
Red sky at night : for brass band. *Chester Music. Unpriced* WMJ (B76-51065)
Learning with traditional rhymes.
Action rhymes. *Ladybird Books. £0.24* ADW/GR (B76-30340) ISBN 0-7214-0439-1
Dancing rhymes. *Ladybird Books. £0.24* ADW/H (B76-30341) ISBN 0-7214-0440-5
Lebermann, Walter.
Concerto, viola & string orchestra, E flat major. *arr.* Konzert Es-dur für Viola und Streicher = Concerto E flat major for viola and strings. (Graun, Johann Gottlieb). 1st ed. *Simrock. £4.00* SQPK/LF (B76-50638)
Partitas, flute, nos.1-6. Sechs Partiten für Flöte. (Tromlitz, Johann George). Zum ersten Mal herausgegeben von Walter Lebermann. *Litolff : Peters. Unpriced* VRPMG (B76-50682)
Symphony, D major. Sinfonie, D-Dur. (Bach, Johann Christian). *Schott. £4.00* MRE (B76-50881)
Leclair, Jean Marie, *b.1697.*
Première récréation de musique, Op.6 : for two violins and basso continuo. *Bärenreiter. £6.00* SNTPWG (B76-50629)
Sonata, violins (2) & continuo, op.13. no.1. Two trio sonatas for two violins and basso continuo. *Oxford University Press. Unpriced* NXNTE (B76-50887) ISBN 0-19-357612-0
Led Zeppelin. (Mylett, Howard). *Panther. £0.60* AKDW/HK/E(P) (B76-34781) ISBN 0-586-04390-x
Ledger, Philip. Three carols for Christmas. *Oxford University Press. Unpriced* EZDP/LF/AY (B76-50425) ISBN 0-19-353246-8
Lee, Carolyn. Linoi : clarinet in A and piano. *Antico. Unpriced* EZDU/AYK (B76-50813)
Lee, Ed. Pop music in school. *Cambridge University Press. £4.75* A/GB(VK) (B76-25953) ISBN 0-521-20836-x
Lees, Benjamin. The trumpet of the swan : for narrator and orchestra. *Boosey and Hawkes. £1.25* KHYE/M (B76-50509)
Lees, Heath.
Breathe on me, breath of God : anthem for 3-part female voice choir unaccompanied. *Roberton. £0.10* FEZDH (B76-50089)
Iona boat song, (For a dead king) : traditional Island air. *Roberton. £0.10* FEZDW (B76-50090)
Two mediaeval carols : for 4-part chorus of mixed voices unaccompanied. *Roberton. Unpriced* EZDP/LF (B76-50059)
Legend : for violin and piano. (Brian, Havergal). *Musica Viva. £2.00* SPJ (B76-50633)
Legend of Robin Hood : for descant recorders, pitched percussion, voices and piano. (Odam, George). *Chester. Unpriced* CQN (B76-50771)
Lehane, Maureen.
Songs
Book 1. (Purcell, Henry). *Galliard : Stainer and Bell. Unpriced* KDW (B76-50480)
Book 2. (Purcell, Henry). *Galliard : Stainer and Bell. Unpriced* KDW (B76-50481) ISBN 0-85249-323-1
Book 3. (Purcell, Henry). *Galliard : Stainer and Bell. Unpriced* KDW (B76-50482) ISBN 0-85249-383-5
Lehár, Franz.
Frederica : operetta in three acts. (Dunn, Bernard). *10 Rathbone St., W1P 2BJ : Glocken Verlag Ltd. £1.00* BLDACF
Friederike. *Vocal score.* Frederica : operetta in three acts. *Glocken. Unpriced* CF (B76-50761)
Zigeunerliebe. *Selections : arr.* Songs from 'Gipsy love'. *Glocken. Unpriced* KDW (B76-50479)
Leichte Stücke, grosser Meister : elektronische Orgel. *Nagel : Bärenreiter. £1.50* RPVK/AAY (B76-50599)
Leonard, Stanley. Vier Scherzduette, K. Anh. 284 dd. Spiegelkanon. *arr.* Mirror canon = Spiegelkanon. (Mozart Wolfgang Amadeus). *Simrock. Unpriced* XPQNSK/AX (B76-51088)
Leonard, Gould and Bolttler's library of unison and part-songs for schools. Longmire, John. Norse cradle song : unison. *Leonard, Gould and Bolttler. £0.09* JFDW (B76-50464)
Let the whole Creation cry : for soprano solo and four-part chorus of mixed voices with organ. (Hanson, Geoffrey). *Roberton. £0.18* DH (B76-50016)
Lethbridge, Lionel.
Les Indes galantes. *Selections : arr.* Four oboe melodies. (Rameau, Jean Philippe). *Oxford University Press. Unpriced* VTPK (B76-50311) ISBN 0-19-358461-1
Six French carols
Set 1. *Banks. Unpriced* FEZDP/LF/AYH (B76-50447)
Set 2. *Banks. Unpriced* FEZDP/LF/AYH (B76-50448)
Levertov, Denise. In praise of Krishna : songs from the Bengali for soprano and nine instruments. (Blake, David). *Novello. £2.00* KFLE/NVNMDW (B76-50863)
Lewis, Huw. Bohemian bell carol : traditional. (Brown, Gerald Edgar). *Universal. Unpriced* JFE/NYLDP/LF (B76-50835)
Liber primus sacrarum cantionum. O quam gloriosum. O quam gloriosum : S.S.A.T.B. (Byrd, William). Revised ed. *Oxford University Press. Unpriced* EZDJ (B76-50417) ISBN 0-19-352060-5
Library Association. *Public Libraries Group.* Introduction to music. *c/o A.L. Bamber, Divisional Library, Timber St., Chippenham, Wilts. : The Group. £0.40* A(T) (B76-19568) ISBN 0-85365-168-x
Library of communication techniques. Manvell, Roger. The technique of film music. Revised and enlarged ed. *Focal Press. £5.00* A/JR (B76-12128) ISBN 0-240-50848-3
Library of unison and part-songs for schools.
Verrall, Pamela Motley. The organ-grinder's carol. (When Jesus Christ was born) : unison. *Leonard, Gould and Bolttler. Unpriced* JFDP/LF (B76-50107)
Verrall, Pamela Motley. Peter Piper's carol : calypso style unison. *Leonard, Gould and Bolttler. Unpriced* JFDP/LF (B76-50108)
Liddell, Claire.
Fine flowers in the valley : Scottish folk ballad. *Roberton. £0.14* EZDW (B76-50071)
Five Orkney scenes : a song cycle for female voice and piano. *Roberton. Unpriced* KFDW (B76-50131)
Ae fond kiss : old Highland melody. *Roberton. £0.14* EZDW (B76-50070)
I'll ay ca' in by yon toon : old Scottish air. *Roberton. £0.10* GEZDW (B76-50096)
Where are the joys? : traditional Scottish air. *Roberton. £0.14* EZDW (B76-50072)
Ye banks and braes. *Roberton. £0.10* EZDW (B76-50073)
Liebestraum no.3, G.298. (Liszt, Franz). *Chappell. Unpriced* QPJ (B76-50573)
Life of Richard Wagner. (Newman, Ernest). *Cambridge University Press. £17.50* BWC(N) (B76-33368) ISBN 0-521-29149-6
Lift up your heads, Opus 44, no.2 : SATB. (Jackson, Francis). *Oxford University Press. Unpriced* DH (B76-50385) ISBN 0-19-350360-3
Ligeti, György.

Quartet, strings, no.2. String quartet no.2. *Schott.* *£4.50* RXNS (B76-50618)
Requiem. *Vocal score.* Requiem für Sopran, Mezzosopran, zwei gemischte Chöre und Orchester. *Litolff : Peters. Unpriced* DGKAV (B76-50011)
Light invisible. (Wills, Arthur). *Weinberger. Unpriced* DH (B76-50784)
Like as the hart : soprano solo and mixed chorus. (Roe, Betty). *Thames. Unpriced* EZDK (B76-50419)
Limites : für einen Geiger oder Bratschisten. (Globokar, Vinko). *Litolff : Peters. Unpriced* SPMJ (B76-50252)
Lines, Marian. The barnstormers. *Selections.* The barnstormers. (Roe, Betty). *Thames. Unpriced* JDW/JM (B76-50457)
Linoi : clarinet in A and piano. *Antico. Unpriced* EZDU/AYK (B76-50813)
Linoi : clarinet in A and piano. (Birtwistle, Harrison). *Universal. Unpriced* VVQPJ (B76-50712)
Lionel Monckton memories. (Monckton, Lionel). *Studio Music. Unpriced* WMK/DW (B76-51073)
Listen! music and nature. (Brace, Geoffrey). *Cambridge University Press. £1.60* A/KB (B76-13569) ISBN 0-521-20706-1
Liszt, Franz.
Christus : oratorio for soli, chorus, organ and orchestra. *Eulenburg. Unpriced* EMDD (B76-50038)
Liebestraum no.3, G.298. *Chappell. Unpriced* QPJ (B76-50573)
Piano music. Klavierwerke = Piano works
Vol.8: Années de pélerinage 3. *Bärenreiter. £3.00* QP/AZ (B76-50561)
Psalm 13. Der 13 Psalm : für Tenor, gemischten Chor und Orchester. *Litolff : Peters. Unpriced* EMDR (B76-50406)
Psalm 13. *Vocal score.* Der 13. Psalm : für Tenor, gemischten Chor und Orchester. *Litolff : Peters. Unpriced* DR (B76-50794)
Salve regina : for 4-part chorus of mixed voices unaccompanied. *Roberton. £0.14* EZDH (B76-50416)
Selections. *arr.* Liszt. *Warren and Phillips. Unpriced* QPK (B76-50582)
Symphonic poem, no.2. Tasso, lamento e trionfo. Tasso, lamento e trionfo. *Eulenburg. Unpriced* MMJ (B76-50874)
Symphonic poem no.4. Orpheus. *Eulenburg. Unpriced* MMJ (B76-50525)
Symphonic poem no.5. Prometheus. Prometheus. *Eulenburg. Unpriced* MMJ (B76-50526)
Symphonic poem no.7. Festklange. *Eulenburg. Unpriced* MMJ (B76-50527)
Symphonic poem no.8 Héroïde funèbre. Héroïde funèbre. *Eulenburg. Unpriced* MMJ (B76-50875)
Symphonic poem, no.9. Hungaria. Hungaria. Revised ed. *Eulenburg. Unpriced* MMJ (B76-50150)
Symphonic poem, no.10. Hamlet. Hamlet. *Eulenburg. Unpriced* MMJ (B76-50876)
Symphonic poem, no.12. Die Ideale. Die Ideale. Revised ed. *Eulenburg. Unpriced* MMJ (B76-50151)
Symphonic poem, no.13, 'Von der Wiege bis zum Grabe'. Von der Wiege bis zum Grabe = From the cradle to the grave : symphonic poem, no.13. *Eulenburg. Unpriced* MMJ (B76-50152)
Thirty songs : for high voice. *Dover Publications : Constable. £2.60* KFTDW (B76-50498)
Two episodes from Lenau's Faust. Procession by night, and, Mephisto waltz. *Eulenburg. Unpriced* MMJ (B76-50528)
Vier kleine Klavierstücke, nos. 3, 4. *arr.* Two Browning choruses : S.A.T.B. unaccompanied. *Boosey and Hawkes. Unpriced* EZDW (B76-50436)
Litanie et motetti. Ave verum corpus. Ave verum corpus : S.A.T.T.B. and organ. (Milani, Francesco). *Oxford University Press. Unpriced* DJ (B76-50022) ISBN 0-19-350357-3
Little piano book : a new way to start. (Phillips, Lois). *Forsyth. Unpriced* Q/AC (B76-50180)
Little piano pieces. Op.20. (Gilbert, Anthony). *Schott. Unpriced* QPJ (B76-50204)
Little prayers. *Vocal score.* Little prayers : for soprano and baritone solos, mixed chorus, and orchestra. (Rorem, Ned). *Boosey and Hawkes. £6.00* DE (B76-50776)
Little suite for strings, Op.26. (Platts, Kenneth). *Edwin Ashdown. £1.00* RXMG (B76-50950)
Livings, Henry. That the medals and the baton be put on view : the story of a village band, 1875-1975. *David and Charles. £3.95* AWM/E(YDJED/X) (B76-00675) ISBN 0-7153-7071-5
Locke, Matthew.
Consort of four parts. *Eulenburg. Unpriced* STNSG (B76-50964)
The flat consort for my Cousin Kemble. *Eulenburg. Unpriced* STNTG (B76-50965)
Musica Britannica : a national collection of music
Vol.38: Matthew Locke : anthems and motets. *Stainer and Bell. Unpriced* C/AYD (B76-50360) ISBN 0-85249-397-5
Loeillet, Jean Baptiste, *of London.* Sonata, treble recorder, oboe & continuo, op.4, no.2. Sonata a tre con fluto e hautboy : for treble recorder, oboe (or treble II) and continuo. *Universal. Unpriced* NWNTE (B76-50885)
Lombardi, Nilson.
Cantilena no.2 : piano. *Arthur Napoleão : Essex Music. Unpriced* QPJ (B76-50907)
Cantilena no.3 : piano. *Arthur Napoleão : Essex Music. Unpriced* QPJ (B76-50908)
Homenagem a Ravel : piano. *Arthur Napoleão : Essex Music. Unpriced* QPJ (B76-50909)
Sex miniaturas : piano. *Arthur Napoleão : Essex Music. Unpriced* QPJ (B76-50910)
Lombardo, Adele. Drakestail : a symphonic fairy tale for children. (Lombardo, Mario). *Chappell. Unpriced* MMJ (B76-50529)
Lombardo, Maria. Hungry for hope. *arr.* Hungry for hope. *Chappell. Unpriced* DW (B76-50030)
Lombardo, Mario. Drakestail : a symphonic fairy tale for children. *Chappell. Unpriced* MMJ (B76-50529)
London, Edwin. Quintet, brass instruments. Brass quintet : 2 trumpets in C, horn in F, trombone, tuba. *Henmar Press : Peters : Peters. Unpriced* WNR (B76-50333)
London. *Greater London Council. See* Greater London Council.
London. *Inner London Education Authority. See* Inner London Education Authority.
London College of Music.
Examinations in pianoforte playing and singing sight reading tests : sight singing tests as set throughout 1975. *Ashdown. Unpriced* Q/EG/AL (B76-50182)
Examinations in pianoforte playing
Grade 1 (primary), Book II. *Ashdown. £0.50* Q/AL (B76-50556)
Grade 2, Book 9. *Edwin Ashdown. Unpriced* Q/AL (B76-50893)
Introductory examinations in pianoforte playing in three steps
Step 2, Book 5. *Ashdown. £0.30* Q/AL (B76-50557)
London in 1826. *See* Hobhouse, Hermione.
London University. *See* University of London.
Londonderry air : traditional. (Burt, James). *Chappell. Unpriced* QPK (B76-50919)
Longmire, John. Norse cradle song : unison. *Leonard, Gould and Bolttler. £0.09* JFDW (B76-50464)
Lorca, Federico García. *See* García Lorca, Federico.
Lord has been gracious unto us = Gott hat uns angenehm gemacht. (Antes, John). *Boosey and Hawkes. £0.40* DH (B76-50379)
Lord in my shepherd, Op.91, no.1. (Berkeley, *Sir* Lennox). *Chester. Unpriced* DR (B76-50401)
Lord make me an instrument of thy peace. Op.84 : S. solo, S.S.A.A.T.T.B.B. (Joubert, John). *Oxford University Press. Unpriced* DH (B76-50386) ISBN 0-19-350359-x
Lord's Prayer plus two hymn tunes for choir or organ solo. (Edwards, D W). *67 Lang Lane, West Kirby, Wirral, Merseyside : D.W. Edwards. Unpriced* DM (B76-50391)

Lorenzo Fernandez, Oscar. Recordações da infância. Na beira do rio. Na beira do rio. *Arthur Napoleão : Essex Music. Unpriced* QPJ (B76-50911)
Lot is fallen unto me : anthem for SATB with divisions and organ. (Phillips, John Charles). *Novello. £0.20* DK (B76-50023)
Louis : the Louis Armstrong story, 1900-1971. (Jones, Max). *Mayflower. £0.95* AMT(P) (B76-01204) ISBN 0-583-12710-x
Love in May : for 4-part female voice choir unaccompanied. (Lyell, Margaret). *Roberton. Unpriced* FEZDW (B76-50820)
Love of three oranges. March. *arr.* March. (Prokofiev, Sergei). *Boosey and Hawkes. £5.00* WMK/AGM (B76-50733)
Lowe, Augustus.
Praise ye the Lord. *Paterson. Unpriced* KDR (B76-50116)

Romance, violin & orchestra, no.1, op.40, G major. *arr.* Beneficence. (Beethoven, Ludwig van). *Fischer; Pinns Farm, West Wellow, Romsey : Edgar New gass. Unpriced* KDW (B76-50118)
Lucas, Hippolyte. Berceuse. *arr.* You will see an angel tonight. (Ropartz, Joseph Guy). *Galaxy : Galliard. Unpriced* DP/LF (B76-50397)
Luening, Otto.
Evangeline. *Vocal score.* Evangeline : opera in 3 acts. *Peters. Unpriced* CC (B76-50760)
Quartet, strings, no.2. String quartet no.2. *Peters. Unpriced* RXNS (B76-50956)
Lullaby. (Scott, Anthony). *Boosey and Hawkes. £0.45* KDW (B76-50485)
Lumsdaine, David.
Easter fresco : for piano, flute, horn, harp and piano. *Universal. Unpriced* KFLE/NUNSDE (B76-50132)
Flights : for 2 pianos. *Universal. Unpriced* QNU (B76-50183)
Kangaroo hunt : for piano and percussion. *Universal. Unpriced* NYLNU (B76-50178)
Lustige Lieder : für akkordprogrammierte Orgel 1 Manue bearbeitet von Willi Draths. *Schott. £1.75* RPVK/DW/AY (B76-50232)
Lute book lullaby : for soprano solo and four-part chorus of mixed voices unaccompanied. (Hanson, Geoffrey). *Roberton. £0.10* EZDP/LF (B76-50058)
Lwowskie piosenki
Część 5: Zbrodnia i Kara ; oraz uzupelnienia poprzednio wydanych cześci. *Kolo Lwowian. £0.75* ADW/G(YMUL) (B76-05915) ISBN 0-9503005-3-5
Lyell, Margaret. Love in May : for 4-part female voice choir unaccompanied. *Roberton. Unpriced* FEZDW (B76-50820)
Lynn, *Dame* Vera. Vocal refrain : an autobiography. *W.H. Allen. £3.00* AKDW/GB/E(P) (B76-00673) ISBN 0-491-01795-2
Lyric fantasias : for viola solo and string orchestra (or string quintet). (Dello Joio, Norman). *Associated Music. Unpriced* RXMPSQ (B76-50238)
Má vlast : a cycle of symphonic poems
No.3: Sarka. (Smetana, Bedřich). *Eulenburg. Unpriced* MMJ (B76-50877)
McCabe, John.
Concertante variations on a theme of Nicholas Maw : for string orchestra. *Novello. £2.25* RXMF/T (B76-50235)
Couples : theme music from the Thames Television series, for piano solo. *Novello. Unpriced* QP/JS (B76-50190)
Maze dances : for violin solo (1973). *Novello. Unpriced* SPH (B76-50958)
Quartet, strings, no.2. String quartet no.2. *Novello. £1.50* RXNS (B76-50240)
McCaldin, Denis. Te Deum. (Berlioz, Hector). *Eulenburg. Unpriced* EMDGKHB (B76-50798)
McCartney, Paul. Paul McCartney in his own words. (Gambaccini, Paul). *78 Newman St., W1P 3LA : Omnibus Press. £1.95* AKDW/GB/E(P) (B76-25962) ISBN 0-8256-3063-0
MacCunn, Hamish. The land of the mountain and the flood. Op.3. *arr.* The land of the mountain and the flood : concert overture, Opus 3. *Paxton. £2.00* WMK (B76-51070)
MacDomnic, Godfrey. Conversations with conductors : Bruno Walter, Sir Adrian Boult, Leonard Bernstein, Ernest Ansermet, Otto Klemperer, Leopold Stokowski. *Robson Books. £4.50* A/EC(M) (B76-33375) ISBN 0-903895-44-7
MacDonald, Hugh. Symphonie funèbre et triomphale. Op.15. Grande symphonie funèbre et triomphale. Op.15. (Berlioz, Hector). *Eulenburg. Unpriced* EUMMDE (B76-50047)
MacDonald, Malcolm, *b.1948.* Schoenberg. *Dent. £4.25* BSET (B76-31120) ISBN 0-460-03143-0
McGinley, Sarah. Music in developmental therapy : a curriculum guide. *University Park Press. £6.25* A(VMWM) (B76-30972) ISBN 0-8391-0895-8
Mack & Mabel : a musical love story. (Stewart, Michael). *French. £1.35* BHKMACM (B76-19250) ISBN 0-573-68074-4
McKee, David. Okki-tokki-unga : action songs for children. *A. and C. Black. £2.75* JFDW/GR (B76-50832) ISBN 0-7136-1685-7
McLaughlin, John. John McLaughlin and the Mahavishnu Orchestra. *Warner-Tamerlane : Blossom. Unpriced* NYG (B76-50888)
Macmillan, Keith, *b.1920.* Contemporary Canadian composers. *Oxford University Press. £11.75* A/D(YSX/XN55/M) (B76-25955) ISBN 0-19-540244-8
Macmillan jazz masters series.
Gitler, Ira. Jazz masters of the Forties. *Collier Books : Collier Macmillan. £1.80* AMT(M/XP10) (B76-12131) ISBN 0-02-060610-9
Hadlock, Richard. Jazz masters of the Twenties. *Collier Books : Collier Macmillan. £1.80* AMT(M/XN10) (B76-12130) ISBN 0-02-060770-9
McNicol, Richard.
Music for wind quintet, 2 flutes, oboe, clarinet, bassoon (or cello)
Volume 1: Six promenades (1878). (Elgar, *Sir* Edward, *bart*). First ed. *Belwin Mills. Unpriced* UNR/AZ (B76-50671)
Volume 2: Harmony music 1 and 2. (Elgar, *Sir* Edward, *bart*). First ed. *Belwin Mills. Unpriced* UNR/AZ (B76-50672)
Volume 3: Harmony music 3 and 4. (Elgar, *Sir* Edward, *bart*). First ed. *Belwin Mills. Unpriced* UNR/AZ (B76-50673)
Maconchy, Elizabeth. Two epitaphs : S.S.A. *Chester. Unpriced* FEZDW (B76-50821)
Maconie, Robin. Stockhausen. *See* Maconie, Robin. Works of Karlheinz Stockhausen.
Maconie, Robin. The works of Karlheinz Stockhausen. *Oxford University Press. £17.50* BSNK (B76-20708) ISBN 0-19-315429-3
MacSweeney, Alix. Children's pieces : for piano. (Satie, Erik). *Novello. £0.60* QPJ (B76-50210)
Madden, John. The babe of Bethlehem : SATB. *Oxford University Press. Unpriced* DP/LF (B76-50396) ISBN 0-19-343060-6
Magic of music. (Baker, Richard, *b.1925*). *Sphere. £0.95* A(X) (B76-29099) ISBN 0-7221-1421-4
Magic of opera. (Knapp, John Merrill). *Hale. £6.50* AC (B76-00668) ISBN 0-7091-5254-x
Magic piano silhouettes.
Beethoven, Ludwig van. Symphony, no.9, op.125, D major, 'Choral'. Freude, schöner Gotterfunken. *arr.* Ode to joy : from 'Choral symphony'. *Chappell. Unpriced* QPK (B76-50579)
Dvořák, Antonín. Symphony, no.9, op.95, E minor, 'From the new world'. Largo. *arr.* Largo. *Chappell. Unpriced* QPK (B76-50580)
Liszt, Franz. Liebestraum no.3, G.298. *Chappell. Unpriced* QPJ (B76-50573)
Mozart, Wolfgang Amadeus. Symphony no.40, K.550, G minor. First movement : arr. Mozart 40. *Chappell. Unpriced* QPK (B76-50584)
Magor, Cliff. The song of a merryman : Ivan Menzies of the D'Oyly Carte Gilbert & Sullivan operas. *Grosvenor Books. £1.00* AKDW/E(P) (B76-19249) ISBN 0-901269-18-2
Magor, Edna. The song of a merryman : Ivan Menzies of the D'Oyly Carte Gilbert & Sullivan operas. (Magor, Cliff). *Grosvenor Books. £1.00* AKDW/E(P) (B76-19249) ISBN 0-901269-18-2
Maguire, John, *b.1902.* Come day, go day, God send Sunday : the songs and life story told in his own words, of John Maguire, traditional singer and farmer from Co. Fermanagh. *Routledge and Kegan Paul. £1.50* AKDW/G/E(YDTF/P) (B76-21366) ISBN 0-7100-8388-2
Mahalia. (Goreau, Laurraine). *Lion Publishing : Aslan. £1.95* AKDW/HJ/L/E(P) (B76-36285) ISBN 0-85648-061-4
Mahler, Gustav.

Mahler. *Warren and Phillips. Unpriced* QPK (B76-50583)

Symphony no.10. A performing version of the draft for the tenth symphony. *Associated Music : Faber Music. Unpriced* MME (B76-50521)

Mahler, Gustav. Symphony no.10. Sonata, viola & piano, 'Homage to Mahler'. Sonata (Homage to Mahler) : for viola and piano. (Tircuit, Heuwell). *Associated Music. Unpriced* SQPE (B76-50255)

Mainardi, Enrico. Einundzwanzig Studien zur Technik des Violoncellospiels. *Schott. £2.80* SR/AF (B76-50961)

Mairants, Ivor.
La Cathedral = The Cathedral : guitar solo. (Barrios, Augustin). *British and Continental Music. Unpriced* TSPMJ (B76-50657)
Finger style guitar in theory and practice
Book 1. *British and Continental : EMI. Unpriced* TS/AC (B76-50971)
Book 1: Basic principles, major and minor scales, chord diagrams and fingerboard chart. *British and Continental : EMI. Unpriced* TS/AF (B76-50977)
Book 2: Instruction for beginners, classical repertoire. *British and Continental : EMI. Unpriced* TS/AF (B76-50978)

Make a joyful noise unto the Lord. Psalm 100 : for 4-part male voice choir with organ or piano or unaccompanied voices. (Head, Michael). *Roberton. £0.18* GDR (B76-50093)

Make a new sound. (Self, George). *Universal Edition. £3.90* AL/E(VF) (B76-13570) ISBN 0-900938-46-3

Make we joye : four carols set to anonymous 15th century texts, for S.A.T.B. (Aston, Peter). *Chappell. Unpriced* EZDP/LF (B76-50807)

Maker and lover of beauty : Ivor Gurney, poet and songwriter. (Moore, Charles Willard). *22 Pheasants Way, Rickmansworth, Herts. : Triad Press. £2.65* BGYU(N) (B76-50358) ISBN 0-902070-16-9

Makin, Denis. Music in Belper (1824-1975). *1 Derwent Ave., Milford, Derby DE5 1RB : The author. £0.60* A(YDHW/XSD152) (B76-50350) ISBN 0-9504990-0-5

Making a simple violin and viola. (Roberts, Ronald). *David and Charles. £4.50* AS/BC (B76-09330) ISBN 0-7153-6964-4

Making early percussion instruments. (Montagu, Jeremy). *Oxford University Press. £2.95* AX/BC (B76-14372) ISBN 0-19-323177-8

Making musical sounds. (Southworth, Mary). *Studio Vist etc.. £0.45* AX/BC (B76-50356) ISBN 0-289-70711-0

Mamlok, Ursula. Five capriccios : oboe and piano. *Peters. Unpriced* VTPJ (B76-50309)

Man in black. (Cash, Johnny). *Hodder and Stoughton. £3.75* AKDW/GCW/E(P) (B76-22082) ISBN 0-340-20627-6

Mancini, Maurice B. Sea of tranquillity : for pianoforte solo. *Anthony Music. Unpriced* QPJ (B76-50912)

Mandnell, John. Quartet, strings (1970). String quartet (1970). *Novello. £1.50* RXNS (B76-50241)

Mandyczewski, Eusebius. Complete piano works for four hands. (Brahms, Johannes). *Dover Publications : Constable. £3.50* QNV/AZ (B76-50894) ISBN 0-486-23271-9

Mannheim 87, 87, 87 : for unison chorus and organ. (Wuorinnen, Charles). *Peters. Unpriced* JDM (B76-50825)

Manvell, Roger. The technique of film music. Revised and enlarged ed. *Focal Press. £5.00* A/JR (B76-12128) ISBN 0-240-50848-3

Mar, Norman del. *See* Del Mar, Norman.

March, Ivan. The Penguin stereo record guide. (Greenfield, Edward). *Penguin. £3.50* A/FF(WT) (B76-03703) ISBN 0-14-046223-6

March-opus '76. (Washburn, Robert). *Boosey and Hawkes. £12.00* UMMGM (B76-50999)

Marco, Tomás. Floreal : música celestial 2, for percussion solo. *Simrock. £1.45* XPMJ (B76-50345)

Mare nostrum : Entdeckung, Gefriedung und Konversion des Mittelmeerraumes durch einen Stamm aus Amazonien, für Contratenor, Bariton, Flöte, Oboe, Gitarre, Harfe, Violoncello und Schlagzeug. (Kagel, Mauricio). *Universal. Unpriced* JNEE/NYEPDX (B76-50113)

Marek, George Richard. Toscanini. *Vision Press. £7.80* A/EC(P) (B76-21367) ISBN 0-85478-463-2

Margaretten, Bill.
Hungry for hope. *arr.* Hungry for hope. (Lombardo, Maria). *Chappell. Unpriced* DW (B76-50030)
The spirit of America. *Chappell. Unpriced* KDW/AYT (B76-50850)

Mariassy, Istvan. Renaissance works for four instruments. *Boosey and Hawkes. £1.75* LNS/AY (B76-50515)

Marischka, E. Eine Nacht in Venedig. *Vocal score.* A night in Venice. (Korngold, Erich). *Weinberger. Unpriced* CF (B76-50364)

Marling, Yvonne Rodd-. *See* Rodd-Marling, Yvonne.

Marne, Denis de. *See* De Marne, Denis.

Marriage of Figaro
Vol.1. (Mozart, Wolfgang Amadeus). *Musica rara. Unpriced* UNNK/CC (B76-50667)
Vol.2. (Mozart, Wolfgang Amadeus). *Musica rara. Unpriced* UNNK/CC (B76-50669)

Marriott, Beryl. Tunes for the band : 70 folk dance melodies with chord symbols. *English Folk Dance and Song Society. Unpriced* LH/G/AYDL (B76-50866) ISBN 0-85418-114-8

Marriott, Roger. Tunes for the band : 70 folk dance melodies with chord symbols. *English Folk Dance and Song Society. Unpriced* LH/G/AYDL (B76-50866) ISBN 0-85418-114-8

Marshall, Madeleine. The singer's manual of English diction. *Shirmer Books : Collier Macmillan. £3.50* AB/ED (B76-23702) ISBN 0-02-871100-9

Marshall, Nicholas. An album for the horn : thirteen easy pieces for horn in F and piano. *Oxford University Press. Unpriced* WTPK/AAY (B76-50344) ISBN 0-19-357745-3

Martín, Juan.
The exciting sound of flamenco. *United Music. Unpriced* TSPMH (B76-50984)

Mary's dream. (Parfrey, Raymond). *Thames. Unpriced* EZDP/LF (B76-50424)

Maske of flowers. *5 Albert Grove, Leeds LS6 4DA : Boethius Press. £3.20* ACPF (B76-10977) ISBN 0-904263-02-9

Masks. Op.3 : for solo flute with glass chimes (ad lib.). (Knussen, Oliver). *Schirmer. Unpriced* VRPMJ (B76-50294)

Mason, Barbara Kirkby-. *See* Kirkby-Mason, Barbara.

Massaino, Tiburtio. Canzon trigesimaquinta : for four antiphonal brass choirs. *Schirmer. Unpriced* WN (B76-50329)

Massenet, Jules.
La Navarraise. Nocturne. *arr.* Nocturne. *Rubank : Novello. Unpriced* VRNSQK (B76-50675)
La Navarraise. Nocturne. *arr.* Nocturne. *Rubank : Novello. Unpriced* VVNSQK (B76-50699)

Massey, Roy. The organists and organs of Hereford Cathedral. (Shaw, Watkins). *Friends of Hereford Cathedral Publications Committee. £0.50* AR/B(YDHRHB/X) (B76-35357) ISBN 0-904642-01-1

Master musicians series.
Day, James. Vaughan Williams. Revised ed. *Dent. £3.75* BVD (B76-01202) ISBN 0-460-03162-7
Dean, Winton. Bizet. 3rd ed.. *Dent. £3.95* BBP (B76-12126) ISBN 0-460-03163-5
Kennedy, Michael, *b.1926.* Richard Strauss. *Dent. £3.95* BSU (B76-14362) ISBN 0-460-03148-1
MacDonald, Malcolm, *b.1948.* Schoenberg. *Dent. £4.25* BSET (B76-31120) ISBN 0-460-03143-0
Norris, Geoffrey, *b.1947.* Rachmaninov. *Dent. £3.50* BRC (B76-04297) ISBN 0-460-03145-7

Masters, Anthony.
The Jesus file. *Voice part.* The Jesus file : a musical nativity. (Hoskins, Graham). *Dobson. Unpriced* JDACN/LF (B76-50099) ISBN 0-234-77244-1
The wind on the heath. *Voice part.* The wind on the heath : children's musical play. (Walker, Chris). *Dobson. Unpriced* JDACN (B76-50098) ISBN 0-234-77245-x

Mathias, William.
Communion service, series 3 : for congregational use with optional S.A.T.B. choir. *Oxford University Press. Unpriced* JDGS (B76-50453) ISBN 0-19-351652-7
Elegy for a prince. Op.59. *Vocal score.* Elegy for a prince. Op.59 : for baritone and orchestra. *Oxford University Press. Unpriced* KGNDX (B76-50508) ISBN 0-19-365582-9
Quintet, wind instruments, op.22. Quintet for flute, oboe, clarinet, horn and bassoon. Op.22. *Oxford University Press. £0.18* UNR (B76-50287) ISBN 0-19-357768-2

Matthews, Colin. Sonata no.4, orchestra, 'Green and gold and blue and white'. Fourth sonata, 'Green and gold and blue and white' : for orchestra. *Novello. £3.00* MME (B76-50143)

Maves, David. Oktoechos : B flat clarinet, horn in F and percussion. *Henmar Press : Peters : Peters. Unpriced* NYHNT (B76-50177)

May, Randy. Gamut : equalizing single strokes, double strokes, and paradiddles around the drum set with simultaneous footwork. *Chappell. Unpriced* XQ/AF (B76-50754)

Mayes, Jerry. Joy waltz : instrumental ensemble. *Charnwood Music. Unpriced* LNHW (B76-50512)

Maynard, John. Good news : new Christian songs for churches and groups. *12 Portland Rd, S.E.25 : Vanguard Music. Unpriced* KDM/AY (B76-50115)

Maynard, Paul. An anthology of early renaissance music. *Dent. £9.95* C/AY(XCSK76) (B76-50001) ISBN 0-460-04300-5

Maynooth College. Léachtaí Cholm Cille VII : an ceol i litríocht la Gaeilge. *Maynooth, Co. Kildare : St Patrick's College. £0.50* A/G(YDM) (B76-34780) ISBN 0-901519-17-0

Maze dances : for violin solo (1973). (McCabe, John). *Novello. Unpriced* SPH (B76-50958)

Mazzolà, Caterino. La Clemenza di Tito : Opera seria in zwei Akten : Textbuch italiebisch-deutsch. (Metastasio, Pietro). *32 Great Titchfield St., W1P 7AD : Bärenreiter. £1.13* BMSAC

Medical and legal professions. *Garland. £400.00 the 28 vol. series* ACLM(XFWK61/ZC) (B76-19251) ISBN 0-8240-0903-7

Meech, Michael. Variations on a well-known theme : for recorder trio, descant, treble, tenor. *Tomus. £0.70* VSNT/T (B76-51034)

Mein Heimatland : Volkslieder für elektronische Orgel. *Schott. Unpriced* RPVK/DM/G/AYE (B76-50942)

Mein junges Leben hat ein End. Variations on 'Mein junges Leben hat ein End'. (Sweelinck, Jan Pieterzoon) *Schirmer. Unpriced* UMK/AT (B76-50283)

Meli, Op.17 : songs on Sappho's poems, for medium voice and orchestra. (Antoniou, Theodore). *Bärenreiter. £3.50* KFVE/MDW (B76-50501)

Mellers, Wilfrid. Twilight of the gods : the Beatles in retrospect. *Faber. £1.50* AKDW/GB/E(P) (B76-33370) ISBN 0-571-10998-5

Memorial music 1 : Man comes from dust = Ki K'shimcho, and, Memorial music 2 : Lord let me know my end, (Psalm 39, Isaiah 40) : for soprano voice with three flutes. (Wyner, Yehudi). *Associated Music. Unpriced* KFLE/VRNTDH (B76-50134)

Memorial music 1. Memorial music 1 : Man comes from dust = Ki K'shimcho, and, Memorial music 2 : Lord let me know my end, (Psalm 39, Isaiah 40) : for soprano voice with three flutes. (Wyner, Yehudi). *Associated Music. Unpriced* KFLE/VRNTDH (B76-50134)

Mendel, Arthur. St John passion. S.245. Johannes-Passion, BWV 245. (Bach, Johann Sebastian). *Bärenreiter. £6.50* EMDD/LK (B76-50405)

Mendelssohn, Felix.
O Haupt voll Blut und Wunden. *Vocal score.* O Haupt voll Blut und Wunden : für Bass, gemischten Chor und Orchester. Zum ersten Mal. *Litolff : Peters. Unpriced* DE (B76-50775)
Quintet, strings, no.1, op.18, A major. String quintet, no.1, A major. Op.18. *Eulenburg. Unpriced* RXNR (B76-50239)
Symphony no.3, op.56, A, 'Scottish'. Symphony no.3 (Scotch) A major, Op.56. *Eulenburg. Unpriced* MME (B76-50869)

Mendoza, Anne. Tops and tails again : eight children's songs with interchangeable accompaniments. *Oxford University Press. Unpriced* JFDW/GJ/AY (B76-50470) ISBN 0-19-330573-9

Menuhin, Yehudi. Violin and viola. *Macdonald and Jane's. £4.50* AS/E (B76-06892) ISBN 0-356-04715-6

Menuhin (Yehudi) music guides. *See* Yehudi Menuhin music guides.

Mercer, Johnny. The good companions. *Vocal score.* The good companions : the musical of the novel by J.B. Priestley. (Previn, André). *Chappell. Unpriced* CM (B76-50763)

Messiaen, Olivier. Conversations with Olivier Messiaen. (Samuel, Claude). *Stainer and Bell. Unpriced* BMKS (B76-18271) ISBN 0-85249-308-8

Metamorphic variations : for orchestra. (Bliss, *Sir* Arthur). *Novello. £3.75* MM/T (B76-50141)

Metaphysical fragments. Our murmers have their musick too. Our murmers have their musick too : for 4-part chorus of mixed voices unaccompanied. (Clark, Keith). *Roberton. £0.10* EZDW (B76-50428)

Metastasio, Pietro. La Clemenza di Tito : Opera seria in zwei Akten : Textbuch italiebisch-deutsch. *32 Great Titchfield St., W1P 7AD : Bärenreiter. £1.13* BMSAC

Method splicing
Part 1: Minor methods. (Chant, H). *19 Lonewood Way, Hadlow, Tonbridge, Kent : Press of John Hilton. £2.00* AXSR/E (B76-35807) ISBN 0-900465-06-9

Mexican trot. (Kenny, Terry A). *Studio Music. Unpriced* WMJ (B76-50727)

Mezö, Imre. Piano music. Klavierwerke = Piano works
Vol.8: Années de pélerinage 3. (Liszt, Franz). *Bärenreiter. £3.00* QP/AZ (B76-50561)

Michael, row the boat ashore : traditional. (Burt, James). *Chappell. Unpriced* KDW/LC (B76-50858)

Michel, Wilfried. Trakturen für Orgel (Tonband, Mikrophon, Kontaktmikrophone). *Bärenreiter. £7.00* RJ (B76-50594)

Mico, Richard. Fantasia no.5 upon ut, re, re, mi, fa, sol, la, (à 4), viol quartet. *Oxford University Press. Unpriced* STNS (B76-50263) ISBN 0-19-341224-1

Middleton, J E. Twas in the moon of wintertime. The Huron carol : old French folk melody. (Younger, John B). *Frederick Harris Music : Lengnick. £0.21* ENYFPNSDP/LF (B76-50799)

Middleton, James Roland. The Easter anthems : SATB and organ. *Banks. Unpriced* DGSKAD/LL (B76-50013)

Mignone, Francisco.
Caixinha de brinquedos. Dança campestre. Dança campestre. *Arthur Napoleão : Essex Music. Unpriced* QPH (B76-50899)
- e o piano canta, também página para un álbum. *Arthur Napoleão : Essex Music. Unpriced* QPJ (B76-50913)
Quatro pecas para 2 flautas doce em do (C) e fa (F). *Arthur Napoleão : Essex Music. Unpriced* VSNU (B76-51036)
Valsa brasileira no.3. *Arthur Napoleão : Essex Music. Unpriced* QPHW (B76-50900)

Mikro-Kontrapunkte Z : für Trompete. (Holzer, Gerhard). *Litolff : Peters. Unpriced* WSPMJ (B76-50748)

Milani, Francesco. Litanie et motetti. Ave verum corpus. Ave verum corpus : S.A.T.T.B. and organ. *Oxford University Press. Unpriced* DJ (B76-50022) ISBN 0-19-350357-3

Miles. The Rolling Stones file. (Jagger, Mick). *78 Newman St., WIP 3LA : Music Sales Ltd. £2.95* AKDW/GB/E(P) (B76-26570) ISBN 0-86001-245-x

Millay, Edna St Vincent. God's world : for unaccompanied mixed chorus, S.S.A.T.B. (Colville, Thomas). *Galaxy : Stainer and Bell. Unpriced* EZDH (B76-50803)

Mills, John.
Music from the student repertoire
Series 1: For first and second year students. *Musical New Services. Unpriced* TPMK/AAY (B76-50966)
Series 2: For first and second year students. *Musical New Services. Unpriced* TPMK/AAY (B76-50967)

Minchin, Leslie. Wiegenlied = Lullaby = Berceuse. Op.49, no.4. (Brahms, Johannes). *Lengnick. £0.30* KDW (B76-50119)

Miniature score. An die Nachgeborenen, Op.42 : Kantate für Mezzosopran, Bariton, gemischten Chor und Orchester. (Einem, Gottfried von). *Boosey and Hawkes. £8.50* EMDE (B76-50796)

Miniature scores:.
Bach, Carl Philipp Emanuel. Die Israeliten in der Wuste

= The Israelites in the wilderness : oratorio for soli, chorus and orchestra. *Eulenburg. Unpriced* EMDD (B76-50037)

Bach, Carl Philipp Emanuel. Magnificat for soli, chorus and orchestra. *Eulenburg. Unpriced* EMDGKK (B76-50040)

Bach, Johann Sebastian. Concerto, harpsichord & string orchestra, BWV 1052, F minor. Concerto, D minor, for harpsichord and string orchestra. BWV 1052. *Eulenburg. Unpriced* RXMPQRF (B76-50237)

Bach, Johann Sebastian. St John passion. S.245. Johannes-Passion, BWV 245. *Bärenreiter. £6.50* EMDD/LK (B76-50405)

Berkeley, *Sir* Lennox. Sinfonia concertante, oboe & chamber orchestra, op.84. Sinfonia concertante for oboe and chamber orchestra. Op.84. *Chester. Unpriced* MPVTE (B76-50880)

Berlioz, Hector. Le Carnival Romain : ouverture caractéristique à grande orchestre. Op.9. *Eulenburg. Unpriced* MMJ (B76-50146)

Berlioz, Hector. Symphonie funèbre et triomphale. Op.15. Grande symphonie funèbre et triomphale. Op.15. *Eulenburg. Unpriced* EUMMDE (B76-50047)

Berlioz, Hector. Te Deum. *Eulenburg. Unpriced* EMDGKHB (B76-50798)

Borodin, Aleksandr Porfirevich. Quartet, strings, no.1, A major. String quartet no.1, A major. *Eulenburg. Unpriced* RXNS (B76-50953)

Delius, Frederick. Concerto, piano, C minor. Piano concerto. *Boosey and Hawkes. Unpriced* MPQF (B76-50157)

Delius, Frederick. Fennimore und Gerda = Fennimore and Gerda. *Boosey and Hawkes. £6.50* CQC (B76-50007)

Dvořák, Antonín. Concerto, cello, op.104, B minor. Cello concerto, B minor. Op.104. *Eulenburg. Unpriced* MPSRF (B76-50535)

Dvořák, Antonín. Concerto, violin, op.53, A minor. Violin concerto, A minor. Op.53. *Eulenburg. Unpriced* MPSF (B76-50533)

Einem, Gottfried von. An die Nachgeborenen, Op.42 : Kantate für Mezzosopran, Bariton, gemischten Chor und Orchester. *Boosey and Hawkes. £8.50* EMDE (B76-50796)

Gilbert, Anthony. Quartet, strings, op.20a. String quartet, Op.20a. *Schott. Unpriced* RXNS (B76-50617)

Hamilton, Iain. Arias : for small orchestra. *Schott. Unpriced* MR/T (B76-50162)

Haydn, Joseph. Mass, no.7, G major, 'Sancti Nicolai'. Missa Sancti Nicolai. *Eulenburg. Unpriced* EMDG (B76-50039)

Holst, Gustav. Savitri, Op 25 : an episode from the Mahābharata. Revised ed. *Eulenburg. Unpriced* CQC (B76-50768)

Kubelík, Rafael. Symphony in one movement. Sinfonie in einem Satz für Orchester. *Litolff : Peters. Unpriced* MME (B76-50520)

Lees, Benjamin. The trumpet of the swan : for narrator and orchestra. *Boosey and Hawkes. £1.25* KHYE/M (B76-50509)

Liszt, Franz. Christus : oratorio for soli, chorus, organ and orchestra. *Eulenburg. Unpriced* EMDD (B76-50038)

Liszt, Franz. Symphonic poem, no.2. Tasso, lamento e trionfo. Tasso, lamento e trionfo. *Eulenburg. Unpriced* MMJ (B76-50874)

Liszt, Franz. Symphonic poem no.4. Orpheus. *Eulenburg. Unpriced* MMJ (B76-50525)

Liszt, Franz. Symphonic poem no.5. Prometheus. Prometheus. *Eulenburg. Unpriced* MMJ (B76-50526)

Liszt, Franz. Symphonic poem no.7. Festklange. *Eulenburg. Unpriced* MMJ (B76-50527)

Liszt, Franz. Symphonic poem no.8 Héroïde funèbre. Héroïde funèbre. *Eulenburg. Unpriced* MMJ (B76-50875)

Liszt, Franz. Symphonic poem, no.9. Hungaria. Hungaria. Revised ed. *Eulenburg. Unpriced* MMJ (B76-50150)

Liszt, Franz. Symphonic poem, no.10. Hamlet. Hamlet. *Eulenburg. Unpriced* MMJ (B76-50876)

Liszt, Franz. Symphonic poem, no.12. Die Ideale. Die Ideale. Revised ed. *Eulenburg. Unpriced* MMJ (B76-50151)

Liszt, Franz. Symphonic poem, no.13, 'Von der Wiege bis zum Grabe'. Von der Wiege bis zum Grabe = From the cradle to the grave : symphonic poem, no.13. *Eulenburg. Unpriced* MMJ (B76-50152)

Liszt, Franz. Two episodes from Lenau's Faust. Procession by night, and, Mephisto waltz. *Eulenburg. Unpriced* MMJ (B76-50528)

Locke, Matthew. Consort of four parts. *Eulenburg. Unpriced* STNSG (B76-50964)

Locke, Matthew. The flat consort for my Cousin Kemble. *Eulenburg. Unpriced* STNTG (B76-50965)

Mathias, William. Quintet, wind instruments, op.22. Quintet for flute, oboe, clarinet, horn and bassoon. Op.22. *Oxford University Press. £0.18* UNR (B76-50287)   ISBN 0-19-357768-2

Mendelssohn, Felix. Symphony no.3, op.56, A, 'Scottish'. Symphony no.3 (Scotch), A major, Op.56. *Eulenburg. Unpriced* MME (B76-50869)

Mozart, Wolfgang Amadeus. Adagio and fugue, string orchestra, K.546, C minor. Adagio and fugue for strings, C minor. K.546. Revised ed. *Eulenburg. Unpriced* RXM/Y (B76-50947)

Mozart, Wolfgang Amadeus. Concerto, piano, no.12, K.414, A major. Piano concerto, A major. K.414. Revised ed. *Eulenburg. Unpriced* MPQF (B76-50158)

Mozart, Wolfgang Amadeus. Concerto, piano, no.26, K.537, D major. Piano concerto D major, K.537. *Eulenburg. Unpriced* MPQF (B76-50878)

Mozart, Wolfgang Amadeus. Concerto, violin, no.3, K.216, G major. Concerto, G major, for violin and orchestra. K.216. *Eulenburg. Unpriced* MPSF (B76-50534)

Mozart, Wolfgang Amadeus. Symphony, no.34, K.338, C major. Symphony, C major. K.338 and Minuetto, C major. K.409. *Eulenburg. Unpriced* MME (B76-50144)

Purcell, Henry. Sonatas, string trio & continuo, no.7-12, Z.796-801. Sonatas of three parts, no.7-12. *Eulenburg. Unpriced* NXNSE (B76-50172)

Rossini, Gioacchino Antonio. Guillaume Tell. Overture. Overture to the opera 'Guillaume Tell'. *Eulenburg. Unpriced* MMJ (B76-50530)

Saint-Saëns, Camille. Concerto, cello, no.1, op.33, A minor. Concerto no.1, A minor for violoncello and orchestra. Op.33. *Eulenburg. Unpriced* MPSRF (B76-50160)

Schwarz-Schilling, Reinhard. Partita für Orchester. *Bärenreiter. £6.00* MMG (B76-50523)

Schwarz-Schilling, Reinhard. Quartet, strings, F minor. Introduction and fugue. arr. Introduktion und Fuge für Streichorchester. *Bärenreiter. £2.50* RXM/Y (B76-50605)

Schwarz-Schilling, Reinhard. Symphony, C major. Symphonie in C für Orchester. *Bärenreiter. £6.50* MME (B76-50522)

Smetana, Bedřich. My fatherland. Sárka. Má vlast : a cycle of symphonic poems No.3: Sarka. *Eulenburg. Unpriced* MMJ (B76-50877)

Mirror canon = Spiegelkanon. (Mozart, Wolfgang Amadeus). *Simrock. Unpriced* XPQNSK/AX (B76-51088)

Miscellanies. arr. Miscellanies : seven pieces for alto saxophone and wind orchestra. (Jacob, Gordon). *Emerson. £2.50* VUSPK (B76-51046)

Missa : Voces choristarum, series 3 : for treble voices with organ. (Rose, Bernard). *Roberton. £0.20* FLDGS (B76-50822)

Missa mundi : for organ. (Camilleri, Charles). *Fairfield Music. £2.50* RJ (B76-50231)

Missae totius anni, 1592. Mass 'O magnum mysterium'. Missa O magnum mysterium : for four voices. (Victoria, Tomás Luis de). *Chester. Unpriced* EZDG (B76-50411)

Missal. Responses. *English.* Sung responses at Mass : music and English translation of the Rite of Mass. (Roman Catholic Church. Liturgy and ritual). *Incorporated Catholic Truth Society. Unpriced* JDGK (B76-50101)

Mitchell, William J. Versuch über die wahre Art das Clavier zu spielen. *English.* Essay on the true art of playing keyboard instruments. (Bach, Carl Philipp Emanuel). *48 Great Marlborough St., W1V 2BN : Eulenburg Books. £3.00* APW/E (B76-15055)   ISBN 0-903873-14-1

Mizusawa, Hiroshi. G.A. Rossini's 'William Tell'. *F. Warne. £2.25* BRRACBN (B76-18578)   ISBN 0-7232-1833-1

Moirologhia for Jani Christou : for bariton sic and piano or bariton sic, piano and instruments. (Antoniou, Theodore). *Bärenreiter. £8.00* KGNDW (B76-50506)

Moisy, Heinz von. Sounds and fills : for drumset. *Simrock. £2.50* XQ/AF (B76-50347)

Moldon, David. A bibliography of Russian composers. *White Lion Publishers. £15.00* A/D(YM/M/T) (B76-28683)   ISBN 0-7284-0101-0

Molich, Theo. O Haupt voll Blut und Wunden. *Vocal score.* O Haupt voll Blut und Wunden : für Bass, gemischten Chor und Orchester. (Mendelssohn, Felix). Zum ersten Mal. *Litolff : Peters. Unpriced* DE (B76-50775)

Molter, Johann Melchior.
  Concerto, flute & string orchestra, G major. H.S.315. Concerto in G major for flute, strings and basso continuo, H.S.315. *Musica rara. Unpriced* RXMPVRF (B76-50612)
  Concerto, flute & string orchestra, G major. H.S.315. Concerto in G major for flute, strings and basso continuo, H.S.315. *Musica rara. Unpriced* VRPK/LF (B76-50681)

Momenti : for piano solo. (Laderman, Ezra). *Oxford University Press. Unpriced* QPJ (B76-50209)

Monckton, Lionel. Lionel Monckton memories. *Studio Music. Unpriced* WMK/DW (B76-51073)

Monologue : for solo violin. (Stoker, Richard). *Ashdown. £0.30* SPMJ (B76-50253)

Monroe, Robert. Most popular finest piano solos : selected from the greatest composers of all time. *Century Music Phoenix. Unpriced* QPK/AAY (B76-50217)

Montagu, Jeremy.
  Early percussion instruments : from the Middle Ages to the Baroque. (Blades, James). *Oxford University Press. £2.95* AX/B(XCG551) (B76-14371)   ISBN 0-19-323176-x
  Making early percussion instruments. *Oxford University Press. £2.95* AX/BC (B76-14372)   ISBN 0-19-323177-8

Monte Carlo opera, 1879-1909. (Walsh, T J.) *Gill and Macmillan : Macmillan. £9.75* AC/E(YHXM/QB/XKU31) (B76-05913)   ISBN 0-7171-0725-6

Moods 1 : for unaccompanied solo oboe. (Overton, David). *Paterson. Unpriced* VTPMJ (B76-50315)

Moog, Helmut. The musical experience of the pre-school child. *48 Great Marlborough St., W1V 2BN : Schott Music. £2.00* A(VCC) (B76-35594)   ISBN 0-901938-06-8

Moore, Charles Willard. Maker and lover of beauty : Ivor Gurney, poet and songwriter. *22 Pheasants Way, Rickmansworth, Herts. : Triad Press. £2.65* BGYU(N) (B76-50358)   ISBN 0-902070-16-9

Moore, Jack.
  An album of popular tunes for the pianOrgan and 40 and 60 bass chord organs. *EMI. Unpriced* RPVK/DW/AY (B76-50941)
  Happy Christmas for chord organ. *EMI. Unpriced* RPVK/DP/LF/AY (B76-50939)
  Happy Christmas for guitar. *EMI. Unpriced* TSPMK/DP/LF/AY (B76-50994)

Moore, Jerrold Northrop. A voice in time : the gramophone of Fred Gaisberg, 1873-1951. *Hamilton. £5.50* A/FD(P) (B76-13200)   ISBN 0-241-89374-7

Moramus edition.
  Antes, John. Die mit Thränen saën. *Vocal score.* Who with weeping soweth = Die mit Thränen saën. *Boosey and Hawkes. £0.30* DH (B76-50377)
  Antes, John. Gelobet sey der Herr. *Vocal score.* All praises be to the Lord = Gelobet sey der Herr. *Boosey and Hawkes. £0.30* DH (B76-50378)
  Antes, John. Gott hat uns angenehm gemacht. *Vocal score.* The Lord has been gracious unto us = Gott hat uns angenehm gemacht. *Boosey and Hawkes. £0.40* DH (B76-50379)
  Antes, John. My heart shall rejoice in His salvation. *Vocal score.* My heart shall rejoice in His salvation. *Boosey and Hawkes. £0.40* DH (B76-50380)
  Antes, John. Sing and rejoice, O daugher of Zion. *Vocal score.* Sing and rejoice, O daughter of Zion. *Boosey and Hawkes. £0.40* DH (B76-50381)
  Antes, John. Unser Seele wartet auf den Herrn. *Vocal score.* Our soul doth wait upon the Lord = Unser Seele wartet auf den Herrn. *Boosey and Hawkes. £0.30* DH (B76-50382)

Morçeaux choisis à l'usage des mains petites de la deuxième année de piano (assez facile) à la moyenne difficulté. (Schumann, Robert). *Chappell. Unpriced* QPJ (B76-50215)

More essays from the world of music : essays from the 'Sunday Times'. (Newman, Ernest). *J. Calder. £7.50* A(D) (B76-34777)   ISBN 0-7145-3549-4

More hidden melodies : six improvisations for piano. (Cooper, Joseph). *Novello. £1.00* QPJ (B76-50570)

Morehen, John. Collected madrigals. (Nicolson, Richard). *Stainer and Bell. Unpriced* EZDU/AZ (B76-50064)   ISBN 0-85249-382-7

Moreman, Philip. Easy favourites : classical guitar. *Chappell. Unpriced* TSPMK/AAY (B76-50660)

Morgan, Hilda. Cantiones sacrae. Hodie Christus natus est. arr. Hodie Christus natus est. (Sweelinck, Jan Pieterzoon). *Roberton. £0.15* FEZDJ/LF (B76-50819)

Morgenstern, Dag. The jazz book. (Berendt, Joachim). *Paladin. £1.50* AMT (B76-33376)   ISBN 0-586-08260-3

Morpheus : wind symphony orchestra. (Sapieyevski, Jerzy). *Peters. Unpriced* UMMJ (B76-51001)

Morris, Christopher. Anthems for choirs Vol.4: Twenty-six anthems for mixed voices by twentieth-century composers. *Oxford University Press. Unpriced* DK/AY (B76-50025)   ISBN 0-19-353016-3

Morris, Max. La Fille du tambour major. *Vocal score.* The drum-major's daughter : comic opera in three acts. (Offenbach, Jacques). *Choudens : United Music. Unpriced* CF (B76-50762)

Morris, Miriam. The key approach to cello playing. *Chappell. Unpriced* SR/AC (B76-50639)

Morris, Reginald Owen.
  Figured harmony at the keyboard
  Part 1. *Oxford University Press. £0.75* QP/R (B76-50896)   ISBN 0-19-321471-7
  Part 2. *Oxford University Press. Unpriced* QP/R (B76-50897)   ISBN 0-19-321472-5

Morton, David. The traditional music of Thailand. *University of California Press. £11.55* BZGH (B76-31121)   ISBN 0-520-01876-1

Morton, Robin. Come day, go day, God send Sunday : the songs and life story told in his own words, of John Maguire, traditional singer and farmer from Co. Fermanagh. (Maguire, John, b.1902). *Routledge and Kegan Paul. £1.50* AKDW/G/E(YDTF/P) (B76-21366)   ISBN 0-7100-8388-2

Most popular finest piano solos : selected from the greatest composers of all time. *Century Music : Phoenix. Unpriced* QPK/AAY (B76-50217)

Most popular series. Most popular finest piano solos : selected from the greatest composers of all time. *Century Music : Phoenix. Unpriced* QPK/AAY (B76-50217)

Motte, Diether de la. *See* La Motte, Diether de.

Mountains o' Mourne. (Newsome, Roy). *Keith Prowse : EMI. Unpriced* WMK (B76-51071)

Moussorgsky, Modeste. *See* Mussorgsky, Modest.

Movie musical from Vitaphone to 42nd Street : as reported in a great fan magazine. *Dover Publications etc. : Constable. £4.55* ACM/JR(YT/XNF8) (B76-12805)   ISBN 0-486-23154-2

Moyes, John, b.1924.
  Action rhymes. *Ladybird Books. £0.24* ADW/GR (B76-30340)   ISBN 0-7214-0439-1
  Dancing rhymes. *Ladybird Books. £0.24* ADW/H (B76-30341)   ISBN 0-7214-0440-5

Mozart, Wolfgang Amadeus.
  Adagio and fugue, string orchestra, K.546, C minor. Adagio and fugue for strings, C minor. K.546. Revised ed. *Eulenburg. Unpriced* RXM/Y (B76-50947)
  Briefe und Afzeichnungen
  Band 7: Register. Gesamtuasg. *32 Great Titchfield St., W1P 7AD : Bärenreiter. £37.50* BMS(N)
  Concerto, piano, no.12, K.414, A major. Piano concerto, A major. K.414. Revised ed. *Eulenburg. Unpriced* MPQF (B76-50158)
  Concerto, piano, no.26, K.537, D major. Piano concerto, D major, K.537. *Eulenburg. Unpriced* MPQF (B76-50878)
  Concerto, violin, no.3, K.216, G major. Concerto, G major, for violin and orchestra. K.216. *Eulenburg. Unpriced* MPSF (B76-50534)
  Contredanse no.21, K.535, G major, 'La Bataille'. arr. Contredanse, 'The battle'. *Oxford University Press.*

Unpriced MK/AH (B76-50516) ISBN 0-19-357927-8
Die Entführung aus dem Serail. K.384. *arr.* The abduction from the Seraglio. *Musica rara. Unpriced* UNNK/CC (B76-50668)
German dance no.76, K.605, no.3. *arr.* The sleigh ride. *Warner. Unpriced* UMMK/AH (B76-51005)
Le Nozze di Figaro. K.492. *arr.* The marriage of Figaro Vol.1. *Musica rara. Unpriced* UNNK/CC (B76-50667)
Le Nozze di Figaro. K.492. *arr.* The marriage of Figaro Vol.2. *Musica rara. Unpriced* UNNK/CC (B76-50669)
Quartet, strings, no.17, K.458, B flat major, 'The hunt'. *arr.* String quartet in B flat. *Emerson. Unpriced* UNRK (B76-51009)
Quartets, strings, nos.14, 16, K.387, 428. *Selections : arr.* Quartet no.2 on themes from Mozart. *Studio Music. Unpriced* WNSK (B76-50742)
Symphony, no.34, K.338, C major. Symphony, C major. K.338 and Minuetto, C major. K.409. *Eulenburg. Unpriced* MME (B76-50144)
Symphony no.40, K.550, G minor. First movement : arr. Mozart 40. *Chappell. Unpriced* QPK (B76-50584)
Vier Scherzduette, K. Anh. 284 dd. Spiegelkanon. *arr.* Mirror canon = Spiegelkanon. *Simrock. Unpriced* XPQNSK/AX (B76-51088)
Mozart 40. (Mozart, Wolfgang Amadeus). *Chappell. Unpriced* QPK (B76-50584)
Mozart : the man, the musician. (Hutchings, Arthur). *Thames and Hudson. £16.00* BMS(N) (B76-34778) ISBN 0-500-01161-3
Mozarts italienische Texte mit deutscher Übersetzung. *See* Internationale Stiftung Mozarteum Salzburg. Mozarts italienische Texte mit deutscher Übersetzung.
M.P. Mussorgsky's 'A night on bare mountain'. (Semba, Taro). *F. Warne. £2.25* BMUAMBN (B76-18581) ISBN 0-7232-1836-6
Mudarra, Alonso. Tres libros de música en cifra para vihuela. Fantasia no.10. *arr.* Fantasia : das Harfenspiel in der Manier von Ludovico nachahmend / von Alonso Mudarra. Welsh Tantz, 'Wascha mesa' / von Hans Neusidler ; für Gitarre solo, eingerichtet von Dieter Kreidler. *Schott. £1.00* TSPMK (B76-50275)
Mudge, Richard. Concerto, trumpet & string orchestra, no.1, B flat major. *arr.* Concerto no.1 for trumpet, strings and continuo. *Boosey and Hawkes. £1.00* WSPK/LF (B76-50343)
Müller-Blattau, Wendelin. Tonsatz und Klanggestaltung bei Giovanni Gabrieli. *32 Great Titchfield St., W.1 : Bärenreiter. £24.00* BG
Munrow, David. Instruments of the Middle Ages and Renaissance. *Oxford University Press, Music Department. £3.50* AL/B(XCD801) (B76-18373) ISBN 0-19-321321-4
Münster University. *See* Westfälische Wilhelmsuniversität.
Musgrave, Thea. Orfeo Z : an improvisation on a theme for solo flute and 15 strings. *Novello. £2.55* RXMPVR (B76-50611)
Musi : für Zupforchester. (Kagel, Mauricio). *Universal. Unpriced* RWMJ (B76-50234)
Music and drama
1975-76. (Careers Research and Advisory Centre). *Bateman St., Cambridge CB2 1LZ : Hobsons Press (Cambridge) Ltd for CRAC. £0.85* A(VQ) (B76-04296) ISBN 0-86021-038-3
Music and musical instruments in the world of Islam. (Jenkins, Jean). *85 Cromwell Rd, SW7 5BW : World of Islam Festival Publishing Co. Ltd. £1.50* BZCWIAL/B(YDB/WJ) (B76-22080) ISBN 0-905035-12-7
Music and revolution, Verdi. (Burrows, Donald). *Open University Press. Unpriced* BVE(N/XHK19) (B76-23700) ISBN 0-335-05059-x
Music and society since 1815. (Raynor, Henry). *Barrie and Jenkins. £6.00* A(XGQ160) (B76-20705) ISBN 0-214-20220-8
Music and the middle class : the social structure of concert life in London, Paris and Vienna. (Weber, William). *Croom Helm. £5.95* A(W/YB/XHK19/Z) (B76-32961) ISBN 0-85664-215-0
Music at Bangor Cathedral Church : some historical notes. (Paul, Leslie Douglas). *The Cathedral Chaplain's House, Glanrafon, Bangor, Caernarvonshire LL57 1LH : Bangor Cathedral. £0.25* AD/LE(YDKPB/X) (B76-24542) ISBN 0-905229-00-2
Music : for flute and harpsichord. (Stout, Alan). *Peters. Unpriced* VRPJ (B76-51020)
Music for GCE 'O' Level. (Corbett, Jane). 2nd ed., revised. *Barrie and Jenkins. £1.95* A (B76-05035) ISBN 0-214-15676-1
Music for Montreal. *arr.* Music for Montreal : the original BBC theme music for the 1976 Olympics. (Young, Peter). *Chappell. Unpriced* QPK/JS (B76-50586)
Music for series 3 : new Communion hymns, Morning and Evening Prayer. (Appleford, Patrick). *Weinberger. Unpriced* DM (B76-50390)
Music for the handicapped child. (Alvin, Juliette). 2nd ed. *Oxford University Press. £2.75* A(VMX) (B76-25691) ISBN 0-19-314920-6
Music for the lute. Easy lute music. *Oxford University Press. Unpriced* TW/AY (B76-50279) ISBN 0-19-358834-x
Music for woodwind quartet. (Diemer, Emma Lou). *Oxford University Press. Unpriced* VNS (B76-51010)
Music from Harter Fell : for brass sextet. (Premru, Raymond). *Chester. Unpriced* WNQ (B76-50738)
Music from the Elizabethan court. *Paxton. £2.55* WMK/AY(XDXT46) (B76-51072)
Music from the student repertoire. Peña, Paco. Toques flamencos. *Selections.* Toques flamencos. *Musical New Services. Unpriced* TSPMJ (B76-50990)
Music from the student repertoire
Series 1: For first and second year students. *Musical New Services. Unpriced* TPMK/AAY (B76-50966)
Series 2: For first and second year students. *Musical New Services. Unpriced* TPMK/AAY (B76-50967)
Series 3: 'A new varietie of lute lessons' : music for the first three years selected from English and continental master lutenists of the sixteenth century. *Musical New Services. Unpriced* TPMK/AAY (B76-50968)
Music fundamentals. (Puopolo, Vito). *Schirmer : Collier Macmillan. £5.25* A/M (B76-25958) ISBN 0-02-871890-9
Music guide to Great Britain : England, Scotland, Wales, Ireland. (Brody, Elaine). *Hale. £5.50* A(YC/BC) (B76-24539) ISBN 0-7091-5662-6
Music hall suite. *Selections : arr.* Three pieces. (Horovitz, Joseph). *Novello. £2.50* WMK (B76-50325)
Music in American life.
A Texas-Mexican cancionero : folksongs of the Lower Border. *University of Illinois Press. £6.50* ADW/G(YUBR) (B76-22856) ISBN 0-252-00522-8
Townsend, Charles R. 'San Antonio Rose' : the life and music of Bob Wills. *University of Illinois Press. £8.75* AKDW/GCW/E(P) (B76-31914) ISBN 0-252-00470-1
White, John Irwin. Git along, little dogies : songs and songmakers of the American West. *University of Illinois Press. £7.00* AKDW/GNF/E(M) (B76-33374) ISBN 0-252-00327-6
Music in Belper (1824-1975). (Makin, Denis). *1 Derwent Ave., Milford, Derby DE5 1RB : The author. £0.60* A(YDHW/XHD152) (B76-50350) ISBN 0-9504990-0-5
Music in developmental therapy : a curriculum guide. *University Park Press. £6.25* A(VMWM) (B76-30972) ISBN 0-8391-0895-8
Music in the 1920s. (Shead, Richard). *Duckworth. £5.95* A(XN9) (B76-35349) ISBN 0-7156-0972-6
Music in the Renaissance. (Brown, Howard Mayer). *Prentice-Hall. £8.00* A(XCR181) (B76-26567) ISBN 0-13-608505-9
Music master
1974. *10 Kingsland High St., E8 2JP : R.P.C. Unpriced* A/FD(WT) (B76-35030) ISBN 0-904520-00-5
1976. *48 Shacklewell La., E8 2EY : John Humphries. £15.00(£22.50 including monthly supplements)* A/FD(WT) (B76-29926) ISBN 0-904520-01-3
Music of a thousand autumns : the Tōgaku style of Japanese court music. (Garfias, Robert). *University of California Press. £17.45* BZHPAL (B76-19253) ISBN 0-520-01977-6
Music of Frank Bridge. (Payne, Anthony, *b.1936*). *14 Barlby Rd, W10 6AR : Thames Publishing. £3.20* BBTP (B76-29100) ISBN 0-905210-02-6
Music through the recorder : a course in musicianship. (Simpson, Kenneth). *Nelson. £1.10* VS/AC (B76-50295) ISBN 0-17-436086-x
Music through the recorder : a course in musicianship Vol.3. (Simpson, Kenneth). *Nelson. £2.25* VS/AC (B76-50683) ISBN 0-17-436085-1
Music time for Brownies : songs for unison voices and instruments. *Girl Guides Association. £0.65* JFE/NYHSDW/AY (B76-50111)
Music titles in translation : a checklist of musical compositions. (Hodgson, Julian). *Bingley etc.. £7.50* AB(TCT/WT) (B76-14368) ISBN 0-85157-198-0
Music when soft voices die : SATB (divisi), with keyboard accompaniment. (Harbison, John). *Associated Music. Unpriced* DW (B76-50028)
Music with ESN children : a guide for the classroom teacher. (Dickinson, Pamela Ingeborg). *NFER. £3.65* A(VMWR) (B76-14728) ISBN 0-85633-085-x
Musica Britannica : a national collection of music
Vol.28: William Byrd : Keyboard music 2. 2nd, revised ed. *Stainer and Bell. Unpriced* C/AYD (B76-50359) ISBN 0-85249-426-2
Vol.38: Matthew Locke : anthems and motets. *Stainer and Bell. Unpriced* C/AYD (B76-50360) ISBN 0-85249-397-5
Musica da camera.
Jenkins, John. Fantasia, viols (2) & organ, A minor. Fantasia, suite 5 : for violin (or treble viol), bass viol (or violoncello) and organ (or harpsichord). *Oxford University Press. Unpriced* NXNT (B76-50886) ISBN 0-19-357410-1
Leclair, Jean Marie, *b.1697.* Sonata, violins (2) & continuo, op.13. no.1. Two trio sonatas for two violins and basso continuo. *Oxford University Press. Unpriced* NXNTE (B76-50887) ISBN 0-19-357612-0
Musica della primavera : for solo clarinet in A. (Jenni, Donald). *Associated Music. Unpriced* VVQPMJ (B76-50322)
Musical experience of the pre-school child. (Moog, Helmut). *48 Great Marlborough St., W1V 2BN : Schott Music. £2.00* A(VCC) (B76-35594) ISBN 0-901938-06-8
Musical instruments. (Diamond, Dorothy Mary). *Macdonald Educational for Chelsea College, University of London. £1.50* AL/E(VG) (B76-30110) ISBN 0-356-05077-7
Musical instruments from odds and ends. (Burton, John Andrew). *Carousel. £0.45* AY/BC (B76-14366) ISBN 0-552-54096-x
Musical instruments in colour. (Gammond, Peter). *Blandford Press. £2.60* AL/B (B76-00667) ISBN 0-7137-0628-7
Musical instruments, made to be played. (Roberts, Ronald). 6th ed. *Dryad Press. £1.95* AL/BC (B76-15863) ISBN 0-85219-095-6
Musical stages : an autobiography. (Rodgers, Richard). *W.H. Allen. £5.95* BRK(N) (B76-32591) ISBN 0-491-01777-4
Musical thoughts & afterthoughts. (Brendel, Alfred). *Robson Books. £5.25* AQ (B76-33377) ISBN 0-903895-43-9
Musicians of Bremen : for 2 counter-tenors, tenor, 2 baritones and bass. (Williamson, Malcolm). *Weinberger. Unpriced* JNAZDX (B76-50473)
Musicologica Hungarica : neue Folge. Bárdos, Kornél. Volksmusikartige Variierungstechnik in den ungarischen Passionen, 15. bis 18. Jahrhundert. *32 Great Titchfield St., W.1 : Bärenreiter. £16.25* ADD/LH(YG/XD301)
Musicplay series.
Burnett, Michael. The poltergoose : for recorder, percussion, voices and piano. *Chester. Unpriced* CQN (B76-50769)
Odam, George. Inca : a project in sound for young performers. *Chester. Unpriced* CQN (B76-50770)
Odam, George. The legend of Robin Hood : for descant recorders, pitched percussion, voices and piano. *Chester. Unpriced* CQN (B76-50771)
Parry, William Howard. The beast of Bettesthorne. *Chester Unpriced* CN (B76-50765)
Musik der Oberpfalz. Grünberger, Theodor. German mass, no.2, G major. *Vocal score.* Zweite deutsche Messe, 'Hier liegt vor deiner Majestät', für Sopran, Alt, Bass ad libitum (solistisch oder chorisch) und Orgel. *Bosse Bärenreiter. £8.75* DE (B76-50367)
Musik für Mallets : 14 Duos und Soli für Malletinstrumente (Vibraphon, Marimbaphon, Xylophon, Stabspiele). (Stahmer, Klaus). *Schott. £3.50* XPQNU (B76-51089)
Musik Israels. (Brod, Max). Revidierte Ausg., mit einen zweiten Teil 'Werden und Entwicklung der Musik in Israel'. *32 Great Titchfield St., W.1 : Bärenreiter Kassel. £10.50* A(YVD)
Musikalischer Andachten, Tl 3. Es danken dir, Gott, die Volker. Es danken dir, Gott, die Volker : solokantate für Tenor, zwei Violinen und Basso continuo. (Hammerschmidt, Andreas). *Bärenreiter. £1.63* KGHE/SNTPWDE (B76-50503)
Musikwissenschaftliche Seminar, *Westfälische Wilhelmsuniversität. Orgelwissenschaftliche Forschungsstelle. Westfälische Wilhelmsuniversität.*
Musique héroïque. *arr.* Heroic music : a suite of twelve marches. (Telemann, Georg Philipp). *Oxford University Press. Unpriced* WSPK/AGM (B76-50342) ISBN 0-19-359067-0
Musorgsky, Modest Petrovich. *See* Mussorgsky, Modest.
Mussorgsky, Modest. M.P. Mussorgsky's 'A night on bare mountain'. (Semba, Taro). *F. Warne. £2.25* BMUAMBN (B76-18581) ISBN 0-7232-1836-6
Mutation : für Männerchor und obligates Klavier. (Kagel, Mauricio). *Universal. Unpriced* GDE (B76-50450)
My fatherland. Šárka. Má vlast : a cycle of symphonic poems
No.3: Sarka. (Smetana, Bedřich). *Eulenburg. Unpriced* MMJ (B76-50877)
My favorite intermissions. My favourite intervals. (Borge, Victor). *Sphere. £0.60* A/D(YB/M) (B76-28392) ISBN 0-7221-1779-5
My favourite intervals. (Borge, Victor). *Sphere. £0.60* A/D(YB/M) (B76-28392) ISBN 0-7221-1779-5
My God and King! : S.A.T.B. organ or piano. (Nelson, Havelock). *Banks. Unpriced* DM (B76-50392)
My heart shall rejoice in His salvation. *Vocal score.* My heart shall rejoice in His salvation. (Antes, John). *Boosey and Hawkes. £0.40* DH (B76-50380)
Mylett, Howard. Led Zeppelin. *Panther. £0.60* AKDW/HK/E(P) (B76-34781) ISBN 0-586-04390-x
Mynall, Frances.
Guitar workshop : a course for guitar groups in two parts Part 1. *Oxford University Press. Unpriced* TSN/AC (B76-50979) ISBN 0-19-322268-x
Part 2. *Oxford University Press. Unpriced* TSN/AC (B76-50980) ISBN 0-19-322269-8
Mynshall, Richard. The Mynshall lute book. *5 Albert Grove, Leeds 6 : Boethius Press. £6.25* ATW(YD) (B76-11505) ISBN 0-904263-03-7
Mynshall lute book. *5 Albert Grove, Leeds 6 : Boethius Press. £6.25* ATW(YD) (B76-11505) ISBN 0-904263-03-7
Na beira do rio. (Lorenzo Fernandez, Oscar). *Arthur Napoleão : Essex Music. Unpriced* QPJ (B76-50911)
Nacht in Venedig. *Vocal score.* A night in Venice. (Korngold, Erich). *Weinberger. Unpriced* CF (B76-50364)
Nachtgedanken : für Orchester. (Killmayer, Wilhelm). *Schott. £7.30* MMJ (B76-50149)
Nagel, Frank. Sonatas, flute. Op.23. Sechs Sonaten für zwei Flöten. (Corrette, Michel). *Heinrichshofen : Peters. Unpriced* VRNUE (B76-50289)
Nagy, Oliver.
Ave Maria : für Sopran, gemischten Chor und Streicher. (Donizetti, Gaetano). *Editio musica : Litolff. Unpriced* ERXMDJ (B76-50407)
Ave Maria. *Vocal score.* Ave Maria : für Sopran, gemischten Chor und Streicher. (Donizetti, Gaetano). *Editio musica : Litolff. Unpriced* DJ (B76-50387)
Psalm 13. *Vocal score.* Der 13. Psalm : für Tenor, gemischten Chor und Orchester. (Liszt, Franz). *Litolff : Peters. Unpriced* DR (B76-50794)
Napoleon's retreat from Wigan. (Harding, Mike). *EMI Music. Unpriced* KEZDW (B76-50495)
Nares, James. Six fugues with introductory voluntaries : for the organ or harpsichord. *Oxford University Press. Unpriced* R/AZ (B76-50227) ISBN 0-19-375611-0
National Foundation for Educational Research in England and Wales. Music with ESN children : a guide for the classroom teacher. (Dickinson, Pamela Ingeborg). *NFER. £3.65* A(VMWR) (B76-14728) ISBN 0-85633-085-x
National Trust. A catalogue of early keyboard instruments : the Benton Fletcher collection. *The Trust. £0.12* APW/B(YDBCF/WJ) (B76-22083)

ISBN 0-7078-0061-7
Navarraise. Nocturne. *arr.* Nocturne. (Massenet, Jules). *Rubank : Novello. Unpriced* VRNSQK (B76-50675)
Navarraise. Nocturne. *arr.* Nocturne. (Massenet, Jules). *Rubank : Novello. Unpriced* VVNSQK (B76-50699)
Naylor, Bernard. Come away, death : song. (Naylor, John). *Roberton. £0.35* KDW (B76-50120)
Naylor, Frank.
Rosen aus dem Suden. Op.388. *arr.* Roses from the south. Op.388 : waltz. (Strauss, Johann, *b.1825*). *Bosworth. Unpriced* MK/AHW (B76-50518)
Suite bergamasque. Clair de lune. *arr.* Clair de lune : piano solo. (Debussy, Claude). *Bosworth. Unpriced* QPK (B76-50920)
Unter Donner und Blitz. Op.324. *arr.* Thunder and lightning = Unter Donner und Blitz, Op.324 : polka. (Strauss, Johann, *b.1825*). *Bosworth. Unpriced* MK/AHVH (B76-50517)
Naylor, John. Come away, death : song. *Roberton. £0.35* KDW (B76-50120)
Nazareth, Ernesto.
Helena : valsa, piano. *Arthur Napoleão : Essex Music. Unpriced* QPHW (B76-50901)
Labirinto : chôro, piano. *Arthur Napoleão : Essex Music. Unpriced* QPJ (B76-50914)
Sarambeque : chôro, piano. *Arthur Napoleão : Essex Music. Unpriced* QPJ (B76-50915)
Neale, John Mason. Peace on earth to men : SATB. (Tate, Phyllis). *Oxford University Press. Unpriced* DP/LF (B76-50399) ISBN 0-19-343057-6
Neaman, Yfrah. The wings of night : for violin solo. (Watkins, Michael Blake). *Novello. Unpriced* SPMJ' (B76-50254)
Neff, Robert. Blues. *Latimer New Dimensions. £5.00* AKDW/HHW (B76-29101) ISBN 0-901539-49-x
Nelson, Havelock.
The lark in the clear air : Irish traditional air. *Banks. Unpriced* GEZDW (B76-50824)
My God and King! : S.A.T.B. organ or piano. *Banks. Unpriced* DM (B76-50392)
Nelson, Robert. Techniques and materials of tonal music : with an introduction to twentieth-century techniques. (Benjamin, Thomas). *Houghton Mifflin. £7.95* A/R (B76-22853) ISBN 0-395-19095-9
Nettel, Reginald. Havergal Brian and his music. *Dobson. £7.50* BBTN(N) (B76-25956) ISBN 0-234-77861-x
Neue Gemeindelieder : neue geistliche Lieder
Heft 3. *Bosse : Bärenreiter. £1.66* JFE/TSDM/AY (B76-50836)
Neunteufel, Erna. La Clemenza di Tito : Opera seria in zwei Akten : Textbuch italiebisch-deutsch. (Metastasio, Pietro). *32 Great Titchfield St., W1P 7AD : Bärenreiter. £1.13* BMSAC
Neusidler, Hans. Tres libros de música en cifra para vihuela. Fantasia no.10. *arr.* Fantasia : das Harfenspiel in der Manier von Ludovico nachahmend / von Alonso Mudarra. Welsh Tantz, 'Wascha mesa' / von Hans Neusidler ; für Gitarre solo, eingerichtet von Dieter Kreidler. (Mudarra, Alonso). *Schott. £1.00* TSPMK (B76-50275)
New, Derek. Hill-billy holiday : trombone duet. *Studio Music. Unpriced* WMPWUNU (B76-51076)
New community mass. (Tamblyn, William). *Chiswick Music. Unpriced* JDG (B76-50100)
New life in country music. (Davis, Paul). *Walker. £1.00* AKDW/GC(M) (B76-35353) ISBN 0-85479-591-x
New York Bartók Archive. Studies in musicology.
Bartók, Béla. Béla Bartók essays. *Faber. £38.50* A/G(D) (B76-36283) ISBN 0-571-10120-8
Bartók, Béla. Turkish folk music from Asia Minor. *Princeton University Press. £12.20* BZC (B76-36284) ISBN 0-691-09120-x
Newgass, E. Praise ye the Lord. (Lowe, Augustus). *Paterson. Unpriced* KDR (B76-50116)
Newgass, Edgar. Romance, violin & orchestra, no.1, op.40, G major. *arr.* Beneficence. (Beethoven, Ludwig van). *Fischer; Pinns Farm, West Wellow, Romsey : Edgar New gass. Unpriced* KDW (B76-50118)
Newman, Ernest. Essays from the world of music : essays from 'The Sunday Times'. *J. Calder. £6.50* A(D) (B76-34776) ISBN 0-7145-3548-6
Newman, Ernest. From the world of music. *See* Newman, Ernest. Essays from the world of music.
Newman, Ernest.
The life of Richard Wagner. *Cambridge University Press. £17.50* BWC(N) (B76-33368) ISBN 0-521-29149-6
More essays from the world of music : essays from the 'Sunday Times'. *J. Calder. £7.50* A(D) (B76-34777) ISBN 0-7145-3549-4
Newsome, Roy. Mountains o' Mourne. *Keith Prowse : EMI. Unpriced* WMK (B76-51071)
Ní Fhlathartaigh, Ríonach. Clár amhrán Bhaile na hInse : clár na n-amhrán i mbarúntacht Bhaile na hInse. *15 Bóthar Ghráinseach an Déin, An Charraig Dhubh, Co. Atha Cliath : An Clóchomhar Tta. £3.50* ADW/G(YDMG/T) (B76-17862) ISBN 0-903758-06-7
Nice, John R van. *See* Van Nice, John R.
Nicholas, W Rhys. 'Pantyfedwen' : i leisiau TTBB. (Evans, M E). Revised ed. *Thames. Unpriced* GDW (B76-50452)
Nicholson, Richard. Consort music for viols in six parts. (Jenkins, John). *Faber Music for the Viola da Gamba Society of Great Britain. Unpriced* STNQR (B76-50963)
Nicolson, Richard.
Collected madrigals. *Stainer and Bell. Unpriced* EZDU/AZ (B76-50064) ISBN 0-85249-382-7
Three consort pieces. *Boosey and Hawkes. £1.50* VSNRK/DW (B76-50299)
Night in Venice. (Korngold, Erich). *Weinberger. Unpriced* CF (B76-50364)
Night of the four moons : alto, alto flute, (doubling piccolo), banjo, electric cello and percussion (one player). (Crumb, George). *Peters. Unpriced* KFQE/NYERNSDW (B76-50136)
Night on bare mountain. *See* Semba, Taro.
Nightingale : English North Countrie song. (Wilkinson, Stephen). *Roberton. £0.18* EZDW (B76-50076)
Nightpiece : for soprano and electronic tape. (Bennett, Richard Rodney). *Universal. Unpriced* KFLE/PVDX (B76-50497)
Nine miniatures : piano solo based on Armenian folk and dance melodies. (Tjeknavorian, Loris). *Basil Ramsey : Roberton. Unpriced* QPJ (B76-50575)
Noble, Harold. Tintern Abbey : elegy for brass band. *Studio Music. Unpriced* WMJ (B76-50728)
Noble, John. Cats : a suite for clarinet and piano. *Cramer. £0.75* VVPG (B76-51050)
Nocturne. (Massenet, Jules). *Rubank : Novello. Unpriced* VRNSQK (B76-50675)
Nocturne. (Massenet, Jules). *Rubank : Novello. Unpriced* VVNSQK (B76-50699)
Norris, Geoffrey, *b.1947.* Rachmaninov. *Dent. £3.50* BRC (B76-04297) ISBN 0-460-03145-7
Norse cradle song : unison. (Longmire, John). *Leonard, Gould and Bolttler. £0.09* JFDW (B76-50464)
North, Nigel. Byrd for the guitar : five pieces. (Byrd, William). *Oxford University Press. Unpriced* TSPMK (B76-50274) ISBN 0-19-355800-9
North country sketches. (Delius, Frederick). *Stainer and Bell. Unpriced* MMJ (B76-50873) ISBN 0-85249-457-2
Northouse, Cameron. Twentieth century opera in England and the United States. *G.K. Hall : Prior. £14.95* AC(XM75/WT) (B76-35928) ISBN 0-86043-002-2
Norton (Charles Eliot) lectures. *See* Charles Eliot Norton lectures.
Norwegian folksongs and dances. Op.17. *Selections : arr.* Three Norwegian pieces. (Grieg, Edvard). *Novello. Unpriced* RXMK (B76-50236)
Notendrucker und Musik verleger in Frankfurt am Main von 1630 bis um 1720 : eine bibliographisch-drucktechnische Untersuchung. (Schaefer, Hartmut). *32 Great Titchfield St., W.1 : Bärenreiter. £28.13* A(S/YEF/XWK91)
Notes : für einen Pianisten. (Globokar, Vinko). *Litolff : Peters. Unpriced* QPJ (B76-50205)
Notes on music. (Joseph, Jack). *38 Ferndale Rd, Gillingham, Kent : Lindley Press. £0.40* A/M (B76-24540) ISBN 0-9504506-0-x
Novello church music. Phillips, John Charles. The lot is fallen unto me : anthem for SATB with divisions and organ. *Novello. £0.20* DK (B76-50023)
Novello short biographies. Palmer, Christopher. Bliss. *Novello. £0.42* BBQ(N) (B76-30335) ISBN 0-85360-064-3
Nozze di Figaro. K.492. *arr.* The marriage of Figaro
Vol.1. (Mozart, Wolfgang Amadeus). *Musica rara. Unpriced* UNNK/CC (B76-50667)
Nozze di Figaro. K.492. *arr.* The marriage of Figaro
Vol.2. (Mozart, Wolfgang Amadeus). *Musica rara. Unpriced* UNNK/CC (B76-50669)
Nuovo ricercare 4 a due voci : für zwei Altblockflöten. (Dolci, Amico). *Heinrichshofen : Peters. Unpriced* VSSNU (B76-50305)
Nuovo ricercare 5 : für Altblockflöte. (Dolci, Amico). *Heinrichshofen : Peters. Unpriced* VSSPMJ (B76-50308)
´O Fiannachta, Pádraig. Léachtaí Cholm Cille VII : an ceol i litríocht la Gaeilge. *Maynooth, Co. Kildare : St Patrick's College. £0.50* A/G(YDM) (B76-34780) ISBN 0-901519-17-0
O Haupt voll Blut und Wunden. *Vocal score.* O Haupt voll Blut und Wunden : für Bass, gemischten Chor und Orchester. (Mendelssohn, Felix). Zum ersten Mal. *Litolff : Peters. Unpriced* DE (B76-50775)
O quam gloriosum : S.S.A.T.B. (Byrd, William). Revised ed. *Oxford University Press. Unpriced* EZDJ (B76-50417) ISBN 0-19-352060-5
Oakshott, Jane. Four French songs from an English song book (Cambridge, University Library Add.MS.5943, ff 161-173) : for voice with 1 and 2 instruments. *Antico. Unpriced* KE/LNUDW/AY (B76-50859)
Oboist's companion
Vol.2. (Rothwell, Evelyn). *Oxford University Press. Unpriced* VT/AC (B76-50691) ISBN 0-19-322336-8
O'Brien, Eugene. Ambages : for piano, four hands. *Schirmer. Unpriced* QNV (B76-50186)
O'Brien, Robert. Die Fledermaus. Fledermaus - Polka. *arr.* Polka française. (Strauss, Johann, *b.1825*). *Oxford University Press. Unpriced* UMMK/AHVH (B76-50665)
Odam, George.
Inca : a project in sound for young performers. *Chester. Unpriced* CQN (B76-50770)
The legend of Robin Hood : for descant recorders, pitched percussion, voices and piano. *Chester. Unpriced* CQN (B76-50771)
Ode to joy : from 'Choral symphony'. (Beethoven, Ludwig van). *Chappell. Unpriced* QPK (B76-50579)
Of German music : a symposium. *Wolff etc.. £6.50* A(YE/X) (B76-14365) ISBN 0-85496-401-0
Offenbach, Jacques.
Les Contes d'Hoffmann. Belle nuit. *arr.* Barcarolle. *Fisher and Lane. £0.30* RPVK/DW (B76-50940)
La Fille du tambour major. *Vocal score.* The drum-major's daughter : comic opera in three acts. *Choudens : United Music. Unpriced* CF (B76-50762)
Oishi, Makoto. P. Dukas' 'The sorcerer's apprentice'. (Yangagihara, Ryohei). *F. Warne. £2.25* BDVAMBN (B76-18582) ISBN 0-7232-1834-x
Okki-tokki-unga : action songs for children. *A. and C. Black. £2.75* JFDW/GR (B76-50832) ISBN 0-7136-1685-7
Oktoechos : B flat clarinet, horn in F and percussion. (Maves, David). *Henmar Press : Peters : Peters. Unpriced* NYHNT (B76-50177)
Old hundredth prelude and doxology : music for organ. (Beeson, Jack). *Boosey and Hawkes. £1.00* RJ (B76-50928)
Oldfield, Mike. In dulci jubilo. *Virgin Music : Chappell. Unpriced* QPK/DP/LF (B76-50219)
Oliver, Stephen.
Three instant operas for children. *Novello. £1.35* CQN (B76-50772)
Tom Jones : a comedy for music, based on the novel by Henry Fielding. *Novello. £0.85* BOLAC (B76-21365) ISBN 0-85360-063-5
Olleson, Edward. Essays on opera and English music : in honour of Sir Jack Westrup. *Blackwell. £7.00* A(YD/XCE841/D) (B76-15050) ISBN 0-631-15890-1
Olor solymaeus. Canzon à 2. Canzon à 2 for cornetto (recorder-trumpet), bassoon (cello-rackett), & basso continuo. (Spiegler, Matthias). *Musica rara. Unpriced* NWNT (B76-50539)
Olsen, Poul Rovsing. Music and musical instruments in the world of Islam. (Jenkins, Jean). *85 Cromwell Rd, SW7 5BW : World of Islam Festival Publishing Co. Ltd. £1.50* BZCWIAL/B(YDB/WJ) (B76-22080) ISBN 0-905035-12-7
On hearing the first cuckoo in spring. *arr.* On hearing the first cuckoo in spring. (Delius, Frederick). *Oxford University Press. Unpriced* WMK (B76-50731) ISBN 0-19-362813-9
One hundred and twenty-five studies for flute. *See* 125 studies for flute.
One hundred hits of the seventies. *Wise, Music Sales. Unpriced* KDW/GB/AY (B76-50852)
Only for guitar : new compositions for solo guitar. (Qualey, David). *Scratchwood Music : EMI. Unpriced* TSPMJ (B76-50272)
Open University.
Contemporary music, case stuwies II. (Bray, Trevor). *Open University Press. £1.60* A(XM76) (B76-50756) ISBN 0-335-00870-4
Music and revolution, Verdi. (Burrows, Donald). *Open University Press. Unpriced* 782.10924 (B76-23700) ISBN 0-335-05059-x
Opera lover's quiz book. (Taylor, Ian, *b.1932*). *Luscombe. £0.95* AC(DE) (B76-15052) ISBN 0-86002-084-3
Orchestra. (Harding, David). *F. Watts. £1.45* AM/B (B76-05039) ISBN 0-85166-558-6
Orfeo Z : an improvisation on a theme for solo flute and 15 strings. (Musgrave, Thea). *Novello. £2.55* RXMPVR (B76-50611)
Orff, Carl. Kleines Konzert nach Lautensätzen aus dem 16. Jahrhundert = Little concerto based on lute pieces from the 16th century : for flute, oboe, bassoon, trumpet, trombone, harpsichord and percussion. New ed. *Schott. £9.00* NYFNPF (B76-50175)
Orga, Ateş. Chopin : his life and times. *Midas Books. £5.95* BCE(N) (B76-29713) ISBN 0-85936-057-1
Organ books
No.5. *Oxford University Press. Unpriced* R/AY (B76-50224) ISBN 0-19-375847-4
No.6. *Oxford University Press. Unpriced* R/AY (B76-50225) ISBN 0-19-375848-2
Organ Club. The Organ Club golden jubilee, 1976. *c/o Jubilee Treasurer, 84 Haynes Rd, Hornchurch, Essex RM11 2HU : Organ Club. £1.80* AR/B(XNF51) (B76-31918) ISBN 0-9505260-0-2
Organ-grinder's carol. (When Jesus Christ was born) : unison. (Verrall, Pamela Motley). *Leonard, Gould and Bolttler. Unpriced* JFDP/LF (B76-50107)
Organists and organs of Hereford Cathedral. (Shaw, Watkins). *Friends of Hereford Cathedral Publications Committee. £0.50* AR/B(YDHRHB/X) (B76-35357) ISBN 0-904642-01-1
Organizational survival in the performing arts : the making of the Seattle Opera. (Salem, Mahmoud). *Praeger Distributed by Martin Robertson. £10.25* AC/E/K/QB(YTXHS) (B76-22516) ISBN 0-275-05670-8
Organs of the Church of St John : a history. (Johnson, David Sturgess). *Mill St., Derby : Church of St John the Evangelist. £0.10* AR/B(YDHWD) (B76-31919) ISBN 0-9505280-0-5
Orgelwissenschaftliche Forschungsstelle, *Westfälische Wilhelmsuniversität.* Veröffentlichungen.
Diederich, Susanne. Originale Registrieranweisungen in der französischen Orgelmusik des 17. und 18. Jahrhunderts : Beziehungen zwischen Orgelbau und Orgelkomposition im Zeitalter Ludwigs XIV. *32 Great Titchfield St., W.1 : Bärenreiter. £11.00* AR(YH/PU/XE201)
Der hannoversche Orgel Christian Vater, 1679-1756. *32 Great Titchfield St., W.1 : Bärenreiter. £13.00* AR/BC(YEH/P)
Originale Registrieranweisungen in der französischen Orgelmusik des 17. und 18. Jahrhunderts : Beziehungen zwischen Orgelbau und Orgelkomposition im Zeitalter Ludwigs XIV. (Diederich, Susanne). *32 Great Titchfield St., W.1 : Bärenreiter. £11.00* AR(YH/PU/XE201)
Ormont, David. Twelve musical plays for children (based on famous fairy tales). (Tobias, Henry). *Henry Tobias : Chappell : Chappell. Unpriced* CN (B76-50006)
Orr, Buxton. Concerto, trombone & brass band. *arr.* Concerto for trombone and brass band. *Novello. £2.55* WUPK/LF (B76-51086)
Orrey, Leslie.

The encyclopedia of opera. *Pitman. £13.50(£10.50 until January 1 1977)* AC(C) (B76-31915)
ISBN 0-273-00237-6
Programme music : a brief survey from the sixteenth century to the present day. *Davis-Poynter. £6.00* A/KB(X) (B76-01879) ISBN 0-7067-0171-2
O'Shaughnessy, Patrick. Yellowbelly ballads : a third selection of Lincolnshire folk-songs, the majority of them from the collection of Percy Aldridge Grainger. *Lincolnshire and Humberside Arts. Unpriced* JE/TSDW/G/AYDGH (B76-50829)
Osmonds : the official story of the Osmond family. (Dunn, Paul H). *W.H. Allen. £2.95* AKDW/GB/E(P) (B76-00672) ISBN 0-491-01835-5
Other flute : a performance manual of contemporary techniques. (Dick, Robert). *Oxford University Press. £6.75* VR/AF (B76-51014) ISBN 0-19-322125-x
Ottone. *Condensed score. Selections.* Three ornamented arias. (Handel, George Frideric). *Oxford University Press. Unpriced* KE/MDW (B76-50128)
ISBN 0-19-345412-2
Our murmers have their musick too : for 4-part chorus of mixed voices unaccompanied. (Clark, Keith). *Roberton. £0.10* EZDW (B76-50428)
Ouverture pour une tragedie classique. Opus 9. (Stekel, Erich Paul). *Paterson. £1.50* MMJ (B76-50532)
Over the hills. The old man from Kilkenny. If. (Parke, Dorothy). *Roberton. £0.15* JFDW (B76-50466)
Overton, David. Moods 1 : for unaccompanied solo oboe. *Paterson. Unpriced* VTPMJ (B76-50315)
Owens, Dewey. Purcell for the harp. (Purcell, Henry). *Schirmer. Unpriced* TQPMK (B76-50266)
Oxford anthems.
Frith, Michael. The river flows, the seasons turn : anthem for S.A.T.B., soprano solo and organ. *Oxford University Press. Unpriced* DH (B76-50015)
Gardner, John. A song for St Cecilia's Day. Op.119 : SATB. *Oxford University Press. Unpriced* DH (B76-50384) ISBN 0-19-350355-7
Jackson, Francis. Lift up your heads, Opus 44, no.2 : SATB. *Oxford University Press. Unpriced* DH (B76-50385) ISBN 0-19-350360-3
Joubert, John. Lord make me an instrument of thy peace. Op.84 : S. solo, S.S.A.A.T.T.B.B. *Oxford University Press. Unpriced* DH (B76-50386) ISBN 0-19-350359-x
Milani, Francesco. Litanie et motetti. Ave verum corpus. Ave verum corpus : S.A.T.T.B. and organ. *Oxford University Press. Unpriced* DJ (B76-50022)
ISBN 0-19-350357-3
Rutter, John. I will lift up mine eyes. *Vocal score.* I will lift up mine eyes : SATB. *Oxford University Press. Unpriced* DR (B76-50402) ISBN 0-19-350353-0
Tallis, Thomas. Cantiones sacrae. Te lucis ante terminum. Te lucis ante terminum : festal and ferial tones, S.A.A.T.B. (unacc.). *Oxford University Press. Unpriced* EZDGKRM (B76-50052) ISBN 0-19-350356-5
Wilbye, John. Homo natus de maliere : S.S.A.T.B. *Oxford University Press. Unpriced* EZDH (B76-50054)
ISBN 0-19-350352-2
Oxford choral songs.
Gardner, John. Five philanders. Contentment. Op.125, no.4. Contentment : S.A.T. unacc. *Oxford University Press. Unpriced* EZDW (B76-50432)
ISBN 0-19-343059-2
Gardner, John. Five philanders. Rejection. Op.125, no.1. Rejection : S.A.T.B. unacc. *Oxford University Press. Unpriced* EZDW (B76-50433) ISBN 0-19-343058-4
Hoddinott, Alun. Two Welsh songs. *Oxford University Press. Unpriced* DW (B76-50403) ISBN 0-19-343061-4
Johnson, Stuart. The gospel train : negro spiritual, two-part (with optional recorders). *Oxford University Press. Unpriced* FDW/LC (B76-50082)
ISBN 0-19-341508-9
Madden, John. The babe of Bethlehem : SATB. *Oxford University Press. Unpriced* DP/LF (B76-50396)
ISBN 0-19-343060-6
Rutter, John. Donkey carol. *arr.* Donkey carol. *Oxford University Press. Unpriced* JFDP/LF (B76-50461)
ISBN 0-19-342052-x
Rutter, John. Donkey carol. *Vocal score.* Donkey carol : S.A.T.B. accompanied. *Oxford University Press. Unpriced* DP/LF (B76-50398) ISBN 0-19-343055-x
Rutter, John. It was a lover and his lass : S.A.T. Bar.B. unacc. *Oxford University Press. Unpriced* EZDW (B76-50074) ISBN 0-19-343056-8
Rutter, John. Two American folk songs : SATB unacc. *Oxford University Press. Unpriced* EZDW (B76-50437)
ISBN 0-19-343048-7
Tate, Phyllis. Peace on earth to men : SATB. *Oxford University Press. Unpriced* DP/LF (B76-50399)
ISBN 0-19-343057-6
Oxford church services.
Holmes, John. The preces and responses ('for trebles') : S.S.A.T.B. unacc. *Oxford University Press. Unpriced* EZDGMM (B76-50412) ISBN 0-19-351651-9
Mathias, William. Communion service, series 3 : for congregational use with optional S.A.T.B. choir. *Oxford University Press. Unpriced* JDGS (B76-50453)
ISBN 0-19-351652-7
Walton, *Sir* William. Magnificat and Nunc dimittis : S.A.T.B. and organ. *Oxford University Press. Unpriced* DGPP (B76-50012) ISBN 0-19-351650-0
Oxford guitar music. Byrd, William. Byrd for the guitar : five pieces. *Oxford University Press. Unpriced* TSPMK (B76-50274) ISBN 0-19-355800-9
Oxford studies of composers. Doe, Paul. Tallis. 2nd ed. *Oxford University Press. £2.20* BTB (B76-15053)
ISBN 0-19-314122-1
P. Dukas' 'The sorcerer's apprentice'. (Yangagihara, Ryohei). *F. Warne. £2.25* BDVAMBN (B76-18582)
ISBN 0-7232-1834-x
Pachelbel, Johann. Canon, violins (3) & continuo, D major. *arr.* Canon in D : variations on a ground bass. *Cramer. £0.39* R/X (B76-50587)
Pagan carols restored
Vol.1. (Iles, Norman). *381 Marine Rd, Morecambe, Lancs. : The author. £0.50* ADP(YD) (B76-15054)
ISBN 0-9500776-4-x
Page, Martin, *b.1938.* For gawdsake don't take me! : the songs, ballads, verses, monologues, etc. of the call-up years, 1939-1963. *Hart-Davis, MacGibbon. £2.95* AKDW/KG(YC/XNU25) (B76-50757)
ISBN 0-246-10859-2
Paget, Michael.
Spirituals reborn
Choral edition. *Cambridge University Press. £3.75* EZDW/LC/AY (B76-50439) ISBN 0-521-08713-9
Melody and guitar edition. Part 1
for male and female voices, with chords for piano and guitar and additional parts for voices. *Cambridge University Press. £1.00* FE/TSDW/LC/AY (B76-50443)
ISBN 0-521-08714-7
Melody and guitar edition. Part 2 : for male and female voices, with chords for piano and guitar and additional parts for voices. *Cambridge University Press. £1.00* FE/TSDW/LC/AY (B76-50444) ISBN 0-521-21332-0
Palmer, Christopher.
Bliss. *Novello. £0.42* BBQ(N) (B76-30335)
ISBN 0-85360-064-3
Delius : portrait of a cosmopolitan. *Duckworth. £9.80* BDL (B76-22079) ISBN 0-7156-0773-1
Palmer, Roy. The rigs of the fair : popular sports and pastimes in the nineteenth century through songs, ballads and contemporary accounts. *Cambridge University Press. £1.25(non-net)* ADW/G(YD/XG61) (B76-12389)
ISBN 0-521-20908-0
Pancake Tuesday : unison (or solo) song. (Carter, Andrew). *Banks. Unpriced* JFDW/LFZ (B76-50110)
'Pantyfedwen' : i leisiau TTBB. (Evans, M E). Revised ed. *Thames. Unpriced* GDW (B76-50452)
Panufnik, Andrzej. Sinfonia di sfere. *Boosey and Hawkes. £10.00* MME (B76-50870)
Papp, Marta.
Psalm 13. Der 13 Psalm : für Tenor, gemischten Chor und Orchester. (Liszt, Franz). *Litolff : Peters. Unpriced* EMDR (B76-50406)
Psalm 13. *Vocal score.* Der 13. Psalm : für Tenor, gemischten Chor und Orchester. (Liszt, Franz). *Litolff : Peters. Unpriced* DR (B76-50794)
Parade : for brass band. (Howarth, Elgar). *Chester Music. Unpriced* WMJ (B76-51060)
Paredes, Américo. A Texas-Mexican cancionero : folksongs of the Lower Border. *University of Illinois Press. £6.50* ADW/G(YUBR) (B76-22856) ISBN 0-252-00522-8
Parfrey, Raymond.
Mary's dream. *Thames. Unpriced* EZDP/LF (B76-50424)
Suite, clarinets (3), no.1. Suite no.1 for three clarinets. *EMI. Unpriced* VVNTG (B76-51047)
Suite, clarinets (3), no.2. Second suite for 3 clarinets. *EMI. Unpriced* VVNTG (B76-51048)
Suite, woodwind quartet, no.1. Suite no.1 for 2 flutes and 2 B flat clarinets. *British and Continental : EMI. Unpriced* VNSG (B76-51012)
Suite, woodwind quartet, no.2. Suite no.2 for 2 flutes and 2 B flat clarinets. *British and Continental. Unpriced* VNSG (B76-51011)
Paris le soir : for brass band. (Lear, W Hogarth). *Chester Music. Unpriced* WMJ (B76-51064)
Parke, Dorothy.
By winding roads. In old Donegal. In old Donegal, and, The fairy tree. *Roberton. £0.10* JFDW (B76-50465)
By winding roads. *Selections.* Over the hills. The old man from Kilkenny. If. *Roberton. £0.15* JFDW (B76-50466)
By winding roads. *Selections.* Three little towns, Blarney. *Roberton. £0.10* JFDW (B76-50467)
By winding roads. The travellers. The travellers, and, The fairy hill. *Roberton. £0.10* JFDW (B76-50468)
By winding roads. Winds. Winds, and, In summer time. *Roberton. £0.20* JFDW (B76-50469)
Tunetime : six easy pieces for the piano. *Roberton. Unpriced* QPJ (B76-50916)
Parrott, Ian. Fanfare and march : for brass quartet. *EMI. Unpriced* WNSGM (B76-50740)
Parry, *Sir* Charles Hubert. And did those feet in ancient time. *arr.* Jerusalem. *Studio Music. Unpriced* WMK/DW (B76-51074)
Parry, John. Piano music. *Selections.* Piano music. (Sullivan, *Sir* Arthur Seymour). *Chappell. Unpriced* QPJ (B76-50216)
Parry, William Howard. The beast of Bettesthorne. *Chester. Unpriced* CN (B76-50765)
Partia für Oboe, 2 Englisch Hörner, 2 Hörner und 2 Fagotte. (Rosetti, Francesco Antonio). Zum ersten Mal. *Bärenreiter. Unpriced* UNPG (B76-51008)
Party time : for instrumental ensemble. (Wright, Francis). *Charnwood Music. Unpriced* LN (B76-50510)
Pasfield, William Reginald. Des Tages Weihe. D.763. *arr.* Where thou reignest. (Schubert, Franz). *Ashdown. £0.12* FLDH (B76-50091)
Pastoral symphony (1970). (Josephs, Wilfred). *Novello. £3.50* MME (B76-50519)
Patchen, Kenneth. Patterns in blue : medium voice, B flat clarinet and piano. (Sargon, Simon). *Boosey and Hawkes. £1.75* KFVE/VVPDW (B76-50502)
Patterns in blue : medium voice, B flat clarinet and piano. (Sargon, Simon). *Boosey and Hawkes. £1.75* KFVE/VVPDW (B76-50502)
Patterson, Paul.
Diversions : for saxophone quartet. *Weinberger. Unpriced* VUNS (B76-50693)
Time piece : for 2 altos, tenor, 2 baritones and bass. *Weinberger. Unpriced* JNGEZAZDX (B76-50840)
Paul, Leslie Douglas. Music at Bangor Cathedral Church : some historical notes. *The Cathedral Chaplain's House, Glanrafon, Bangor, Caernarvonshire LL57 1LH : Bangor Cathedral. £0.25* AD/LE(YDKPB/X) (B76-24542)
ISBN 0-905229-00-2
Paul Bunyan : an operetta in two acts and a prologue. (Auden, Wystan Hugh). *38 Russell Sq., WC1B 5DA : Faber Music Limited for Faber. £0.80* BBUACF (B76-10251) ISBN 0-571-10015-5
Paul McCartney in his own words. (Gambaccini, Paul). *78 Newman St., W1P 3LA : Omnibus Press. £1.95* AKDW/GB/E(P) (B76-25962) ISBN 0-8256-3063-0
Paul McCartney story. (Tremlett, George). *White Lion Publishers. £3.25* AKDW/GB/E(P) (B76-34782)
ISBN 0-7274-0118-1
Päuler, Bernhard.
Duets, clarinets, op.10. nos.1-3. Drei Duos für zwei Klarinetten. Opus 10. (Gambaro, Giovanni Battista). *Litolff : Peters. Unpriced* VVNU (B76-50702)
Symphony, D major. Sinfonie D-dur für Kammerorchester. (Cambini, Giovanni Giuseppe). Zum ersten Mal. *Litolff : Peters. Unpriced* MRE (B76-50882)
Paulik, Anton. Eine Nacht in Venedig. *Vocal score.* A night in Venice. (Korngold, Erich). *Weinberger. Unpriced* CF (B76-50364)
Pavane & galliard, 'The Earl of Salisbury'. Pavane. *arr.* The 'Earl of Salisbury' carol. (Byrd, William). *Banks. Unpriced* EZDP/LF (B76-50422)
Payne, Anthony. Concerto, orchestra. Concerto for orchestra. *Chester. Unpriced* MMF (B76-50871)
Payne, Anthony, *b.1936.* The music of Frank Bridge. *14 Barlby Rd, W10 6AR : Thames Publishing. £3.20* BBTP (B76-29100) ISBN 0-905210-02-6
Peace on earth to men : SATB. (Tate, Phyllis). *Oxford University Press. Unpriced* DP/LF (B76-50399)
ISBN 0-19-343057-6
Peake, Mervyn. Six songs of Mervyn Peake : for high voice, two clarinets and piano. (Walker, Robert). *Ramsey : Roberton. Unpriced* KFTE/VVNTQDW (B76-50499)
Pearsall, Ronald. Popular music of the twenties. *David and Charles etc.. £4.95* A/GB(XN10) (B76-32590)
ISBN 0-7153-7036-7
Peeters, Flor.
Serenade for carillon. Opus 61. *Peters. Unpriced* QXPJ (B76-50222)
Sonatina, carillon, no.2. Op.46. Sonatina 2. Opus 46 : carillon. *Peters. Unpriced* QXPE (B76-50221)
Pelléas et Mélisande. Op.80. Sicilienne. *arr.* Sicilienne. (Fauré, Gabriel). *Boosey and Hawkes. £3.95* MK/AHVQ (B76-50140)
Pember, Ron. Jack the Ripper : a musical play. *French. £0.90* BPEMACM (B76-10909) ISBN 0-573-08042-9
Peña, Paco. Toques flamencos. *Selections.* Toques flamencos. *Musical New Services. Unpriced* TSPMJ (B76-50990)
Penderecki, Krzysztof. Magnificat : für Bass solo, 7 Männerstimmen, 2 gemischte Chore (je 24 stimmig), Knabenstimmen und Orchester. *Schott. £10.00* EMDGKK (B76-50041)
Penetrations VI (1972-II) : for voice, chamber ensemble, lights, electronic music and electronic extensions. (Lanza, Alcides). *Boosey and Hawkes. Unpriced* KE/PV (B76-50860)
Penguin stereo record guide. (Greenfield, Edward). *Penguin. £3.50* A/FF(WT) (B76-03703) ISBN 0-14-046223-6
People look east : Advent carol, for four-part chorus of mixed voices unaccompanied. (Hanson, Geoffrey). *Roberton £0.10* EZDP/LEZ (B76-50806)
People of Sion : introit for Advent II (Populus Sion), A.T.B. (Jackson, Francis). *Banks. Unpriced* DH (B76-50783)
Pepper, Harry S.
Frederica : operetta in three acts. (Dunn, Bernard). *10 Rathbone St., W1P 2BJ : Glocken Verlag Ltd. £1.00* BLDACF
Friederike. *Vocal score.* Frederica : operetta in three acts. (Lehár, Franz). *Glocken. Unpriced* CF (B76-50761)
Percussion Studio.
Fink, Siegfried. Studien für Drums = Studies for drums Vol.1: Elementary. *Simrock. £2.00* XQ/AF (B76-50753)
Fink, Siegfried. Studien für Pauken = Studies for timpani Vol.1: Elementary. *Simrock. £4.00* XR/AF (B76-50755)
Marco, Tomás. Floreal : música celestial 2, for percussion solo. *Simrock. £1.45* XPMJ (B76-50345)
Moisy, Heinz von. Sounds and fills : for drumset. *Simrock. £2.50* XQ/AF (B76-50347)
Percy Grainger. (Bird, John, *b.1941*). *Elek. £10.00* BGRT(N) (B76-35350) ISBN 0-236-40004-5
Pergolesi, Giovanni Battista. Concerto, flute, two violins & continuo, D major. Concerto per il flauto solo, 2 violini e basso continuo (D-dur). *Heinrichshofen : Peters. Unpriced* NURNTF (B76-50164)
Perry merry dixy : 106 nursery and infant songs, old and new. *Schott. Unpriced* JFDW/GK/AY (B76-50109)
ISBN 0-901938-08-4
Pert, Morris. Four Japanese verses, Op.2 : for soprano and piano. *Weinberger. Unpriced* KFLDW (B76-50862)
Peter Piper's carol : calypso style, unison. (Verrall, Pamela Motley). *Leonard, Gould and Bolttler. Unpriced* JFDP/LF (B76-50108)
Peter Warlock Society. Warlock and Delius. (Tomlinson, Fred). *14 Barlby Rd, W10 6AR : Thames Publishing for the Peter Warlock Society. £1.50* BDL(Z) (B76-27764)
ISBN 0-905210-05-0
Petit concertiste. Schumann, Robert. Morçeaux choisis à l'usage des mains petites de la deuxième année de piano (assez facile) à la moyenne difficulté. *Chappell. Unpriced*

QPJ (B76-50215)
Petite ballerina : accordion solo. (Saint John, A M). *Charnwood Music. Unpriced* RSPMHW (B76-50603)
Petits concerts. Opus 16 : leichte Duos für Altblockflöten (Querflöten, Oboen, Violinen oder andere Melodieninstrumente)
Concerts 1-3. (Aubert, Jacques). *Heinrichshofen : Peters. Unpriced* VSSNUG (B76-50306)
Concerts 4-6. (Aubert, Jacques). *Heinrichshofen : Peters. Unpriced* VSSNUG (B76-50307)
Phelps, Ruth. Inca : a project in sound for young performers. (Odam, George). *Chester. Unpriced* CQN (B76-50770)
Phillips, John Charles. The lot is fallen unto me : anthem for SATB with divisions and organ. *Novello. £0.20* DK (B76-50023)
Phillips, Lois. The little piano book : a new way to start. *Forsyth. Unpriced* Q/AC (B76-50180)
Phorminx : for solo harp. (Capanna, Robert). *Schirmer. Unpriced* TQPMJ (B76-50265)
'Photoplay Magazine'. The movie musical from Vitaphone to 42nd Street : as reported in a great fan magazine. *Dover Publications etc. : Constable. £4.55* ACM/JR(YT/XNF8) (B76-12805) ISBN 0-486-23154-2
Physics of music. *See* Wood, Alexander.
Piano. (Kentner, Louis). *Macdonald and Jane's. £3.95* AQ/B (B76-10253) ISBN 0-356-04713-x
Piano : a history. (Ehrlich, Cyril). *Dent. £6.95* AQ/B(X) (B76-20709) ISBN 0-460-04246-7
Piano music. *Selections.* Piano music. (Sullivan, *Sir* Arthur Seymour). *Chappell. Unpriced* QPJ (B76-50216)
Piano tuning : a simple and accurate method for amateurs. (Fischer, Jerry Cree). Abridged ed.. *Dover Publication etc. : Constable. £2.10* AQ/P (B76-31127) ISBN 0-486-23267-0
Pianto delle Muse, in morte di Lord Byron = The weeping of the Muse on the death of Lord Byron : canzone for soloists, chorus and piano. (Rossini, Gioacchino Antonio). *Novello. £0.75* EZDW (B76-50815)
Pic-a-pic-a-polka : instrumental ensemble. (Wright, Francis). *Charnwood Music. Unpriced* LNHVH (B76-50511)
Pickles, Sydney. Events in tune. *EMI. Unpriced* QPJ (B76-50917)
Picton, Howard. Concerto, horns (2), keyboard & string orchestra, D major. Concerto in D major for fortepiano, 2 horns and strings. (Steffan, Joseph Anton). *Oxford University Press, for the University of Hull. Unpriced* RXMPWTNTPWF (B76-50613) ISBN 0-19-713421-1
Pidgeon, John. Eric Clapton : a biography. *Panther. £0.60* ATS/HK/E(P) (B76-27135) ISBN 0-586-04292-x
Pidoux, Pierre. Musikalischer Andachten, Tl 3. Es danken dir, Gott, die Volker. Es danken dir, Gott, die Volker : solokantate für Tenor, zwei Violinen und Basso continuo. (Hammerschmidt, Andreas). *Bärenreiter. £1.63* KGHE/SNTPWDE (B76-50503)
Pinson, Bob. 'San Antonio Rose' : the life and music of Bob Wills. (Townsend, Charles R). *University of Illinois Press. £8.75* AKDW/GCW/E(P) (B76-31914) ISBN 0-252-00470-1
Piper in the meadow. (Barratt, Bob). *Ambleside Music. Unpriced* WMK (B76-51069)
Pitfield, Thomas Baron. Eleven miniatures for harp. *Peters. Unpriced* TQPMJ (B76-50970)
Plato. Triptych, no.2. Op.30. Shadowplay, Op.30 : music theatre from book 7 of the Republic of Plato. (Goehr, Alexander). *Schott. Unpriced* C/JR (B76-50002)
Platts, Kenneth.
An Advent carol. Opus 25 : for treble voices and piano. *Ashdown. £0.08* FLDP/LEZ (B76-50092)
Little suite for strings, Op.26. *Edwin Ashdown. £1.00* RXMG (B76-50950)
Songs from the stable : for children's voices and instruments. *Edwin Ashdown. £2.00* JFE/LPDP/LF (B76-50834)
Play and sing : a third book for descant recorder and/or other instruments. *Holmes McDougall. Unpriced* VSRPLK/AAY (B76-51042)
Play and sing : for descant recorder and-or other instruments
3rd book. *Holmes-McDougall. £1.05* VSRPMK/AAY (B76-51043) ISBN 0-7157-0848-1
Play guitar. (Goran, Ulf). *Oxford University Press. £1.30* TS/AC (B76-50651) ISBN 0-19-322210-8
Play suite : seven simple quartets for beginner brass ensemble. (Stephen, John). *British and Continental : EMI. Unpriced* WNSG (B76-50335)
Plumley, Gwendolen Alice. El tanbur : the Sudanese lyre or the Nubian kissar. *c/o Book Production Consultants, 12 Hills Rd, Cambridge CB2 1PG : Town and Gown Press. £1.25* BZNDAT (B76-13572) ISBN 0-905107-02-0
Pocket book of 288 guitar chords : with fingering chord arrangements. (Conway, Pat). *International Music. Unpriced* TS/RC (B76-50269)
Pocket book of mandoline chords : 288 chords with fingering chord arrangements. (Conway, Pat). *International Music. Unpriced* TX/RC (B76-50280)
Pocket book of tenor banjo chords : (288 chords with fingering). (Conway, Pat). *International Music. Unpriced* TTV/RC (B76-50278)
Poet and peasant overture : (selections). (Suppé, Franz von). *Fisher and Lane. Unpriced* RPVK (B76-50937)
Poet in the suburbs : for unaccompanied mixed voices. (Fleischmann, Aloys). *Oxford University Press. Unpriced* EZDX (B76-50077) ISBN 0-19-336108-6
Poets' requiem. *Vocal score.* The poets' requiem : mixed chorus, soprano solo and orchestra. (Rorem, Ned). *Boosey and Hawkes. £5.00* DX (B76-50404)
Point and counterpoint : an account of the founding and first twenty-five years of the Canford Summer School of Music. (Hale, Noel). *250 Purley Way, Croydon CR9 4QD : Belwin Mills Music Limited. £0.80* A(VS/YDFKC/X) (B76-35347) ISBN 0-9503671-3-3
Polka française. (Strauss, Johann, *b.1825*). *Oxford University Press. Unpriced* UMMK/AHVH (B76-50665)
Poltergoose : for recorder, percussion, voices and piano. (Burnett, Michael). *Chester. Unpriced* CQN (B76-50769)
Pont, Kenneth. Donkey carol. *arr.* Donkey carol. (Rutter, John). *Oxford University Press. Unpriced* JFDP/LF (B76-50461) ISBN 0-19-342052-x
Poos, Heinrich. Ein jegliches hat seine Zeit : Suite für Männerchor, Sopransolo, Sprecher, in der Fassung für zwei Klaviere, Pauken und Schlagzeug (1 Spieler). *Schott. £19.20* ENYLNSDE (B76-50800)
Pop music in school. *Cambridge University Press. £4.75* A/GB(VK) (B76-25953) ISBN 0-521-20836-x
Popplewell, Richard. Puck's shadow : for organ. *Oxford University Press. Unpriced* RJ (B76-50934) ISBN 0-19-375657-9
Popular Italian madrigals of the sixteenth century : for mixed voices. *Oxford University Press. Unpriced* EZDU/AYJ (B76-50063) ISBN 0-19-343646-9
Popular music of the twenties. (Pearsall, Ronald). *David and Charles etc.. £4.95* A/GB(XN10) (B76-32590) ISBN 0-7153-7036-7
Popular songs for the recorder : outstanding selections published complete with lyrics and guitar diagrams plus a six page introduction to playing the recorder. *Wise : Music Sales. Unpriced* VSPMK/DW/GB/AY (B76-51038)
Popular songs of nineteenth-century America : complete original sheet music for 64 songs. *Dover Publications : Constable. £4.20* KDW/GB/AYT(XG101) (B76-50854) ISBN 0-486-23270-0
Porter, Andrew. Der Ring des Nibelungen. *English & German.* The ring. (Wagner, Richard). *Dawson. £15.00* BWCAC (B76-31122) ISBN 0-7129-0698-3
Post-partitions : piano. (Babbitt, Milton). *Peters. Unpriced* QPJ (B76-50198)
Poston, Elizabeth.
The apple tree : Christmas music from 'The Cambridge hymnal'. *Cambridge University Press. £4.00* DP/LF/AY (B76-50791) ISBN 0-521-21479-3
The Cambridge hymnal. *Choral score.* The Cambridge hymnal : vocal edition. *Cambridge University Press. £1.50* DADM (B76-50008) ISBN 0-521-20398-8
Powell, Sandy. 'Can you hear me, mother?' : Sandy Powell's lifetime of music-hall. *Jupiter Books. £3.50* A/JV/E(P) (B76-13584) ISBN 0-904041-38-7
Praeger special studies in US economic, social and political issues. Salem, Mahmoud. Organizational survival in the performing arts : the making of the Seattle Opera. *Praeger : Distributed by Martin Robertson. £10.25* AC/E/K/QB(YTXHS) (B76-22516) ISBN 0-275-05670-8
Praise ye the Lord. (Lowe, Augustus). *Paterson. Unpriced* KDR (B76-50116)
Prausnitz, Frederick. Triptych, no.3. Op.31. Sonata about Jerusalem. Op.31 : cantata. (Goehr, Alexander). *Schott. Unpriced* C/JR (B76-50003)
Prausnitz, Frederik. Triptych, no.2. Op.30. Shadowplay, Op.30 : music theatre from book 7 of the Republic of Plato. (Goehr, Alexander). *Schott. Unpriced* C/JR (B76-50002)
Preces and responses ('for trebles') : S.S.A.T.B. unacc. (Holmes, John). *Oxford University Press. Unpriced* EZDGMM (B76-50412) ISBN 0-19-351651-9
Prelude and paragrams. (Washburn, Robert). *Oxford University Press. Unpriced* UMMJ (B76-50664)
Première liste générale des disques à saphir Phrynis de 30 centimètres de diamètre. *19 Glendale Rd, Bournemouth BH6 4JA : Talking Machine Review. £0.60* A/FD(WT) (B76-50352) ISBN 0-902338-23-4
Première récréation de musique, Op.6 : for two violins and basso continuo. (Leclair, Jean Marie, *b.1697*). *Bärenreiter. £6.00* SNTPWG (B76-50629)
Premru, Raymond. Music from Harter Fell : for brass sextet. *Chester. Unpriced* WNQ (B76-50738)
Prentice-Hall history of music series. Brown, Howard Mayer. Music in the Renaissance. *Prentice-Hall. £8.00* A(XCR181) (B76-26567) ISBN 0-13-608505-9
Preparatory course for guitar. (Wright, Francis). *Charnwood Music. Unpriced* TS/AC (B76-50973)
Pretzels : a musical revue. (Forster, John). *French. £1.25* BFNRACP (B76-06889) ISBN 0-573-68071-x
Previn, André. The good companions. *Vocal score.* The good companions : the musical of the novel by J.B. Priestley. *Chappell. Unpriced* CM (B76-50763)
Price, Beryl. Airs from seven lands. *Oxford University Press. Unpriced* VRPK/DW/AY (B76-51024) ISBN 0-19-358304-6
Price, Tim Rose-. *See* Rose-Price, Tim.
Price-Thomas, Brian.
Action rhymes. *Ladybird Books. £0.24* ADW/GR (B76-30340) ISBN 0-7214-0439-1
Dancing rhymes. *Ladybird Books. £0.24* ADW/H (B76-30341) ISBN 0-7214-0440-5
Priestley, John Boynton. The good companions. *Vocal score.* The good companions : the musical of the novel by J.B. Priestley. (Previn, André). *Chappell. Unpriced* CM (B76-50763)
Primary course for guitar. (Wright, Francis). *Charnwood Music. Unpriced* TS/AC (B76-50974)
Primary music groups. *British and Continental : EMI. Unpriced* NYESK/AAY (B76-50174)
Primo libro delle musiche. Primo ballo. Suite in 6 parts for 6 recorders. (Allegri, Lorenzo). *Dolmetsch : Chappell. Unpriced* VSNQH (B76-51029)
Primrose, William. Violin and viola. (Menuhin, Yehudi). *Macdonald and Jane's. £4.50* AS/E (B76-06892) ISBN 0-356-04715-6
Pringle, John. Music and musical instruments in the world of Islam. (Jenkins, Jean). *85 Cromwell Rd, SW7 5BW : World of Islam Festival Publishing Co. Ltd. £1.50* BZCWIAL/B(YDB/WJ) (B76-22080) ISBN 0-905035-12-7
Prismen : für Soloinstrumente, (Flöte, Oboe, Klarinette in B, Harfe, Schlagzeug) und Orchester von Wolfgang Fortner. (Fortner, Wolfgang). *Schott. £11.20* MPVR (B76-50879)
Probe, no.13. Folk song : music arranged by John and Susanne Bailey, text by John Bailey. *SCM Press. Unpriced* JEZDW/G/AYC (B76-50106) ISBN 0-334-00492-6
Procession by night, and, Mephisto waltz. (Liszt, Franz). *Eulenburg. Unpriced* MMJ (B76-50528)
Proctor, Charles. Chaconne for organ. *Weinberger. Unpriced* RHJN (B76-50588)
Prodigal sister : a new black musical. (Franklin, J E). *French. £1.35* BGSEACM (B76-50357) ISBN 0-573-68075-2
Professional register of private teachers of music 1975-76. *48 Gloucester Place, W1H 3HJ : The Society. £1.00* A(VC/M/BC) (B76-14360) ISBN 0-902900-08-0
Programme music : a brief survey from the sixteenth century to the present day. (Orrey, Leslie). *Davis-Poynter. £6.00* A/KB(X) (B76-01879) ISBN 0-7067-0171-2
Progressive sight reading for accordion students : a collection of graded exercises
Book 1: Stage 1 to stage 5. (Romani, G). *Charnwood Music. Unpriced* RS/EG (B76-50944)
Book 2: Stage 4 to stage 8. (Romani, G). *Charnwood Music. Unpriced* RS/EG (B76-50945)
Projects in sound. (Dennis, Brian). *Universal Edition. £2.00* AL/E(VG) (B76-22854) ISBN 0-900938-45-5
Prokofiev, Sergei. The love of three oranges. March. *arr.* March. *Boosey and Hawkes. £5.00* WMK/AGM (B76-50733)
Prometheus. (Liszt, Franz). *Eulenburg. Unpriced* MMJ (B76-50526)
Promise me you'll sing 'Mud'! : the autobiography of Ian Wallace. (Wallace, Ian, *b.1919*). *18 Brewer St., W1R 4AS : John Calder. £5.75* AKGX/E(P) (B76-00669) ISBN 0-7145-3500-1
Propes, Steve. Those oldies but goodies : a guide to 50's record collecting. *Collier Books : Collier Macmillan. £0.95* A/FD/GB/YT(XPK11) (B76-12802) ISBN 0-02-061430-6
Protestant church music : a history. (Blume, Friedrich). *Gollancz. £15.00* ADGTCW(X) (B76-01876) ISBN 0-575-01996-4
Psalm 130 : for double choir, S.A.T.B.-S.A.T.B. (Schütz, Heinrich). *Chiswick Music. Unpriced* EZDR (B76-50061)
Psalmen Davids. De profundis. Psalm 130 : for double choir, S.A.T.B.-S.A.T.B. (Schütz, Heinrich). *Chiswick Music. Unpriced* EZDR (B76-50061)
Public Libraries Group. *See* Library Association. *Public Libraries Group.*
Puccini, Giacomo. Puccini. *Warren and Phillips. Unpriced* QPK/DW (B76-50585)
Puccini : a critical biography. (Carner, Mosco). 2nd ed. *Duckworth. £14.00* BPU (B76-22081) ISBN 0-7156-0795-2
Puck's shadow : for organ. (Popplewell, Richard). *Oxford University Press. Unpriced* RJ (B76-50934) ISBN 0-19-375657-9
Puffin easy readers. Ten green bottles. *Puffin Books. £0.50* ADW/GJ (B76-14369) ISBN 0-14-050144-4
Pulkingham, Betty. Fresh sounds. *Hodder and Stoughton. Unpriced* JDM/AY (B76-50826) ISBN 0-340-20622-5
Puopolo, Vito. Music fundamentals. *Schirmer : Collier Macmillan. £5.25* A/M (B76-25958) ISBN 0-02-871890-9
Purcell, Henry.
Complete trumpet repertoire of Henry Purcell. *Musica rara. Unpriced* WS (B76-50338)
Purcell for the harp. *Schirmer. Unpriced* TQPMK (B76-50266)
Sonatas, string trio & continuo, no.7-12, Z.796-801. Sonatas of three parts, no.7-12. *Eulenburg. Unpriced* NXNSE (B76-50172)
Songs
Book 1. *Galliard : Stainer and Bell. Unpriced* KDW (B76-50480)
Book 2. *Galliard : Stainer and Bell. Unpriced* KDW (B76-50481) ISBN 0-85249-323-1
Book 3. *Galliard : Stainer and Bell. Unpriced* KDW (B76-50482) ISBN 0-85249-383-5
The works of Henry Purcell
Vol.5: Twelve sonatas of three parts. *Novello. £10.00* NXNTE (B76-50173)
Purcell for the harp. (Purcell, Henry). *Schirmer. Unpriced* TQPMK (B76-50266)
Purvis, Jennie. Music in developmental therapy : a curriculum guide. *University Park Press. £6.25* A(VMWM) (B76-30972) ISBN 0-8391-0895-8
Q.M.B. Edition.
Grundman, Clare. Tuba rhapsody : for tuba and symphonic band. *Boosey and Hawkes. £30.00* UMPWV (B76-51007)
Tull, Fisher. Credo for symphonic band. *Boosey and Hawkes. £15.00* UMMJ (B76-50663)
Q.M.B. edition.
Washburn, Robert. Epigon IV. *Boosey and Hawkes. £15.00* UMMJ (B76-51003)
Washburn, Robert. Epigon IV. *Boosey and Hawkes.*

£15.00 UMMJ (B76-51004)
Washburn, Robert. March-opus '76. *Boosey and Hawkes. £12.00* UMMGM (B76-50999)
Q.M.B. Edition, 385. Gillis, Don. Symphony 'X', (Big 'D'). *Boosey and Hawkes. £0.35* UMME (B76-50662)
Qualey, David. Only for guitar : new compositions for solo guitar. *Scratchwood Music : EMI. Unpriced* TSPMJ (B76-50272)
Quartet no.2 on themes from Mozart. (Mozart, Wolfgang Amadeus). *Studio Music. Unpriced* WNSK (B76-50742)
Quatro pecas para 2 flautas doce em do (C) e fa (F). (Mignone, Francisco). *Arthur Napoleão : Essex Music. Unpriced* VSNU (B76-51036)
Quattro versioni originale della 'Ritirata notturna di Madrid'. (Boccherini, Luigi). *Universal. Unpriced* MMK (B76-50154)
Quiet showman : Sir David Webster and the Royal Opera House. (Haltrecht, Montague). *Collins. £6.00* AC(WB/XPD28/P) (B76-03866) ISBN 0-00-211163-2
Quine, Hector.
Cantata no.22: Jesus nahm zu sich die Zwölfe. Ertodt' uns durch dein' Güte. *arr.* Sanctify us by thy goodness : chorale. (Bach, Johann Sebastian). *Oxford University Press. Unpriced* TSNUK/DM (B76-50982) ISBN 0-19-355297-3
Cantata no.208: Was mir behagt. Schafe konnen sicher weiden. *arr.* Sheep may safely graze : aria. (Bach, Johann Sebastian). *Oxford University Press. Unpriced* TSNUK/DW (B76-50983) ISBN 0-19-355298-1
Easy modern guitar music : ten pieces by British composers. *Oxford University Press. Unpriced* TS/AY (B76-50654) ISBN 0-19-358419-0
Selections. *arr.* Bach for the guitar : nine pieces. (Bach, Johann Sebastian). *Oxford University Press. Unpriced* TSPMK (B76-50273) ISBN 0-19-355300-7
The watermill. *arr.* The watermill. (Binge, Ronald). *Oxford University Press. Unpriced* TSPMJ (B76-50658) ISBN 0-19-355510-7
Rachmaninoff, Sergei. Romance and scherzo. *arr.* Romance and scherzo. *Oxford University Press. Unpriced* SQPK (B76-50637) ISBN 0-19-358441-7
Rachmaninov, Serge. *See* Rachmaninoff, Sergei.
Rachmaninov. (Norris, Geoffrey, *b.1947*). *Dent. £3.50* BRC (B76-04297) ISBN 0-460-03145-7
Radcliffe, Philip. E.J. Dent : a centenary memoir. *22 Pheasants Way, Rickmansworth, Herts. : Triad Press for the E.J. Dent Centenary Committee. £1.50* A(VX/P) (B76-20005) ISBN 0-902070-18-5
Radford, Winifred. The interpretation of French song. (Bernac, Pierre). *Gollancz. £7.50* AKDW/E(YH) (B77-00346) ISBN 0-575-02207-8
Ragtime classics : ten piano rags. *Paxton. £1.25* QPHXJ/AY (B76-50564)
Ragtime guitar : complete instructions and exercises, 37 raggy songs, 23 Scott Joplin rags, the Scott Joplin school of ragtime. *Chappell. Unpriced* KE/TSDW/HXJ/AY (B76-50130)
Ragtime rarities : complete original music for 63 piano rags. *Dover Publications : Constable. £4.55* QPHXJ/AY (B76-50565) ISBN 0-486-23157-7
Rainbow and the cuckoo : for oboe and string trio. (Tate, Phyllis). *Oxford University Press. Unpriced* NVTNS (B76-50884) ISBN 0-19-359024-7
Rakhmaninov, Serge. *See* Rachmaninoff, Sergei.
Rameau, Jean Philippe. Les Indes galantes. *Selections : arr.* Four oboe melodies. *Oxford University Press. Unpriced* VTPK (B76-50311) ISBN 0-19-358461-1
Ramsbotham, Alexander. Liber primus sacrarum cantionum. O quam gloriosum. O quam gloriosum : S.S.A.T.B. (Byrd, William). Revised ed. *Oxford University Press. Unpriced* EZDJ (B76-50417) ISBN 0-19-352060-5
Randall, Julia. Pièces de clavecin, livre 3, ordre 13. Les Roseaux. *arr.* Les Roseaux = The reeds. (Couperin, François). *Oxford University Press. Unpriced* VTPK (B76-50310) ISBN 0-19-355910-2
Rastall, Richard.
Four French songs from an English song book (Cambridge, University Library Add.MS.5943, ff 161-173) : for voice with 1 and 2 instruments. *Antico. Unpriced* KE/LNUDW/AY (B76-50859)
Lachrimae. (Dowland, John). 1st ed., reprinted. *5 Albert Grove, Leeds 6 : Boethius Press. £6.60* BDTARWNR (B76-10254) ISBN 0-904263-04-5
Ratcliffe, Desmond. An Erik Satie entertainment : a selection of songs and piano music. (Satie, Erik). *Novello. Unpriced* QPJ (B76-50212)
Ratione in musica : Festschrift Erich Schenk, zu 5.Mai 1972. *32 Great Titchfield St., W.1 : Bärenreiter Kassel. £18.00* A(ZC)
Raven, Jon. The rigs of the fair : popular sports and pastimes in the nineteenth century through songs, ballads and contemporary accounts. *Cambridge University Press. £1.25(non-net)* ADW/G(YD/XG61) (B76-12389) ISBN 0-521-20908-0
Raynor, Henry. Music and society since 1815. *Barrie and Jenkins. £6.00* A(XGQ160) (B76-20705) ISBN 0-214-20220-8
Rea, William A. Inia Te Wiata's Maori songbook : favourite songs and chants as arranged and recorded by Inia Te Wiata. (Te Wiata, Inia). *A.H. & A.W. Reed. Unpriced* KDW/G/AYXR (B76-50491) ISBN 0-589-00877-3
'Record Mirror'. 20 years of British record charts, 1955-1975. *Queen Anne Press. £0.75* ADW/GB/FD(XPQ21/WT) (B76-08789) ISBN 0-362-00263-0
Recordações da infância. Na beira do rio. Na beira do rio. (Lorenzo Fernandez, Oscar). *Arthur Napoleão : Essex Music. Unpriced* QPJ (B76-50911)
Recorder music for beginners. *Boosey and Hawkes. £1.25* VSRPK/AAY (B76-51041)
Red and green Christmas. *arr.* Red and green Christmas : for SATB chorus and keyboard. (Cattouse, Nadia). *Galaxy : Galliard. Unpriced* DP/LF (B76-50393)
Red sky at night : for brass band. (Lear, W Hogarth). *Chester Music. Unpriced* WMJ (B76-51065)
Redlich, Hans F. Adagio and fugue, string orchestra, K.546, C minor. Adagio and fugue for strings, C minor. K.546. (Mozart, Wolfgang Amadeus). Revised ed. *Eulenburg. Unpriced* RXM/Y (B76-50947)
Redlich, Hans Ferdinand. Symphony, no.34, K.338, C major. Symphony, C major. K.338 and Minuetto, C major. K.409. (Mozart, Wolfgang Amadeus). *Eulenburg. Unpriced* MME (B76-50144)
Rédoublement : für einen Klarinettisten. (Globokar, Vinko). *Litolff : Peters. Unpriced* VVPMJ (B76-50320)
Redwood, Christopher. A Delius companion. *John Calder Distributed by Calder and Boyars. £7.50* BDL (B76-17646) ISBN 0-7145-3526-5
Reflections on Wagner's 'Ring'. (Culshaw, John). *Secker and Warburg. £3.50* BWCAC (B76-13571) ISBN 0-436-11801-7
Reid, Alistair. Compass : cello, contra bass, tenor, bass and electronics. (Reynolds, Roger). *Peters. Unpriced* JNGE/SRPLSSDX (B76-50114)
Reiser, Dave. What a spot! : a musical farce in three acts. (Sharkey, Jack). *French. £1.45* BSGNHACM (B76-30339) ISBN 0-573-61814-3
Rejection : S.A.T.B. unacc. (Gardner, John). *Oxford University Press. Unpriced* EZDW (B76-50433) ISBN 0-19-343058-4
Rejoice and sing : sacred songs for Christmas, for treble voices and piano (or organ). (Ridout, Alan). *Chappell. Unpriced* JFLDP/LF (B76-50839)
Reminiscences of Scriabin : for treble and sopranino recorders. (Dench, Chris). *17 Dempster Rd, S.W.18 : The composer. Unpriced* VSNU (B76-50301)
Renaissance works for four instruments. *Boosey and Hawkes. £1.75* LNS/AY (B76-50515)
Repertoire der Flötenpartien aus dem Kantaten und Oratorienwerk
Band 1: Kantaten BWV 8-102, Matthaus Passion, Oster-Oratorium. (Bach, Johann Sebastian). *Litolff : Peters. Unpriced* VR (B76-50288)
Report on the music examination in 1974 relating to the proposed single system of examining at 16+. (Associated Examining Board for the General Certificate of Education). *Wellington House, Aldershot, Hants. GU11 1BQ : The Board. £0.50* A(VK/AL) (B76-15048) ISBN 0-901893-07-2
Reproductions of early music. The Mynshall lute book. *5 Albert Grove, Leeds 6 : Boethius Press. £6.25* ATW(YD) (B76-11505) ISBN 0-904263-03-7
Res/as/ex/ins-pirer : für einen Blechbläser. (Globokar, Vinko). *Litolff : Peters. Unpriced* WPMJ (B76-50337)
Resources of music. Pop music in school. *Cambridge University Press. £4.75* A/GB(VK) (B76-25953) ISBN 0-521-20836-x
Resources of music series. The rigs of the fair : popular sports and pastimes in the nineteenth century through songs, ballads and contemporary accounts. *Cambridge University Press. £1.25(non-net)* ADW/G(YD/XG61) (B76-12389) ISBN 0-521-20908-0
Reubke, Julius. Sonata, organ 'The 94th psalm'. The 94th psalm. Sonata for organ. *Oxford University Press. Unpriced* RE (B76-50229) ISBN 0-19-375685-4
Reutter, Hermann. Trost der Nacht : Chorvariationen für vierstimmigen gemischten Chor a cappella oder mit Flöte und Klavier ad lib. *Schott. £5.20* EZDH (B76-50804)
Reverberations : interviews with the world's leading musicians. (Jacobson, Robert). *Vision Press. £5.95* AL/E(M) (B76-15049) ISBN 0-85478-453-5
Reynolds, David. Weber in London, 1826. *Wolff. £1.95* BWL(YDB/XHF) (B76-22852) ISBN 0-85496-403-7
Reynolds, Roger. Compass : cello, contra bass, tenor, bass and electronics. *Peters. Unpriced* JNGE/SRPLSSDX (B76-50114)
Rhodes, Phillip. Trio, strings. Trio for strings : violin, viola, violoncello. *Peters. Unpriced* RXNT (B76-50244)
Ricci, Robert. The language of twentieth century music : a dictionary of terms. (Fink, Robert). *Schirmer Books : Collier Macmillan. £5.50* A(XMA77/C) (B76-05036) ISBN 0-02-870600-5
Richard, Keith. The Rolling Stones file. (Jagger, Mick). *78 Newman St., WIP 3LA : Music Sales Ltd. £2.95* AKDW/GB/E(P) (B76-26570) ISBN 0-86001-245-x
Richard Strauss. (Kennedy, Michael, *b.1926*). *Dent. £3.95* BSU (B76-14362) ISBN 0-460-03148-1
Richard Wagner. (Gál, Hans). *Gollancz. £5.50* BWC (B76-05038) ISBN 0-575-01847-x
Richter, Werner. Selections. *Flute parts.* Repertoire der Flötenpartien aus dem Kantaten und Oratorienwerk
Band 1: Kantaten BWV 8-102, Matthaus Passion, Oster-Oratorium. (Bach, Johann Sebastian). *Litolff : Peters. Unpriced* VR (B76-50288)
Ricker, Ramon L. Mein junges Leben hat ein End. Variations on 'Mein junges Leben hat ein End'. (Sweelinck, Jan Pieterzoon). *Schirmer. Unpriced* UMK/AT (B76-50283)
Ridgeon, John.
Brass for beginners. *Boosey and Hawkes. £2.00* W/AC (B76-50717)
How brass players do it : a book of lip building and flexibility exercises. *Belwin Mills. Unpriced* W/EH/AF (B76-50718)
Ridley, Edward Alexander Keane. Wind instruments of European art music. (Horniman Museum). *Inner London Education Authority. £0.45* AU/B(YDBL) (B76-21368) ISBN 0-7168-0545-6
Ridout, Alan. Rejoice and sing : sacred songs for Christmas, for treble voices and piano (or organ). *Chappell. Unpriced* JFLDP/LF (B76-50839)
Riethmuller Heinrich.
Weinachten an der Heimorgel
Band 1. *Anton J. Benjamin. £1.90* RPVK/DP/LF/AY (B76-50600)
Band 2. *Anton J. Benjamin. £1.90* RPVK/DP/LF/AY (B76-50601)
Right on : from blues to soul in Black America. (Haralambos, Michael). *2 Greycoat Place, SW1P 1SB : Eddison Press Ltd. £2.50* AKDW/HHW/E(M) (B76-20008) ISBN 0-85649-016-4
Rigs of the fair : popular sports and pastimes in the nineteenth century through songs, ballads and contemporary accounts. *Cambridge University Press. £1.25(non-net)* ADW/G(YD/XG61) (B76-12389) ISBN 0-521-20908-0
Ring, Layton.
Sinfonia, allemande, correnti e sarabande a 5 e 6. Op.5. *Selections : arr.* Two suites a 6 : for 6 recorders. (Bononcini, Giovanni Maria). *Universal. Unpriced* VSNQK/AHG (B76-51030)
Sonata, treble recorder, oboe & continuo, op.4, no.2. Sonata a tre con fluto e hautboy : for treble recorder, oboe (or treble II) and continuo. (Loeillet, Jean Baptiste, *of London*). *Universal. Unpriced* NWNTE (B76-50885)
Ring. (Wagner, Richard). *Dawson. £15.00* BWCAC (B76-31122) ISBN 0-7129-0698-3
Ring des Nibelungen. *English & German.* The ring. (Wagner, Richard). *Dawson. £15.00* BWCAC (B76-31122) ISBN 0-7129-0698-3
Rise of romantic opera. (Dent, Edward Joseph). *Cambridge University Press. £6.50* AC(XG41) (B77-00341) ISBN 0-521-21337-1
Ritmi dispari : Sonatine für Klarinette in B und Klavier von Wolfgang Hildemann. (Hildemann, Wolfgang). *Schott. £1.75* VVPEM (B76-50704)
River flows, the seasons turn : anthem for S.A.T.B., soprano solo and organ. (Frith, Michael). *Oxford University Press. Unpriced* DH (B76-50015)
Roberton, Hugh S. Iona boat song, (For a dead king) : traditional Island air. (Lees, Heath). *Roberton. £0.10* FEZDW (B76-50090)
Roberton female choir series. Lyell, Margaret. Love in May : for 4-part female voice choir unaccompanied. *Roberton. Unpriced* FEZDW (B76-50820)
Roberton male voice series.
Burtch, Mervyn. Epilogue : for four-part male voice choir unaccompanied. *Roberton. £0.10* GEZDH (B76-50823)
Head, Michael. I will lift up mine eyes : Psalm 121, for 4-part male voice choir with optional organ or piano. *Roberton £0.14* GEZDR (B76-50095)
Head, Michael. Make a joyful noise unto the Lord. Psalm 100 : for 4-part male voice choir with organ or piano or unaccompanied voices. *Roberton. £0.18* GDR (B76-50093)
Roberton mixed voice series. Burtch, Mervyn. Three sonnets of John Donne : for four-part choir of mixed voices unaccompanied. *Roberton. £0.28* EZDW (B76-50814)
Roberts, Ronald.
Making a simple violin and viola. *David and Charles. £4.50* AS/BC (B76-09330) ISBN 0-7153-6964-4
Musical instruments, made to be played. 6th ed. *Dryad Press. £1.95* AL/BC (B76-15863) ISBN 0-85219-095-6
Robin, Jacqueline. Morçeaux choisis à l'usage des mains petites de la deuxième année de piano (assez facile) à la moyenne difficulté. (Schumann, Robert). *Chappell. Unpriced* QPJ (B76-50215)
Robinson, Marjorie. The violin and viola. *F. Watts. £1.75* AS/B (B77-00349) ISBN 0-85166-595-0
Robinson, Paul. Karajan. *Macdonald and Jane's. £3.95* A/EC(P) (B76-35356) ISBN 0-354-04031-6
Roche, Jerome. Litanie et motetti. Ave verum corpus. Ave verum corpus : S.A.T.T.B. and organ. (Milani, Francesco). *Oxford University Press. Unpriced* DJ (B76-50022) ISBN 0-19-350357-3
Rocherolle, Eugénie R.
Along the sand : SSAA chorus and piano with optional alto. *Warner : Blossom. Unpriced* FDW (B76-50081)
Christmas lullaby : unison, two part or SSA chorus and piano. *Warner : Blossom. Unpriced* JDP/LF (B76-50455)
Rock file
4. *Panther. £1.25* ADW/GB (B76-25952) ISBN 0-586-04370-5
Rocking. (Roe, Betty). *Thames. Unpriced* FE/NYFPNTDP/LF (B76-50442)
Rodd-Marling, Yvonne. Singing : the physical nature of the vocal organ : a guide to the unlocking of the singing voice. (Husler, Frederick). *Hutchinson. £6.50* AB/E (B76-26571) ISBN 0-09-126860-5
Rodgers, Richard.
The best of Rodgers and Hart. *Chappell. Unpriced* KDW (B76-50121)
Musical stages : an autobiography. *W.H. Allen. £5.95* BRK(N) (B76-32591) ISBN 0-491-01777-4
Rodgers and Hammerstein clarinet classics. *Williamson. Unpriced* VVPK/DW (B76-50710)
Rodgers and Hammerstein clarinet classics. (Rodgers, Richard). *Williamson. Unpriced* VVPK/DW (B76-50710)
Roe, Betty.
An ABC of music for actors. *14 Barlby Rd, W10 6AR : Thomas Publishing. £0.30* A/M (B76-05037) ISBN 0-905210-00-x

The barnstormers. *Selections.* The barnstormers. *Thames. Unpriced* JDW/JM (B76-50457)
Like as the hart : soprano solo and mixed chorus. *Thames. Unpriced* EZDK (B76-50419)
Rocking. *Thames. Unpriced* FE/NYFPNTDP/LF (B76-50442)
Rogers, Maurice. Piano album. (Satie, Erik). *Cramer. Unpriced* QPJ (B76-50211)
Rokos, Kitty. Vibrato on the violin. (Hauck, Werner). *Bosworth. £3.00* AS/EV (B76-09329) ISBN 0-900180-71-4
Roll the old chariot along (with other things) : a quodlibet. (Hudson, Hazel). *Ashdown. £0.15* FDW/LC (B76-50440)
Rolla, Alessandro. Duets, violins, nos 1-3. Drei Duos für zwei Violinen. Zum ersten Mal herausgegeben von Ulrich Drüner. *Litulff : Peters. Unpriced* SNU (B76-50631)
Rolling Stones. (Jasper, Tony). *Octopus Books. £1.99* AKDW/GB/E(P) (B76-31917) ISBN 0-7064-0549-8
Rolling Stones file. (Jagger, Mick). *78 Newman St., WIP 3LA : Music Sales Ltd. £2.95* AKDW/GB/E(P) (B76-26570) ISBN 0-86001-245-x
Rolling Stones story. (Tremlett, George). *White Lion Publishers. £3.25* AKDW/GB/E(P) (B76-28394) ISBN 0-7274-0123-8
Roman Catholic Church. *Liturgy and ritual.* Missal. Responses. *English.* Sung responses at Mass : music and English translation of the Rite of Mass. *Incorporated Catholic Truth Society. Unpriced* JDGK (B76-50101)
Romance and scherzo. *arr.* Romance and scherzo. (Rachmaninoff, Sergei). *Oxford University Press. Unpriced* SQPK (B76-50637) ISBN 0-19-358441-7
Romance, violin & orchestra, no.1, op.40, G major. *arr.* Beneficence. (Beethoven, Ludwig van). *Fischer; Pinns Farm, West Wellow, Romsey : Edgar New gass. Unpriced* KDW (B76-50118)
Romani, G.
Joy waltz : instrumental ensemble. (Mayes, Jerry). *Charnwood Music. Unpriced* LNHW (B76-50512)
Progressive sight reading for accordion students : a collection of graded exercises
Book 1: Stage 1 to stage 5. *Charnwood Music. Unpriced* RS/EG (B76-50944)
Book 2: Stage 4 to stage 8. *Charnwood Music. Unpriced* RS/EG (B76-50945)
Romantic music for flute and piano. *Boosey and Hawkes. Unpriced* VRPK/AAY (B76-51023)
Rooftop ballet. Rooftop ballet and Underwater ballet : two piano solos. (Bailey, Freda O). *Regina Music. Unpriced* QPJ (B76-50902)
Rooley, Anthony. Music from the student repertoire
Series 3: 'A new varietie of lute lessons' : music for the first three years selected from English and continental master lutenists of the sixteenth century. *Musical New Services. Unpriced* TPMK/AAY (B76-50968)
Rooper, Jasper. Cantata for all seasons. *Vocal score.* Cantata for all seasons : for solos and mixed voices with orchestra or organ. *Thames. Unpriced* DE (B76-50368)
Rooster rag : a cantata in popular style for unison voices (with divisions) and piano, with guitar chord symbols. (Hurd, Michael). *Novello. £0.50* FDX (B76-50441)
Ropartz, Joseph Guy. Berceuse. *arr.* You will see an angel tonight. *Galaxy : Galliard. Unpriced* DP/LF (B76-50397)
Ropesight : Jasper Whitfield Snowdon's introduction to the art of change ringing, as revised by William Snowdon. (Snowdon, Jasper Whitfield). *22 Duke St., Burton Latimer, Northants. : C. Groome. £2.50* AXSR/E(XA1935) (B76-35804) ISBN 0-905334-00-0
Rorem, Ned.
Little prayers. *Vocal score.* Little prayers : for soprano and baritone solos, mixed chorus, and orchestra. *Boosey and Hawkes. £6.00* DE (B76-50776)
The poets' requiem. *Vocal score.* The poets' requiem : mixed chorus, soprano solo and orchestra. *Boosey and Hawkes. £5.00* DX (B76-50404)
Sky music : ten pieces for solo harp. *Boosey and Hawkes. £2.00* TQPMJ (B76-50650)
To Jane : music by Ned Rorem. *Boosey and Hawkes. £1.00* KDW (B76-50483)
Where we came. *Boosey and Hawkes. £1.25* KDW (B76-50484)
Rose, Bernard.
Behold, I make all things new : anthem for four-part mixed choir with organ. *Roberton. £0.15* EZDK (B76-50805)
Missa : Voces choristarum, series 3 : for treble voices with organ. *Roberton. £0.20* FLDGS (B76-50822)
Rose, Gregory. Vespers for Mary Magdalen : for 21 solo voices, (5 sopranos, 5 altos, 5 tenors, 6 basses). *Novello. £0.42* EZDE (B76-50048)
Rose, Margaret. Norse cradle song : unison. (Longmire, John). *Leonard, Gould and Bolttler. £0.09* JFDW (B76-50464)
Rose, Philip. Shenandoah : a musical. (Udell, Peter). *French. £1.25* BGGTACM (B76-06888) ISBN 0-573-68073-6
Rose-Price, Tim. Time piece : for 2 altos, tenor, 2 baritones and bass. (Patterson, Paul). *Weinberger. Unpriced* JNGEZAZDX (B76-50840)
Rosen, Charles. Arnold Schoenberg. *See* Rosen, Charles. Schoenberg.
Rosen, Charles.
The classical style : Haydn, Mozart, Beethoven. Revised ed. *Faber. £9.00* A(X) (B76-35348) ISBN 0-571-04916-8
Schoenberg. *Fontana. £0.75* BSET (B76-34779) ISBN 0-00-633558-6
Schoenberg. *Marion Boyars : Distributed by Calder and Boyars. £4.25* BSET (B76-14361) ISBN 0-7145-2566-9

Rosen aus dem Suden. Op.388. *arr.* Roses from the south. Op.388 : waltz. (Strauss, Johann, *b.1825*). *Bosworth. Unpriced* MK/AHW (B76-50518)
Roses from the south. Op.388 : waltz. (Strauss, Johann, *b.1825*). *Bosworth. Unpriced* MK/AHW (B76-50518)
Rosetti, Francesco Antonio. Partia für Oboe, 2 Englisch Hörner, 2 Hörner und 2 Fagotte. Zum ersten Mal. *Bärenreiter. Unpriced* UNPG (B76-51008)
Ross. Swingtime in Tottenham. (Green, Benny). *Basset Chambers, 27 Bedfordbury, W.C.2 : Lemon Tree Press Ltd. £1.25* AMT(P/XP11) (B76-35803) ISBN 0-904291-11-1
Ross, Stella. Wassailing. (Holder, Ray). *Thames Music. Unpriced* JDP/LF (B76-50454)
Ross, William. Ross's collection of pipe music. *E.P. £6.95* VY/AY (B76-51055) ISBN 0-7158-1201-7
Rossini, Gioacchino. G.A. Rossini's 'William Tell'. (Mizusawa, Hiroshi). *F. Warne. £2.25* BRRACBN (B76-18578) ISBN 0-7232-1833-1
Rossini, Gioacchino Antonio.
Ave Maria : for four-part chorus of mixed voices with piano. *Roberton. £0.14* DH (B76-50018)
Guillaume Tell. Overture. Overture to the opera 'Guillaume Tell'. *Eulenburg. Unpriced* MMJ (B76-50530)
Messe solennelle. Kyrie. *Vocal score.* Kyrie. *Roberton. £0.28* DGB (B76-50778)
Il pianto delle Muse, in morte di Lord Byron = The weeping of the Muse on the death of Lord Byron : canzone for soloists, chorus and piano. *Novello. £0.75* EZDW (B76-50815)
Rossini, Giocchino Antonio. Cinderella in Salerno. *Vocal score.* Cinderella in Salerno : an opera for schools in three acts based on Rossini's 'La Cenerentola'. (Walker, Raymond). *Novello. £1.70* CN (B76-50766)
Rossiter, Frank Raymond. Charles Ives and his America. *Gollancz. £8.50* BIV(N) (B76-20007) ISBN 0-575-02103-9
Ross's collection of pipe music. *E.P. £6.95* VY/AY (B76-51055) ISBN 0-7158-1201-7
Rostirolla, Giancarlo. Duo tessuti con diversi solfeggiamenti. *Selections.* Duetti per due strumenti, soprani e tenori. (Giamberti, Giuseppe). *Heinrichshofen : Peters. Unpriced* VSSNU (B76-50689)
Rostropovich, Mstislav Leopoldovich. Suite, cello, no.3. Op.87. Third suite for cello. Op.87. (Britten, Benjamin, *Baron Britten*). *Faber Music. Unpriced* SRPMG (B76-50647)
Rothwell, Evelyn.
The oboist's companion
Vol.2. *Oxford University Press. Unpriced* VT/AC (B76-50691) ISBN 0-19-322336-8
A tune book for oboe. *Oxford University Press. Unpriced* VTPMK/AAY (B76-51044) ISBN 0-19-358667-3
Routh, Francis. Gloria tibi trinitas, Op.29 : a meditation on the Festival of the Trinity : organ solo. *Boosey and Hawkes. £1.40* RJ (B76-50595)
Roy, Jeroo. The voice of music. (Willson, Robina Beckles). *Heinemann. £4.50* A (B76-22073) ISBN 0-434-97258-4
Royal School of Church Music. English churgh music : essays, reports and reviews
1976. *Addington Place, Croydon CR9 5AD : Royal School of Church Music. £1.50* A/LD(YD/D) (B76-50353) ISBN 0-85402-062-4
Royds, Graham. Catalogue of the Hans Ferdinand Redlich Collection of musical books and scores : (including material on the Second Viennese School). (University of Lancaster. *Library*). *University Library, Bailrigg, Lancaster LA1 4YH : The University. £3.00* A(T) (B76-31432) ISBN 0-901699-35-7
Rubank symphonic band library. Walters, Harold L. Dynamite brass. *Rubank : Novello. Unpriced* UMMJ (B76-51002)
Rubbra, Edmund. Four short songs : for medium voice. *Lengnick. Unpriced* KDW (B76-50122)
Rubsamen, Walter Howard.
The medical and legal professions. *Garland. £400.00 the 28 vol. series* ACLM(XFWK61/ZC) (B76-19251) ISBN 0-8240-0903-7
Topical and nautical operas. *Garland. £400.00 the 28 volume series* ACLM(XFWK61/ZC) (B76-20707) ISBN 0-8240-0913-4
Ruf, Hugo. Première récréation de musique, Op.6 : for two violins and basso continuo. (Leclair, Jean Marie, *b.1697*). *Bärenreiter. £6.00* SNTPWG (B76-50629)
Rush, Leonard. German dance no.76, K.605, no.3. *arr.* The sleigh ride. (Mozart, Wolfgang Amadeus). *Warner. Unpriced* UMMK/AH (B76-51005)
Rushby-Smith, John. Quartet, saxophones. Saxophone quartet. *Simrock. £4.50* VUNS (B76-50694)
Russell, Kay. In the picture
Songbook 1. *19 Scullamus, Isle of Skye : Aquila. Unpriced* KADW (B76-50841) ISBN 0-7275-0144-5
Russell, Raymond. A catalogue of early keyboard instruments : the Benton Fletcher collection. (National Trust). *The Trust. £0.12* APW/B(YDBCF/WJ) (B76-22083) ISBN 0-7078-0061-7
Russell, Ross. Bird lives! *Quartet Books. £2.25* AMT(P) (B76-31128) ISBN 0-7043-3094-6
Russian masters : for piano. *EMI. Unpriced* QP/AYM (B76-50895)
Rutter, John.
Bang. *Choral Score.* Bang! *Oxford University Press. Unpriced* DACM (B76-50773) ISBN 0-19-338051-x
Donkey carol. *arr.* Donkey carol. *Oxford University Press. Unpriced* JFDP/LF (B76-50461) ISBN 0-19-342052-x
Donkey carol. *Vocal score.* Donkey carol : S.A.T.B. accompanied. *Oxford University Press. Unpriced* DP/LF (B76-50398) ISBN 0-19-343055-x
Gloria. *Vocal score.* Gloria for mixed voices with brass, percussion and organ. *Oxford University Press. Unpriced* DGC (B76-50369) ISBN 0-19-338062-5
I will lift up mine eyes. *Vocal score.* I will lift up mine eyes : SATB. *Oxford University Press. Unpriced* DR (B76-50402) ISBN 0-19-350353-0
It was a lover and his lass : S.A.T. Bar.B. unacc. *Oxford University Press. Unpriced* EZDW (B76-50074) ISBN 0-19-343056-8
Two American folk songs : SATB unacc. *Oxford University Press. Unpriced* EZDW (B76-50437) ISBN 0-19-343048-7

Saarbrücker Studien zur Musikwissen-schaft. Müller-Blattau, Wendelin. Tonsatz und Klanggestaltung bei Giovanni Gabrieli. *32 Great Titchfield St., W.1 : Bärenreiter. £24.00* BG
Sacrae symphoniae, bk.2. Hodie completi sunt. Hodie sompleti sunt, Magnificat antiphon for Whit Sunday : double chorus SATB-SATB. (Gabrieli, Giovanni). *83 Stilehall Gdns, W4 3BT : Chiswick Music. Unpriced* EZDGKH/LN (B76-50051)
Sadleir, Dick. Primary music groups. *British and Continental : EMI. Unpriced* NYESK/AAY (B76-50174)
Sadler, Graham. Sonata, violins (2) & continuo, op.13. no.1. Two trio sonatas for two violins and basso continuo. (Leclair, Jean Marie, *b.1697*). *Oxford University Press. Unpriced* NXNTE (B76-50887) ISBN 0-19-357612-0
Saëns, Camille Saint-. *See* Saint-Saëns, Camille.
Sainsbury, Diana. Toques flamencos. *Selections.* Toques flamencos. (Peña, Paco). *Musical New Services. Unpriced* TSPMJ (B76-50990)
St John, A M. April jaunt : elementary accordion solo. *Charnwood Music. Unpriced* RSPMJ (B76-50604)
Saint John, A M. Petite ballerina : accordion solo. *Charnwood Music. Unpriced* RSPMHW (B76-50603)
St John march. *arr.* The St John march. (Kennedy, James). *Studio Music. Unpriced* WMK/AGM (B76-50327)
St John passion. S.245. Johannes-Passion, BWV 245. (Bach, Johann Sebastian). *Bärenreiter. £6.50* EMDD/LK (B76-50405)
St John the Evangelist, *Derby.* The organs of the Church of St John : a history. (Johnson, David Sturgess). *Mill St., Derby : Church of St John the Evangelist. £0.10* AR/B(YDHWD) (B76-31919) ISBN 0-9505280-0-5
St Martin's organ series. Pachelbel, Johann. Canon, violins (3) & continuo, D major. *arr.* Canon in D : variations on a ground bass. *Cramer. £0.39* R/X (B76-50587)
St Patrick's College, *Maynooth. See* Maynooth College.
Saint-Saëns, Camille. Concerto, cello, no.1, op.33, A minor. Concerto no.1, A minor for violoncello and orchestra. Op.33. *Eulenburg. Unpriced* MPSRF (B76-50160)
Salem, Mahmoud. Organizational survival in the performing arts : the making of the Seattle Opera. *Praeger Distributed by Martin Robertson. £10.25* AC/E/K/QB(YTXHS) (B76-22516) ISBN 0-275-05670-8
Salles, Annita. A Tecnica na palma da mão : aproximação de elementos que compõem a técnica e evolução do estado moderno de órgão. *Fermata do Brasil : Essex Music. Unpriced* R/AF (B76-50223)
Saloon bar favourites. *Chappell. Unpriced* JDW/AY (B76-50456)
Salter, Lionel.
Eighteenth-century violin sonatas
Book 1. *Associated Board of the Royal Schools of Music. £1.00* SPE/AY (B76-50247)
Book 2. *Associated Board of the Royal Schools of Music. £1.00* SPE/AY (B76-50248)
Salvation Army Brass Band Journal (Festival series)
Nos.369-372: On parade : march / by Eilev Herikstad. We are an army : selection / by Robert Redhead. Radiant pathway : duet, for basses E flat and B flat / by Leslie Condon. Thou must leave thy lowly dwelling / by Hector Berlioz ; arr. Ray Steadman-Allen. *Salvationist Publishing and Supplies. Unpriced* WM/AY (B76-50719)
Nos.373-376: Happy in the fight : cornet duet / by Ray Steadman-Allen. Marche militaire française / by C. Saint-Saëns. Towards the victory : prelude and fugue / by Kenneth Downie. The word of grace : trombone solo / by Norman Bearcroft. *Salvationist Publishing and Supplies. Unpriced* WM/AY (B76-50720)
Salvation Army Brass Band Journal (General series)
Nos.1673-1676: Guardian of our way : selection / by James Curnow. Sparkling slides : trombone foursome / by Ray Steadman-Allen. O God of Bethel / transcription by Charles Skinner. Atlanta Temple : march / by Edwin S. Stanyon. *Salvationist Publishing and Supplies. Unpriced* WM/AY (B76-50721)
Salvation Army Brass Band Journal (Triumph series)
Nos.789-792: Schaffhausen march / by Eilir Herikstad. Healing waters : selection / by Leslie Condon. The pilgrim band : meditation / by Derek Jordan. Ilford young people : march / by W.J. Hopkins. *Salvationist Publishing and Supplies. Unpriced* WM/AY (B76-50722)
Nos.793-796: Young campaigners : march / by Erik Silfverberg. A Scottish suite / by Michael Kenyon. Emmaus : hymn tune arrangements / by Robert Schramm. Consistency : cornet solo / by John Birch. *Salvationist Publishing and Supplies. Unpriced* WM/AY (B76-50723)
Nos.797-800: Bound for Canaan's shore : march / by Bruce Broughton. The golden rule : suite / by Philip Catelinet. Melcombe : hymn tune arrangement / by David Greenthorne. The decisive step : meditation / by Paul Marti. *Salvationist Publishing and Supplies.*

Unpriced WM/AY (B76-50724)
Salve regina : for 4-part chorus of mixed voices unaccompanied. (Liszt, Franz). *Roberton. £0.14* EZDH (B76-50416)
Samet, Shelley. Music in developmental therapy : a curriculum guide. *University Park Press. £6.25* A(VMWM) (B76-30972) ISBN 0-8391-0895-8
Sammlung kleiner Stücke für Violoncello = Collection of small pieces for violoncello : duets and solos from the 18th century
Vol.1: For beginners. *Schott. £2.25* SRNU/AY (B76-50643)
Sams, Eric. The songs of Robert Schumann. 2nd ed. *48 Great Marlborough St., W1V 2BN : Eulenburg Books. £4.50* BSGADW (B76-10252) ISBN 0-903873-17-6
Samuel, Claude. Conversations with Olivier Messiaen. *Stainer and Bell. Unpriced* BMKS (B76-18371) ISBN 0-85249-308-8
'San Antonio Rose' : the life and music of Bob Wills. (Townsend, Charles R). *University of Illinois Press. £8.75* AKDW/GCW/E(P) (B76-31914) ISBN 0-252-00470-1
Sanctify us by thy goodness : chorale. (Bach, Johann Sebastian). *Oxford University Press. Unpriced* TSNUK/DM (B76-50982) ISBN 0-19-355297-3
Sandberg, Carl. Spring grass : part song, SATB. (Kreutz, Robert). *Boosey and Hawkes. Unpriced* EZDW (B76-50069)
Sandburg, Carl. Patterns in blue : medium voice, B flat clarinet and piano. (Sargon, Simon). *Boosey and Hawkes. £1.75* KFVE/VVPDW (B76-50502)
Sandon, Nicholas. Masses. (Sheppard, John). *Stainer and Bell. Unpriced* EZDG (B76-50410) ISBN 0-85249-392-4
Sans day carol : Cornish, S.A.T.B. unacc. (Carter, Andrew). *Banks. Unpriced* EZDP/LF (B76-50423)
Sansom, Clive A.
Film and TV themes for the recorder : outstanding selections published complete with lyrics and guitar diagrams plus a six page introduction to playing the recorder. *Wise : Music Sales. Unpriced* VSPMK/DW/JR/AY (B76-51039)
Happiness blues : for S.A.T.B. (or S.S.A., S.A.B., T.T.B.) with instrumental accompaniment. *Paterson. Unpriced* ELDW (B76-50036)
Popular songs for the recorder : outstanding selections published complete with lyrics and guitar diagrams plus a six page introduction to playing the recorder. *Wise : Music Sales. Unpriced* VSPMK/DW/GB/AY (B76-51038)
Sentimental mood. *Studio Music. Unpriced* WMJ (B76-51066)
Sapieyevski, Jerzy. Morpheus : wind symphony orchestra. *Peters. Unpriced* UMMJ (B76-51001)
Sappho. Meli, Op.17 : songs on Sappho's poems, for medium voice and orchestra. (Antoniou, Theodore). *Bärenreiter. £3.50* KFVE/MDW (B76-50501)
Sarambeque : chôro, piano. (Nazareth, Ernesto). *Arthur Napoleão : Essex Music. Unpriced* QPJ (B76-50915)
Sargon, Simon. Patterns in blue : medium voice, B flat clarinet and piano. *Boosey and Hawkes. £1.75* KFVE/VVPDW (B76-50502)
Sassmannshaus, Egon.
Früher Anfang auf dem Cello : eine Violoncelloschule für Kinder ab 4 Jahren
Band 1. *Bosse : Bärenreiter. £3.75* SR/AC (B76-50640)
Früher Anfang auf der Geige : eine Violinschule für Kinder ab 4 Jahren
Band 1. *Bosse : Bärenreiter. £3.75* S/AC (B76-50621)
Satie, Erik.
Children's pieces : for piano. *Novello. £0.60* QPJ (B76-50210)
An Erik Satie entertainment : a selection of songs and piano music. *Novello. Unpriced* QPJ (B76-50212)
Piano album. *Cramer. Unpriced* QPJ (B76-50211)
Trios gymnopédies : piano solo. *Leonard, Gould and Bolttler. £0.45* QPJ (B76-50213)
Trois gymnopédies. Trois gymnopédies, et Trois gnossiennes. *United Music. Unpriced* QPJ (B76-50214)
Trois gymnopédies. *arr.* Three gymnopédies : flute (or oboe) and piano. *Fentone Music : Breitkopf and Härtel. Unpriced* VRPJ (B76-50291)
Sato, Satoru. M.P. Mussorgsky's 'A night on bare mountain'. (Semba, Taro). *F. Warne. £2.25* BMUAMBN (B76-18581) ISBN 0-7232-1836-6
Save me, O God : for 4-part chorus of mixed voices with piano or organ. (Boyce, William). *Roberton. £0.18* DK (B76-50389)
Savitri, Op 25 : an episode from the Mahābharata. (Holst, Gustav). Revised ed. *Eulenburg. Unpriced* CQC (B76-50768)
Scales and studies for guitar. (Kish, Gabriell). *Frederick Harris : Lengnick. £1.95* TS/AF (B76-50975)
Scarecrow : for unison voices and piano. (Clements, John). *Elkin. £0.12* JFDW (B76-50463)
Scarlatti, Alessandro. Dixit Dominus : for SATB soli and chorus, string orchestra and organ continuo. *Novello. £1.20* ERXMDGKJ (B76-50046)
Schackner, Alan Blackie. Blues harp and marine band. *Warner : Blossom. Unpriced* VX/AC (B76-51054)
Schaefer, Hartmut. Die Notendrucker und Musik verleger in Frankfurt am Main von 1630 bis um 1720 : eine bibliographisch-drucktechnische Untersuchung. *32 Great Titchfield St., W.1 : Bärenreiter. £28.13* A(S/YEF/XWK91)
Schafer, Robert Murray. Son of Heldenleben. *Universal. Unpriced* MMJ (B76-50531)
Schenk, Erich. De ratione in musica : Festschrift Erich Schenk, zu 5.Mai 1972. *32 Great Titchfield St., W.1 : Bärenreiter Kassel. £18.00* A(ZC)
Schering, Arnold. Concerto, harpsichord & string orchestra, BWV 1052, F minor. Concerto, D minor, for harpsichord and string orchestra. BWV 1052. (Bach, Johann Sebastian). *Eulenburg. Unpriced* RXMPQRF (B76-50237)
Scherzo, 'Encore for winds'. (Walker, James). *Schirmer. Unpriced* UN (B76-50285)
Schilling, Reinhard Schwarz-. *See* Schwarz-Schilling, Reinhard.
Schilling, Richard Schwarz-. *See* Schwarz-Schilling, Reinhard.
Schoenberg. (MacDonald, Malcolm, *b.1948*). *Dent. £4.25* BSET (B76-31120) ISBN 0-460-03143-0
Schoenberg. (Rosen, Charles). *Fontana. £0.75* BSET (B76-34779) ISBN 0-00-633558-6
Schoenberg. (Rosen, Charles). *Marion Boyars : Distributed by Calder and Boyars. £4.25* BSET (B76-14361) ISBN 0-7145-2566-9
Schöne Müllerin. D.795 : für Gesang und Klavier. (Schubert, Franz). *Litolff : Peters. Unpriced* KDW (B76-50847)
Schonthal, Ruth. Sonata breve : for piano. *Oxford University Press. Unpriced* QPE (B76-50193)
Schönzeler, Hans Hubert.
Die Israeliten in der Wuste = The Israelites in the wilderness : oratorio for soli, chorus and orchestra. (Bach, Carl Philipp Emanuel). *Eulenburg. Unpriced* EMDD (B76-50037)
Of German music : a symposium. *Wolff etc.. £6.50* A(YE/X) (B76-14365) ISBN 0-85496-401-0
Schönzeler, Hans-Hubert. Richard Wagner. (Gál, Hans). *Gollancz. £5.50* BWC (B76-05038) ISBN 0-575-01847-x
School of English Church Music. *See* Royal School of Church Music.
Schottisches Balladen-Büchlein : die schönsten schottischen Balladen, für Singstimme, Melodieinstrumente und Gitarre. *Heinrichstofen : Peters. Unpriced* JE/LPLTSDW/G/AYDL (B76-50459)
Schroeder, Hermann. Variationen über den Tonus peregrinus : für Orgel. *Schott. £2.25* R/T (B76-50228)
Schubert, Franz.
Franz Peter Schubert : his greatest songs, 38 lieder with new singable translations. *Copa : Phoenix Music. Unpriced* KDW (B76-50846)
Gesänge zur Feier des heiligen Opfers der Messe. D.872. Zum Sanctus. *arr.* Zum Sanctus : for 4-part chorus of mixed voices with organ or piano. *Roberton. £0.14* DH (B76-50019)
Die schöne Müllerin. D.795 : für Gesang und Klavier. *Litolff : Peters. Unpriced* KDW (B76-50847)
Schwanengesang. D.957 : für Gesang und Klavier. *Litolff : Peters. Unpriced* KDW (B76-50848)
Des Tages Weihe. D.763. *arr.* Where thou reignest. *Ashdown. £0.12* FLDH (B76-50091)
Schubert : a biographical study of his songs. (Fischer-Dieskau, Dietrich). *Cassell. £5.95* BSFAKDW (B76-33372) ISBN 0-304-29002-5
Schulgottesdienst für Grund-und Hauptschulen : für Mittelschulen und Familiengottesdienst, Lieder und Text. *Boose : Bärenreiter. £1.31* JFE/TSDM/AY (B76-50837)
Schuller, Gunther.
Seven studies on themes of Paul Klee : for orchestra. *Universal. Unpriced* MMJ (B76-50153)
Trio, oboe, horn, viola. Trio for oboe, horn and viola. *Associated Music. Unpriced* NVNT (B76-50167)
Schumann, Robert. Morçeaux choisis à l'usage des mains petites de la deuxième année de piano (assez facile) à la moyenne difficulté. *Chappell. Unpriced* QPJ (B76-50215)
Schumann. (Walker, Alan, *b.1930*). *Faber. £3.25* BSG(N) (B76-21364) ISBN 0-571-10269-7
Schütz, Heinrich. Psalmen Davids. De profundis. Psalm 130 : for double choir, S.A.T.B.-S.A.T.B. *Chiswick Music. Unpriced* EZDR (B76-50061)
Schwanengesang. D.957 : für Gesang und Klavier. (Schubert, Franz). *Litolff : Peters. Unpriced* KDW (B76-50848)
Schwarz, Gerard R. Pavans, galiards, almains and other short airs. *Selections : arr.* Suite of Elizabethan dances. (Holborne, Antony). *Schirmer. Unpriced* WNRK/AH (B76-50334)
Schwarz-Schilling, Reinhard.
Partita für Orchester. *Bärenreiter. £6.00* MMG (B76-50523)
Quartet, strings, F minor. Introduction and fugue *arr.* Introduktion und Fuge für Streichorchester. *Bärenreiter. £2.50* RXM/Y (B76-50605)
Symphony, C major. Symphonie in C für Orchester. *Bärenreiter. £6.50* MME (B76-50522)
Schwierigkeiten und Unfälle mit 1 Choral. (Zehm, Friedrich). *Schott. £4.50* UMJ (B76-50282)
Scotland. *Education Department. See* Great Britain. *Scottish Education Department.*
Scott, Anthony. Lullaby. *Boosey and Hawkes. £0.45* KDW (B76-50485)
Scott Joplin and the ragtime era. (Gammond, Peter). *Abacus. £1.25* BJRP(N) (B76-29712) ISBN 0-349-11412-9
Scottish Education Department. *See* Great Britain. *Scottish Education Department.*
Scriven, R C. The poltergoose : for recorder, percussion, voices and piano. (Burnett, Michael). *Chester. Unpriced* CQN (B76-50769)
Sculthorpe, Peter. Sun music : for voices and percussion. *Faber Music. Unpriced* ENYLDW (B76-50045)
Sea of tranquillity : for pianoforte solo. (Mancini, Maurice B). *Anthony Music. Unpriced* QPJ (B76-50912)
Searle, Humphrey.
Five, Op.61 : for guitar. *Faber Music. Unpriced* TSPMJ (B76-50991)
Symphonic poem, no.2. Tasso, lamento e trionfo. Tasso, lamento e trionfo. (Liszt, Franz). *Eulenburg. Unpriced* MMJ (B76-50874)
Symphonic poem no.7. Festklange. (Liszt, Franz). *Eulenburg. Unpriced* MMJ (B76-50527)
Symphonic poem no.8 Héroïde funèbre. Héroïde funèbre. (Liszt, Franz). *Eulenburg. Unpriced* MMJ (B76-50875)
Symphonic poem, no.9. Hungaria. Hungaria. (Liszt, Franz). Revised ed. *Eulenburg. Unpriced* MMJ (B76-50150)
Symphonic poem, no.10. Hamlet. Hamlet. (Liszt, Franz). *Eulenburg. Unpriced* MMJ (B76-50876)
Symphonic poem, no.12. Die Ideale. Die Ideale. (Liszt, Franz). Revised ed. *Eulenburg. Unpriced* MMJ (B76-50151)
Seaside park : march, symphonic band. (Goldman, Richard Franko) *Boosey and Hawkes. £4.00* UMMGM (B76-50998)
Seasons of man : mixed chorus and two trumpets. (Tull, Fisher). *Boosey and Hawkes. £0.20* EWSNUDH (B76-50408)
Sechs Saiten sehn Finger : Grundlagen und Ubunger für Unterricht und Selbststudium des klassischen, spanischen und begleitenden Gitarrenspiels. (Wangler, Rudolf). *Bärenreiter. £4.50* TS/AC (B76-50653)
Second classical and romantic album for horn in F and piano. *Oxford University Press. Unpriced* WTPK/AAY (B76-50750) ISBN 0-19-356528-5
Second pentatonic song book. *Schott. Unpriced* JDW/G/PP/AY (B76-50828)
Secundus tomus musici operis. Alleluia. In resurrectione tua. *arr.* In resurrectione tua Christe. (Handl, Jacob). *Associated Music. Unpriced* WNK/DJ (B76-50331)
Seemann, Carl.
Klavierwerke
Band 1. (Brahms, Johannes). *Litolff : Peters. Unpriced* QP/AZ (B76-50559)
Band 2. (Brahms, Johannes). *Litolff : Peters. Unpriced* QP/AZ (B76-50560)
Waltzes, piano 2 hands, op.39. Walzer für Klavier zu zwei Händen. Opus 39. (Brahms, Johannes). *Litolff : Peters. Unpriced* QNUHW (B76-50558)
Seesaw : a musical. (Fields, Dorothy). *French. £1.25* BCMEACM (B76-06887) ISBN 0-573-68069-8
Seidl, Uwe. Neue Gemeindelieder : neue geistliche Lieder
Heft 3. *Bosse : Bärenreiter. £1.66* JFE/TSDM/AY (B76-50836)
Selectissimae cantiones. In monte Oliveti. In monte Oliveti : responsory, S.A.A.T.B.B. (Lasso, Orlando di). *Chiswick Music. Unpriced* EZDGKH/LHM (B76-50050)
Self, George. Make a new sound. *Universal Edition. £3.90* AL/E(VF) (B76-13570) ISBN 0-900938-46-3
Semba, Taro. M.P. Mussorgsky's 'A night on bare mountain'. *F. Warne. £2.25* BMUAMBN (B76-18581) ISBN 0-7232-1836-6
Senator, Ronald. Streets of London. *Boosey and Hawkes. £2.20* JFE/NYFSNSDW (B76-50471)
Sentimental mood. (Sansom, Clive A). *Studio Music. Unpriced* WMJ (B76-51066)
Serenade for carillon. Opus 61. (Peeters, Flor). *Peters. Unpriced* QXPJ (B76-50222)
Series for school and amateur orchestra.
Chabrier, Emmanuel. España. *arr.* España : rhapsody for orchestra *Bosworth. Unpriced* MK (B76-50139)
Strauss, Johann, *b.1825.* Unter Donner und Blitz. Op.324. *arr.* Thunder and lightning = Unter Donner und Blitz, Op.324 : polka. *Bosworth. Unpriced* MK/AHVH (B76-50517)
Set of five. Improvisation. Improvisation : for the piano. (Van Appledorn, Mary Jeanne). *Boosey and Hawkes. Unpriced* QPJ (B76-50576)
Seven chords and fifty songs : with photo-chord positions and bigrams for guitar, mandolin, banjo and ukulele. *Belwin Mills Music. Unpriced* TPMK/DW/AY (B76-50264)
Seven duos for guitar. *British and Continental : EMI. Unpriced* TSNUK/AAY (B76-50655)
Seven league boots. (Siebert, Edrich). *Studio Music. Unpriced* WMJ (B76-51067)
Seven romantics. *Cramer. £0.60* VVPK/AAY (B76-50709)
Seven studies on themes of Paul Klee : for orchestra. (Schuller, Gunther). *Universal. Unpriced* MMJ (B76-50153)
Seven wild mushrooms and a waltz : easy pieces for prepared piano. (Greene, Arthur). *Galaxy : Galliard. Unpriced* QPJ (B76-50572)
Seventeenth and eighteenth century sonatas, concerti and overtures. Telemann, Georg Philipp. Concerto, trumpets (3), oboes (2), timpani & string orchestra, D major. Concerto for 3 clarini (trumpets), timpani, 2 oboes, strings, and basso continuo. *Musica rara. Unpriced* RXMPNYHNQF (B76-50610)
Sewell, Penelope. Classical guitar : a complete course
Book 1. *Thames. Unpriced* TS/AC (B76-50652) ISBN 0-905210-04-2
Sex miniaturas : piano. (Lombardi, Nilson). *Arthur Napoleão : Essex Music. Unpriced* QPJ (B76-50910)
Sextets : violin and piano. (Babbitt, Milton). *Peters. Unpriced* SPJ (B76-50249)
Shadowplay, Op.30 : music theatre from book 7 of the Republic of Plato. (Goehr, Alexander). *Schott. Unpriced* C/JR (B76-50002)
Shakespeare, William.
Come away, death : song. (Naylor, John). *Roberton. £0.35* KDW (B76-50120)

It was a lover and his lass : S.A.T. Bar.B. unacc. (Rutter, John). *Oxford University Press. Unpriced* EZDW (B76-50074) ISBN 0-19-343056-8
Twelfth night. *Selections : arr.* Five Shakespeare songs : voice and piano. (Amram, David). *Peters. Unpriced* KDW (B76-50117)
Shaliapin, Fedor Ivanovich. Chaliapin : an autobiography. *White Lion Publishers. £6.50* AKGX/E(P) (B76-07530) ISBN 0-7274-0191-2
Sharkey, Jack. What a spot! : a musical farce in three acts. *French. £1.45* BSGNHACM (B76-30339) ISBN 0-573-61814-3
Sharp, Cecil. The crystal spring : English folk songs. *Oxford University Press. £4.95* JE/TSDW/G/AYD (B76-50105) ISBN 0-19-330518-6
Sharp, Cecil James. Country dance tunes. Sets 3-8, 10 and 11. *EP Publishing. £4.00* QPK/AH/H/AYD (B76-50218) ISBN 0-7158-1166-5
Sharpe, Frederick. The church bells of Herefordshire : their inscriptions and founders
Vol.5: Summarised accounts of the bells at the Reformation and the present day and details of bellfounders. *'Derwen', Launton, Oxon. : The author. £3.20* AXSR/B(YDHR) (B76-09332) ISBN 0-9500835-9-3
Shaw, Barry. Guitar workshop : a course for guitar groups in two parts
Part 1. (Mynall, Frances). *Oxford University Press. Unpriced* TSN/AC (B76-50979) ISBN 0-19-322268-x
Shaw, Bernard. Wagner in Bayreuth. *15 Mortimer Terrace, N.W.5 : Broadsheet King. Unpriced* BWCAC/E(YEB) (B76-35352) ISBN 0-902617-17-6
Shaw, George Bernard. *See* Shaw, Bernard.
Shaw, Harry. Guitar workshop : a course for guitar groups in two parts
Part 2. (Mynall, Frances). *Oxford University Press. Unpriced* TSN/AC (B76-50980) ISBN 0-19-322269-8
Shaw, Pat. The crystal spring : English folk songs. *Oxford University Press. £4.95* JE/TSDW/G/AYD (B76-50105) ISBN 0-19-330518-6
Shaw, Watkins.
Magnificat and Nunc dimittis in E. (Wesley, Samuel Sebastian). *Oxford University Press. Unpriced* DGPP (B76-50375) ISBN 0-19-395317-x
The organists and organs of Hereford Cathedral. *Friends of Hereford Cathedral Publications Committee. £0.50* AR/B(YDHRHB/X) (B76-35357) ISBN 0-904642-01-1
Shead, Richard. Music in the 1920s. *Duckworth. £5.95* A(XN9) (B76-35349) ISBN 0-7156-0972-6
Sheaf of sonnets. Op.36. (Kleyn, Howard). *Sonia Archer Lengnick. Unpriced* DW (B76-50795)
Sheep may safely graze : aria. (Bach, Johann Sebastian). *Oxford University Press. Unpriced* TSNUK/DW (B76-50983) ISBN 0-19-355298-1
Shelley, Percy Bysshe.
Music when soft voices die : SATB (divisi), with keyboard accompaniment. (Harbison, John). *Associated Music. Unpriced* DW (B76-50028)
To Jane : music by Ned Rorem. (Rorem, Ned). *Boosey and Hawkes. £1.00* KDW (B76-50483)
Shenandoah : a musical. (Udell, Peter). *French. £1.25* BGGTACM (B76-06888) ISBN 0-573-68073-6
Sheppard, John. Masses. *Stainer and Bell. Unpriced* EZDG (B76-50410) ISBN 0-85249-392-4
Sherman, Richard M.
The slipper and the rose. *Selections : arr.* The slipper and the rose. The story of Cinderella. *Noel Gay Music. Unpriced* WMK/CM (B76-50328)
The slipper and the rose. *Selections: arr.* The slipper and the rose : the story of Cinderella, an album of songs. *Noel Gay Music. Unpriced* KDW/JR (B76-50492)
Sherman, Robert. My favourite intervals. (Borge, Victor). *Sphere. £0.60* A/D(YB/M) (B76-28392) ISBN 0-7221-1779-5
Sherman, Robert B.
The slipper and the rose. *Selections : arr.* The slipper and the rose. The story of Cinderella. (Sherman, Richard M). *Noel Gay Music. Unpriced* WMK/CM (B76-50328)
The slipper and the rose. *Selections: arr.* The slipper and the rose : the story of Cinderella, an album of songs. (Sherman, Richard M). *Noel Gay Music. Unpriced* KDW/JR (B76-50492)
Shewan, Douglas. Octet, wind instruments. Wind octet. *Hansen House. Unpriced* UNN (B76-50286)
Shields, Hugh. Eigse cheol tíre = Irish folk music studies
Vol.2 : 1974-1975. *3 Sydenham Rd, Dundrum, Dublin 14 : Folk Music Society of Ireland. £1.00* A/G(YDM) (B76-35799) ISBN 0-905733-00-2
Shifrin, Seymour. Quartet, strings, no.3. String quartet, no.3. *Peters. Unpriced* RXNS (B76-50957)
Short and easy pieces for organ. *Oxford University Press. Unpriced* R/AY (B76-50226) ISBN 0-19-375856-3
Shostakovich, Dmitrii Dmitrievich. Sonata for viola and piano. Op.147. *Anglo-Soviet Music Press : Boosey and Hawkes. £5.00* SQPE (B76-50635)
Sibelius
Vol.1: 1865-1905. (Tawaststjerna, Erik). *Faber. £12.50* BSH(N) (B76-30336) ISBN 0-571-08832-5
Sicilienne. (Fauré, Gabriel). *Boosey and Hawkes. £3.95* MK/AHVQ (B76-50140)
Sieben Hauptwerke aus dem Klavierschaften. (Bach, Carl Philipp Emanuel). *Heinrichshofen : Peters. Unpriced* QPJ (B76-50566)
Sieben Ricercari (1689) : Violoncello solo. (Gabrielli, Domenico). *Schott. £2.00* SRPMJ (B76-50260)
Siebert, Edrich.
Funiculi, funicula. *arr.* Funiculi - finicula sic. (Denza, Luigi). *8 Hurst Green Close, Hurst Green, Oxted : Paul. Unpriced* WMK/DW (B76-50734)
Für Elise. G.173. *arr.* Für Elise. (Beethoven, Ludwig van). *Paul. Unpriced* QPK (B76-50918)
Für Elise. G.173. *arr.* Für Elise. (Beethoven, Ludwig van). *Paul. Unpriced* WRPK (B76-51084)
The piper in the meadow. (Barratt, Bob). *Ambleside Music. Unpriced* WMK (B76-51069)
Quartets, strings, nos.14, 16, K.387, 428. *Selections : arr.* Quartet no.2 on themes from Mozart. (Mozart, Wolfgang Amadeus). *Studio Music. Unpriced* WNSK (B76-50742)
Quartets, strings, ops.64, 77. *Selections: arr.* Quartet no.3 on themes from Haydn. (Haydn, Joseph). *Studio Music. Unpriced* WNSK (B76-50741)
Seven league boots. *Studio Music. Unpriced* WMJ (B76-51067)
The slipper and the rose. *Selections : arr.* The slipper and the rose. The story of Cinderella. (Sherman, Richard M). *Noel Gay Music. Unpriced* WMK/CM (B76-50328)
Three gifts. *arr.* Three gifts : trio for trombones. (Waterworth, R). *D. Rahter. £2.75* WMK (B76-50732)
Toccata, organ, S.565, D minor. *arr.* Toccata in D minor. (Bach, Johann Sebastian). *Studio Music. Unpriced* WMK (B76-50730)
Siegfriedp' : für Violoncello. (Kagel, Mauricio). *Universal. Unpriced* SRPMJ (B76-50648)
Silent waters. Opus 72 : for flute and piano. (Simpson, Lionel). *EMI. Unpriced* VRPJ (B76-51019)
Silver threads among the gold : cornet solo. (Boddington, Stanley H). *Studio Music. Unpriced* WMPWR/T (B76-50735)
Silverman, Jerry. Folksongs for flute, with guitar chords : 200 favourites. *Chappell. Unpriced* VRPLTSK/DW/G/AY (B76-51025)
Simpson, Adrienne. Easy lute music. *Oxford University Press. Unpriced* TW/AY (B76-50279) ISBN 0-19-358834-x
Simpson, Bland. Diamond studs : the life of Jesse James. (Wann, Jim). *French. £1.60* BSHLACM (B77-00344) ISBN 0-573-68076-0
Simpson, Kenneth.
Music through the recorder : a course in musicianship. *Nelson. £1.10* VS/AC (B76-50295) ISBN 0-17-436086-x
Music through the recorder : a course in musicianship
Vol.3. *Nelson. £2.25* VS/AC (B76-50683) ISBN 0-17-436085-1
Simpson, Lionel.
Quartet, brass instruments, no.2. Brass quartet no.2, Opus 106, sic. *British and Continental. Unpriced* WNS (B76-51083)
Silent waters. Opus 72 : for flute and piano. *EMI. Unpriced* VRPJ (B76-51019)
Sonata, flute & piano, op.67. Sonata for flute. Op.67. *British and Continental : EMI. Unpriced* VRPE (B76-50290)
Simpson, Robert. Quartet, strings, no.4. Quartet n.4 (1973) : first violin, second violin, viola, cello. *Lengnick. £11.50* RXNS (B76-50619)
Sinatra. (Wilson, Earl). *W.H. Allen. £5.00* AKDW/GB/E(P) (B76-35802) ISBN 0-491-01967-x
Sinatra, the man and his music. *Wise : Music Sales. Unpriced* KDW/GB/AYT (B76-50853)
Sinfonia di sfere. (Panufnik, Andrzej). *Boosey and Hawkes. £10.00* MME (B76-50870)
Sinfoniae drammaticae, T1.2. Symphonische Hymnen : für grosses Orchester. (Hartmann, Karl Amadeus). *Schott. £11.00* MMJ (B76-50524)
Sinfonie in einem Satz für Orchester. (Kubelík, Rafael). *Litolff : Peters. Unpriced* MME (B76-50520)
Sinfonietta. Cambini, Giovanni Giuseppe. Symphony, D major. Sinfonie D-dur für Kammerorchester. Zum ersten Mal. *Litolff : Peters. Unpriced* MRE (B76-50882)
Sing and rejoice, O daugher of Zion. *Vocal score.* Sing and rejoice, O daughter of Zion. (Antes, John). *Boosey and Hawkes. £0.40* DH (B76-50381)
Sing to the Lord : a collection of twelve anthems. *Novello. £0.75* DH/AY (B76-50021)
Singer, Otto. Concerto, piano, C minor. *arr.* Piano concerto. (Delius, Frederick). *Boosey and Hawkes. Unpriced* QNUK/LF (B76-50184)
Singer's manual of English diction. (Marshall, Madeleine). *Shirmer Books : Collier Macmillan. £3.50* AB/ED (B76-23702) ISBN 0-02-871100-9
Singing : the physical nature of the vocal organ : a guide to the unlocking of the singing voice. (Husler, Frederick). *Hutchinson. £6.50* AB/E (B76-26571) ISBN 0-09-126860-5
Six easy pieces for 3 cellos (or violas da gamba). *British and Continental. Unpriced* SRNTK/AAY (B76-50642)
Six French carols
Set 1. *Banks. Unpriced* FEZDP/LF/AYH (B76-50447)
Six fugues with introductory voluntaries : for the organ or harpsichord. (Nares, James). *Oxford University Press. Unpriced* R/AZ (B76-50227) ISBN 0-19-375611-0
Six miniatures : for guitar. (Drabble, L H). *Charnwood Music. Unpriced* TSPMJ (B76-50659)
Six romantic pieces. *Oxford University Press. Unpriced* VVPK/AAY (B76-50318) ISBN 0-19-355331-7
Six songs of Mervyn Peake : for high voice, two clarinets and piano. (Walker, Robert). *Ramsey : Roberton. Unpriced* KFTE/VVNTQDW (B76-50499)
Skelton, Geoffrey. Wagner at Bayreuth : experiment and tradition. New and revised ed. *White Lion Publishers. £5.75* BWCAC/E(YEB) (B76-14367) ISBN 0-85617-068-2
Skupnik, Reinhard. Der hannoversche Orgel Christian Vater, 1679-1756. *32 Great Titchfield St., W.1 : Bärenreiter. £13.00* AR/BC(YEH/P)
Sky music : ten pieces for solo harp. (Rorem, Ned). *Boosey and Hawkes. £2.00* TQPMJ (B76-50650)
Sky songs. (Benger, Richard). *Edwin Ashdown. £0.40* JFDW (B76-50462)
Slack, Roy.
Four play three. *British and Continental. Unpriced* RXNS (B76-50620)
Rumba : for brass band. *EMI. Unpriced* WMHVKK (B76-50726)
A toye : for trumpet and piano. *British and Continental : EMI. Unpriced* WSPJ (B76-50339)
Sleigh ride. (Mozart, Wolfgang Amadeus). *Warner. Unpriced* UMMK/AH (B76-51005)
Slipper and the rose. *Selections : arr.* The slipper and the rose. The story of Cinderella. (Sherman, Richard M). *Noel Gay Music. Unpriced* WMK/CM (B76-50328)
Slipper and the rose. *Selections: arr.* The slipper and the rose : the story of Cinderella, an album of songs. (Sherman, Richard M). *Noel Gay Music. Unpriced* KDW/JR (B76-50492)
Smart, *Sir* George. Beethoven : a Victorian tribute based on the papers of Sir George Smart. (Young, Percy Marshall). *Dobson. £5.00* A/EC(P/ZD) (B76-33367) ISBN 0-234-77672-2
Smet, Robin de. *See*
De Smet, Robin.
De Smet, Robin.
Smetana, Bedřich. My fatherland. Šárka. Má vlast : a cycle of symphonic poems
No.3: Sarka. *Eulenburg. Unpriced* MMJ (B76-50877)
Smith, Gregg. America's bicentennial songs from the great sentimental age, 1850-1900, Stephen C. Foster to Charles E. Ives : for unison, two- and four-part vocal ensembles with piano accompaniment. *Schirmer. Unpriced* CB/AYT (B76-50004)
Smith, John Rushby-. *See* Rushby-Smith, John.
Smith, Jon. Electric music : a practical manual for musicians. (Jenkins, John, *b.1936*). *David and Charles. £4.95* APV (B76-33378) ISBN 0-7153-6815-x
Smith, Pat.
Christmas things to sing. *Arnold. Unpriced* JFDW/LF (B76-50833) ISBN 0-560-02721-4
Things to sing. *Arnold. Unpriced* JFDW (B76-50830) ISBN 0-560-02720-6
Smith, Ronald. Alkan
Vol.1: The enigma. *Kahn and Averill. £3.00* BAO (B76-07533) ISBN 0-900707-39-9
Smith, Stella Jackson-. *See* Jackson-Smith, Stella.
Smith, Virginia.
The orchestra. (Harding, David). *F. Watts. £1.45* AM/B (B76-05039) ISBN 0-85166-558-6
The violin and viola. (Robinson, Marjorie). *F. Watts. £1.75* AS/B (B77-00349) ISBN 0-85166-595-0
Smith : a musical. (Dubey, Matt). *French. £1.25* BDUACM (B76-00671) ISBN 0-573-68066-3
Snider, Lee. Twelve musical plays for children (based on famous fairy tales). (Tobias, Henry). *Henry Tobias : Chappell : Chappell. Unpriced* CN (B76-50006)
Snowdon, Jasper Whitfield. Ropesight : Jasper Whitfield Snowdon's introduction to the art of change ringing, as revised by William Snowdon. *22 Duke St., Burton Latimer, Northants. : C. Groome. £2.50* AXSR/E(XA1935) (B76-35804) ISBN 0-905334-00-0
Snowdon, William. Ropesight : Jasper Whitfield Snowdon's introduction to the art of change ringing, as revised by William Snowdon. (Snowdon, Jasper Whitfield). *22 Duke St., Burton Latimer, Northants. : C. Groome. £2.50* AXSR/E(XA1935) (B76-35804) ISBN 0-905334-00-0
Snowdon (Jasper) change ringing series. *See* Jasper Snowdon change ringing series.
Solitary reaper. Op.96 : for soprano, clarinet and piano. (Wordsworth, William, *b.1908*). *Roberton. £0.75* KFLE/VVPDW (B76-50135)
Some hallucinations : unison song. (Williams, Patrick). *Bosworth. Unpriced* JFDW (B76-50831)
Sommer, Jürgen. Leichte Stücke, grosser Meister : elektronische Orgel. *Nagel : Bärenreiter. £1.50* RPVK/AAY (B76-50599)
Son of Heldenleben. (Schafer, Robert Murray). *Universal. Unpriced* MMJ (B76-50531)
Sonata about Jerusalem. Op.31 : cantata. (Goehr, Alexander). *Schott. Unpriced* C/JR (B76-50003)
Sonata breve : for piano. (Schonthal, Ruth). *Oxford University Press. Unpriced* QPE (B76-50193)
Sonata capriccioso : clarinet and piano. (Hughes, Eric). *Emerson. Unpriced* VVPE (B76-51049)
Song for every season. (Copper, Bob). *Paladin. £1.25* ADW/G(YDCR) (B76-02079) ISBN 0-586-08229-8
Song for St Cecilia's Day. Op.119 : SATB. (Gardner, John). *Oxford University Press. Unpriced* DH (B76-50384) ISBN 0-19-350355-7
Song of a merryman : Ivan Menzies of the D'Oyly Carte Gilbert & Sullivan operas. (Magor, Cliff). *Grosvenor Books. £1.00* AKDW/E(P) (B76-19249) ISBN 0-901269-18-2
Song of Ireland : songs. *Wise : Music Sales. £2.95* KDW/AYDM (B76-50849)
Songs and hymns from Sweden. *Stainer and Bell. Unpriced* DM/AYND (B76-50787) ISBN 0-85249-440-8
Songs from the stable : for children's voices and instruments. (Platts, Kenneth). *Edwin Ashdown. £2.00* JFE/LPDP/LF (B76-50834)
Songs from White Horse Inn and other favourites. (Stolz, Robert). *Chappell. Unpriced* KDW (B76-50486)
Songs of Robert Schumann. (Sams, Eric). 2nd ed. *48 Great Marlborough St., W1V 2BN : Eulenburg Books. £4.50* BSGADW (B76-10252) ISBN 0-903873-17-6
Sonny boy! : the world of Al Jolson. (Anderton, Barrie). *Jupiter Books. £3.95* AKDW/GB/E(P) (B76-12797) ISBN 0-904041-35-2
Soodlum's selection of Irish ballads with guitar chords

Vol.1. *153 Downpatrick Rd, Dublin 12 : International Music Publications. Unpriced* AKDW/K/G(YDM) (B76-07531) ISBN 0-905326-00-8
Vol.2. *153 Downpatrick Rd, Dublin 12 : International Music Publications. Unpriced* AKDW/K/G(YDM) (B76-07532) ISBN 0-905326-01-6
Sorcerer's apprentice. *See* Yanagihara, Ryohei.
Sound of Philadelphia. (Cummings, Tony). *Eyre Methuen. £2.75* ADW/GB(YTLD/X) (B76-04295) ISBN 0-413-34080-5
Sound projects. (Walker, Robert, *b.1936*). *Oxford University Press, Music Department. £1.25* A(VG) (B76-21743) ISBN 0-19-321804-6
Sound study : for eight double basses. (Drew, Lucas). *Schirmer. Unpriced* SSNN (B76-50261)
Sounds and fills : for drumset. (Moisy, Heinz von). *Simrock. £2.50* XQ/AF (B76-50347)
Sounds of music. (Taylor, Charles Alfred). *British Broadcasting Corporation. £6.50* A/B (B76-10250) ISBN 0-563-12228-5
Sounds remembered : violin and piano. (Bassett, Leslie). *Peters. Unpriced* SPJ (B76-50250)
Southworth, Mary. How to make musical sounds. *Adaptations.* Making musical sounds. (Southworth, Mary). *Studio Vista etc.. £0.45* AX/BC (B76-50356) ISBN 0-289-70711-0
Southworth, Mary. Making musical sounds. *Studio Vis etc.. £0.45* AX/BC (B76-50356) ISBN 0-289-70711-0
Spacious firmament on high : anthem for SSATTB unaccompanied. (Beaumont, Adrian). *Roberton. £0.18* EZDH (B76-50414)
Sparke, Philip. Concert prelude. *R. Smith. Unpriced* WMJ (B76-51068)
Spatlese. Op.218 : in sechs Teilen, für Bariton und Klavier. (Křenek, Ernst). *Bärenreiter. £7.50* KGNDX (B76-50507)
Spencer, Stewart. Wagner 1976 : a celebration of the Bayreuth festival. *c/o 25 Balcombe St., NW1 6HE : The Wagner Society. £3.75* BWC(D) (B77-00342) ISBN 0-905800-00-1
Spiegler, Matthias. Olor solymaeus. Canzon à 2. Canzon à 2 for cornetto (recorder-trumpet), bassoon (cello-rackett), & basso continuo. *Musica rara. Unpriced* NWNT (B76-50539)
Spink, Ian. Cavalier songs. *Stainer and Bell. Unpriced* KE/TDW (B76-50129) ISBN 0-85249-325-8
Spinner, Leopold. Sonatina, cello & piano. Op.26. Sonatina for violoncello and piano. Op.26. *Boosey and Hawkes. £5.00* SRPE (B76-50644)
Spirit of America. *Chappell. Unpriced* KDW/AYT (B76-50850)
Spirituals reborn
Choral edition. *Cambridge University Press. £3.75* EZDW/LC/AY (B76-50439) ISBN 0-521-08713-9
Melody and guitar edition. Part 1 for male and female voices, with chords for piano and guitar and additional parts for voices. *Cambridge University Press. £1.00* FE/TSDW/LC/AY (B76-50443) ISBN 0-521-08714-7
Melody and guitar edition. Part 2 : for male and female voices, with chords for piano and guitar and additional parts for voices. *Cambridge University Press. £1.00* FE/TSDW/LC/AY (B76-50444) ISBN 0-521-21332-0
Spring grass : part song, SATB. (Kreutz, Robert). *Boosey and Hawkes. Unpriced* EZDW (B76-50069)
Spring overture. (Lane, Philip). *R. Smith. Unpriced* WMJ (B76-51062)
Staehelin, Dieter. Sieben Ricercari (1689) : Violoncello solo. (Gabrielli, Domenico). *Schott. £2.00* SRPMJ (B76-50260)
Stafford, W J. The Charlton memorial tune book : a collection of tunes for the Northumbrian small-pipes and the fiddle. *5 Denebank, Monkseaton : Northumbrian Pipers' Society. Unpriced* VYQPMJ (B76-50716) ISBN 0-902510-03-7
Stahmer, Klaus. Musik für Mallets : 14 Duos und Soli für Malletinstrumente (Vibraphon, Marimbaphon, Xylophon, Stabspiele). *Schott. £3.50* XPQNU (B76-51089)
Stambler, Irwin. Encyclopedia of folk country and Western music. *St Martin's Press : St James Press. £5.00* A/GCW(C) (B76-00666) ISBN 0-900997-24-9
Stanbrook Abbey hymnal. Revised ed. *Stanbrook Abbey, Callow End, Worcester WR2 4TD : Stanbrook Abbey Music. Unpriced* DM/AY (B76-50786)
Stanley, Harry. 'Can you hear me, mother?' : Sandy Powell's lifetime of music-hall. (Powell, Sandy). *Jupiter Books. £3.50* A/JV/E(P) (B76-13584) ISBN 0-904041-38-7
Statham, Heathcote. Two posthumous organ pieces. *Ramsey : Roberton. Unpriced* RJ (B76-50596)
Steele, John. Dixit Dominus : for SATB soli and chorus, string orchestra and organ continuo. (Scarlatti, Alessandro). *Novello. £1.20* ERXMDGKJ (B76-50046)
Steffan, Joseph Anton. Concerto, horns (2), keyboard & string orchestra, D major. Concerto in D major for fortepiano, 2 horns and strings. *Oxford University Press, for the University of Hull. Unpriced* RXMPWTNTPWF (B76-50613) ISBN 0-19-713421-1
Stekel, Erich Paul. Ouverture pour une tragedie classique. Opus 9. *Paterson. £1.50* MMJ (B76-50532)
Stephen, John. Play suite : seven simple quartets for beginner brass ensemble. *British and Continental : EMI. Unpriced* WNSG (B76-50335)
Stephens, Norris L. Clock music. *arr.* Ten pieces for a musical clock. (Handel, George Frideric). *Schirmer. Unpriced* XSQMK (B76-50348)
Stephenson, Kurt.
Klavierwerke
Band 1. (Brahms, Johannes). *Litolff : Peters. Unpriced* QP/AZ (B76-50559)
Band 2. (Brahms, Johannes). *Litolff : Peters. Unpriced* QP/AZ (B76-50560)
Waltzes, piano 2 hands, op.39. Walzer für Klavier zu zwei Händen. Opus 39. (Brahms, Johannes). *Litolff : Peters. Unpriced* QNUHW (B76-50558)
'Sterling'. (Carter, Sydney Horace). *19 Glendale Rd, Bournemouth BH6 4JA : 'Talking Machine Review'. £1.60* A/FE(P/X) (B76-09865) ISBN 0-902338-22-6
Sternfeld, Frederick William. Essays on opera and English music : in honour of Sir Jack Westrup. *Blackwell. £7.00* A(YD/XCE841/D) (B76-15050) ISBN 0-631-15890-1
Stevenson, Ronald. Canonic studies. (Ziehn, Bernhard). 1st ed. reprinted. *Kahn and Averill. £4.50* A/RM (B76-35798) ISBN 0-900707-38-0
Stewart, Michael. Mack & Mabel : a musical love story. *French. £1.35* BHKMACM (B76-19250) ISBN 0-573-68074-4
Stockhausen. *See* Maconie, Robin.
Stoker, Richard. Monologue : for solo violin. *Ashdown. £0.30* SPMJ (B76-50253)
Stokes, Richard. The Fischer-Dieskau book of Lieder : the texts of over 750 songs in German. *Gollancz : Pan Books. £7.50* AKDW(YE) (B76-33373) ISBN 0-575-01852-6
Stolz, Robert. Songs from White Horse Inn and other favourites. *Chappell. Unpriced* KDW (B76-50486)
Stone, David. Pelléas et Mélisande. Op.80. Sicilienne. *arr.* Sicilienne. (Fauré, Gabriel). *Boosey and Hawkes. £3.95* MK/AHVQ (B76-50140)
Stone, Ruth M. African music oral data : a catalog of field recordings, 1902-1975. *Indiana University Press Distributed by Bell. £12.00* BZK/FD(WT) (B76-50759) ISBN 0-253-30262-5
Story of pop. *Adaptations.* Superstars of the 70's. *Octopus Books. £1.99* AKDW/GB/E(M/XQK7) (B76-34774) ISBN 0-7064-0447-5
Story of the piano. (Van Barthold, Kenneth). *British Broadcasting Corporation. £3.50* AQ/B(X) (B76-05040) ISBN 0-563-12580-2
Story of unique piano tuition. (Ashburnham, George). 3rd ed.. *22 Effingham Close, Sutton, Surrey SM2 6AG : Ashburnham School of Music. £1.15* AQ/E(P) (B76-05916) ISBN 0-905329-00-7
Stout, Alan.
Music : for flute and harpsichord. *Peters. Unpriced* VRPJ (B76-51020)
Sonata, cello & piano. Sonata, violoncello and piano. *Peters. Unpriced* SRPE (B76-50258)
Strand wind series. Further progressive steps. *R. Smith. Unpriced* WMK/AAY (B76-50326)
Stratification of musical rhythm. (Yeston, Maury). *Yale University Press. £6.00* A/NM (B76-18372) ISBN 0-300-01884-3
Strauss, Johann, *b.1825.*
An der schönen blauen Donau. Op.314. *arr.* The blue Danube. *Fisher and Lane. Unpriced* RPVK/AHW (B76-50938)
Die Fledermaus. Fledermaus - Polka. *arr.* Polka française. *Oxford University Press. Unpriced* UMMK/AHVH (B76-50665)
Eine Nacht in Venedig. *Vocal score.* A night in Venice. (Korngold, Erich). *Weinberger. Unpriced* CF (B76-50364)
Rosen aus dem Suden. Op.388. *arr.* Roses from the south. Op.388 : waltz. *Bosworth. Unpriced* MK/AHW (B76-50518)
Seven Strauss waltzes : for descant, treble recorders and piano. *Chappell. Unpriced* VSNTQK/AHW (B76-51035)
Unter Donner und Blitz. Op.324. *arr.* Thunder and lightning = Unter Donner und Blitz, Op.324 : polka. *Bosworth. Unpriced* MK/AHVH (B76-50517)
Stravinsky, Soulima. Chantefaibles : 10 chansons pour enfants. *Peters. Unpriced* KDW (B76-50487)
Streets of London. (Senator, Ronald). *Boosey and Hawkes. £2.20* JFE/NYFSNSDW (B76-50471)
Streisand : an unauthorised biography. (Jordan, René). 1st British ed. *W.H. Allen. £3.95* AKDW/GB/E(P) (B76-11504) ISBN 0-491-01775-8
Strenuous life : a ragtime two-step. (Joplin, Scott). *Schirmer. Unpriced* WNK/AHXJ (B76-50330)
Strenuous life. *arr.* The strenuous life : a ragtime two-step. (Joplin, Scott). *Schirmer. Unpriced* WNK/AHXJ (B76-50330)
Structural functions in music. (Berry, Wallace). *Prentice-Hall. £8.40* A/LZ (B76-11503) ISBN 0-13-853903-0
Student's music library, historical and critical studies. Nettel, Reginald. Havergal Brian and his music. *Dobson. £7.50* BBTN(N) (B76-25956) ISBN 0-234-77861-x
Studies in musicology. *See* New York Bartók Archive. Studies in musicology.
Style in piano playing. (Cooper, Peter, *b.1918*). *John Calder : Distributed by Calder and Boyars. £6.50* AQ/E (B76-15056) ISBN 0-7145-3512-5
Suchoff, Benjamin.
Béla Bartók essays. (Bartók, Béla). *Faber. £38.50* A/G(D) (B76-36283) ISBN 0-571-10120-8
Turkish folk music from Asia Minor. (Bartók, Béla). *Princeton University Press. £12.20* BZC (B76-36284) ISBN 0-691-09120-x
Suite à la mode : fourteen pieces for piano. (Wolford, Darwin). *Boosey and Hawkes. £2.00* QPG (B76-50562)
Suite bergamasque. Clair de lune. *arr.* Clair de lune : piano solo. (Debussy, Claude). *Bosworth. Unpriced* QPK (B76-50920)
Suite of Elizabethan dances. (Holborne, Antony). *Schirmer. Unpriced* WNRK/AH (B76-50334)
Suite on English folk tunes, 'A time there was ...' Op.90 : for orchestra. (Britten, Benjamin). *Faber Music. Unpriced* MRG (B76-50163)
Sullivan, Sir Arthur Seymour. Piano music. *Selections.* Piano music. *Chappell. Unpriced* QPJ (B76-50216)
Sulyok, Imre. Piano music. Klavierwerke = Piano works Vol.8: Années de pélerinage 3. (Liszt, Franz). *Bärenreiter. £3.00* QP/AZ (B76-50561)
Sumerlin, Macon. Jalapeño : SATB chorus and piano. *Warner : Blossom. Unpriced* DW (B76-50031)
Sumsion, Herbert. Fifty hymns for band
Book 2: General, Passiontide and Easter. *Oxford University Press. Unpriced* MK/DM/AY (B76-50868) ISBN 0-19-363060-5
Sun music : for voices and percussion. (Sculthorpe, Peter). *Faber Music. Unpriced* ENYLDW (B76-50045)
Sung responses at Mass : music and English translation of the Rite of Mass. (Roman Catholic Church. *Liturgy and ritual*). *Incorporated Catholic Truth Society. Unpriced* JDGK (B76-50101)
Sunset trail : a collection of songs of the American West with text and illustrations. *EMI. Unpriced* KDW/AYT (B76-50851)
Superband meets Mr Boogie. (Balent, Andrew). *Warner Blossom. Unpriced* UMJ (B76-50281)
Supersound series for young bands.
Balent, Andrew. Got the spirit! *Warner : Blossom. Unpriced* UMMK/DW/LC (B76-51006)
Mozart, Wolfgang Amadeus. German dance no.76, K.605, no.3. *arr.* The sleigh ride. *Warner. Unpriced* UMMK/AH (B76-51005)
Superstars of the 70's. *Octopus Books. £1.99* AKDW/GB/E(M/XQK7) (B76-34774) ISBN 0-7064-0447-5
Suppé, Franz von. Dichter und Bauer. Overture. *Selections: arr.* Poet and peasant overture : (selections). *Fisher and Lane. Unpriced* RPVK (B76-50937)
Swann, Donald. Red and green Christmas. *arr.* Red and green Christmas : for SATB chorus and keyboard. (Cattouse, Nadia). *Galaxy : Galliard. Unpriced* DP/LF (B76-50393)
Swarenski, H. D'un cahier d'esquisses : piano solo. (Debussy, Claude). *Peters. Unpriced* QPJ (B76-50201)
Swarsenski, H.
Berceuse héroïque : piano solo. (Debussy, Claude). *Peters. Unpriced* QPJ (B76-50200)
Danse bohémienne : piano solo. (Debussy, Claude). *Peters. Unpriced* QPH (B76-50196)
Swedish march, and, Fanfare. (Gregson, Edward). *R. Smith. Unpriced* WMJ (B76-51059)
Sweelinck, Jan Pieterzoon.
Cantiones sacrae. Hodie Christus natus est. *arr.* Hodie Christus natus est. *Roberton. £0.15* FEZDJ/LF (B76-50819)
Mein junges Leben hat ein End. Variations on 'Mein junges Leben hat ein End'. *Schirmer. Unpriced* UMK/AT (B76-50283)
Swingtime in Tottenham. (Green, Benny). *Basset Chambers, 27 Bedfordbury, W.C.2 : Lemon Tree Press Ltd. £1.25* AMT(P/XP11) (B76-35803) ISBN 0-904291-11-1
Symphonic poem, no.2. Tasso, lamento e trionfo. Tasso, lamento e trionfo. (Liszt, Franz). *Eulenburg. Unpriced* MMJ (B76-50874)
Symphonic poem no.4. Orpheus. (Liszt, Franz). *Eulenburg. Unpriced* MMJ (B76-50525)
Symphonic poem no.5. Prometheus. Prometheus. (Liszt, Franz). *Eulenburg. Unpriced* MMJ (B76-50526)
Symphonic poem no.7. Festklange. (Liszt, Franz). *Eulenburg. Unpriced* MMJ (B76-50527)
Symphonic poem no.8 Héroïde funèbre. Héroïde funèbre. (Liszt, Franz). *Eulenburg. Unpriced* MMJ (B76-50875)
Symphonic poem, no.9. Hungaria. Hungaria. (Liszt, Franz). Revised ed. *Eulenburg. Unpriced* MMJ (B76-50150)
Symphonic poem, no.10. Hamlet. Hamlet. (Liszt, Franz). *Eulenburg. Unpriced* MMJ (B76-50876)
Symphonic poem, no.12. Die Ideale. Die Ideale. (Liszt, Franz). Revised ed. *Eulenburg. Unpriced* MMJ (B76-50151)
Symphonie funèbre et triomphale. Op.15. Grande symphonie funèbre et triomphale. Op.15. (Berlioz, Hector). *Eulenburg. Unpriced* EUMMDE (B76-50047)
Symphonische Hymnen : für grosses Orchester. (Hartmann, Karl Amadeus). *Schott. £11.00* MMJ (B76-50524)
Symphony 'X', (Big 'D'). (Gillis, Don). *Boosey and Hawkes. £0.35* UMME (B76-50662)
Szántó, Theodor. Concerto, piano, C minor. *arr.* Piano concerto. (Delius, Frederick). *Boosey and Hawkes. Unpriced* QNUK/LF (B76-50184)
Szathmáry, Zsigmond. Requiem. *Vocal score.* Requiem für Sopran, Mezzosopran, zwei gemischte Chöre und Orchester. (Ligeti, György). *Litolff : Peters. Unpriced* DGKAV (B76-50011)
Tages Weihe. D.763. *arr.* Where thou reignest. (Schubert, Franz). *Ashdown. £0.12* FLDH (B76-50091)
'Talking Machine Review'.
The catalogue of the United States Everlasting Indestructible cylinders, 1908-1913. (Annand, Herbert Harry). 2nd ed. *19 Glendale Rd, Bournemouth BH6 4JA : The Talking Machine Review International. £0.45* A/FE(WT) (B76-27984) ISBN 0-902338-21-8
Première liste générale des disques à saphir Phrynis de 30 centimètres de diamètre. *19 Glendale Rd, Bournemouth BH6 4JA : Talking Machine Review. £0.60* A/FD(WT) (B76-50352) ISBN 0-902338-23-4
'Sterling'. (Carter, Sydney Horace). *19 Glendale Rd, Bournemouth BH6 4JA : 'Talking Machine Review'. £1.60* A/FE(P/X) (B76-09865) ISBN 0-902338-22-6
Tall wind : soprano, flute, oboe, guitar and violoncello. (Ung, Chinary). *Peters. Unpriced* KFLE/NVPNSDW (B76-50133)

Tallis, Thomas. Cantiones sacrae. Te lucis ante terminum. Te lucis ante terminum : festal and ferial tones, S.A.A.T.B. (unacc.). *Oxford University Press. Unpriced* EZDGKRM (B76-50052) ISBN 0-19-350356-5

Tallis. (Doe, Paul). 2nd ed. *Oxford University Press. £2.20* BTB (B76-15053) ISBN 0-19-314122-1

Tamblyn, Bill.
Psalmen Davids. De profundis. Psalm 130 : for double choir, S.A.T.B.-S.A.T.B. (Schütz, Heinrich). *Chiswick Music. Unpriced* EZDR (B76-50061)
Sacrae symphoniae, bk.2. Hodie completi sunt. Hodie sompleti sunt, Magnificat antiphon for Whit Sunday : double chorus SATB-SATB. (Gabrieli, Giovanni). *83 Stilehall Gdns, W4 3BT : Chiswick Music. Unpriced* EZDGKH/LN (B76-50051)
Selectissimae cantiones. In monte Oliveti. In monte Oliveti : responsory, S.A.A.T.B.B. (Lasso, Orlando di). *Chiswick Music. Unpriced* EZDGKH/LHM (B76-50050)

Tamblyn, William. New community mass. *Chiswick Music. Unpriced* JDG (B76-50100)

Tanbur : the Sudanese lyre or the Nubian kissar. (Plumley, Gwendolen Alice). *c/o Book Production Consultants, 12 Hills Rd, Cambridge CB2 1PG : Town and Gown Press. £1.25* BZNDAT (B76-13572) ISBN 0-905107-02-0

Taschenpartituren.
Bach, Johann Sebastian. St John passion. S.245. Johannes-Passion, BWV 245. *Bärenreiter. £6.50* EMDD/LK (B76-50405)
Schwarz-Schilling, Reinhard. Partita für Orchester. *Bärenreiter. £6.00* MMG (B76-50523)
Schwarz-Schilling, Reinhard. Quartet, strings, F minor. Introduction and fugue. *arr.* Introduktion und Fuge für Streichorchester. *Bärenreiter. £2.50* RXM/Y (B76-50605)

Taschpartituren. Schwarz-Schilling, Reinhard. Symphony, C major. Symphonie in C für Orchester. *Bärenreiter. £6.50* MME (B76-50522)

Tasso, lamento e trionfo. (Liszt, Franz). *Eulenburg. Unpriced* MMJ (B76-50874)

Tate, Phyllis.
Explorations around a troubadour song : for piano solo. *Oxford University Press. Unpriced* QPJ (B76-50574) ISBN 0-19-373809-0
Peace on earth to men : SATB. *Oxford University Press. Unpriced* DP/LF (B76-50399) ISBN 0-19-343057-6
The rainbow and the cuckoo : for oboe and string trio. *Oxford University Press. Unpriced* NVTNS (B76-50884) ISBN 0-19-359024-7

Tatham, Dick. Elton John. *Octopus Books : Phoebus. £1.99* AKDW/GB/E(P) (B76-28395) ISBN 0-7064-0548-x

Tawaststjerna, Erik. Sibelius
Vol.1: 1865-1905. *Faber. £12.50* BSH(N) (B76-30336) ISBN 0-571-08832-5

Taylor, Charles Alfred. Sounds of music. *British Broadcasting Corporation. £6.50* A/B (B76-10250) ISBN 0-563-12228-5

Taylor, Dorothy.
Action rhymes. *Ladybird Books. £0.24* ADW/GR (B76-30340) ISBN 0-7214-0439-1
Dancing rhymes. *Ladybird Books. £0.24* ADW/H (B76-30341) ISBN 0-7214-0440-5

Taylor, Ian, *b.1932.* The opera lover's quiz book. *Luscombe. £0.95* AC(DE) (B76-15052) ISBN 0-86002-084-3

Taylor, Paul Arden. Bach goes to sea : saxophone trio (S.A.B.). *Emerson. Unpriced* VUNT (B76-50696)

Taylor, Ron. Twenty-four Christmas carols for classical guitar. *Wise : Music Sales. Unpriced* TSPMK/DP/LF/AY (B76-50995)

Taylor, Stainton de Boufflers. Two centuries of music in Liverpool : a scrap-book of information concerning musical activities both professional and amateur. *Long Lane, Aintree, Liverpool : Rockliff Brothers Limited. £4.50* A(YDJF/XYN201) (B76-25957) ISBN 0-9505143-0-6

T.B. *See* B., T.

Tchaikovsky, Peter. Four anthems : for mixed chorus. *Ramsey : Roberton. Unpriced* EZDGTC (B76-50413)

Tchaikowsky, André. Concerto, piano, op.4. *arr.* Concerto for piano and orchestra, Op.4. *Weinberger. Unpriced* QNUK/LF (B76-50185)

Te lucis ante terminum : festal and ferial tones, S.A.A.T.B. (unacc.). (Tallis, Thomas). *Oxford University Press. Unpriced* EZDGKRM (B76-50052) ISBN 0-19-350356-5

Te Wiata, Inia. Inia Te Wiata's Maori songbook : favourite songs and chants as arranged and recorded by Inia Te Wiata. *A.H. & A.W. Reed. Unpriced* KDW/G/AYXR (B76-50491) ISBN 0-589-00877-3

Teaching music-reading in class. (Todd, Dennis). *Evans Bros. £0.95* A(VF) (B76-06886) ISBN 0-237-29164-9

Teaching primary science. Diamond, Dorothy Mary. Musical instruments. *Macdonald Educational for Chelsea College, University of London. £1.50* AL/E(VG) (B76-30110) ISBN 0-356-05077-7

Technique of film music. (Manvell, Roger). Revised and enlarged ed. *Focal Press. £5.00* A/JR (B76-12128) ISBN 0-240-50848-3

Techniques and materials of tonal music : with an introduction to twentieth-century techniques. (Benjamin, Thomas). *Houghton Mifflin. £7.95* A/R (B76-22853) ISBN 0-395-19095-9

Telemann, Georg Philipp.
Concerto, trumpets (3), oboes (2), timpani & string orchestra, D major. Concerto for 3 clarini (trumpets), timpani, 2 oboes, strings, and basso continuo. *Musica rara. Unpriced* RXMPNYHNQF (B76-50610)
Musique héroïque. *arr.* Heroic music : a suite of twelve marches. *Oxford University Press. Unpriced* WSPK/AGM (B76-50342) ISBN 0-19-359067-0

Ten folk songs on the gospel and life. *Weinberger. Unpriced* JDM/AY (B76-50102)

Ten for guitar. *Fentone Music : Breitkopf and Härtel. Unpriced* TSPMK/DW/AY (B76-50277)

Ten green bottles. *Puffin Books. £0.50* ADW/GJ (B76-14369) ISBN 0-14-050144-4

Ten traditional melodies : easy duos for descant recorder and guitar. *Ricordi. £0.95* VSRPLTSK (B76-50688)

Tender tyrant, Nadia Boulanger : a life devoted to music : a biography. (Kendall, Alan, *b.1939*). *Macdonald and Jane's. £5.95* A(VC/P) (B76-29098) ISBN 0-356-08403-5

Tennyson, Alfred, *Baron Tennyson.* Lullaby. (Scott, Anthony). *Boosey and Hawkes. £0.45* KDW (B76-50485)

Terpsichore : die Tänze der Barockzeit, für zwei Sopranblockflöten. *Noetzel : Peters. Unpriced* VSRNU/AY (B76-50302)

Terri, Salli. A child of God : American folk song for four-part chorus of mixed voices and solo (or soli) unaccompanied. *Roberton. £0.20* EZDW (B76-50816)

Terri, Salli. Choral series. Terri, Salli. A child of God : American folk song for four-part chorus of mixed voices and solo (or soli) unaccompanied. *Roberton. £0.20* EZDW (B76-50816)

Texas-Mexican cancionero : folksongs of the Lower Border. *University of Illinois Press. £6.50* ADW/G(YUBR) (B76-22856) ISBN 0-252-00522-8

Texte deutscher Lieder. *English.* The Fischer-Dieskau book of Lieder : the texts of over 750 songs in German. *Gollancz : Pan Books. £7.50* AKDW(YE) (B76-33373) ISBN 0-575-01852-6

Thackray, Roy. The heavenly archer. *Chester. Unpriced* CQN (B76-50365)

That the medals and the baton be put on view : the story of a village band, 1875-1975. (Livings, Henry). *David and Charles. £3.95* AWM/E(YDJED/X) (B76-00675) ISBN 0-7153-7071-5

Theory of change ringing : an introduction. (Cleaver, A W T). *36 Great Clarendon St., Oxford : J. Hannon and Co. (Publishers) Oxford. £0.60* AXSR/E (B76-35358) ISBN 0-904233-10-3

Things to sing. (Smith, Pat). *Arnold. Unpriced* JFDW (B76-50830) ISBN 0-560-02720-6

Third classical and romantic album for horn in F and piano. *Oxford University Press. Unpriced* WTPK/AAY (B76-50749) ISBN 0-19-356530-7

Thirty-one pieces of the 16th-18th centuries : for treble recorder and piano. *Universal. Unpriced* VSSPK/AAY (B76-50690)

Thomas, Brian Price-. *See* Price-Thomas, Brian.

Thomas, Elizabeth. Frog went a-courtin' : traditional American song, SATBB unaccompanied. *Roberton. £0.14* EZDW (B76-50075)

Thomas, J C. Chasin' the Trane : the music and mystique of John Coltrane. *Elm Tree Books. £4.50* AMT(P) (B76-10255) ISBN 0-241-89340-2

Thomas Aquinas, *Saint.* Bone pastor, panis vere : SATB unacc. (Harness, Marjorie). *Banks. Unpriced* EZDJ (B76-50055)

Thompson, Charles. Bing : the authorised biography. *Star Books. £0.70* AKDW/GB/E(P) (B76-25963) ISBN 0-352-39887-6

Thomson, Ross. *See* Ross.

Thomson, Virgil.
Cantata on poems of Edward Lear. Half an alphabet. Half an alphabet : canons for chorus, for four-part chorus of mixed voices with piano accompaniment. *Schirmer. Unpriced* DW/X (B76-50034)
Cantata on poems of Edward Lear. The Akond of Swat. The Akond of Swat : for four-part chorus of mixed voices with baritone solo and piano accompaniment. *Schirmer. Unpriced* DW (B76-50032)
Cantata on poems of Edward Lear. The Jumblies. The Jumblies : for four-part chorus of mixed voices with soprano solo and piano accompaniment. *Schirmer. Unpriced* DW (B76-50033)

Those oldies but goodies : a guide to 50's record collecting. (Propes, Steve). *Collier Books : Collier Macmillan. £0.95* A/FD/GB/YT(XPK11) (B76-12802) ISBN 0-02-061430-6

Three carols for Christmas. *Oxford University Press. Unpriced* EZDP/LF/AY (B76-50425) ISBN 0-19-353246-8

Three carols of the nativity : for S.A.T.B. (James, Donald). *Chappell. Unpriced* EZDP/LF (B76-50810)

Three consort pieces. (Nicolson, Richard). *Boosey and Hawkes. £1.50* VSNRK/DW (B76-50299)

Three epitaphs : for voices and percussion. (Withams, Eric L). *Boosey and Hawkes. £0.35* FE/XPQDW (B76-50088)

Three gifts. *arr.* Three gifts : trio for trombones. (Waterworth, R). *D. Rahter. £2.75* WMK (B76-50732)

Three gymnopédies : flute (or oboe) and piano. (Satie, Erik). *Fentone Music : Breitkopf and Härtel. Unpriced* VRPJ (B76-50291)

Three instant operas for children. (Oliver, Stephen). *Novello. £1.35* CQN (B76-50772)

Three Norwegian pieces. (Grieg, Edvard). *Novello. Unpriced* RXMK (B76-50236)

Three songs for America. *arr.* Three songs for America : bass voice and instruments (woodwind quintet and string quintet). (Amran, David). *Peters. Unpriced* KGXDW (B76-50137)

Three songs for America : bass voice and instruments (woodwind quintet and string quintet). (Amran, David). *Peters. Unpriced* KGXDW (B76-50137)

Three songs for America : bass voice and instruments (woodwind quintet and string quintet). (Amran, David). *Peters. Unpriced* KGXE/MRDW (B76-50138)

Three sonnets of John Donne : for four-part choir of mixed voices unaccompanied. (Burtch, Mervyn). *Roberton. £0.28* EZDW (B76-50814)

Three variations on a Japanese theme : for four guitars. (Croucher, Terence). *109 St Leonard's Rd, Leicester : Clarendon Music. £0.75* TSNS/T (B76-50981)

Threlfall, Robert.
Concerto, piano, C minor. Piano concerto. (Delius, Frederick). *Boosey and Hawkes. Unpriced* MPQF (B76-50157)
Concerto, piano, C minor. *arr.* Piano concerto. (Delius, Frederick). *Boosey and Hawkes. Unpriced* QNUK/LF (B76-50184)
Concerto, violin & cello. Concerto for violin & violoncello. (Delius, Frederick). *Stainer and Bell. Unpriced* MPSPLSRF (B76-50159) ISBN 0-85249-399-1
Dance rhapsody no.2. (Delius, Frederick). *Stainer and Bell. Unpriced* MMJ (B76-50872) ISBN 0-85249-458-0
Eventyr. Once upon time, after Asbjornsen's folklore. (Delius, Frederick). *Stainer and Bell. Unpriced* MMJ (B76-50148) ISBN 0-85249-398-3
North country sketches. (Delius, Frederick). *Stainer and Bell. Unpriced* MMJ (B76-50873) ISBN 0-85249-457-2
Romance for cello and piano. (Delius, Frederick). First ed. *Boosey and Hawkes. £1.00* SRPJ (B76-50645)

Tichenor, Trebor Jay. Ragtime rarities : complete original music for 63 piano rags. *Dover Publications : Constable. £4.55* QPHXJ/AY (B76-50565) ISBN 0-486-23157-7

Tidy, Bill. For gawdsake don't take me! : the songs, ballads, verses, monologues, etc. of the call-up years, 1939-1963. *Hart-Davis, MacGibbon. £2.95* AKDW/KG(YC/XNU25) (B76-50757) ISBN 0-246-10859-2

Tierney, Harry. Irene : song album. *EMI. Unpriced* KDW (B76-50844)

Tiffin, Robert. Musical instruments. (Diamond, Dorothy Mary). *Macdonald Educational for Chelsea College, University of London. £1.50* AL/E(VG) (B76-30110) ISBN 0-356-05077-7

Tigers : satirical anti-war opera in a prologue and three acts. (Brian, Havergal). Centennial ed. *7 Gaitside Drive, Aberdeen : Aberdeen Branch of the Havergal Brian Society. £0.40* BBTNAC (B76-30338) ISBN 0-9505185-0-6

Tillman, June. Exploring sound : creative musical projects for teachers. *Galliard etc.. £2.50* A/D(VJ) (B76-22855) ISBN 0-85249-310-x

Tilmouth, Michael.
Consort of four parts. (Locke, Matthew). *Eulenburg. Unpriced* STNSG (B76-50964)
The flat consort for my Cousin Kemble. (Locke, Matthew). *Eulenburg. Unpriced* STNTG (B76-50965)
The works of Henry Purcell
Vol.5: Twelve sonatas of three parts. (Purcell, Henry). *Novello. £10.00* NXNTE (B76-50173)

Time and motion study III : 16 solo voices with percussion and electronic amplification. (Ferneyhough, Brian). *Peters. Unpriced* EPV (B76-50801)

Time piece : for 2 altos, tenor, 2 baritones and bass. (Patterson, Paul). *Weinberger. Unpriced* JNGEZAZDX (B76-50840)

Tintern Abbey : elegy for brass band. (Noble, Harold). *Studio Music. Unpriced* WMJ (B76-50728)

Tircuit, Heuwell.
Quartet, strings, no.3, 'Drama in musica'. String quartet no.3, 'Drama in musica'. *Associated Music. Unpriced* RXNS (B76-50242)
Sonata, viola & piano, 'Homage to Mahler'. Sonata (Homage to Mahler) : for viola and piano. *Associated Music. Unpriced* SQPE (B76-50255)

Tjeknavorian, Loris. Nine miniatures : piano solo based on Armenian folk and dance melodies. *Basil Ramsey : Roberton. Unpriced* QPJ (B76-50575)

To Jane : music by Ned Rorem. (Rorem, Ned). *Boosey and Hawkes. £1.00* KDW (B76-50483)

Tobias, Henry. Twelve musical plays for children (based on famous fairy tales). *Henry Tobias : Chappell : Chappell. Unpriced* CN (B76-50006)

Today is the first day ... (of the rest of my life) : SATB chorus and piano, (optional flute, recorder or harmonica). (Artman, Ruth). *Warner : Blossom. Unpriced* DH (B76-50014)

Todd, Dennis. Teaching music-reading in class. *Evans Bros. £0.95* A(VF) (B76-06886) ISBN 0-237-29164-9

Tom Jones. *See* Fielding, Henry.

Tomblings, Philip. Behold, I show you a mystery : anthem for SATB and optional organ. *St Gregory Publications. Unpriced* EZDK (B76-50056)

Tombstone-Arizona : a concert overture for brass band. (Wood, Gareth). *R. Smith. Unpriced* WMJ (B76-50729)

Tomlinson, Fred. Warlock and Delius. *14 Barlby Rd, W10 6AR : Thames Publishing for the Peter Warlock Society. £1.50* BDL(Z) (B76-27764) ISBN 0-905210-05-0

Tomlinson, Geoffrey. Norwegian folksongs and dances. Op.17. *Selections : arr.* Three Norwegian pieces. (Grieg, Edvard). *Novello. Unpriced* RXMK (B76-50236)

Tonal perspective series for tuned percussion.
Senator, Ronald. Streets of London. *Boosey and Hawkes. £2.20* JFE/NYFSNSDW (B76-50471)
Withams, Eric L. Three epitaphs : for voices and percussion. *Boosey and Hawkes. £0.35* FE/XPQDW (B76-50088)

Tongues of fire : for organ. (Wills, Arthur). *Weinberger. Unpriced* RJ (B76-50597)

Tonsatz und Klanggestaltung bei Giovanni Gabrieli. (Müller-Blattau, Wendelin). *32 Great Titchfield St., W.1 : Bärenreiter. £24.00* BG

Top pop scene
1976. *Purnell. £0.85* AKDW/GB/E(M) (B76-31913)

ISBN 0-361-03505-5
Topical and nautical operas. *Garland. £400.00 the 28 volume series* ACLM(XFWK61/ZC) (B76-20707) ISBN 0-8240-0913-4
Tops and tails again : eight children's songs with interchangeable accompaniments. *Oxford University Press. Unpriced* JFDW/GJ/AY (B76-50470) ISBN 0-19-330573-9
Toques flamencos. *Selections.* Toques flamencos. (Peña, Paco). *Musical New Services. Unpriced* TSPMJ (B76-50990)
Toscanini. (Marek, George Richard). *Vision Press. £7.80* A/EC(P) (B76-21367) ISBN 0-85478-463-2
Tószeghy, Richard. Béla Bartók essays. (Bartók, Béla). *Faber. £38.50* A/G(D) (B76-36283) ISBN 0-571-10120-8
Touches in popular doubles methods. (Crabtree, Anthony John). *202 Attenborough La., Beeston, Nottingham NG9 6AL : The author. £1.75* AXSR/E (B76-35805) ISBN 0-904233-11-1
Townsend, Charles R. 'San Antonio Rose' : the life and music of Bob Wills. *University of Illinois Press. £8.75* AKDW/GCW/E(P) (B76-31914) ISBN 0-252-00470-1
Toye : for trumpet and piano. (Slack, Roy). *British and Continental : EMI. Unpriced* WSPJ (B76-50339)
Traditional music of Thailand. (Morton, David). *University of California Press. £11.55* BZGH (B76-31121) ISBN 0-520-01876-1
Trakturen für Orgel (Tonband, Mikrophon, Kontaktmikrophone). (Michel, Wilfried). *Bärenreiter. £7.00* RJ (B76-50594)
Trapp Family. Enjoy your recorder. The Trapp family recorder method : a new complete method of instruction for the recorder, including exercises, revisions, trill charts, ornaments and embellishments, duets, trios and quartets
Vol.1. New ed. *Schott. Unpriced* VS/AC (B76-50296) ISBN 0-901938-50-5
Trapp family. The Trapp family recorder method : a new complete method of instruction for the recorder, including exercises, revisions, trill charts, ornaments and embellishments, duets, trios and quartets
Book 1: Treble sopranino (or bass). New ed. *Schott. Unpriced* VS/AC (B76-50297) ISBN 0-901938-51-3
Trapp family recorder method : a new complete method of instruction for the recorder, including exercises, revisions, trill charts, ornaments and embellishments, duets, trios and quartets
Book 1: Treble sopranino (or bass). (Trapp family). New ed. *Schott. Unpriced* VS/AC (B76-50297) ISBN 0-901938-51-3
Vol.1. (Trapp Family). New ed. *Schott. Unpriced* VS/AC (B76-50296) ISBN 0-901938-50-5
Traum, Happy. The guitarist's picture chords. *Wise Music Sales. Unpriced* TS/RC (B76-50270) ISBN 0-86001-205-0
Travellers, and, The fairy hill. (Parke, Dorothy). *Roberton. £0.10* JFDW (B76-50468)
Tremlett, George.
The David Essex story. *White Lion Publishers. £3.25* AKDW/GB/E(P) (B76-16550) ISBN 0-7274-0113-0
The Paul McCartney story. *White Lion Publishers. £3.25* AKDW/GB/E(P) (B76-34782) ISBN 0-7274-0118-1
The Rolling Stones story. *White Lion Publishers. £3.25* AKDW/GB/E(P) (B76-28394) ISBN 0-7274-0123-8
Tres libros de música en cifra para vihuela. Fantasia no.10. *arr.* Fantasia : das Harfenspiel in der Manier von Ludovico nachahmend / von Alonso Mudarra. Welsh Tantz, 'Wascha mesa' / von Hans Neusidler ; für Gitarre solo, eingerichtet von Dieter Kreidler. (Mudarra, Alonso). *Schott. £1.00* TSPMK (B76-50275)
Tresis : for guitar, flute (or violin) and cello. (Balada, Leonardo). *Schirmer. Unpriced* NVRNT (B76-50168)
Trevor, Caleb H.
Organ books
No.5. *Oxford University Press. Unpriced* R/AY (B76-50224) ISBN 0-19-375847-4
No.6. *Oxford University Press. Unpriced* R/AY (B76-50225) ISBN 0-19-375848-2
Trevor, Caleb Henry.
Four eighteenth century concerto movements for organ with and without pedals. *EMI. Unpriced* RK/LF/AY (B76-50936)
Short and easy pieces for organ. *Oxford University Press. Unpriced* R/AY (B76-50226) ISBN 0-19-375856-3
Triad Press bibliographical series. Felix Weingartner : recollections & recordings. *22 Pheasants Way, Rickmansworth, Herts. : Triad Press. £5.95* A/EC(P) (B76-17083) ISBN 0-902070-17-7
Trinity of organs : notes on the history of the organs in three Ipswich public buildings. (Woodward, Michael, *b.1928*). *c/o The Chief Executive, Civic Centre, Civic Drive, Ipswich IP1 2EE : Borough of Ipswich. £0.50* AR/B(YDDLI) (B76-09328) ISBN 0-904023-08-7
Trinket : a piano solo. (Bonner, Stuart). *Sonia Archer Lengnick. Unpriced* QPJ (B76-50903)
Trionto del tempo / by Orlando di Lasso ; and, Ecco l'alma beata / by Giovanni Croce ; arranged for ten recorders in 2 choirs by Dennis A. Bamforth. (Lasso, Orlando di). *Tomus. Unpriced* VSMK/DH (B76-50298)
Trios gymnopédies : piano solo. (Satie, Erik). *Leonard, Gould and Bolttler. £0.45* QPJ (B76-50213)
Triptych, no.2. Op.30. Shadowplay, Op.30 : music theatre from book 7 of the Republic of Plato. (Goehr, Alexander). *Schott. Unpriced* C/JR (B76-50002)
Triptych, no.3. Op.31. Sonata about Jerusalem. Op.31 : cantata. (Goehr, Alexander). *Schott. Unpriced* C/JR (B76-50003)
Tristan : preludes for piano, electronic tapes and orchestra. (Henze, Hans Werner). *Schott. £11.00* MPQ (B76-50156)
Trois ésquisses : for flute/piccolo, oboe and harpsichord. (Bevan, Clifford). *British and Continental : EMI. Unpriced* NWPNT (B76-50169)
Trois gymnopédies. Trois gymnopédies, et Trois gnossiennes. (Satie, Erik). *United Music. Unpriced* QPJ (B76-50214)
Trois gymnopédies. *arr.* Three gymnopédies : flute (or oboe) and piano. (Satie, Erik). *Fentone Music : Breitkopf and Härtel. Unpriced* VRPJ (B76-50291)
Trollope, J Armiger. Grandsire. 3rd ed. *22 Duke St., Burton Latimer, Kettering, Northants. : Christopher Groome. £2.50* AXSR/E (B76-35806) ISBN 0-904233-09-x
Tromlitz, Johann George. Partitas, flute, nos.1-6. Sechs Partiten für Flöte. Zum ersten Mal herausgegeben von Walter Lebermann. *Litolff : Peters. Unpriced* VRPMG (B76-50682)
Trost der Nacht : Chorvariationen für vierstimmigen gemischten Chor a cappella oder mit Flöte und Klavier ad lib. (Reutter, Hermann). *Schott. £5.20* EZDH (B76-50804)
Trowell, Brian. Invitation to medieval music
3: Music of the mid-fifteenth century (1). *Stainer and Bell. Unpriced* CB/AY(XCH301) (B76-50362) ISBN 0-85249-316-9
True glory. (Aston, Peter). *Royal School of Church Music. Unpriced* DH (B76-50782)
Truffert, André. Chantefaibles : 10 chansons pour enfants. (Stravinsky, Soulima). *Peters. Unpriced* KDW (B76-50487)
Trumpet excursions : seven easy pieces for trumpet and piano. (Williams, Christopher). *Chappell. Unpriced* WSPJ (B76-50340)
Trumpet of the swan : for narrator and orchestra. (Lees, Benjamin). *Boosey and Hawkes. £1.25* KHYE/M (B76-50509)
Tuba rhapsody : for tuba and symphonic band. (Grundman, Clare). *Boosey and Hawkes. £30.00* UMPWV (B76-51007)
Tudor church music.
Byrd, William. Liber primus sacrarum cantionum. O quam gloriosum. O quam gloriosum : S.S.A.T.B. Revised ed. *Oxford University Press. Unpriced* EZDJ (B76-50417) ISBN 0-19-352060-5
Gibbons, Orlando. Hosanna to the Son of David : S.S.A.A.T.T.B. *Oxford University Press. Unpriced* EZDK (B76-50418) ISBN 0-19-352078-8
Tull, Fisher.
Credo for symphonic band. *Boosey and Hawkes. £15.00* UMMJ (B76-50663)
Fantasy on L'Homme armé : oboe and piano. *Boosey and Hawkes. £1.25* VTPJ (B76-50692)
The love of three oranges. March. *arr.* March. (Prokofiev, Sergei). *Boosey and Hawkes. £5.00* WMK/AGM (B76-50733)
The seasons of man : mixed chorus and two trumpets. *Boosey and Hawkes. £0.20* EWSNUDH (B76-50408)
Tune book for oboe. *Oxford University Press. Unpriced* VTPMK/AAY (B76-51044) ISBN 0-19-358667-3
Tunes for the band : 70 folk dance melodies with chord symbols. *English Folk Dance and Song Society. Unpriced* LH/G/AYDL (B76-50866) ISBN 0-85418-114-8
Tunetime : six easy pieces for the piano. (Parke, Dorothy). *Roberton. Unpriced* QPJ (B76-50916)
Tunnard, Thomas. Versicles and responses : SATB. *Banks. Unpriced* EZDGMM (B76-50053)
Turkish folk music from Asia Minor. (Bartók, Béla). *Princeton University Press. £12.20* BZC (B76-36284) ISBN 0-691-09120-x
Turner, John.
December music : trio for recorders, descant, treble, tenor. *Tomus. Unpriced* VSNT (B76-50300)
Four diversions : for descant recorder and piano. *Forsyth. Unpriced* VSRPJ (B76-51040)
Twarz, Waldemar. Kleine Tänze. (Handel, George Frideric). *Heinrichshoffen : Peters. Unpriced* SNTK/AH (B76-50245)
Twas in the moon of wintertime. The Huron carol : old French folk melody. (Younger, John B). *Frederick Harris Music : Lengnick. £0.21* ENYFPNSDP/LF (B76-50799)
Twelfth night. *Selections : arr.* Five Shakespeare songs : voice and piano. (Amram, David). *Peters. Unpriced* KDW (B76-50117)
Twelve madrigals : for SSA(A). *Novello. £1.00* EZDU/AY (B76-50062)
Twelve musical plays for children (based on famous fairy tales). (Tobias, Henry). *Henry Tobias : Chappell. Unpriced* CN (B76-50006)
Twelve trumpet tunes with piano accompaniment. *Oxford University Press. Unpriced* WSPK/AAY (B76-50744) ISBN 0-19-355320-1
Twentieth century opera in England and the United States. (Northouse, Cameron). *G.K. Hall : Prior. £14.95* AC(XM75/WT) (B76-35928) ISBN 0-86043-002-2
Twenty-four Christmas carols for classical guitar. *Wise : Music Sales. Unpriced* TSPMK/DP/LF/AY (B76-50995)
Twenty years of British record charts, 1955-1975. *See* 20 years of British record charts, 1955-1975.
Twilight of the gods : the Beatles in retrospect. (Mellers, Wilfrid). *Faber. £1.50* AKDW/GB/E(P) (B76-33370) ISBN 0-571-10998-5
Two acts for three players : clarinet, percussion, piano. (Finney, Rose Lee). *Henmar Press : Peters : Peters. Unpriced* NYFVNT (B76-50176)
Two Browning choruses : S.A.T.B. unaccompanied. (Liszt, Franz). *Boosey and Hawkes. Unpriced* EZDW (B76-50436)
Two centuries of music in Liverpool : a scrap-book of information concerning musical activities both professional and amateur. (Taylor, Stainton de Boufflers). *Long Lane, Aintree, Liverpool : Rockliff Brothers Limited. £4.50* A(YDJF/XYN201) (B76-25957) ISBN 0-9505143-0-6
Two episodes from Lenau's Faust. Procession by night, and, Mephisto waltz. (Liszt, Franz). *Eulenburg. Unpriced* MMJ (B76-50528)
Two epitaphs : S.S.A. (Maconchy, Elizabeth). *Chester. Unpriced* FEZDW (B76-50821)
Two for the seesaw. *See* Gibson, William, b.1914.
Two harvest carols : for four-part chorus of mixed voices unaccompanied. (Hanson, Geoffrey). *Roberton. £0.10* EZDP/LP (B76-50060)
Two mediaeval carols : for 4-part chorus of mixed voices unaccompanied. (Lees, Heath). *Roberton. Unpriced* EZDP/LF (B76-50059)
Two pieces for flute. (Davies, Peter Maxwell). *Boosey and Hawkes. £2.00* VRPMJ (B76-51027)
Two posthumous organ pieces. (Statham, Heathcote). *Ramsey : Roberton. Unpriced* RJ (B76-50596)
Two revival preludes : for trumpet and organ. (Farrell, Graham). *Galaxy : Galliard. Unpriced* WSPLR (B76-50745)
Two Welsh songs. (Hoddinott, Alun). *Oxford University Press. Unpriced* DW (B76-50403) ISBN 0-19-343061-4
Udell, Peter. Shenandoah : a musical. *French. £1.25* BGGTACM (B76-06888) ISBN 0-573-68073-6
Uhma, Stefan. Lwowskie piosenki
Część 5: Zbrodnia i Kara ; oraz uzupelnienia poprzednio wydanych części. *Kolo Lwowian. £0.75* ADW/G(YMUL) (B76-05915) ISBN 0-9503005-3-5
Unanswered question : six talks at Harvard. (Bernstein, Leonard). *Harvard University Press. £12.75* A (B76-22251) ISBN 0-674-92000-7
Underwater Ballet. Rooftop ballet. Rooftop ballet and Underwater ballet : two piano solos. (Bailey, Freda O). *Regina Music. Unpriced* QPJ (B76-50902)
Ung, Chinary. Tall wind : soprano, flute, oboe, guitar and violoncello. *Peters. Unpriced* KFLE/NVPNSDW (B76-50133)
Unger. Kleine Tänze. (Handel, George Frideric). *Heinrichshoffen : Peters. Unpriced* SNTK/AH (B76-50245)
Unison songs.
Benger, Richard. Sky songs. *Edwin Ashdown. £0.40* JFDW (B76-50462)
Davies, Laurence Hector. Gather gladness from the skies : spring carol, unison or SATB. *Ashdown. £0.08* JDP (B76-50103)
United States Everlasting Indestructible Company. The catalogue of the United States Everlasting Indestructible cylinders, 1908-1913. (Annand, Herbert Harry). 2nd ed. *19 Glendale Rd, Bournemouth BH6 4JA : The Talking Machine Review International. £0.45* A/FE(WT) (B76-27584) ISBN 0-902338-21-8
Unity capsule : solo flute. (Ferneyhough, Brian). *Peters. Unpriced* VRPMJ (B76-51028)
University of Cambridge. *Fitzwilliam Museum. See* Fitzwilliam Museum.
University of Cambridge. *Library. MSS.(Add.MS.5943, ff 161-173)* Four French songs from an English song book (Cambridge, University Library Add.MS.5943, ff 161-173) : for voice with 1 and 2 instruments. *Antico. Unpriced* KE/LNUDW/AY (B76-50859)
University of Lancaster. *Library.* Catalogue of the Hans Ferdinand Redlich Collection of musical books and scores : (including material on the Second Viennese School). *University Library, Bailrigg, Lancaster LA1 4YH : The University. £3.00* A(T) (B76-31432) ISBN 0-901699-35-7
University of London. *Chelsea College of Science and Technology. See* Chelsea College of Science and Technology.
University of Münster. *See* Westfälische Wilhelmsuniversität.
University paperbacks. Blunt, *Sir* Anthony. French art and music since 1500. *Methuen. £1.35* A(YH/X) (B76-50351) ISBN 0-416-81650-9
Unser Seele wartet auf den Herrn. *Vocal score.* Our soul doth wait upon the Lord = Unser Seele wartet auf den Herrn. (Antes, John). *Boosey and Hawkes. £0.30* DH (B76-50332)
Unter Donner und Blitz. Op.324. *arr.* Thunder and lightning = Unter Donner und Blitz, Op.324 : polka. (Strauss, Johann, *b.1825*). *Bosworth. Unpriced* MK/AHVH (B76-50517)
Useful tunes for guitar
No.5: Hot cross buns : trad. and Auld lang syne : trad. *Charnwood Music. Unpriced* TSPMK
Valbonesi, Ruggero. Five interludes : for clarinet solo. *British and Continental : EMI. Unpriced* VVPMJ (B76-50321)
Valsa brasileira no.3. (Mignone, Francisco). *Arthur Napoleão : Essex Music. Unpriced* QPHW (B76-50900)
Valse des guitares : instrumental ensemble. (Wright, Francis). *Charnwood Music. Unpriced* LNHW (B76-50513)
Van Appledorn, Mary Jeanne. Set of five. Improvisation. Improvisation : for the piano. *Boosey and Hawkes. Unpriced* QPJ (B76-50576)
Van Barthold, Kenneth. The story of the piano. *British Broadcasting Corporation. £3.50* AQ/B(X) (B76-05040) ISBN 0-563-12580-2
Van Beethoven, Ludwig. *See* Beethoven, Ludwig van.
Van Diemen's land : a choral fantasy for mezzo soprano, bass, 2 tenors, baritones, male speaker and a capella. (Bauld, Alison). *Novello. £1.30* EZDX (B76-50818)
Van Nice, John R.

Blessing and glory : for full chorus of mixed voices with organ. (Boyce, William). *Roberton. £0.14* DK (B76-50388)

Save me, O God : for 4-part chorus of mixed voices with piano or organ. (Boyce, William). *Roberton. £0.18* DK (B76-50389)

Varèse, Louise. Varèse : a looking-glass diary Vol.1: 1883-1928. *48 Great Marlborough St., W1V 2BN : Eulenburg Books. £3.00* BVB(N) (B76-12127)
ISBN 0-903873-04-4

Variationen über den Tonus peregrinus : für Orgel. (Schroeder, Hermann). *Schott. £2.25* R/T (B76-50228)

Variations on 'Mein junges Leben hat ein End'. (Sweelinck, Jan Pieterzoon). *Schirmer. Unpriced* UMK/AT (B76-50283)

Vaughan, Henry. My God and King! : S.A.T.B. organ or piano. (Nelson, Havelock). *Banks. Unpriced* DM (B76-50392)

Vaughan Williams. (Day, James). Revised ed. *Dent. £3.75* BVD (B76-01202)   ISBN 0-460-03162-7

Vermeer, Hans Dieter. Sonatina, mandoline & piano, Kinsky 43, D minor. *arr.* Sonatine, d-moll, für zwei Gitarren. (Beethoven, Ludwig van). *Schott. £0.90* TSNUK/AEM (B76-50271)

Verrall, Pamela Motley.
Clarinets in chorus : 14 international folksongs. *Rahter. £2.75* VVNTK/DW/G/AY (B76-50700)
The organ-grinder's carol. (When Jesus Christ was born) : unison. *Leonard, Gould and Bolttler. Unpriced* JFDP/LF (B76-50107)
Peter Piper's carol : calypso style, unison. *Leonard, Gould and Bolttler. Unpriced* JFDP/LF (B76-50108)
Seven romantics. *Cramer. £0.60* VVPK/AAY (B76-50709)

Verse, op.7b : for 8 solo voices. (Connolly, Justin). *Novello. £1.00* JNAYDW (B76-50472)

Versuch über die wahre Art das Clavier zu spielen. *English.* Essay on the true art of playing keyboard instruments. (Bach, Carl Philipp Emanuel). *48 Great Marlborough St., W1V 2BN : Eulenburg Books. £3.00* APW/E (B76-15055)   ISBN 0-903873-14-1

Vespers for Mary Magdalen : for 21 solo voices, (5 sopranos, 5 altos, 5 tenors, 6 basses). (Rose, Gregory). *Novello. £0.42* EZDE (B76-50048)

Vester, Frans. 125 easy classical studies for flute : taken from classical flute methods. *Universal. Unpriced* VR/AF/AY (B76-51015)

Vibrato on the violin. (Hauck, Werner). *Bosworth. £3.00* AS/EV (B76-09329)   ISBN 0-900180-71-4

Victor Jara : his life and songs. (Jara, Victor). *Elm Tree Books : Essex House Publishing. Unpriced* KDW (B76-50845)   ISBN 0-241-89520-0

Victoria, Tomás Luis de. Missae totius anni, 1592. Mass 'O magnum mysterium'. Missa O magnum mysterium : for four voices. *Chester. Unpriced* EZDG (B76-50411)

'Vienna charm' : waltz : an organ solo. (Ashburnham, George). *Effingham Close, Sutton : Ashburnham School of Music. Unpriced* RJ (B76-50589)

Vier Grotesken : für 11 Bläser und Schlagzeüg. (Wanek, Friedrich K). *Schott. £10.50* UMJ (B76-50997)

Vier Scherzduette, K. Anh. 284 dd. Spiegelkanon. *arr.* Mirror canon = Spiegelkanon. (Mozart, Wolfgang Amadeus). *Simrock. Unpriced* XPQNSK/AX (B76-51088)

Vieuxtemps, Henri. Cinq melodies inédités. *Chappell. Unpriced* KDW (B76-50123)

Viola Bibliothek. Hessenberg, Kurt. Sonata, viola & piano. Opus 94. Sonate für Bratsche und Klavier. Opus 94. *Schott. £5.00* SQPE (B76-50634)

Viola da Gamba Society of Great Britain. Consort music for viols in six parts. (Jenkins, John). *Faber Music for the Viola da Gamba Society of Great Britain. Unpriced* STNQR (B76-50963)

Viola d'amore. (Danks, Harry). *7 Summit Gardens, Halesowen, West Midlands B63 4SP : Bois de Boulogne. £15.40* ASQQ/B (B76-17084)   ISBN 0-900998-15-6

Viola method from the third to the first position for individual and class tuition. (Dinn, Freda). *Schott. Unpriced* SR/AF (B76-50257)   ISBN 0-901938-53-x

Violin and viola. (Menuhin, Yehudi). *Macdonald and Jane's. £4.50* AS/E (B76-06892)   ISBN 0-356-04715-6

Violin and viola. (Robinson, Marjorie). *F. Watts. £1.75* AS/B (B77-00349)   ISBN 0-85166-595-0

Vocal refrain : an autobiography. (Lynn, *Dame* Vera). *W.H. Allen. £3.00* AKDW/GB/E(P) (B76-00673)
ISBN 0-491-01795-2

Voice in time : the gramophone of Fred Gaisberg, 1873-1951. (Moore, Jerrold Northrop). *Hamilton. £5.50* A/FD(P) (B76-13200)   ISBN 0-241-89374-7

Voice of music. (Willson, Robina Beckles). *Heinemann. £4.50* A (B76-22073)   ISBN 0-434-97258-4

Voices and instruments. (Feldman, Morton). *Universal. Unpriced* ENYHDW (B76-50044)

Voices no.1 : for four-part chorus of mixed voices a cappella. (Balada, Leonardo). *Schirmer. Unpriced* EZDW (B76-50066)

Voix instrumentalisée : für einen Bassklarinettisten. (Globokar, Vinko). *Litolff : Peters. Unpriced* VVUPMJ (B76-50323)

Volkonsky, Andrei. Sonata, viola & piano. Sonate für Viola und Klavier. *Belaieff : Peters. Unpriced* SQPE (B76-50636)

Volkslieder in leichten Sätzen : für zwei Sopranflöten. *Nagel : Bärenreiter. £1.25* VSRNUK/DW/G/AYE (B76-50686)

Volksmusikartige Variierungstechnik in den ungarischen Passionen, 15. bis 18. Jahrhundert. (Bárdos, Kornél). *32 Great Titchfield St., W.1 : Bärenreiter. £16.25* ADD/LH(YG/XD301)

Von der Wiege bis zum Grabe = From the cradle to the grave : symphonic poem, no.13. (Liszt, Franz). *Eulenburg. Unpriced* MMJ (B76-50152)

Von Einem, Gottfried. *See* Einem, Gottfried von.

Von Grimmelshausen, Jakob Christophel. *See* Grimmelshausen, Jakob Christophel von.

Von Moisy, Heinz. *See* Moisy, Heinz von.

Von Suppé, Franz. *See* Suppé, Franz von.

Von Weber, Carl Maria, *Freiherr. See* Weber, Carl Maria von, *Freiherr.*

Von Westernhagen, Curt. *See* Westernhagen, Curt von.

Voxman, Himie.
Die Entführung aus dem Serail. K.384. *arr.* The abduction from the Seraglio. (Mozart, Wolfgang Amadeus). *Musica rara. Unpriced* UNNK/CC (B76-50668)
Le Nozze di Figaro. K.492. *arr.* The marriage of Figaro Vol.1. (Mozart, Wolfgang Amadeus). *Musica rara. Unpriced* UNNK/CC (B76-50667)
Le Nozze di Figaro. K.492. *arr.* The marriage of Figaro Vol.2. (Mozart, Wolfgang Amadeus). *Musica rara. Unpriced* UNNK/CC (B76-50669)

Vulliamy, Graham. Pop music in school. *Cambridge University Press. £4.75* A/GB(VK) (B76-25953)
ISBN 0-521-20836-x

Wachsmann, Paul. Cinq melodies inédités. (Vieuxtemps, Henri). *Chappell. Unpriced* KDW (B76-50123)

Wagner, Marian. Lwowskie piosenki
Część 5: Zbrodnia i Kara ; oraz uzupelnienia poprzednio wydanych cześci. *Kolo Lwowian. £0.75* ADW/G(YMUL) (B76-05915)   ISBN 0-9503005-3-5

Wagner, Richard.
Der Ring des Nibelungen. *English & German.* The ring. *Dawson. £15.00* BWCAC (B76-31122)
ISBN 0-7129-0698-3

Wagner. *Warren and Phillips. Unpriced* QPK (B76-50922)

Wagner, Wolf Siegfried. The Wagner family albums, Bayreuth 1876-1976. *Thames and Hudson. £5.95* BWCB(XKR101/EM) (B76-19493)
ISBN 0-500-01158-3

Wagner 1976 : a celebration of the Bayreuth festival. *c/o 25 Balcombe St., NW1 6HE : The Wagner Society. £3.75* BWC(D) (B77-00342)   ISBN 0-905800-00-1

Wagner at Bayreuth : experiment and tradition. (Skelton, Geoffrey). New and revised ed. *White Lion Publishers. £5.75* BWCAC/E(YEB) (B76-14367)
ISBN 0-85617-068-2

Wagner family albums, Bayreuth 1876-1976. *Thames and Hudson. £5.95* BWCB(XKR101/EM) (B76-19493)
ISBN 0-500-01158-3

Wagner in Bayreuth. (Shaw, Bernard). *15 Mortimer Terrace, N.W.5 : Broadsheet King. Unpriced* BWCAC/E(YEB) (B76-35352)   ISBN 0-902617-17-6

Wagner Society. Wagner 1976 : a celebration of the Bayreuth festival. *c/o 25 Balcombe St., NW1 6HE : The Wagner Society. £3.75* BWC(D) (B77-00342)
ISBN 0-905800-00-1

Wales, Tony. We wunt be druv : songs and stories from Sussex. *Galliard : English Folk Dance and Song Society. £2.80* ADW/G(YDCR) (B76-17456)
ISBN 0-85249-307-x

Walker, Alan, *b.1930.* Schumann. *Faber. £3.25* BSG(N) (B76-21364)   ISBN 0-571-10269-7

Walker, Arthur Dennis. Symphony, no.34, K.338, C major. Symphony, C major. K.338 and Minuetto, C major. K.409. (Mozart, Wolfgang Amadeus). *Eulenburg. Unpriced* MME (B76-50144)

Walker, Chris. The wind on the heath. *Voice part.* The wind on the heath : children's musical play. *Dobson. Unpriced* JDACN (B76-50098)   ISBN 0-234-77245-x

Walker, James. Scherzo, 'Encore for winds'. *Schirmer. Unpriced* UN (B76-50285)

Walker, Raymond. Cinderella in Salerno. *Vocal score.* Cinderella in Salerno : an opera for schools in three acts based on Rossini's 'La Cenerentola'. *Novello. £1.70* CN (B76-50766)

Walker, Richard, *b.1925.* Maker and lover of beauty : Ivor Gurney, poet and songwriter. (Moore, Charles Willard). *22 Pheasants Way, Rickmansworth, Herts. : Triad Press. £2.65* BGYU(N) (B76-50358)   ISBN 0-902070-16-9

Walker, Robert. Six songs of Mervyn Peake : for high voice, two clarinets and piano. *Ramsey : Roberton. Unpriced* KFTE/VVNTQDW (B76-50499)

Walker, Robert, *b.1936.* Sound projects. *Oxford University Press, Music Department. £1.25* A(VG) (B76-21743)
ISBN 0-19-321804-6

Wallace, Ian, *b.1919.* Promise me you'll sing 'Mud'! : the autobiography of Ian Wallace. *18 Brewer St., W1R 4AS : John Calder. £5.75* AKGX/E(P) (B76-00669)
ISBN 0-7145-3500-1

Walmsley, Henry. God is gone up on high : melody from Corner, 1625. *Banks. Unpriced* DP/LL (B76-50027)

Walsh, T J. Monte Carlo opera, 1879-1909. *Gill and Macmillan : Macmillan. £9.75* AC/E(YHXM/QB/XKU31) (B76-05913)
ISBN 0-7171-0725-6

Walters, David. Epilogue : for four-part male voice choir unaccompanied. (Burtch, Mervyn). *Roberton. £0.10* GEZDH (B76-50823)

Walters, Harold L.
Dynamite brass. *Rubank : Novello. Unpriced* UMMJ (B76-51002)
La Navarraise. Nocturne. *arr.* Nocturne. (Massenet, Jules). *Rubank : Novello. Unpriced* VRNSQK (B76-50675)
La Navarraise. Nocturne. *arr.* Nocturne. (Massenet, Jules). *Rubank : Novello. Unpriced* VVNSQK (B76-50699)

Walton, *Sir* William.
Magnificat and Nunc dimittis : S.A.T.B. and organ. *Oxford University Press. Unpriced* DGPP (B76-50012)

ISBN 0-19-351650-0

Quartet, strings & piano. Quartet for violin, viola, cello and piano. Revised ed. *Oxford University Press. Unpriced* NXNS (B76-50171)   ISBN 0-19-359414-5

Wanek, Friedrich K. Vier Grotesken : für 11 Bläser und Schlagzeüg. *Schott. £10.50* UMJ (B76-50997)

Wangler, Rudolf. Sechs Saiten sehn Finger : Grundlagen und Ubunger für Unterricht und Selbststudium des klassischen, spanischen und begleitenden Gitarrenspiels. *Bärenreiter. £4.50* TS/AC (B76-50653)

Wann, Jim. Diamond studs : the life of Jesse James. *French. £1.60* BSHLACM (B77-00344)   ISBN 0-573-68076-0

Warlock, Peter.
The everlasting voices. *Thames. Unpriced* KDW (B76-50488)
On hearing the first cuckoo in spring. *arr.* On hearing the first cuckoo in spring. (Delius, Frederick). *Oxford University Press. Unpriced* WMK (B76-50731)
ISBN 0-19-362813-9

Warlock, Peter. *For works of this composer under other names see also Heseltine, Philip.*

Warlock (Peter) Society. *See* Peter Warlock Society.

Warlock and Delius. (Tomlinson, Fred). *14 Barlby Rd, W10 6AR : Thames Publishing for the Peter Warlock Society. £1.50* BDL(Z) (B76-27764)   ISBN 0-905210-05-0

Warrack, John. Weber's legacy. Weber in London, 1826. *Wolff. £1.95* BWL(YDB/XHF) (B76-22852)
ISBN 0-85496-403-7

Washburn, Robert.
Epigon IV. *Boosey and Hawkes. £15.00* UMMJ (B76-51004)
Intrada for band. *Oxford University Press. Unpriced* UMMJ (B76-50284)
March-opus '76. *Boosey and Hawkes. £12.00* UMMGM (B76-50999)
Prelude and paragrams. *Oxford University Press. Unpriced* UMMJ (B76-50664)

Washington, Henry. Missae totius anni, 1592. Mass 'O magnum mysterium'. Missa O magnum mysterium : for four voices. (Victoria, Tomás Luis de). *Chester. Unpriced* EZDG (B76-50411)

Wassail of Figgy Duff. *arr.* The wassail of Figgy Duff : for mixed chorus and keyboard, traditional words. (Flanders, Michael). *Galaxy : Galliard. Unpriced* DP/LF (B76-50394)

Wassailing. (Holder, Ray). *Thames Music. Unpriced* JDP/LF (B76-50454)

Wastall, Peter.
Babylon's falling : a jazz spiritual, for voices, recorders, guitars (optional) and piano. *Boosey and Hawkes. £1.75* FE/NWSDW/LC (B76-50083)
Classical music for flute and piano. *Boosey and Hawkes. Unpriced* VRPK/AAY (B76-51022)
Did't my Lord deliver Daniel : a jazz spiritual for voices, recorders, guitars (optional) and piano. *Boosey and Hawkes. £1.75* FE/NWSDW/LC (B76-50084)
Joshua fought the battle of Jericho : a jazz spiritual, for voices, recorders, guitars (optional) and piano. *Boosey and Hawkes. £1.75* FE/NWSDW/LC (B76-50086)
Romantic music for flute and piano. *Boosey and Hawkes. Unpriced* VRPK/AAY (B76-51023)

Watermill. (Binge, Ronald). *Weinberger. Unpriced* VVPK (B76-50706)

Watermill. *arr.* The watermill. (Binge, Ronald). *Oxford University Press. Unpriced* TSPMJ (B76-50658)
ISBN 0-19-355510-7

Watermill. *arr.* The watermill. (Binge, Ronald). *Weinberger. Unpriced* VVPK (B76-50706)

Waterworth, R. Three gifts. *arr.* Three gifts : trio for trombones. *D. Rahter. £2.75* WMK (B76-50732)

Watkins, Michael Blake. The wings of night : for violin solo. *Novello. Unpriced* SPMJ (B76-50254)

Watson, Dennis. Dance of the penguins : elementary accordion solo. *Charnwood Music. Unpriced* RSPMH (B76-50602)

Watts, Leonard Leslie. 'Sterling'. (Carter, Sydney Horace). *19 Glendale Rd, Bournemouth BH6 4JA : 'Talking Machine Review'. £1.60* A/FE(P/X) (B76-09865)
ISBN 0-902338-22-6

Waxman, Donald.
Fifty études : for piano
Book 1. *Galaxy : Galliard. Unpriced* QPJ (B76-50577)
Book 2. *Galaxy : Galliard. Unpriced* QPJ (B76-50578)
Book 3: Lower advanced. *Galaxy : Stainer and Bell. Unpriced* (B76-50891)
The wassail of Figgy Duff. *arr.* The wassail of Figgy Duff : for mixed chorus and keyboard, traditional words. (Flanders, Michael). *Galaxy : Galliard. Unpriced* DP/LF (B76-50394)

W.D. *See* D., W.

We come to the river = Wir erreichen den Fluss : Handlungen für Musik. (Henze, Hans Werner). *Schott. £39.20* CQC (B76-50767)

We wunt be druv : songs and stories from Sussex. *Galliard : English Folk Dance and Song Society. £2.80* ADW/G(YDCR) (B76-17456)   ISBN 0-85249-307-x

Weait, Christopher. Variations, bassoon. Variations for solo bassoon. *Harmuse : Lengnick. £1.25* VWPM/T (B76-51053)

Weber, Carl Maria von, *Freiherr.* Rondo, two pianos, op.60, no.8, in B flat major. *arr.* Rondo in B flat. Op.60, no.8.

Oxford University Press. Unpriced VVPK/AW (B76-50319) ISBN 0-19-359503-6
Weber, William. Music and the middle class : the social structure of concert life in London, Paris and Vienna. *Croom Helm. £5.95* A(W/YB/XHK19/Z) (B76-32961) ISBN 0-85664-215-0
Weber in London, 1826. *Wolff. £1.95* BWL(YDB/XHF) (B76-22852) ISBN 0-85496-403-7
Weber's legacy. *See* Warrack, John.
Weelkes, Thomas.
Alleluia! I heard a voice : anthem for SATBB or SSATB. Revised edition. *Oxford University Press. Unpriced* DK (B76-50024) ISBN 0-19-352090-7
Invitation to madrigals
9: for S.S.A.T.B. *Staines and Bell. Unpriced* EZDU/AY (B76-50812) ISBN 0-85249-345-2
9: for S.S.A.T.B. *Stainer and Bell. Unpriced* EZDU/AY (B76-50811) ISBN 0-85249-346-0
Weihnachtskonzert : für Orgel. (Genzmer, Harald). *Litolff : Peters. Unpriced* RF/LF (B76-50230)
Weinachten an der Heimorgel
Band 1. *Anton J. Benjamin. £1.90* RPVK/DP/LF/AY (B76-50600)
Band 2. *Anton J. Benjamin. £1.90* RPVK/DP/LF/AY (B76-50601)
Weinachtslieder in leichten Sätzen : für zwei Sopranflöten. *Nagel : Bärenreiter. £1.25* VSRNUK/DP/LF/AYE (B76-50685)
Weir, Gillian. Missa mundi : for organ. (Camilleri, Charles). *Fairfield Music. £2.50* RJ (B76-50231)
Weisberg, Arthur. The art of wind playing. *Schirmer Books : Collier Macmillan. £5.00* AU/E (B76-05041) ISBN 0-02-872800-9
Wendt, Johann Nepomuk.
Die Entführung aus dem Serail. K.384. *arr.* The abduction from the Seraglio. (Mozart, Wolfgang Amadeus). *Musica rara. Unpriced* UNNK/CC (B76-50668)
Le Nozze di Figaro. K.492. *arr.* The marriage of Figaro Vol.1. (Mozart, Wolfgang Amadeus). *Musica rara. Unpriced* UNNK/CC (B76-50667)
Le Nozze di Figaro. K.492. *arr.* The marriage of Figaro Vol.2. (Mozart, Wolfgang Amadeus). *Musica rara. Unpriced* UNNK/CC (B76-50669)
Wesley, Samuel Sebastian. Magnificat and Nunc dimittis in E. *Oxford University Press. Unpriced* DGPP (B76-50375) ISBN 0-19-395317-x
Wessely, Othman. De ratione in musica : Festschrift Erich Schenk, zu 5.Mai 1972. *32 Great Titchfield St., W.1 : Bärenreiter Kassel. £18.00* A(ZC)
West Yorkshire and Lindsey Regional Examining Board for the Certificate of Secondary Education. Report on the music examination in 1974 relating to the proposed single system of examining at 16+. (Associated Examining Board for the General Certificate of Education). *Wellington House, Aldershot, Hants. GU11 1BQ : The Board. £0.50* A(VK/AL) (B76-15048) ISBN 0-901893-07-2
Westernhagen, Curt von. The forging of the 'Ring' : Richard Wagner's composition sketches for 'Der Ring des Nibelungen'. *Cambridge University Press. £7.50* BWCAC (B77-00343) ISBN 0-521-21293-6
Westfälische Wilhelmsuniversität. *Musikwissenschaftliche Seminar. See* Musikwissenschaftliche Seminar. *Westfälische Wilhelmsuniversität.*
Westfälische Wilhelmsuniversität. *Orgelwissenschaftliche Forschungsstelle. See* Orgelwissenschaftliche Forschungsstelle. *Westfälische Wilhelmsuniversität.*
Weston, Pamela.
The clarinet teacher's companion. *Hale : Distributed to the music trade by Breitkopf and Härtel. £2.00* AVV/E(VC) (B76-14370) ISBN 0-7091-5482-8
Fifty classical studies for clarinet. *Fentone Music. Unpriced* VV/AF/AY (B76-50698)
Westrup, *Sir* Jack. Everyman's dictionary of music. (Blom, Eric). 5th ed. *Dent. £1.95* A(C) (B76-31911) ISBN 0-460-02151-6
Westrup, *Sir* Jack Allan. Essays on opera and English music : in honour of Sir Jack Westrup. *Blackwell. £7.00* A(YD/XCE841/D) (B76-15050) ISBN 0-631-15890-1
Wette, Adelheid. Hänsel und Gretel. *Adaptations.* Hansel and Gretel : a fairy opera in three acts. (Hammond, Tom). *48 Great Marlborough St., W1V 2BN : Schott and Co. Ltd. £0.50* BHUAC (B76-18375) ISBN 0-901938-14-9
Wette, Adelheid. Hänsel und Gretel. *Vocal score.* Hansel and Gretel : opera in two acts. (Humperdinck, Engelbert). *Boosey and Hawkes. £9.00* CC (B76-50005)
What a spot! : a musical farce in three acts. (Sharkey, Jack). *French. £1.45* BSGNHACM (B76-30339) ISBN 0-573-61814-3
What Child is this? : Old English melody. (Balent, Andrew). *Warner : Blossom. Unpriced* JDP/LF (B76-50827)
Wheatley, Dorothy.
Christmas things to sing. (Smith, Pat). *Arnold. Unpriced* JFDW/LF (B76-50833) ISBN 0-560-02721-4
Things to sing. (Smith, Pat). *Arnold. Unpriced* JFDW (B76-50830) ISBN 0-560-02720-6
When we went to Liza's house : 6 piano pieces. (Ezell, Helen Ingle). *Oxford University Press. Unpriced* QPJ (B76-50904)
Where are the joys? : traditional Scottish air. (Liddell, Claire). *Roberton. £0.14* EZDW (B76-50072)
Where thou reignest. (Schubert, Franz). *Ashdown. £0.12* FLDH (B76-50091)
Where we came. (Rorem, Ned). *Boosey and Hawkes. £1.25* KDW (B76-50484)
Which song and when : a handbook of selected song titles from 1880 to 1974. (Blacklock, Robert Shedden). *10 Antigua St., Edinburgh EH1 3NH : Bandparts Music Stores Ltd. £0.40* ADW/GB(XL95/WT) (B76-06890) ISBN 0-9504826-0-9
Whistling, Carl Friedrich. Handbuch der musikalischen Litteratur. 1817 ed. reprinted with the ten supplements, 1818-1827. *Garland; 2 Rugby St., WC1N 3QU Distributed by George Prior Associated Publishers Ltd. £33.35* A(TC) (B76-04592) ISBN 0-8240-1064-7
White, E B. The trumpet of the swan : for narrator and orchestra. (Lees, Benjamin). *Boosey and Hawkes. £1.25* KHYE/M (B76-50509)
White, John Irwin. Git along, little dogies : songs and songmakers of the American West. *University of Illinois Press. £7.00* AKDW/GNF/E(M) (B76-33374) ISBN 0-252-00327-6
Whittaker, Anthony F. Theme music : single stave edition for organ, piano, guitar. *Anthony Music. £0.50* TSPMK (B76-50992)
Whittall, Arnold. The forging of the 'Ring' : Richard Wagner's composition sketches for 'Der Ring des Nibelungen'. (Westernhagen, Curt von). *Cambridge University Press. £7.50* BWAC (B77-00343) ISBN 0-521-21293-6
Whittall, Mary. The forging of the 'Ring' : Richard Wagner's composition sketches for 'Der Ring des Nibelungen'. (Westernhagen, Curt von). *Cambridge University Press. £7.50* BWAC (B77-00343) ISBN 0-521-21293-6
Whitton, Kenneth Stuart. Schubert : a biographical study of his songs. (Fischer-Dieskau, Dietrich). *Cassell. £5.95* BSFAKDW (B76-33372) ISBN 0-304-29002-5
Whitworth, John. The preces and responses ('for trebles') : S.S.A.T.B. unacc. (Holmes, John). *Oxford University Press. Unpriced* EZDGMM (B76-50412) ISBN 0-19-351651-9
Who with weeping soweth = Die mit Thränen saën. (Antes, John). *Boosey and Hawkes. £0.30* DH (B76-50377)
Whone, Herbert. The integrated violinist. *Gollancz. £4.75* AS/CY (B76-27768) ISBN 0-575-02148-9
Wiegenlied = Lullaby = Berceuse. Op.49, no.4. (Brahms, Johannes). *Lengnick. £0.30* KDW (B76-50119)
Wilbye, John. Homo natus de maliere : S.S.A.T.B. *Oxford University Press. Unpriced* EZDH (B76-50054) ISBN 0-19-350352-2
Wilford, Charles. Ragtime classics : ten piano rags. *Paxton. £1.25* QPHXJ/AY (B76-50564)
Wilkins, Nigel. Three madrigals for voices and/or instruments. (Bartolino da Padova). *Antico. Unpriced* EZDU (B76-50426)
Wilkinson, Stephen.
Consider well : Irish melody. *Roberton. £0.18* GEZDP/LF (B76-50094)
The nightingale : English North Countrie song. *Roberton. £0.18* EZDW (B76-50076)
Willcocks, David. Hymns for choirs. *Oxford University Press. Unpriced* DM/AY (B76-50026) ISBN 0-19-353556-4
William Tell. *See* Mizusawa, Hiroshi.
Williams, Christopher. Trumpet excursions : seven easy pieces for trumpet and piano. *Chappell. Unpriced* WSPJ (B76-50340)
Williams, John, *b.1932.* Jaws. *Theme: arr.* Jaws : theme from the film, piano solo. *Leeds Music. £0.30* QPK/JR (B76-50220)
Williams, Patrick. Some hallucinations : unison song. *Bosworth. Unpriced* JFDW (B76-50831)
Williamson, Malcolm. The musicians of Bremen : for 2 counter-tenors, tenor, 2 baritones and bass. *Weinberger. Unpriced* JNAZDX (B76-50473)
Willner, A M. Zigeunerliebe. *Selections : arr.* Songs from 'Gipsy love'. (Lehár, Franz). *Glocken. Unpriced* KDW (B76-50479)
Wills, Arthur.
The child for today : a carol sequence for SATB and organ. *Novello. £0.90* DPDE/LF (B76-50792)
The light invisible. *Weinberger. Unpriced* DH (B76-50784)
Tongues of fire : for organ. *Weinberger. Unpriced* RJ (B76-50597)
Willson, Robina Beckles. The voice of music. *Heinemann. £4.50* A (B76-22073) ISBN 0-434-97258-4
Wilson, Earl. Sinatra. *W.H. Allen. £5.00* AKDW/GB/E(P) (B76-35802) ISBN 0-491-01967-x
Wilson, Geoffrey. La Fille du tambour major. *Vocal score.* The drum-major's daughter : comic opera in three acts. (Offenbach, Jacques). *Choudens : United Music. Unpriced* CF (B76-50762)
Wilson, Robert Barclay.
The apron of flowers : for flute and piano. *EMI. Unpriced* VRPJ (B76-51021)
Sonata, piano. Sonata for piano. *Cramer. £0.45* QPE (B76-50194)
Wind instruments of European art music. (Horniman Museum). *Inner London Education Authority. £0.45* AU/B(YDBL) (B76-21368) ISBN 0-7168-0545-6
Wind on the heath. *Voice part.* The wind on the heath : children's musical play. (Walker, Chris). *Dobson. Unpriced* JDACN (B76-50098) ISBN 0-234-77245-x
Winding, Thomas. My favourite intervals. (Borge, Victor). *Sphere. £0.60* A/D(YB/M) (B76-28392) ISBN 0-7221-1779-5
Winds, and, In summer time. (Parke, Dorothy). *Roberton. £0.20* JFDW (B76-50469)
Wine of peace : for organ. (Camilleri, Charles). *Roberton. £0.30* RJ (B76-50929)
Wings of night : for violin solo. (Watkins, Michael Blake). *Novello. Unpriced* SPMJ (B76-50254)
Winters, Geoffrey.
Contredanse no.21, K.535, G major, 'La Bataille'. *arr.* Contredanse, 'The battle'. (Mozart, Wolfgang Amadeus). *Oxford University Press. Unpriced* MK/AH (B76-50516) ISBN 0-19-357927-8
Sonatina. piano, op.29. Sonatina for piano. Op.29. *Chappell. Unpriced* QPEM (B76-50195)
Wishart, Peter.
Songs
Book 1. (Purcell, Henry). *Galliard : Stainer and Bell. Unpriced* KDW (B76-50480)
Book 2. (Purcell, Henry). *Galliard : Stainer and Bell. Unpriced* KDW (B76-50481) ISBN 0-85249-323-1
Book 3. (Purcell, Henry). *Galliard : Stainer and Bell. Unpriced* KDW (B76-50482) ISBN 0-85249-383-5
With 100 kazoos. (Bedford, David). *Universal. Unpriced* NV (B76-50166)
With Christmas in mind : thirty-seven songs of today. *Music Sales. £2.95* KDW/GB/AY (B76-50125) ISBN 0-86001-059-7
Withams, Eric L. Three epitaphs : for voices and percussion. *Boosey and Hawkes. £0.35* FE/XPQDW (B76-50088)
Woehl, Waldemar. Le Journal de printemps. Partie 3, 4. Suiten = Suites for four strings or wind instruments and basso continuo. (Fischer, Johann Caspar Ferdinand). *Bärenreiter. £6.00* NXNRG (B76-50540)
Wolford, Darwin. Suite à la mode : fourteen pieces for piano. *Boosey and Hawkes. £2.00* QPG (B76-50562)
Wonderful world of folk : piano, vocal, organ, guitar. *Chappell. Unpriced* TSPMK/DW/AY (B76-50996)
Wood, Alexander. Alexander Wood's the physics of music. 7th ed. *Chapman and Hall etc.. £5.50* A/B (B76-23699) ISBN 0-412-13250-8
Wood, Gareth. Tombstone-Arizona : a concert overture for brass band. *R. Smith. Unpriced* WMJ (B76-50729)
Woodward, G R. Ding dong! merrily on high : 16th cent. French tune. (Carter, Andrew). *Banks. Unpriced* FEZDP/LF (B76-50446)
Woodward, Michael, *b.1928.* A trinity of organs : notes on the history of the organs in three Ipswich public buildings. *c/o The Chief Executive, Civic Centre, Civic Drive, Ipswich IP1 2EE : Borough of Ipswich. £0.50* AR/B(YDDLI) (B76-09328) ISBN 0-904023-08-7
Wordsworth, William, *b.1770.* The solitary reaper. Op.96 : for soprano, clarinet and piano. (Wordsworth, William, *b.1908*). *Roberton. £0.75* KFLE/VVPDW (B76-50135)
Wordsworth, William, *b.1908.* The solitary reaper. Op.96 : for soprano, clarinet and piano. *Roberton. £0.75* KFLE/VVPDW (B76-50135)
Working Group on Provision for Children of Exceptional Gifts in Music and Dance. Gifted young musicians and dancers : report of a Working Group i.e. Working Group on Provision for Children of Exceptional Gifts in Music and Dance set up to consider their general and specialised education. *H.M.S.O. £0.80* A(VMMX/YDL) (B76-24278) ISBN 0-11-491405-2
Works of Karlheinz Stockhausen. (Maconie, Robin). *Oxford University Press. £17.50* BSNK (B76-20708) ISBN 0-19-315429-3
World of Islam Festival Trust. Music and musical instruments in the world of Islam. (Jenkins, Jean). *85 Cromwell Rd, SW7 5BW : World of Islam Festival Publishing Co. Ltd. £1.50* BZCWIAL/B(YDB/WJ) (B76-22080) ISBN 0-905035-12-7
World of your 100 best tunes. *Chappell. Unpriced* QPK/AAY (B76-50923)
World record markets. (Electric and Musical Industries). 3rd ed. *23 Ridgmount St., WC1E 7AH : Henry Melland for EMI. £2.50* A/FD(K) (B76-28828) ISBN 0-9500730-1-6
Worldes blis : motet for orchestra on a thirteenth century English monody. (Davies, Peter Maxwell). *Boosey and Hawkes. £10.00* MMJ (B76-50147)
World's favorite easy violin pieces. *Ashley : Phoenix. Unpriced* SPK/AAY (B76-50959)
World's favorite intermediate violin pieces. *Ashley : Phoenix. Unpriced* SPK/AAY (B76-50960)
World's favourite series. World's favorite easy violin pieces. *Ashley : Phoenix. Unpriced* SPK/AAY (B76-50959)
World's favourite series. World's favorite intermediate violin pieces. *Ashley : Phoenix. Unpriced* SPK/AAY (B76-50960)
Wright, Curtis. Olor solymaeus. Canzon à 2. Canzon à 2 for cornetto (recorder-trumpet), bassoon (cello-rackett), & basso continuo. (Spiegler, Matthias). *Musica rara. Unpriced* NWNT (B76-50539)
Wright, Francis.
Elementary course for guitar. *Charnwood Music. Unpriced* TS/AC (B76-50972)
Etude barcarolle : for instrumental ensemble. *Charnwood Music. Unpriced* LNQ (B76-50514)
Forty-eight exercises for accordion. *Charnwood Music. Unpriced* RS/AF (B76-50943)
Party time : for instrumental ensemble. *Charnwood Music. Unpriced* LN (B76-50510)
Pic-a-pic-a-polka : instrumental ensemble. *Charnwood Music. Unpriced* LNHVH (B76-50511)
Preparatory course for guitar. *Charnwood Music. Unpriced* TS/AC (B76-50973)
Primary course for guitar. *Charnwood Music. Unpriced* TS/AC (B76-50974)
Valse des guitares : instrumental ensemble. *Charnwood Music. Unpriced* LNHW (B76-50513)
Wright, Rosemary. Useful tunes for guitar
No.5: Hot cross buns : trad. and Auld lang syne : trad. *Charnwood Music. Unpriced* TSPMK
Writing down music. (Boustead, Alan). *Oxford University Press. £3.75* A(QU) (B76-14363) ISBN 0-19-317104-x
Wüllner, Franz. Geistliche Lieder aus Schmelli's

Gesangbuch und dem Notenbuch der Anna Magdelena
Buch. Jesus ist das schönste Licht. S.474. *arr.* Jesus is the
loveliest light. (Bach, Johann Sebastian). *Roberton. £0.10*
EZDM (B76-50420)

Wuorinen, Charles. Flute variations 2 : flute solo. *Peters.*
Unpriced VRPM/T (B76-51026)

Wuorinnen, Charles. Mannheim 87, 87, 87 : for unison
chorus and organ. *Peters. Unpriced* JDM (B76-50825)

Wyner, Yehudi. Memorial music 1. Memorial music 1 : Man
comes from dust = Ki K'shimcho, and, Memorial music
2 : Lord let me know my end, (Psalm 39, Isaiah 40) : for
soprano voice with three flutes. *Associated Music.*
Unpriced KFLE/VRNTDH (B76-50134)

Yangagihara, Ryohei. P. Dukas' 'The sorcerer's apprentice'.
F. Warne. £2.25 BDVAMBN (B76-18582)
ISBN 0-7232-1834-x

Ye banks and braes. (Liddell, Claire). *Roberton. £0.10*
EZDW (B76-50073)

Yeats, William Butler. The everlasting voices. (Warlock,
Peter). *Thames. Unpriced* KDW (B76-50488)

Yeats-Edwards, Paul. English church music : a bibliography.
White Lion Publishers. £15.00 A/LD(T) (B76-50000)
ISBN 0-7285-0020-5

Yehudi Menuhin music guides.
Brymer, Jack. Clarinet. *Macdonald and Jane's. £4.50*
AVV/E (B76-36286) ISBN 0-356-08414-0
Kentner, Louis. Piano. *Macdonald and Jane's. £3.95*
AQ/B (B76-10253) ISBN 0-356-04713-x
Menuhin, Yehudi. Violin and viola. *Macdonald and Jane's.*
£4.50 AS/E (B76-06892) ISBN 0-356-04715-6

Yellowbelly ballads : a third selection of Lincolnshire
folk-songs, the majority of them from the collection of
Percy Aldridge Grainger. *Lincolnshire and Humberside*
Arts. Unpriced JE/TSDW/G/AYDGH (B76-50829)

Yelverton, Vera. Music for GCE 'O' Level. (Corbett, Jane).
2nd ed., revised. *Barrie and Jenkins. £1.95* A
(B76-05035) ISBN 0-214-15676-1

Yeston, Maury. The stratification of musical rhythm. *Yale*
University Press. £6.00 A/NM (B76-18372)
ISBN 0-300-01884-3

You will see an angel tonight. (Ropartz, Joseph Guy).
Galaxy : Galliard. Unpriced DP/LF (B76-50397)

Young, Percy Marshall.
Beethoven : a Victorian tribute based on the papers of Sir
George Smart. *Dobson. £5.00* A/EC(P/ZD)
(B76-33367) ISBN 0-234-77672-2
Schlaginstrumente = Percussion instruments : a method of
instruction
Part 1: Kleine Trommel = Side drum. (Keune,
Eckehardt). *Bärenreiter. £6.25* X/AC (B76-50751)

Young, Peter. Music for Montreal. *arr.* Music for Montreal :
the original BBC theme music for the 1976 Olympics.
Chappell. Unpriced QPK/JS (B76-50586)

Young horn-player : a series of graded arrangements for
horn in F and piano
Vol.1. *Oxford University Press. Unpriced* VTPK/AAY
(B76-50312) ISBN 0-19-357459-4
Vol.2. *Oxford University Press. Unpriced* VTPK/AAY
(B76-50313) ISBN 0-19-357461-6
Vol.3. *Oxford University Press. Unpriced* VTPK/AAY
(B76-50314) ISBN 0-19-357463-2

Younger, John B. Twas in the moon of wintertime. The
Huron carol : old French folk melody. *Frederick Harris*
Music : Lengnick. £0.21 ENYFPNSDP/LF (B76-50799)

Yuzuru. *Vocal score.* Yuzuru = The twilight heron : opera
in one act. (Dan, Ikuma). *Boosey and Hawkes. Unpriced*
CC (B76-50363)

Zehm, Friedrich.
Klarinetten im Duett : 8 Stücke für 2 Klarinetten gleicher
Stimmung. *Schott. £1.75* VVNU (B76-50317)
Schwierigkeiten und Unfälle mit 1 Choral. *Schott. £4.50*
UMJ (B76-50282)

Zehn Stücke für Kinder zum Spielen und Träumen, 'De la
musique avant toute chose'. (Françaix, Jean). *Schott.*
£2.40 QPJ (B76-50905)

Zempléni, Kornél. Piano music. Klavierwerke = Piano
works
Vol.8: Années de pélerinage 3. (Liszt, Franz). *Bärenreiter.*
£3.00 QP/AZ (B76-50561)

Ziehn, Bernhard. Canonic studies. 1st ed. reprinted. *Kahn*
and Averill. £4.50 A/RM (B76-35798)
ISBN 0-900707-38-0

Ziehn, Bernhard. Canonical studies. *See* Ziehn, Bernhard.
Canonic studies.

Zum Sanctus : for 4-part chorus of mixed voices with organ
or piano. (Schubert, Franz). *Roberton. £0.14* DH
(B76-50019)

Zwei Miniaturen : für Trompete (B) und Schlagwerk.
(Konietzny, Heinrich). *Bosse : Barenreiter. £6.00*
WSPLX (B76-50746)

Subject Index

List of Music Publishers

While every effort has been made to check the information given in this list with the publishers concerned, the British Library cannot hold itself responsible for any errors or omissions.

ACUFF-ROSE Music Ltd. 16 St George St., London W1. *Tel:* 01-629-0392. *Grams:* Acufrose London.

AFFILIATED MUSIC Publishers Ltd. 138 Charing Cross Rd, London WC2H 0LD. *Tel:* 01-836-9351.

AMERICAN UNIVERSITY PUBLISHERS Group, Ltd. 70 Great Russell St., London WC1B 3BY. *Tel:* 01-405-0182. *Grams:* Amunpress.

ANTICO Edition. North Harton, Lustleigh, Newton Abbot, Devon TQ13 9SG. *Tel:* Lustleigh (064-77)-260.

ARDMORE AND BEECHWOOD, Ltd. 21 Denmark St., London WC2H 8WE *Tel:* 01-836-3856.

ARNOLD. E.J. Arnold & Son Ltd. Butterley St., Leeds LS10 1AX.

ARS VIVA. 48 Great Marlborough St., London W1V 2BN.

ASCHERBURG, HOPWOOD AND CREW, Ltd. 50 New Bond St., London W1A 2BR. *Tel:* 01-629-7600. *Grams:* Symphony London.

ASHDOWN. Edwin, Ltd. 275–281 Cricklewood Broadway, London NW2 6QR. *Tel:* 01-450-5237.

ASHLEY-FIELDS Music, Ltd. 61 Frith St., London W1V 5TA. *Tel:* 01-734-7462. *Grams:* Fieldmus London.

ASSOCIATED BOARD OF THE ROYAL SCHOOLS OF MUSIC. (Publications Dept), 14 Bedford Sq., London WC1B 3JG. *Tel:* 01-636-6919. *Grams:* Musexam London WC1.

ASSOCIATED MUSIC Publishers, Inc. c/o G. Schirmer Ltd, 140 Strand, London WC2R 1HH. *Tel:* 01-836-4011.

BANKS and Son (Music) Ltd. Stonegate, York.

BARENREITER Ltd. 32 Great Titchfield St., London W1. *Tel:* 01-580-9008.

BAYLEY AND FERGUSON, Ltd. 65 Berkeley St., Glasgow C3. *Tel:* Central 7240. *Grams:* Bayley Glasgow.

B.B.C. *See* British Broadcasting Corporation.

BELWIN-MILLS Music, Ltd. 250 Purley Way, Croydon CR9 4QD. *Tel:* 01-681-0855. *Grams:* Belmilmus Croydon.

BERRY MUSIC Co. Ltd. 10 Denmark St., London WC2H 8LU. *Tel:* 01-836-1653.

BLOSSOM Music, Ltd. 139 Piccadilly, London W1. *Tel:* 01-629-7211. *Grams:* Leedsmusik London W1.

BODLEY HEAD. The Bodley Head, Ltd. 9 Bow St., London WC2E 7AL. *Tel:* 01-836-9081. *Grams:* Bodleian London WC2.

BOOSEY AND HAWKES Music Publishers, Ltd. 295 Regent St., London W1A 1BR. *Tel:* 01-580-2060. *Grams:* Sonorous London W1. *Trade:* The Hyde, Edgware Rd, London NW9 6JN. *Tel:* 01-305-3861. *Grams:* Sonorous London NW9.

BOSWORTH and Co., Ltd. 14–18 Heddon St., London W1R 8DP. *Tel:* 01-734-0475. *Grams:* Bosedition London W1.

BOURNE MUSIC Ltd. 34/36 Maddox St., London W1R 9PD. *Tel:* 01-493-6412. *Grams:* Bournemusic London W1.

BREGMAN VOCCO AND CONN, Ltd. 50 New Bond St., London W1A 1BR. *Tel:* 01-629-7600. *Grams:* Symphony London.

BREITKOPF AND HARTEL (London) Ltd. 8 Horse and Dolphin Yard, London W1V 7LG. *Tel:* 01-437-3342. *Grams:* Breitkopfs London W1.

BRITISH AND CONTINENTAL Music Agencies, Ltd. 8 Horse and Dolphin Yard, London W1V 7LG. *Tel:* 01-437-3342.

BRITISH BROADCASTING CORPORATION. BBC Publications, 35 Marylebone High St., London W1M 4AA. *Tel:* 01-580-5577. *Grams:* Broadcasts London. *Telex:* 265781.

CAMBRIDGE UNIVERSITY PRESS. Bentley House, P.O. Box 92, 200 Euston Rd., London NW1 2DB. *Tel:* 01-387-5030. *Grams:* Cantabrigia London NW1. *Telex:* 27335. *Editorial and Production:* The Pitt Building, Trumpington St., Cambridge CB2 1RP. *Tel:* Cambridge 58331. *Grams:* Unipress Cambs. *Telex:* 817256.

CAMPBELL CONNELLY and Co., Ltd. 10 Denmark St., London WC2. *Tel:* 01-863-1653.

CARY. L.J. Cary and Co. Ltd. 50 New Bond St., London W1A 2BR. *Tel:* 01-629-7600. *Grams:* Symphony London W1.

CENTRAL COUNCIL OF CHURCH BELL RINGERS. c/o "Monsal", Bredon, Tewkesbury, Glos. GL20 7LY.

CHAPPELL and Co., Ltd. 50 New Bond St., London W1A 1DR. *Tel:* 01-629-7600. *Grams:* Symphony London. *Telex:* 268403.

CHARNWOOD MUSIC Publishing Co. 5 University Rd, Leicester.

CHESTER. J. and W. Chester/Edition Wilhelm Hansen London Ltd. Eagle Court, London EC1M 5QD. *Tel:* 01-253-6276. *Grams:* Guarnerius London EC1.

CLIFFORD ESSEX Music Co. Ltd. 20 Earlham St., London WC2. *Tel:* 01-836-2810. *Grams:* Triomphe London WC2.

COLLIER MACMILLAN Publishers. Division of Cassell and Collier Macmillan Publishers Ltd., 35 Red Lion Sq., London WC1R 4SG. *Tel:* 01-242-6281.

Connelly, Campbell and Co., Ltd. *See* Campbell Connelly.

CONSTABLE and Co., Ltd. 10 Orange St., London WC2H 7EG. *Tel:* 01-930-0801. *Grams:* Dhagoba London WC2H 7EG. *Trade:* Tiptree, Essex. *Tel:* 0621-81-6362.

CRAMER. J.B. Cramer and Co., Ltd. 99 St. Martin's Lane, London WC2N 4AZ. *Tel:* 01-240-1612.

CRANZ and Co. Ltd. Alderman's House, Bishopsgate, London EC2. *Tel:* 01-283-4266. *Grams:* Cranz Usually London.

Curwen. J. Curwen and Sons, Ltd. *See* Faber Music.

DANIEL. The C.W. Daniel Co. Ltd. 60 Muswell Rd. London N10. *Tel:* 01-444-8650.

DAVID AND CHARLES (Publishers) Ltd. South Devon House, Railway Station, Newton Abbot, Devon TQ12 2BP. *Tel:* 0626-3521. *Telex:* 42904.

DE WOLFE, Ltd. 80–82 Wardour St., London W1V 3LF. *Tel:* 01-437-4933. *Grams:* Musicall London.

DICK JAMES MUSIC Ltd. 71 New Oxford St., London WC1A 1DP. *Tel:* 01-836-4864.

EFDS. *See* English Folk Dance and Song Society.

EGRET HOUSE. 93 Chancery La., London WC2.

ELKIN and Co., Ltd. Borough Green, Sevenoaks, Kent. *Tel:* 0732-88-3261. *Grams:* Novellos Sevenoaks.

EMERSON. June Emerson Wind Music. Windmill Farm, Ampleforth, York.

EMI MUSIC. 20 Manchester Sq., London W1. *Tel:* 01-486-4488.

ENGLISH FOLK DANCE AND SONG SOCIETY. Cecil Sharp House, 2 Regent's Park Rd, London NW1 7AY. *Tel:* 01-485-2206.

EP PUBLISHING. EP Group of Companies. Bradford Rd. East Ardsley, Wakefield, Yorkshire. *Tel:* Wakefield 823971 (0924). *Grams:* Edpro Wakefield. *London Office:* 27 Maunsel St., London SW1P 2QS. *Tel:* 01-834-1067.

Essex, C. Clifford Essex Music Co. Ltd. *See* Clifford Essex.

ESSEX MUSIC Group. Essex House, 68 Oxford St., London W1. *Tel:* 01-636-7906. *Grams:* Sexmus London. *Trade:* Music Sales Ltd, 78 Newman St., London W1.

EULENBURG. Ernst, Ltd. 48 Great Marlborough St., London W1V 2BN. *Tel:* 01-437-1246.

FABER MUSIC, Ltd. 38 Russell Sq., London WC1B 5DA. *Tel:* 01-636-1344. *Grams:* Fabbaf London WC1.

FAMOUS CHAPPELL, Ltd. 50 New Bond St., London W1A 2BR. *Tel:* 01-629-7600. *Grams:* Symphony London.

FELDMAN. B. Feldman and Co. Ltd. 64 Dean St., London W1. *Tel:* 01-437-9336. *Grams:* Humfriv London WC2.

FENETTE MUSIC. 138–140 Charing Cross Rd, London WC2H 0LD.

FORSYTH Brothers, Ltd. 190 Grays Inn Rd, London WC1X 8EW. *Tel:* 01-837-4768.

Fox. Sam Fox Publishing Co. (London) Ltd. *See* Sam Fox.

FRANCIS, DAY AND HUNTER, Ltd.
138 Charing Cross Rd, London WC2H 0LD.
Tel: 01-836-6699. *Grams:* Arpeggio London
WC2.

FRANK MUSIC Co., Ltd. 50 New Bond St.,
London W1A 2BR. *Tel:* 01-629-7600.
Grams: Symphony London.

FREEMAN. H. Freeman, Ltd. 64 Dean St.,
London W1. *Tel:* 01-437-9336.

Galliard. *See* Stainer and Bell.

GLOCKEN Verlag, Ltd. 10–16 Rathbone St.,
London W1P 2BJ. *Tel:* 01-580-2827.
Grams: Operetta London W1.

GOOD NEWS CRUSADE. 32a Fore St., St Austell,
Cornwall PL25 5EP. *Tel:* St Austell 2716.

GRAHAM. Frank Graham. 6 Queen's Terrace,
Newcastle upon Tyne. *Tel:* Newcastle upon Tyne
813067.

GWASG PRIFYSGOL CYMRU. *See* University of
Wales Press.

Hansen. Edition Wilhelm Hansen London Ltd.
See Chester.

HANSEN Publications Ltd. 21–25 Earle St.,
London EC2. *Tel:* 01-267-0237.

Hart. F. Pitman Hart and Co., Ltd. *See* Pitman
Hart.

HINRICHSEN Edition Ltd. 10 Baches St.,
London N1 6DN. *Tel:* 01-253-1638.
Grams: Musipeters London.

HORTON TRUST. 1 Sherbourne Rd, Great
Horton, Bradford, West Yorkshire BD7 1RB.
Tel: Bradford (0274) 26975.
Grams: Hortrust Bradford.

HUGHES A'I FAB. (Hughes and Son) Publishers,
Ltd. 29 Rivulet Rd, Wrexham, Clwyd.
Tel: Wrexham 4340.

IMPERIA MUSIC CO. Ltd. 21 Denmark St.,
London WC2. *Tel:* 01-836-6699.
Grams: Maritunes London WC2.

INTER-ART Music Publishers. 10–16 Rathbone St.
London W1P 2BJ. *Tel:* 01-580-2827.
Grams: Operetta London W1.

James. Dick James Music Ltd. *See* Dick James
Music.

KALMUS. Alfred A. Kalmus, Ltd. 2–3 Fareham St.,
London W1V 4DU. *Tel:* 01-437-5203.
Grams: Alkamus London W1.

KEITH PROWSE MUSIC Publishing Co., Ltd.
21 Denmark St., London WC2H 8NE.
Tel: 01-836-5501.

LEEDS MUSIC, Ltd. 139 Piccadilly, London W1.
Tel: 01-629-7211. *Grams:* Leedsmusik London.

LENGNICK. Alfred Lengnick and Co., Ltd.
Purley Oaks Studios, 421a Brighton Rd,
South Croydon, Surrey CR2 6YR.
Tel: 01-660-7646.

LEONARD, GOULD AND BOLTTLER.
99 St Martin's Lane, London WC2N 4AZ.
Tel: 01-240-1612.

LONDON PRO MUSICA. 42 Christchurch Ave.,
London NW6.

LONGMAN Group Ltd. Longman House,
Burnt Mill, Harlow, Essex. *Tel:* Harlow 26721.
Trade: Pinnacles, Harlow, Essex.
Tel: Harlow 29655. *Grams:* 81259.

MORRIS. Edwin H. Morris and Co., Ltd.
52 Maddox St., London W1. *Tel:* 01-629-7600.

MOZART EDITION (Great Britain) Ltd.
199 Wardour St., London W1V 3FA.
Tel: 01-734-3711.

MUSIC SALES Ltd. 78 Newman St., London W1.
Tel: 01-636-9033.

MUSICA RARA. 2 Great Marlborough St.,
London W1. *Tel:* 01-437-1576.

MUSICA VIVA. 558 Galleywood Rd, Chelmsford,
Essex CM2 8BX.

NATIONAL FEDERATION OF WOMEN'S
INSTITUTES. 39 Eccleston St.,
London SW1W 9NT. *Tel:* 01-730-7212.
Grams: Fedinsti London SW1.

NOVELLO and Co., Ltd. Borough Green,
Sevenoaks, Kent TN15 8DT. *Tel:* 0732-88-3261.
Grams: Novellos Sevenoaks.

OCTAVA Music Co., Ltd. *See* Weinberger.

OXFORD UNIVERSITY PRESS
(Music Department). 44 Conduit St.,
London W1R 0DE. *Tel:* 01-734-5364.
Grams: Fulscore London W1.

PATERSON. Paterson's Publications, Ltd.
38 Wigmore St., London W1H 0EX.
Tel: 01-935-3551. *Grams:* Paterwia London W1.

PAXTON. Borough Green, Sevenoaks,
Kent TN15 8DT.

PENGUIN Books, Ltd. Bath Rd, Harmondsworth,
Middx. *Tel:* 01-759-1984. *Grams:* Penguinook
West Drayton. *Telex:* 263130.
London Office: 17 Grosvenor Gardens,
London SW1.

PETERS Edition. 10 Baches St., London N1 6DN.
Tel: 01-253-1638. *Grams:* Musipeters London.

PHOENIX. 61 Frith St., London W1V 5TA.

PITMAN HART. F. Pitman Hart, and Co., Ltd.
99 St Martin's Lane, London WC2N 4AZ.
Tel: 01-240-1612.

Pro Musica. *See* London Pro Musica.

Prowse. Keith Prowse Music Publishing Co. Ltd.
See Keith Prowse Music.

R. SMITH and Co. Ltd. 210 Strand,
London WC2R 1AP. *Tel:* 01-353-1166.

RAHTER. D. Rahter. Lyra House, 67 Belsize La.,
London NW3. *Tel:* 01-794-8038.

REGINA MUSIC Publishing Co., Ltd. Old Fun Rd,
Leeds LS10 2AA. *Tel:* Leeds 700527.

RICORDI. G. Ricordi and Co. (London), Ltd.
The Bury, Church St., Chesham, Bucks HP5 1JG.
Tel: Chesham 3311. *Grams:* Ricordi Chesham.

ROBBINS Music Corporation, Ltd. 138 Charing
Cross Rd, London WC2H 0LD.
Tel: 01-836-6699.

ROBERTON Publications. The Windmill,
Wendover, Aylesbury, Bucks. HP22 6JJ.
Tel: Wendover (0296) 623107.

ROYAL SCHOOL OF CHURCH MUSIC.
Addington Palace, Croydon CR9 5AD.
Tel: 01-654-7676. *Grams:* Cantoris Croydon.

ROYAL SCOTTISH COUNTRY DANCE SOCIETY.
12 Coates Cres., Edinburgh EH3 7AF.
Tel: 031-225-3854.

SALVATIONIST PUBLISHING AND SUPPLIES,
Ltd. 117 Judd St., London WC1H 9NN.
Tel: 01-387-1656. *Grams:* Savingly London
WC1.

SAM FOX Publishing Co. (London) Ltd.
21 Denmark St., London WC2H 8NE.
Tel: 01-836-6699.

SCHAUER AND MAY, 67 Belsize La.,
London NW3. *Tel:* 01-794-8038.

SCHIRMER. G. Schirmer Ltd. (Music Publishers).
140 Strand, London WC2R 1HH.
Tel: 01-836-4011.

SCHOFIELD AND SIMS, Ltd. 35 St John's Rd,
Huddersfield, Yorkshire HD1 5DT.
Tel: Huddersfield 30684.
Grams: Schosims Huddersfield.

SCHOOLMASTER PUBLISHING Co. Ltd.
Derbyshire House, Lower St., Kettering,
Northants. NN16 8BB. *Tel:* 053687-3407.

SCHOTT and Co. Ltd. 48 Great Marlborough St.,
London W1V 2BN. *Tel:* 01-437-1246.
Grams: Shotanco London.

SCHROEDER, A. A. Schroeder Music Publishing
Co., Ltd. 15 Berkeley St., London W1
Tel: 01-493-2506.

SCHROEDER AND GUNTHER Inc. c/o G.
Schirmer Ltd., 140 Strand, London WC2R 1HH.
Tel: 01-836-4011.

SIMROCK. N. Simrock. Lyra House, 67 Belsize La.,
London NW3 5AX. *Tel:* 01-749-8038.

Smith. R. Smith and Co. Ltd. *See* R. Smith.

ST GREGORY PUBLISHING Co. 4 West Hill Rd,
Hoddesdon, Herts. *Tel:* Hoddesdon 64433.

ST MARTINS PUBLICATIONS, Ltd
No longer publishing.

STAINER AND BELL Ltd. 82 High Rd,
London N2 9PW. *Tel:* 01-444-9135.

STOCKWELL. Arthur H. Stockwell, Ltd. Elms
Court, Ilfracombe, Devon EX34 8BA.
Tel: C2716-2557. *Grams:* Stockwell, Ilfracombe.

STUDIO MUSIC Co. 89–91 Vicarage Rd,
London NW10 2UA. *Tel:* 01-459-6194.

THAMES MUSIC. 39–41 New Bond St., London
W1. *Tel:* 01-499-5961.

THAMES Publishing. 14 Barlby Rd,
London W10 6AR. *Tel:* 01-969-3579.

TOMUS Publications. Carne House, Parsons La.,
Bury, Lancs. BL9 0JT. *Tel:* 061-764-1099.

UNITED MUSIC Publishers Ltd. 1 Montague St.,
London WC1B 5BS. *Tel:* 01-636-5171.

UNIVERSAL Edition (London), Ltd. 2 Fareham St.,
Dean St., London W1V 4DU. *Tel:* 01-437-5203.
Grams: Alkamus London W1.

UNIVERSITY OF ILLINOIS PRESS.
See American University Publishers.

UNIVERSITY OF TEXAS PRESS, Ltd.
See American University Publishers.

UNIVERSITY OF WALES PRESS. Merthyr House,
James St., Cardiff CF1 6EU. *Tel:* Cardiff 31919.

VANGUARD MUSIC Ltd. 19 Charing Cross Rd,
London WC2. *Tel:* 01-839-3655.

WARREN AND PHILLIPS. 196 Grays Inn Rd,
London WC1X 8EW.

WEINBERGER. Joseph Weinberger Ltd.
10–16 Rathbone St., London W1P 2BJ.
Tel: 01-580-2827. *Grams:* Operetta London W1.

WISE Publications. 78 Newman St., London W1.
Tel: 01-636-0933.

WOLFE Publishing, Ltd. 10 Earlham St.,
London WC2H 9LP. *Tel:* 01-240-2935.

YORKE Edition. 8 Cecil Rd, London W3 0DA.
Tel: 01-992-1068.